METHODS IN PSYCHOPHYSIOLOGY

METHODS IN
PSYCHOPHYSIOLOGY

Clinton C. Brown, Ph.D.

Associate Professor of Medical Psychology,
Johns Hopkins University
School of Medicine

THE WILLIAMS & WILKINS COMPANY

Baltimore • 1967

N-8

Copyright ©, 1967

The Williams & Wilkins Co.
428 E. Preston Street
Baltimore, Md. 21202 U.S.A.

Made in the United States of America

Library of Congress Catalog Card Number 66-24500

Printed and Composed at the

WAVERLY PRESS, INC.
Mt. Royal & Guilford Aves.
Baltimore, Md. 21202 U.S.A.

Note on the cover design: The contrast between ancient and modern attempts at designating affective
reaction types is illustrated by the sample of a modern
polygraph tracing and the superimposed woodcuts
illustrating the four temperaments. The latter are
from the First German Calendar printed in Augsburg
about 1480. They represent the sanguine, melancholy,
choleric, and phlegmatic disposition depicted in typical activity. It is an interesting and enlightening task
to match the titles to the illustrations. (Illustrations
from: Saturn and Melancholy, Klebansky, R., Thos.
Nelson and Sons, 1964.)

Table of Contents

Contributors

CLINTON C. BROWN, PH.D., Associate Professor of Medical Psychology, Department of Psychiatry and Behavioral Science, Johns Hopkins University School of Medicine.

CHESTER W. DARROW, PH.D., Chief, Division of Psychophysiology, Institute for Juvenile Research and Associate Professor of Physiology, Medical School of the University of Illinois.

ROSCOE A. DYKMAN, PH.D., Professor of Psychology and Director of the Research Laboratory, Department of Psychiatry, University of Arkansas Medical Center.

ROBERT EDELBERG, B.S., PH.D., Professor of Psychophysiology and Professor of Physiology, Department of Psychiatry, Neurology and Behavioral Sciences, University of Oklahoma Medical Center.

LESLIE A. GEDDES, PH.D., M.E.E., Professor of Physiology, Baylor University College of Medicine; Assistant Professor of Physiology, University of Texas Dental College; Assistant Professor of Physiology, Texas A and M College of Veterinary Medicine; Chief, Section of Biomedical Engineering, Baylor University.

JAMES W. JOHNSTON, JR., B.S., M.F., PH.D., Associate Professor of Physiology, Department of Physiology and Biophysics, Georgetown University Schools of Medicine and Dentistry.

RUTH A. KATZ, B.S., Psychophysiology Research Unit, Spring Grove State Hospital.

THOMAS J. LUPARELLO, M.D., Assistant Professor of Psychiatry, Department of Psychiatry, State University of New York, Downstate Medical Center.

R. STUART MACKAY, PH.D., Space Sciences Laboratory and Division of Medical Physics, University of California at Berkeley.

CURTIS MARSHALL, M.D., C.M., Associate Professor of Neurosurgery, Johns Hopkins University School of Medicine.

KEITH MURRAY, PH.D., Executive Secretary, Experimental Psychology B Study Section, Division of Research Grants, National Institutes of Health.

FREDRICK OLMSTED, M.D., Research Division of the Cleveland Clinic Foundation.

STANISLAUS RADVAN-ZIEMNOWICZ, M.D.,. Director, Brain Research Foundation.

LOUIS SIEGEL, B.S.E.E., Technical Associate in Radiation Biology and Biophysics, University of Rochester School of Medicine and Dentistry.

MARVIN STEIN, M.D., Professor and Chairman, Department of Psychiatry, State University of New York, Downstate Medical Center, College of Medicine.

GEORGE F. SUTHERLAND, M.D., Associate Professor of Psychiatry, University of Maryland, School of Medicine.

HARDY W. TROLANDER, B.S., President, Yellow Springs Instrument Company.

GEORGE N. WEBB, B.E., M.S., Assistant Professor of Biomedical Engineering, Johns Hopkins University School of Medicine.

BERNARD WEISS, PH.D., Associate Professor of Radiation Biology and Biophysics; Associate Professor in the Center for Brain Research, University of Rochester.

Preface:
Measuring Biological Processes

The amount of medical research activity, reflected by the magnitude of the financial support, has experienced a phenomenal growth in the last several decades. In 1947, a total of $88 million was spent by the Federal government and all other sources on medical research. Ten years later the total endowment was $330 million and experts have predicted that by 1970 the national medical research expenditures will have reached the $1 billion mark.

These funds are granted to researchers to broaden and deepen medical knowledge, to ensure the prolongation of life, to alleviate suffering, and to produce an increase in the physical and mental capabilities of the population.

Such expenditures represent a degree of support and consequent intensity of research effort which would have been incomprehensible to workers in the period prior to World War II. Research in that era was a part-time occupation, performed on makeshift or borrowed equipment on after-hours time.

Yet this present affluence of medical research has produced a unique set of problems based upon the abundance of materials, information, and techniques.

Contemporary instrumentation makes use of complex apparatus developed by biomedical electronics engineers and is based upon advances made in the general field of electronics. Such equipment is exquisitely sensitive and flexible and its use is mandatory in most psychophysiologic studies, but it requires the services of experts to maintain, is difficult to operate by the uninitiated, and the user must possess considerable electronic sophistication before he can realize its full capabilities.

Contemporary life sciences researchers employ techniques derived from such diverse fields as biochemistry, biology, medicine, information, theory, and statistical mathematics. Such procedures enhance the amount and kind of information one can obtain from a behavioral study but to use them appropriately one must either develop considerable expertise in the field or is forced to consult the services of a specialist.

Biotelemetry techniques and subminiaturization of its equipment have provided the investigator with a powerful tool to analyze biological activity over extended periods of time in either remote or naturalistic locations. Yet this process produces such a mass of data that computer analysis is required to extract the significant information. Again, the proper use of such facilities requires that the investigator must learn to write computer programs, and often, to reinforce his mathematical background in order to do so.

The improved procedures and apparatus of modern behavioral science, the speedier methods of data analysis, and the increased emphasis placed upon publication have produced a literature explosion of no mean proportions. The preliminary library research on a planned investigation requires not only the search of half a hundred journals, but the more tedious process of locating critical reports often buried in obscure, foreign language publications. Experts in other fields must be contacted to clear up obscurities or interpret strange technical terms.

The undertaking of contemporary psychophysiologic research requires therefore that one must possess more than a mere smattering of information in many adjacent fields, that a small army of technicians, engineers, and scientific consultants must lend their skill and knowledge to the preparation, planning, and execution.

Despite his favorable position of adequate financial support, the possession of sensitive equipment, high speed analytical methods, and libraries of information, the present day investigator has been evicted from his ivory tower. The community of science is immensely interdependent. Reciprocal communication across broad areas of science is a necessity, not a luxury. Teamwork within the life sciences, with the clinical practitioner, with members of allied professions in the pharmaceutical, chemical, and electronic industries is a necessity. This teamwork requires effective communication, a mutual knowledge of the basics in other fields, and a facility with the terminology.

This book represents an attempt to further the communication within a specialty and a means for representing its techniques to the other members of the scientific community. It was conceived as a single source for the presentation of the latest developments of the most used and potentially most useful methods and procedures in psychophysiology. The authors are specialists, leaders in their fields, selected not only for their technical knowledge but for their ability to communicate their subject matter clearly, precisely, and completely.

The needs for this book are evident. The procedures of psychophysiology are typically highly technical. To this time there has been an unfortunate diversity of "standard practice" which not only has made it difficult to compare results between investigators but often, has resulted in confusion and error in measurement. In each of the following chapters the writers have traced the development of a measure, discussed the physiological phenomena they describe, and have proposed a procedure for measurement which is optimum for sensitivity and accuracy. A number have proposed standard terminology and units of measurement. The reader is presented with the optimum technique and the rationale for its use.

The audience to which this book is directed is a heterogeneous one. It includes not only the psychophysiologist who wishes to standardize the measurement techniques he now employs or to adopt new techniques, but the clinical practitioner, the teacher, and the research worker who wish to acquire the best of current information and technology.

CLINTON C. BROWN, PH.D.

1
Electrical Properties of the Skin*

ROBERT EDELBERG, B.S., Ph.D.

When a voltage is applied to a pair of electrodes placed upon the surface of the body, the skin, of all structures traversed by the current path, offers by far the greatest relative resistance to its passage, accounting for at least 80% of the total resistance. This is not altogether unexpected in view of the special role of this organ as the last layer between the organism and its external environment. The skin must constitute a barrier which prevents undue leakage of water and salts, and it appropriately offers considerable hindrance to the movement of ions, in which form virtually all transfer of electric charge in an aqueous system takes place. The conductance (or in reciprocal terms, resistance) measured between a pair of electrodes in large part reflects the leakiness of this ionic barrier, and its level and variations can serve as an indication of the state of the skin.

Although Féré (1888) is generally credited with discovery of reflex variation of skin resistance, it has been pointed out by Landis and DeWick (1929) that changes in the electrical resistance of the skin had in fact been described much earlier by Vigouroux (1879), who attributed them to vasomotor activity. When Féré (1888) demonstrated that rapid fluctuations of skin resistance could occur in response to emotional stimulation, the translucent integument was transformed into a transparent window for looking into inner experience, although, it must be conceded, not without considerable distortion. In 1927, Richter produced conclusive evidence, confirming earlier indications that an intact sympathetic innervation was necessary to elicit the reflex in humans, and the measure took on added significance. By 1930, with improvement in sensitivity and frequency response of string and mirror galvanometers, and a

*Many of the experimental findings reported in this chapter originated in a series of research projects conducted over a 9-year period and were supported by research grants and a Senior Research Fellowship from the National Institute of Health, by the USAF Office of Scientific Research, by the USAF Aero Medical Laboratory, and by the NASA Manned Spacecraft Center. The preparation of this manuscript was in part supported by Research Grant MH-08656, National Institute of Mental Health.

growing interest in the physiological aspects of psychological behavior, there was a gradual acceleration of the utilization of this tool, in some cases as an indicator of central nervous events, more often as a crude "emotion indicator."

Since the beginning of this century, hundreds of studies have appeared as evidence of efforts to correlate base levels or transient alterations of conductance or resistance with behavioral states with varying degrees of success. In a few instances electrodermal measures were used for dermatological research (e.g. Perry, Wright, Mount, & Leland, 1958) or for neurological diagnosis (e.g. Fries & Richter, 1964), but for the most part these measures have served as indices of psychological behavior or drug effect. One exception is high frequency impedance which, because of its special relevance to structure, has been used primarily for dermatological purposes (Gougerot, 1947).

During the first several decades after the discovery of the electrodermal reflex, a great controversy raged over the nature of its peripheral physiology. Féré had suggested a vascular basis. When in 1890 Tarchanoff demonstrated that potential changes occurred between two electrodes placed on dissimilar skin sites, even in the absence of applied current, and that these, too, could be elicited by emotional stimulation, the foundation was laid for interpretation of this phenomenon as a change in the permeability of a selective membrane, with many subsequent indications that the site of this action was the human sweat gland. There were nevertheless strong adherents of Féré's original vascular hypothesis, with McDowall (1933) as a leading proponent, but in an extended series of studies it became clear that this vascular hypothesis was untenable for explaining the resistance changes if not the potential changes. Much of this history has been reviewed by Mc Cleary (1950), Rothman (1954, Ch. 2), and Wang (1957). While recent pharmacological experiments by Lader and Montagu (1962) seem to have given the final coup to the vascular hypothesis as far as skin resistance changes are concerned, a vascular component of the *potential* response has not been fully excluded. It has also been contended that the site of the electrical changes is in a cellular layer in addition to the sweat gland (Richter, 1929; Edelberg & Wright, 1964), but this hypothesis is still being debated. As a working hypothesis one may regard the electrodermal reflex as an increase in the total permeability of a selective cutaneous membrane in response to the arrival of impulses carried by cholinergic sympathetic nerves. The nature of this effect has important bearing on the techniques and methodology used in its measurement.

The Physics of Electrodermal Measurement

Skin resistance is not purely ohmic (dissipative) since the electromotive force (emf) does not develop instantaneously upon application of the external source but rises exponentially. Similarly, upon opening the battery circuit there is an exponential decay of the induced emf not an abrupt cessation. In fact, as has been discussed by Gildemeister (1923) and by Rein (1929), this system represents largely an *apparent* resistance, actually a polarization potential and has the electrical characteristics of a complex capacitative network. The skin may be regarded as a resistor in series with a leaky capacitor (Montagu, 1964). Rather than being of fixed value, as indicated by Montagu, the capacitor may be considered more accurately as consisting of a fixed structural capacitor in parallel with a polarization capacitance whose value varies inversely with a power function of the frequency (Fricke, 1932).

In physical terms we may measure either the electrical conductivity (C or G) of the skin (SC),* (or its derived measure, skin resistance (SR), skin potential (SP), i.e. the potential across the skin in the absence of imposed current or skin impedance (SZ) at any specified frequency. The reciprocal of impedance, admittance, has also been used (Montagu, 1964). Forbes (1964) has recently discussed various considerations governing a choice among these measures. These all represent base levels, but may show gradual shifts over extended periods of time (i.e. minutes or hours). Each of these measures may represent a rapid transient shift in response to neural impulses or local excitation requiring fractions of seconds or at most a few seconds to reach peak values and recovering usually in less than a minute. Such transients may be collectively designated as electrodermal responses (EDR). They are known variously as the galvanic skin response (GSR), galvanic skin reflex (GSR), psychogalvanic reflex (PGR), skin potential response (SPR), electrodermogram (EDG), skin resistance response (SRR), or skin conductance response (SCR). One of the problems in this field at present clearly is to arrive at a standard nomenclature and abbreviations for these terms. In the case of the measurement of conductance, resistance, or impedance in which an external current source is required, the various measures, both base levels and responses, are in common called *exosomatic*. Resistance responses have been known also as the Féré phenomenon or in the German literature as the Veraguth phenomenon, after the author of the term "psychogalvanic reflex." The most common term now used, applicable equally well to the skin resistance response or to the skin conductance response, is the GSR.

When no external current is applied and the measurement is simply of the endogenous potential between electrodes on two dissimilar pieces of skin, or between an electrode placed on the surface and one within the body, the method is described as *endosomatic* and the terms skin potential or electrodermal potential apply. Change in this potential is commonly designated as skin potential response (SPR). The change in skin potential has also been known, after its discoverer, as the Tarchanoff reflex. In many cases the term *endosomatic GSR* has been used to denote skin potential response, but this is in fact a misnomer

---

*The abbreviations used by the author do not necessarily agree with those found in the literature.

since these potentials are not related to galvanic current flow if properly measured. Unlike the exosomatic response which is always a fall in resistance, the direction of a potential response may be positive, negative, biphasic, or triphasic.

In addition to potential responses of central reflex origin, there is also the Ebbecke response (1921), a change in skin potential elicited by local stimulation of the skin and always positive in direction. Whether it involves a direct activation of the end organ or is an axon reflex remains to be determined.

Units

The unit of apparent resistance, even though not ohmic, is the ohm or more commonly the kilohm (1000 ohms) or simply K. This term has meaning only if expressed in terms of resistance afforded by each unit area of surface, i.e. *as specific resistance*. For unit conversion this is expressed as ohms·cm² rather than ohms/cm². Dimensional analysis then indicates that total resistance equals specific resistance divided by area. Specific resistance generally ranges from 10 K·cm² to 500 K·cm². The physical unit for conductance is the reciprocal ohm or mho. However, because skin resistance under ordinary conditions is at least 10 K·cm², conductance is more conveniently expressed in terms of reciprocal megohms or micromhos (μmho). A useful equation to help in the conversion of resistance to conductance is:

$$C \ (\mu\text{mho}) \ = \ \frac{1000}{R(\text{in kilohms})} \qquad (1)$$

It should be noted that one cannot make this same conversion of *change* in resistance (ΔR) to change in conductance (ΔC). To make such a transformation the following relation is useful.

$$\Delta C = C_2 - C_1 = \frac{1}{R_2} - \frac{1}{R_1} = - \frac{\Delta R}{R_1 R_2} \qquad (2)$$

If R is only a small fraction of the total resistance, $R_1 \cdot R_2$ is approximately equal to the square of the resistance, whence

$$\Delta C \approx - \frac{\Delta R}{R^2} \qquad (3)$$

Specific conductance is expressed in μmho/cm², indicating that specific conductance *times* area yields total conductance. Conductance and resistance are frequently expressed in terms of their logs and it may be of use to point out that since

$$C = \frac{1}{R}$$

$$\log C = - \log R$$

If one is using a recording system in which the readout of R is logarithmically compressed, one can simplify data conversion by the above relation. In terms of micromhos and K

$$\log\ C = 3\ -\ \log\ R \tag{4}$$

Values for specific conductance characteristically range from 2 to 100 μmho/cm^2.

Impedance, like resistance, is expressed in ohms.cm^2, but the frequency of the applied current must be specified and the phase angle is normally given, since this allows calculation of an equivalent resistance-capacitance network. Impedance curves have been determined by Hozawa (1928), Barnett (1938), and Plutchik and Hirsch (1963). Specific impedance is of the order of 70% of DC value at 100 cps, 25% at 1,000 cps, and 5% at 10,000 cps. The phase angle becomes relatively constant above 1,000 cps with values ranging from 55° to 83° reported.

Potentials are expressed in terms of millivolts with the polarity shown and the reference clearly stated. For example, a value for palmar skin may be expressed as −25 mv with respect to the ear lobe, meaning that the palm is 25 mv more negative than the ear lobe which served as the companion (reference) electrode site. Potentials of the skin surface with respect to the inside of the body characteristically vary from +10 to −60 mv. They are not expressed in area specific terms because they are independent of electrode area if the impedance of the voltmeter is high enough. Skin potential responses may be as high as 10 mv but are more commonly of the order of 1 to 2 mv.

The Electrode

Electric charge is carried by electrons in the circuitry associated with the measurement of bioelectric characteristics; in the aqueous organism it is carried by ions. This significant difference in the two systems implies a boundary between them, namely the solid-water interface at the surface of the electrode, with peculiar characteristics. It is at this phase boundary that ions become atoms and conversely, and it is in this critical zone of oxidation and reduction where recording difficulties are also concentrated, appearing in the form of electrode bias, polarization or slow wave, or "pop" artifact. The following section is devoted to a discussion of these problems.

In neurophysiological measurements of *action potential*, there have not been stringent requirements with regard to electrode characteristics because of the capacitative coupling of the devices used to measure such AC potentials. In the case of DC measurements, however, an electrode pair may contribute a significant error to the measurement if it has any appreciable electrode bias, i.e. any potential difference between the pair not originating in the system under observation. Further, in the specific case of skin resistance measurement, unlike most other biological measurements, one must apply a relatively high density of direct current to the electrodes. It is necessary that these electrodes show (1) absence of bias potential and (2) capability of handling a high current density without polarizing. The development of a *bias potential* is often incorrectly termed *polarization*, but is in fact only a manifestation of a difference in the surfaces of the two electrodes such that their half-cell potentials with respect to the electrolyte medium are dissimilar. True polarization on the other hand is a phenomenon in which as a result of current passage, a counter electromotive force arises at the interface between the electrode and the electrolyte, due either to an energy barrier in the oxidation-reduction reaction at the electrode surface or to a limitation placed upon ion transfer by the rate of diffusion of ions to or from the interface (Hozawa, 1931).

The development of a given level of polarization in an exosomatic measurement will introduce an error the relative size of which varies according to the intensity of the voltage or current applied. In a constant current system, using 1 μamp of current, a polarization potential of 1 mv will result in an error of 1 K in the measured resistance, while at 10 μamp, 1 mv corresponds to an error of only 0.1 K. In a constant voltage system, the error will vary with the applied voltage. With 1 v applied, a 1-mv polarization potential will produce an error of 0.1% in the measurement. With some electrodes the polarization potential at 10 μamp/cm^2 may easily amount to 100 to 200 mv.

Bias potentials may be a source of error in either endosomatic or exosomatic measurement but are more serious in the former since they can easily amount to an error of 100% in base potential readings. Their contribution to base resistance levels is of far less consequence because of the comparatively high potentials generated by the passage of applied current, and per mv is the same as for polarization potentials. Bias potentials do not constitute a problem in the measurement of skin potential *responses* unless they exceed a few millivolts and become a source of exosomatic current.

Testing for bias or polarization. *Bias potential.* The two electrodes under test are best tested as matched pairs, although they can be measured separately against a stable reference electrode for equality of half-cell potential. In general, the simplest method is to immerse the pair of electrodes in saline having the approximate composition of the electrolyte medium to be used and to measure the potential with a high impedance, sensitive DC voltmeter. For electrodermal measurement, if this potential is 1 mv or less, the pair is considered acceptable although it is normally possible to reduce this potential to less than 0.1 mv.

Polarization. Polarization tendency must be determined by the behavior manifested during the passage of current. A pair of electrodes showing very little bias potential may polarize readily when they carry current. The level of polarization depends both on electrolyte concentration and on current density. At very low currents its magnitude is negligible but may be very appreciable at the electrodermal current level. It is therefore important to test the electrodes under the same conditions as will be encountered in the electrodermal measurement. The same set up may be used as for determination of bias potential except that the voltage across the pair is measured during passage of the direct current strength in question. The impedance of the pair at 1000 cps or higher is separately determined, and this value used as the ohmic resistance. Ohm's law, using the ohmic resistance and the current strength of the DC determination, gives the expected voltage. The difference between the measured and expected voltage is a measure of the polarization potential.

A simpler method rests on the knowledge that the electrolyte media used in electrodermal measurements have relatively low resistance. For example, the specific resistance of 0.1 N NaCl is only about 100 ohms.cm. Consequently, if two electrodes, each 1 cm² are placed in this solution 1 cm apart, and 10 μamp of current delivered through them, the predicted voltage will be only 1 mv. Any voltage above this level measured under these conditions can be attributed to polarization. Another indication of whether or not polarization is occurring at any given current strength can be obtained by suddenly reversing polarity of current and noting any change in voltage level (other than sign). One last test consists of observing the oscilloscope trace at the moment a step voltage is applied to the electrode pair through a series resistor (e.g. 1 megohm). The magnitude of the deviation from a square wave response in the development of the full potential is an indication of the degree of polarization.

It may be desirable for general application to know the limits of reversible or nonpolarizable behavior for a given electrode pair. This can be determined by the point at which the current-voltage curve deviates from linearity as current is increased. Such a curve may be measured conveniently on an X-Y recorder or on a polargraph of the type commonly used for oxygen determinations, but it can also be determined by plotting individual voltages developed at a series of increasing current strengths. It should be noted that polarization of skin is a normal phenomenon so that testing of electrode polarization must be done in vitro.

Prevention of bias potentials. The prevention of bias potentials is primarily a matter of method of preparation of the electrode. There is a voluminous literature on the construction of stable, nonpolarizable electrodes (e.g. Janz & Taniguchi, 1953; O'Connell & Tursky, 1960) and if these are prepared in a similar fashion their half-cell potentials should be equal and the bias between any pair low. O'Connell, Tursky, and Orne (1960) have examined various types of half-cells for stability and bias and find the silver-silver chloride sponge electrode to be superior to others tested, but point to the difficulty of its preparation and care. The silver-silver chloride disc electrode runs a fairly close second and is simpler to prepare. The commonly used zinc-zinc chloride electrode proved to be unacceptable for potential measurement despite the fact that Lykken (1959) found the zinc-zinc sulfate electrode best of all for skin resistance measurement. After much trial and error, I have adopted a relatively simple process to produce low bias, relatively stable silver-silver chloride electrodes. The bright silver electrode is first carefully covered with an insulating cement in the region where the lead wire has been soldered on, so that only silver is accessible to the solution. Its surface is wiped with a solvent to remove grease and washed in water. The electrode is connected to the negative terminal of a 1.5-v battery and immersed in 1 M NaCl with a second strip of silver acting as the anode and the current allowed to flow long enough for bubbles to develop over the surface. This reduces any oxide or sulfide coating. The polarity is then reversed and anodizing continued until the surface is a uniform brownish-purple. Coatings which are very thick tend to flake off and should be avoided. Electrode pairs are stored dry and when used are tested at 3-day intervals. If bias develops, both electrodes are heated in a gentle gas flame until the first change of color occurs; this invariably reduces bias to less than 1 mv. There are conflicting views on the best method for storage of the commonly used silver-silver chloride electrode, i.e. whether wet or dry and whether in light or darkness. According to Janz and Taniguchi (1953) it is doubtful that this electrode is appreciably light-sensitive but dissolved oxygen in solution was shown to have a deteriorating effect. Some authors suggest storing the pair short-circuited in solution. In the absence of comparative experiments on the effects of wet and dry storage, I assume in practice that any method of storage is acceptable for *electrodermal* application provided members of each pair are treated similarly.

Prevention of polarization. One method for prevention of polarization is the use of a large electrode to reduce current density through the surface. Since the current is dictated by the bioelectric requirements of the skin, the current density through the electrode is relatively predetermined. However, the surface area can be increased by using the walls as well as the roof of the electrode chamber as electrode surface or by using an electrode with a high surface to volume ratio, for example, the silver-silver chloride sponge electrode (O'Connell & Tursky, 1960). Of special help in handling the polarization problem is the two-element electrode first reported by Barnett (1938) and adopted by Lykken (1959). In this arrangement the constant current is carried by one electrode to a delineated area of skin. A second electrode, acting as a voltage probe, monitors the potential developed at the skin surface. When used with a high impedance amplifier, there is negligible current in the measuring circuit and hence negligible polarization error. Any polarization occurring at the current-furnishing electrode does not influence total current flow which is controlled by external circuitry. The system has two disadvantages in that (1) it cannot be used with the constant voltage system to be described later, and (2) the geometry of these electrodes makes them especially susceptible to error if there is any appreciable resistance in the electrode medium. However, if the paste is reasonably conductive, i.e. has a specific resistance of less than 200 ohms, this system can be used to great advantage.

No matter which technique is used to reduce polarization, it will be more effective if *reversible* electrodes are used. These consist of a metal in contact with a solution of its own ions and are reversible in the sense that the oxidation-reduction takes place through a readily reversible reaction, e.g. $Ag^+ + e \rightleftarrows Ag^0$, and therefore has a low energy barrier, implying less polarization. Common reversible half-cells used in electrochemical or bioelectrical measurement are $Hg-Hg^+$, $Ag-Ag^+$, and $Zn-Zn^{++}$, in the form of the calomel, the anodized silver, and the $Zn - ZnSO_4$ electrodes, respectively.

Lead, zinc, or bright silver electrodes have been frequently used with NaCl as the electrolyte. These constitute a nonreversible system since until part of the electrode dissolves by an electrolytic or auto-oxidative process it is not in contact with a solution of its own ions. Thus zinc in a sodium chloride medium is much more easily polarized than zinc in a zinc sulfate medium. Similarly, bright silver in a sodium chloride medium constitutes quite a different system than chloridized (anodized) silver in the same solution.

Stability of electrodes during use. Changes in the concentration of the ionic environment produce a change in the local half-cell potential resulting in a spurious potential reading. Provision must therefore be made for maintaining the constancy of the ionic cloud in the vicinity of the metallic surface. In the case of Ag-AgCl, the concentration of Ag^+ is determined by the concentration of Cl^- in conformance with the solubility product, $K_{sp} = (Ag^+)(Cl^-) = 1.56 \times 10^{-10}$. It becomes clear that the concentration of Cl^- in the medium must be maintained the same at both electrodes or a bias will develop in the course of the measurement. Because of the low K_{sp} of AgCl, a concentration of NaCl even as low as 0.05 M is sufficient to depress the concentration of Ag^+ to a value of 3×10^{-9} M, a level well below the range of significant biological activity. The silver-silver chloride electrode is generally preferable to the most popular alternate, $Zn-ZnCl_2$ or $Zn-ZnSO_4$, because it is more stable, owing to the lesser tendency for silver to dissolve, and because its use requires no other agent in the medium than the biologically acceptable compound sodium chloride.

Many electrodes will fortuitously set up a local environment of their own ions since they go into solution rather readily. Such materials, e.g. copper, being more reactive with the aqueous medium will be more susceptible to change in the ionic concentration in the electrode vicinity, thereby producing artifacts seen both as sudden transients, termed "pop" artifacts, and as slow wave artifacts according to the rate at which the concentration changes occur. Aluminum and stainless steel are particularly susceptible to "pop" artifacts; solder, bright silver, and copper tend to produce slow wave artifact.

Not all electrode artifact is caused by change in local electrolyte concentration. If a silver-silver chloride electrode is momentarily lifted from the solution so that the surface is exposed to air, it will show a rather extended period of drift upon being replaced in the solution. As pointed out by Janz and Taniguchi (1953), the oxygen tension at the surface of the electrode is a significant determinant of half-cell potential and is probably the primary cause of this effect.

Electrode medium. The interface between the metallic plate and the skin must be filled with a conductive medium. In the case of so-called "dry electrodes, it is the fortuitous accumulation of sweat or transpired moisture which fills this function. This is not only unpredictable as regards rate of formation but as shown by Edelberg (1966) can be reabsorbed into the body. More commonly (and much more dependably) a medium of known composition is interposed between the metallic electrode and the skin. This medium must possess several characteristics. (1) It must be of high enough viscosity to remain in place during application and subsequent use. (2) Its composition must be consistent with the electrochemical requirements of the electrode system. (3) It must be compatible with the biological system, producing minimum change in base level or response amplitude as a consequence of continuing exposure. Of these three, the last is most commonly violated. As demonstrated elsewhere (Edelberg, Greiner, & Burch, 1960), multivalent ions such as Ca^{++}, Zn^{++}, Al^{+++}, or $SO_4^=$ have a potentiating action on GSR. Other ions such as K^+ attenuate GSR amplitude. This action is a function of concentration and polarity of current as well as ion size; at low concentrations, i.e. less than 0.1 M, the effect is slight. One popular electrode has been the Zn-$ZnSO_4$ electrode which as demonstrated by Lykken is very stable but is actually unacceptable for electrodermal measurement because of the specific action of Zn^{++} on the amplitude of the GSR. Commonly available electrode pastes designed for application in electroencephalography or electrocardiography are designed to produce lowered skin resistance and hence are made with high salt concentration. This eventuates in a progressive fall in skin resistance and GSR amplitude over a period of approximately 1 hr (Edelberg & Burch, 1962). It has been found desirable to use a paste with a NaCl concentration approximating that in human sweat which is variable but falls within the range of 0.015 to 0.06 M (Rothman, 1954, Ch. 7). An appropriate choice is 0.05 and tests have shown that raising this value to 0.1 does not result in any deleterious effects even after relatively long exposures. Moreover, the contamination of a paste of such concentration by sweating under the electrode would produce minimal change in NaCl concentration. Its specific resistance is of the order of 200 ohms.cm, low enough to satisfy electrode chamber requirements. As shown above, this concentration would also be adequate to depress the Ag^+ concentration derived from an Ag-AgCl electrode to a negligible concentration.

Starch paste has been used effectively as a *thickening agent*. Although it has the advantage of availability, it suffers from variability in consistency and susceptibility to bacterial or fungus liquefaction. Preservatives help solve this second problem. The paste is prepared by uniformly suspending 6 gm of corn starch in 100 cc of 0.05 M NaCl and bringing to a gentle boil while continuously stirring. Boiling is interrupted 30 sec after it starts and the mixture immediately poured into containers and capped. Starch paste made by adding 0.02% propyl-p-hydroxybenzoate and 0.1% methyl-p-hydroxybenzoate to the NaCl diluent as a preservative has been shown to have no measureable specific effect in a 24-hr exposure, but its use for several days has not been tested.

A preferred medium, derived from a formula by Day and Lippitt (1964) is formed by stirring 3 gm of polyvinylpyrrolidone (PVP K-90, Antara Chemicals, New York, New York) and 2 gm of hydroxymethyl cellulose (Natrosol, HR-250, Hercules Powder Company, Wilmington, Delaware) into 80 ml of 0.05 M NaCl. The resulting suspension is allowed to stand overnight to reach its final degree of viscosity. It too liquifies in about 10 days but the addition of 0.01% thymol retards this process. A commonly available commercial preparation which has rather similar properties and an acceptable NaCl concentration is K-Y surgical jelly (Johnson's Professional Products Co., New Brunswick, N.J.).

The above media have a viscosity high enough for them to be used in the cup-shaped electrode chambers commonly used. However, with electrodes of other designs, for example a sponge pad, low viscosity may be tolerated and in this case a solution may be used without a thickening agent.

Physical construction and application of the electrode. Although a large variety of electrode configurations have found their way into the literature, they fall essentially into four basic types. All must delineate a fixed area of skin if exosomatic recordings are to be made. This is accomplished either by the use of a direct mask, by containing the electrode medium in a chamber with the opening surrounded by a flange which is pressed or cemented against the skin, or by the use of an unprotected electrode of known contact area. The types may be briefly described as follows.

Masked electrodes. In these, a layer of waterproof pressure-sensitive adhesive having a cutout of known area is applied to clean, dry skin. The exposed skin is covered with electrode paste and an electrode plate larger than the cutout is taped over the area (Edelberg & Burch, 1962).

Unmasked electrodes. Metal plates cut to an exact area are applied to skin, either dry or with a thin layer of paste on the plate. Care is taken to prevent spread of the paste to adjacent skin. A variant of this method is the use of sponge discs filled with a liquid or jelly electrolyte and sandwiched between the skin and the metal plate (Kennedy & Travis, 1948).

Chamber electrodes. These may be cup-type chambers which are filled and cemented or strapped to the skin (e.g. Richter, 1929; Venables & Sayer, 1963; Rickles, 1964). They may also be open chambers, essentially gaskets, which are usually fastened to the skin prior to filling with electrode paste (e.g. Lykken, 1959), but may also be filled before applying (e.g. Day & Lippitt, 1964).

Liquid electrodes. These consist of vessels filled with an electrolyte in contact with a nonpolarizable electrode (e.g. Darrow, 1929). This method has been adapted by Lykken and Rose (1959) for measurement of GSR in rats. Although generally not designed for fixed area, the liquid electrode has been used successfully by me with a masking technique. A disc of pressure-sensitive tape is pressed firmly to the surface of the finger. Next a coating of rubber paper cement is applied over the entire finger, nail included. Two thin coatings are more effective than a single thick coating. When almost dry, the protective disc is removed exposing the delineated site. Two fingers prepared in this manner are immersed in separate baths each connected via an agar-KCl salt bridge to a chamber of 1 M KCl containing an Ag-AgCl electrode. The end of the salt bridge dips into a perforated plastic tube which acts as a barrier to prevent contamination of the contact electrolyte with KCl.

Consideration should be given in the design of electrode chambers to principles of surface conformity. For example, the tip of the finger is relatively spherical. Since the intersection of a plane with a sphere is circular, a circular electrode is in order for use on the finger tip. A different configuration is desirable for the shaft of the finger which is a cylinder. Since the intersection of a plane with a cylinder, parallel to the axis, is a rectangle, the optimum flange contact for a given electrode size is here achieved with a relatively long, narrow, or at least ellipsoid opening.

Cements or adhesives are superior to the use of straps in conjunction with the chamber method because the tension required in the absence of adhesive to produce a pressure seal against the skin may produce circulatory occlusion. This will in time cause reduction of GSR amplitude (Wilcott, 1958a; Edelberg, 1964a). Eastman 910 adhesive is an excellent pressure-sensitive cement, but more common ones are also suitable if a cement is to be used. Unfortunately, the application of an electrode which is filled with paste is troublesome because of the tendency for the aqueous material to contaminate the flange and thereby weaken the subsequent bond. One method for avoiding this involves the use of protected double-coated pressure-sensitive tape such as Stomaseal (Minnesota Mining and Manufacturing Company). Electrode application with the use of this adhesive is described by Day and Lippitt (1964). Even more effective are the methods calling for application of the empty gasket-type chamber to dry skin. Filling is accomplished by injection through a hole in the electrode or by pressing the paste through a grid electrode. If the medium is conductive enough and the depth of paste is not too great, a simple bar electrode may be used along the diameter of the chamber, a modification proposed by Dr. Thomas Adams.* Precautions are taken to ensure that the paste entirely covers the site, and a cover is applied. In electrodes of the chamber type in which an airtight seal has been formed and a hypertonic medium used, osmotic swelling will frequently

---

*T. Adams, personal communication, 1965.

cause the electrode to pop off after only an hour or two of use. This can be obviated either by the use of an isotonic medium or, following a suggestion from Dr. Albert F. Ax,* the addition of a rubber membrane to the cap to allow equalization of pressure. The chamber methods have two distinct advantages over the direct masking method. (1) There is less tendency for the medium to move relative to the metal plate; hence, less movement artifact. (2) There is a greater reservoir of paste between the electrode and the skin; hence, less susceptibility to change induced by cutaneous absorption or secretion. However, the direct masking method does have the advantages of simplicity of application, ease of cleaning and ease of fabrication, and has been used satisfactorily for many years.

The *silver cloth electrode* represents an innovation which has been used at this laboratory with much success. Cloth has the advantage of easy conformance with a surface and is excellent for use with the direct masking technique. Furthermore, it is essentially a grid; therefore, a reservoir of low viscosity electrolyte held in a sponge backing will filter through as needed to fill the interstices between it and the skin. Its large surface area per unit of electrode site area is still another advantage in preventing polarization and has allowed accurate measurements even without anodizing. It can, however, be easily anodized. Morrison (1958) reported the development of such an electrode for "dry" application but described the development of serious artifacts after 2 days of wearing. This trouble undoubtedly developed at the junction with the wire lead, as it became gradually contaminated with electrolyte from sweat. It has been found at this laboratory that careful insulation of this junction eliminates the artifact problem. One further modification of her method was to use an electrode paste rather than use the dry electrode. The objections to the use of a dry electrode have been discussed by Blank and Finesinger (1946). The silver cloth electrode with these two modifications has been so satisfactory on all counts that it has been adopted at this laboratory as the method of choice. In making the modification for the attachment of the lead, a tab of silver cloth is left on one edge of the electrode. The wire is twisted firmly around this tab and the tab and wire are well insulated with either molten dental impression wax or a flexible cement such as Pliobond (Goodyear). The tab is folded out of the way over the sponge backing of the electrode and cemented down. When this electrode is used with the long term medium to be described in a later section, masking becomes unnecessary. Silver cloth is manufactured by American Tent Company, Canton, Mississippi and by Swift Textile Metalizing and Laminating Corporation, Hartford, Connecticut.

Spacing of electrodes. It is commonly believed that electrodes must be spaced rather far apart so that the current path proceeds transversely through the sites rather than laterally across the skin surface. With pastes of low salt-concentration, i.e. 0.05 M NaCl, this is a relatively unfounded concern even if

---

*A. F. Ax, personal communication, 1965.

leakage occurs at the periphery of the electrode site since the lateral conductivity is extremely low relative to the transverse because of the very thin cross-section of the lateral conducting layer. The relative lateral and transverse distribution of current from an electrode was measured by delivering a current from one microelectrode while measuring the potential generated at various distances away with a second microelectrode voltage probe. As shown in Figure 1.1, even with sweaty skin the applied voltage is completely attenuated at distances greater than 2 mm from the electrode. One way of demonstrating this effect was to slide an electrode steadily toward another while observing the resistance. This did not fall until the separation was less than 3 mm, even when the skin was smeared with a thin layer of conducting medium. Another way of demonstrating this effect was to smear a metal electrode with conducting paste and apply it to dry skin. After stabilization, sliding the electrode sideways did not increase conductivity even though a trail of paste was now including a much greater area.

Anatomical locations.   The palmar and plantar surfaces have long been recognized as the most active in displaying electrodermal responses. Because of the very high concentration of sweat glands in these areas this observation has been viewed as support for the sweat gland as the effector for this reflex. Other areas, however, which contain far fewer sweat glands do show exosomatic activity of just as high amplitude, for example the dorsal surface of the fingers (Edelberg, 1964a). Endosomatic activity may sometimes be observed on the dorsum of the foot and on the arms and legs to a degree approaching that of the palms or soles in amplitude. Despite the relatively high exosomatic activity on the palms and soles, these sites do not represent the most conductive ones on the body, this position being claimed by the scalp. The likely reason for this is the hair con-

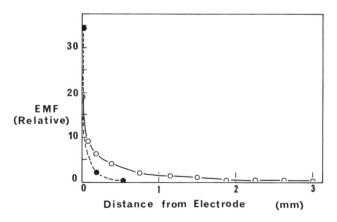

FIG. 1.1. Decay of potential as a function of distance from an exosomatic microelectrode. Measurements were made on human skin using a moveable microelectrode voltage probe. O, moderately moist skin; ●, drier skin in same area several minutes later.

centration in this region, since the hair follicle has been shown to be the most accessible route for percutaneous absorption (Rothman, 1954, Ch. 3). A comparison of the relative skin conductance at various anatomical points is presented in Table 1.1. Relative GSR amplitude is also tabulated for some of these

TABLE 1.1 *Survey of skin conductance and skin conductance response amplitude at various points on the body.*
Values are expressed in terms of average ratio to the values for the palmar surface of the finger.

Site	N	Relative Con-ductance	N	Relative GSR Amplitude
Finger				
Palmar	All	1.00	All	1.00
Dorsal.	14	0.64	20	0.90
Hand				
Palmar (thenar, hypothenar, and center)	12	1.21	6	1.38
Dorsal.	5	0.32		
Wrist				
Volar	11	0.38	5	0.13
Dorsal.	5	0.36		
Forearm				
Volar	19	0.43		
Dorsal.	3	0.37		
Upper arm				
Medial	12	0.16		
Lateral	5	0.18		
Deltoid	5	0.26		
Shoulder				
Ventral	9	0.33		
Neck				
Ventral	8	0.53		
Dorsal.	6	0.84		
Forehead				
Midway between eye and scalp	5	1.55		
Scalp				
Coronal suture.	7	4.41		
Parieto-occipital	7	2.96		
Chest				
Lateral wall, midaxillary line, level of 6th rib	9	0.35		
Ventral, 1 in. below nipple	10	0.47		
Sternum, at level of nipples	8	0.87		
Back				
Interscapular, level of inferior angle	9	0.64		
Abdomen				
Lateral	9	0.57		
Ventral, 1 in. below navel	8	0.62		

TABLE 1.1   *(Continued)*

Site	N	Relative Con- ductance	N	Relative GSR Amplitude
Thigh				
Lateral	5	0.28		
Leg				
Lower lateral	6	0.60		
Foot				
Dorsal.	14	0.53	9	0.20
Medial, over abductor				
hallucis muscle	8	1.26	15	1.70
Lateral			5	0.68
Plantar				
Heel	8	1.32	14	0.88
Arch	9	0.91	10	0.60
Ball	8	0.89	14	0.61
Toe	8	1.27	3	0.38

sites. The average resting potential relative to the inside of the body also varies predictably according to anatomical region. A comparison of some of these against skin-drilled sites is shown in Table 1.2. The relative amplitude of skin potential responses from these sites is also tabulated.

TABLE 1.2   *Skin potential and relative skin potential response (SPR) amplitude at various sites.* Reference is a skin-drilled site. SPR is expressed in ratio of total activity to that of the palmar surface of the finger.

Site	N	Skin Potential	N	Relative SPR Activity
Finger		*mv*		
Palmar	25	−39.0	All	1.00
Dorsal	13	−24.8	12	0.57
Forearm				
Over ulnar bone, 2 in. from elbow . . .	13	−15.2	12	0.07
Ear				
Inner aspect of ear lobe.	25	−14.1	24	0.05
Leg				
Over tibial bone, 2 in. above junction				
with foot	13	− 9.2	39	0.18
Foot				
Dorsal.			7	0.23
Lateral, near sole.			6	1.52
Medial, over abductor hallucis muscle. .	13	−36.2	12	1.94
Plantar				
Heel.			12	3.87
Ball			12	1.89

Attention should be drawn to one of those sites which, because of its conveni- ent location and activity level, is highly promising for use in sleep runs, long term runs, or runs in which hands must be free. This site is on the medial side of the foot over the *abductor hallucis muscle* adjacent to the plantar surface and midway between the first phalange and a point directly beneath the ankle. The area is one which is not susceptible to damage by standing or walking, and its location along the shaft of the foot allows effective securing of the electrode without slippage.

The choice of site depends in part on the type of electrode to be used and in part upon the experimental design. Thus, the fingers lend themselves readily to masking and to affixing a plate type electrode with tape. If the thenar or hypo- thenar eminence is used, the electrode will tend to slip unless it is either cemented in place or clipped on as in the method of Clark and Lacey (1950). Use of the nonpreferred hand for electrode application is a useful standardization because it allows the other hand to be free for experiments involving writing or manipu- lation. If the finger is used, it has been found desirable to use the middle seg- ment rather than the tip, because of the higher frequency of cuts and scratches on the tip. The effect of these on response amplitude has been described else- where (Edelberg & Burch, 1962). Palmar sites are conventionally used but the activity of the dorsal surface of the finger has been found to be equal to, and frequently greater than, that of the palmar surface.

Temperature effects. Like most biological processes, SR, GSR, and SPR are very susceptible to temperature effects. Skin resistance increases by about 3% for a drop in temperature of 1°C. This relation is rather predictable and un- complicated. GSR on the other hand undergoes a complex change when the temperature at the site is altered. In the first moments of a rapid temperature change, amplitude increases by about 5%/degree C but within a few min- utes returns to control level (Maulsby & Edelberg, 1960). If, however, local surface temperature is dropped to below 20° C, GSR amplitude, after the initial rise and return to base line, falls progressively over a 30-min period in the ma- jority of subjects, eventually disappearing entirely in many cases. The influence of temperature upon SPR is even more complex because of the differential effects upon the positive and negative waves. Yokota, Takahashi, Kondo, and Fujimori (1959) have attempted to describe these differential effects which are further complicated by regional differences. The relationship is so complex that the interested reader is advised to consult the original paper. In interpreting the results of Yokota et al one should bear in mind the interaction between positive and negative amplitudes in a biphasic wave, due to their partial mutual cancel- lation (Holmquest & Edelberg, 1964).

Aside from direct effects of temperature on the effector, there is the secondary effect of hypoxia resulting from thermally-induced vasoconstriction. In a study in which the temperature of the site was artificially maintained constant while vasoconstriction was induced by nearby cooling to 15°C, the amplitude of

GSR fell to 81% of its resting level in a period of 8 to 15 min (Edelberg, 1964b). The effect increased at this rate if the cooling was continued. Interestingly, resistance level was not changed by this maneuver.

These various observations make it clear that temperature must be maintained relatively constant for valid electrodermal measurement. Furthermore, if field conditions result in total body surface cooling, a secondary effect mediated by vasoconstriction must be anticipated. This is of special relevance when subjects run during winter months come in from outdoors even though the laboratory be thermostatically controlled. In practice it has been found that a full hour may be necessary to reverse thermal vasoconstriction. If the feet are used as sites of measurement the effect may be even greater.

As has been reported by Wenger (1943) and by Costiloe and Schneider (1964), there is a significant seasonal variation in skin conductance. There are furthermore significant although generally low correlations with a number of other environmental factors such as pressure, humidity, and air contamination (Wenger & Gustafson, 1962; Wenger & Cullen, 1962).

Electrode pressure. Pressure on the electrode area should be as low as possible in keeping with the securing of the electrode, largely because the local occlusion of blood flow occasioned by relatively slight constriction may produce a severe attentuation of GSR and especially of the positive wave of the SPR. The implication of this effect on choice of electrode configuration has already been discussed. The chamber electrode, if sealed and hypertonic, may produce a considerable pressure of osmotic origin. Changes in pressure may act as a local stimulus producing the Ebbecke wave which resembles an artifact but represents a true biological response. The result of pressing an electrode against the skin is frequently an Ebbecke response rather than an effect due to a shortening of the transverse path from electrode plate to skin. This response, like true artifact, has a very short latency, and the criterion used by Prideaux (1920) to distinguish artifact from electrodermal activity does not always hold. The geometric effect with any paste of reasonable conductivity can be shown to be rather negligible provided the plate to skin space is entirely filled.

Current density and area. This parameter has been the basis of rather heated debate, largely because electrodermal measurements began before adequate instrumentation had come of age. Insufficient sensitivity of the recording system could be counteracted in part by the use of higher applied current sources. These levels, dictated by the limits of amplification, became relatively standard among many investigators. When, with the arrival of better amplifiers, it was demonstrated that appreciably lower limits of applied current were in order, there was a predictable controversy. Grings (1953) called attention to the fall in SR which accompanies increasing current density. The range of linear behavior for a sample of subjects was later shown to be in the region of 10 μamp/cm^2 (Edelberg et al, 1960). Beyond this limit, the level of resistance and the amplitude of GSR both fell significantly. Evidence was presented in this work to show that these higher currents, if maintained, would produce a progressively more serious effect. Wenger and Gustafson (1962) also demonstrated a time effect, showing that intermittent imposition of currents, 12.7 μamp/cm^2, produced a much less serious reduction of resistance than did steady application. This latter observation has especially serious implications for long term runs, such as sleep studies, in which steady currents of at least 10 μamp/cm^2 are used.

Recently, a series of voltage-current curves was run on a population of 40 subjects, using an X-Y recorder so that a complete curve could be determined in 5 sec. This technique greatly contributed to the accuracy of the curve and revealed that the limiting factor for linearity is the voltage developed rather than the current applied; subjects with very low resistance could tolerate much higher current densities, e.g. 75 μamp/cm^2 in the linear range. At very high resistances such as may be encountered in sleep, the subject could tolerate perhaps as little as 4 μamp/cm^2 before their curves became nonlinear. The voltage cutoff which allowed inclusion of the entire population in a linear range was approximately 0.8 v across a single site. This seems contradictory of early results in which the upper limit for linearity was around 16 μamp/cm^2 . While this may be due to a population or seasonal difference, it is more likely that the discrepancy is to be explained on the basis of the time of exposure. This supposition was in fact demonstrated by the effect of halting the change of voltage during determination of the curve; a distinct bend was produced as the current flow at the fixed voltage point spontaneously increased. This confirms the observations of Wenger and Gustafson (1962).

Despite the complicating temporal effect, this author is inclined to accept the conclusion that exosomatic limits should be expressed in terms of voltage rather than current. The temporal effect would indicate that the tolerable level of 0.8 v across a single site obtained in these short exposures is too high. The voltage limit reported in the earlier study ranged from 0.4 to 1.5 v across a single site. On this basis it seems reasonable, pending better data, to adopt a value of 0.5 v across each site as a limit for exosomatic measures. This discussion also implies that a constant voltage system is to be preferred over a constant current system.

Methods of Measurement

Until such time as conductance and potential measures may be shown to have different significance, most investigators, it seems will continue to regard them as alternative ways of measuring a common type of behavior. The choice then depends upon their respective operational advantages, some of which are enumerated below.

Advantages of the exosomatic method. (1) Conductance (or resistance) measures are always unidirectional and are therefore simpler to analyze. (2) They are less affected by electrode bias. (3) There has been a wealth of literature built up around base levels of conductance; reliable correlations with certain behavioral or pathological states and relatively reliable relations of response amplitude to base level have been found (although subject to controversy). No satisfactory relations have been as yet demonstrated with skin potentials. (4) When constant current is used, considerably less gain is normally required. (5) No inactive reference is required.

Advantages of the endosomatic method. (1) It is more physiological insofar as no current is applied to the skin. This is of especial advantage in long term runs. (2) Since essentially no current flow occurs, electrode polarization is not a problem.(3) The accessory circuitry is simpler, although a bucking circuit must be used. If condenser coupling with *long* time-constant is used, even the bucking circuit may be eliminated. (4) The positive and negative waves may have independent behavioral significance (Edelberg, 1963).

General considerations in exosomatic measurement. Ohm's law lays the basis for exosomatic measurements despite the fact that skin resistance is largely apparent. If one expresses it as $R = E/I$, *resistance* is seen to be directly proportional to the voltage, E, which develops when current, I, is held constant. If expressed in terms of *conductance*, C, where $C = I/R$, it is seen that conductance or conductance change can be measured directly in terms of current since $C = I/E$. These relations form the basis of the two major systems used today. Some of the early systems, e.g. Veraguth (1909), were actually of the constant voltage type, since the experimenter merely placed a battery across the subject and measured current flow through a galvanometer. The Wheatstone Bridge was also used, starting with Féré (1888), and is presently still the most common system for exosomatic measures. It is convenient for accurate determination of base resistance and at the same time allows balancing out of the greater part of the generated potential so that higher amplification can be used to observe the fluctuations in the envelope. Up to the early 1930's, most applications of the Wheatstone Bridge were accomplished under conditions which optimized its sensitivity, namely with the four arms approximately equal. Under this condition, power through the subject and bridge sensitivity are greatest for any given bridge voltage, but neither voltage across, nor current through, the subject is maintained constant when the subject resistance changes. To my knowledge, it was Davis (1929a) who first emphasized the importance of controlling current strength and who introduced an electronic circuit for maintaining constant current (1929b). Richter (1929), was independently making constant current measurements of skin resistance with a circuit that called for manual adjustment of voltage to keep a galvanometer deflection constant. Such a circuit was suitable for measurement of base level but not of response. Shortly afterwards Darrow (1932) introduced a constant-current Wheatstone Bridge circuit which is still in widespread use.

Principles of bridge measurement. It seems profitable in view of the numerous forms of bridge circuitry to examine certain principles of bridge application. Let us first recognize that a Wheatstone Bridge is designed for use either at balance, when no current flows in the meter circuit, or with such a high impedance meter that even at off-balance settings, no meter current flows. It is only under these two circumstances that the conventional analysis of bridge circuits (as opposed to a network) is valid. When a subject becomes an arm of a bridge under these conditions, one pair of bridge arms serves only as a voltage reference, in effect as a bucking battery to cancel out the major portion of the voltage developed across the subject so that meter sensitivity can be greatly increased. In Fig. 1.2, when the subject experiences a GSR, the high impedance voltmeter, V_s, across R_s reads the same change as the one across the bridge. V_b, but the bridge meter, V_b, fluctuates approximately about zero, V_s, about the subject's total voltage.

Consider only the single arm of this bridge, $\overline{ABC}$. The voltage across the series resistor is

$$e_1 = \frac{R_k}{R_k + R_s} \cdot E_b \tag{5}$$

where E_b is the bridge supply voltage. Let the subject undergo a small change in resistance, ΔR. The new voltage across R_k is

$$e_2 = \frac{R_k}{R_k + R_s + \Delta R} \cdot E_b$$

The change in voltage, reflected equally but oppositely across either R_k or R_s, is

$$\Delta e = e_2 - e_1 = E_b R_k \left(\frac{1}{R_k + R_s + \Delta R} - \frac{1}{R_k + R_s} \right) \tag{6}$$

$$\Delta e = - E_b R_k \cdot \frac{\Delta R}{(R_k + R_s)(R_k + R_s + \Delta R)} \tag{7}$$

Case 1: Constant current. If $R_k \gg R_s$, current is essentially constant and the equation is approximately reduced to

$$\Delta e \approx - E_b R_k \cdot \frac{\Delta R}{R_k^2} = - \frac{E_b}{R_k} \cdot \Delta R \approx - I \Delta R \tag{8}$$

Case 2: Constant voltage. If $R_k \ll R_s$ the voltage across the subject is essentially constant and

$$R_k + R_s \approx R_s$$

$$R_k + R_s + \Delta R \approx R_s + \Delta R$$

Hence, from Equation 6

$$\Delta e \approx E_b R_k \left(\frac{1}{R_s + \Delta R} - \frac{1}{R_s} \right) \tag{9}$$

$$\approx E_b R_k \left(C_2 - C_1 \right) = E_b R_k \Delta C$$

Case 3. Consider the case formerly used in electrodermal bridges in which $R_k \approx R_s$

$$\Delta e = E_b R_k \left(\frac{1}{R_k + R_s + \Delta R} - \frac{1}{R_k + R_s} \right)$$

$$\approx E_b R_k \left(\frac{1}{2R_s + \Delta R} - \frac{1}{2R_s} \right)$$

$$\approx \frac{E_b R_k}{2} \left(\frac{1}{R_s + \frac{\Delta R}{2}} - \frac{1}{R_s} \right)$$

or

$$\Delta e \approx \frac{E_b R_k}{4} \cdot \frac{\Delta R}{R_s \left(R_s + \frac{\Delta R}{2} \right)} \tag{10}$$

an expression in which Δe is proportional to neither a resistance change nor a conductance change.

The constant voltage and the constant current systems may thus be regarded as extremes of an asymmetrical bridge. When R_k is much greater than R_s, for example by 50 times, subject current is relatively constant despite major shifts in subject resistance. When R_k is far less than R_s, e.g. one-fiftieth, the voltage across S is virtually constant and the system measures conductance directly. Since the balancing arms of the bridge $\overline{ADC}$ serve only to supply reference voltage, a bucking system may be conveniently substituted as has been done by Withers (1956). A simpler circuit is shown in Fig. 1.3. The circuit constants have been selected for a constant current of 8 μamp through sites 1 cm². For smaller sites, the series resistors, R_a and R_k should be increased in inverse proportion to site area.

Comparison of Constant Current and Constant Voltage Systems

There is an excellent physiological justification for the use of a constant voltage system. If a constant *voltage* is applied to the skin, each element will draw an amount of current in proportion to its conductivity. Consider an ele-

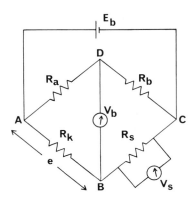

FIG. 1.2. General circuit for Wheatstone Bridge used in electrodermal measurement. R_s, Subject resistance.

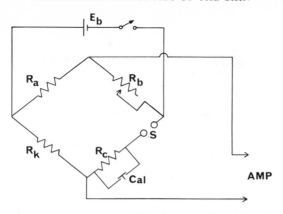

FIG. 1.3. Constant current system providing 8 μamp. E_b = 90 v; R_a and R_k = 11.25 megohms each; R_b = 500 K; R_c = 1 K.

ment of epidermis which has been demonstrated to account for a large part of the total conductivity of the skin (Edelberg, 1961). If sweat glands open or close, the amount of current going through this element remains unchanged, as does the absolute contribution of this area to total effect. Conversely, change in epidermal conductivity does not alter the electrical effect of a given change in a sweat gland.

By contrast, if a constant *current* is imposed, the available current will divide itself among the various elements in accordance with their relative conductivity. If for some reason the epidermis should become more resistant, more current will transit the sweat glands. If a portion of the sweat glands close down, the remainder will receive more current. This also implies that a given physiological change in a sweat gland will produce a greater voltage change if the epidermal shunt is closed down. Also, assuming certain sweat glands can "close down" while others continue normal operation, the same physiological change in a given sweat gland will produce a greater electrical change as more sweat glands become inactive. In circuit terms, the conductances of units in parallel and changes in these conductances are directly additive; their resistances are not. Although this may be considered irrelevant since one can directly convert net conductance to net resistance, physiologically the two may not be directly interchangeable. If because of decreased conductivity in some elements, an unduly high current density is experienced by others, there may well be an "injury" effect or at least a depressant effect exerted on these over-exposed units, even though total current remains at an otherwise tolerable level. This may explain why voltage, rather than current, appears to be the appropriate criterion for limit on linearity (see p. 19).

The constant voltage system is not without its own problems. Its effectiveness as a measuring system is premised on the assumption that the site consists of a

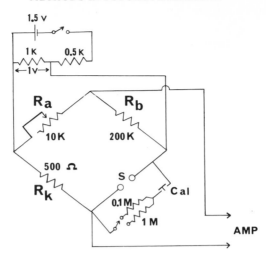

FIG. 1.4. Constant voltage system providing 0.5 v across each site with direct reading of conductance on linear potentiometer.

group of parallel units, each exposed to the standard voltage. In such a system any unknown series resistance creates a far more serious effect than in the constant current system. With a dry corneum, for example, a constant current system will reflect an error in base resistance, but the absolute fluctuations in resistance due to activity of the membrane in series with the corneum will be unaffected. In the constant voltage system, where $\Delta I = E \Delta C$, any drop in voltage occurring across the corneum reduces the value of E, the proportionality constant in the above equation, and hence gives an unduly low indication of the magnitude of the membrane change. It obviously follows that a well hydrated skin site is necessary in the constant voltage system.

The area requirements of both exosomatic systems must be considered in selection of circuit constants. In the constant current system, current intensity must be varied in inverse relation to the size of the site. Thus no change of site area can be made without correcting current strength to maintain density constant. The constant voltage system places no requirement of this sort on the operator, but as the site is made progressively smaller, less current is drawn and the sensitivity of the system is reduced. As the size of the constant voltage site is made higher, and its resistance therefore lower, attention must be given to the size of the series resistor used for current determination. This may become an appreciable fraction of the subject resistance, and therefore violate a basic requirement for maintaining constant voltage. Provisions can be made in the circuit for altering this in conjunction with electrode size, bearing in mind, however, that this changes the calibration. If an essentially unlimited gain is available, this resistor may be made very low, e.g. 50 ohms, and the system may be applied to any subject having a resistance of 2000 ohms or more for the site used.

A system embodying these principles is shown in Fig. 1.4. In building such a conductance circuit it is most convenient to be able to use the vernier on a 10-turn linear potentiometer for direct reading of conductance. As long as the product $R_B \times R_K = 10^n$, where n is a whole number, the readings on R_a will be some decimal multiple of the conductance. In the example given, each 100 ohms on R_a is equivalent to a subject conductance of 1 μmho. The 1-v source places 0.5 v across each site.

Unfortunately for the constant voltage system, the measurement of subject current is far less efficient than the measurement of subject voltage. For example, with a subject resistance of 100 K, a constant current system using 10 μamp will generate 1 v across the subject and will show a deflection of 10 mv for a 1 K change. A constant voltage system of 1 v under these same conditions with a series resistor as high as 5 K will show a deflection of only 0.5 mv.

One perplexing problem of the constant voltage system is that of the uncontrolled current through the subject. Almost no choice of constant voltage is suitable for the entire range of conductances. If the subject's resistance should fall to the low range of the distribution of the population, i.e. 10 K $\cdot$cm^2, voltage would have to be limited to 0.1 v to restrict current to 10 μamp/cm^2. This choice of voltage would aggravate the already serious amplification problem resulting from the inefficiency involved in measuring current. Higher voltages, e.g. 1 v, producing a current of only 10 μamp at a resistance of 100 K, would at a resistance of 10 K result in 100 μamp. One further difficulty of this system is in the choice of the series resistance. The series resistor if made low enough to produce essentially constant voltage at all subject conductances would make the amplification requirement even higher, thereby raising problems of signal-noise level as well as availability of instruments. If it is made high enough for use with an amplifier of reasonably high gain, the error in constancy of voltage becomes unacceptable.

Hagfors (1964) has developed a circuit which circumvents this latter problem provided the system is in balance by using the basic circuit in Fig. 1.5. As long as the meter resistance is negligible and the system is near balance, the voltage drop across R_m is negligible. Conductance change in R_s produces a proportional current change through the meter. In practice, Hagfors uses a variable shunt across the subject to make the total conductance of subject + shunt equal to that of R_k. Although this system when in balance is superior to the bridge circuit in terms of constancy of voltage across the subject, it suffers from the same limitations in terms of the impedance of the meter. If this becomes too low, its sensitivity becomes too low; if it is made high enough for common use, it no longer faithfully reflects changes in conductance.

Lykken and Roth (1961) have also provided a solution to this problem, by using a transistorized amplifier with an input impedance of only 100 ohms for

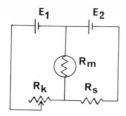

FIG. 1.5. Basic constant voltage circuit, after Hagfors. $E_1 = E_2$. At balance $R_k = R_s$.

measurement of current. They *select* levels of constant voltage to limit current to 10 μamp.

Besides amplifier gain, input impedance and source impedance limitations of the recording system must be considered. Whether a bridge system or a bucking system is used, the impedance of the amplifier should be high relative to the resistance of the source. In the constant voltage system, the series resistor will normally be 1 K or less (it must not be greater than 5% of the subject's resistance) and an amplifier with as little as 100-K input impedance is acceptable. This source impedance is low enough to be compatible with the requirements of most transistorized amplifiers which usually demand a value of 10 K or less. With the constant current system, the amplifier is placed across the subject (bucking system) or across the subject and the balancing arm (bridge system). Since the subject resistance may at times reach 0.5 megohm or more, the impedance of the amplifier must be considerable, preferably 100 megohms, to prevent its becoming an appreciable shunt. Thus, an amplifier of the common variety having 1-megohm input impedance placed across a subject with 250-K resistance will shunt 20% of the "constant" current, and the measured resistance across the subject will thereby be in error by 20%. This high source impedance also poses a problem when using transistorized amplifiers, causing them to become nonlinear and noisy.

It becomes clear that the choice between constant current and constant voltage systems, like that between endosomatic and exosomatic methods, poses a compromise. A summary of some of their relative advantages is presented below.

Advantages of the constant current system. (1) It requires lower amplification, of the order of 1/10 that of the constant voltage system. (2) It limits current density at very low levels of subject resistance to levels known to be tolerable. Constant voltage may produce unduly high currents at low subject resistance. (3) At low subject resistance, it consumes less battery power. (4) It limits current density through the electrode, regardless of subject resistance, and hence limits electrode polarization. (5) In cases where the dry horny layer offers a high resistance the base level but *not* response amplitude is affected.

Advantages of the constant voltage system. (1) The development of high voltages and an accompanying "injury" effect at high subject resistance is avoided. (2) The system in a sense is self-correcting for peripheral effect of base level on response amplitude. Thus less gain change is required. (3) The source impedance seen by the amplifier is low and constant, contrary to the case with constant current. (4) Deflections are in terms of conductance units. This eliminates one step in ultimate data reduction, since conductance or log conductance has been commonly adopted as the most appropriate measure. (5) The current flowing through one element of the electrode site is independent of what is flowing through the others. (6) Under certain conditions, the constant voltage system may be used for sites of different size without circuit adjustment. This is not true of constant current circuits.

Endosomatic Contamination of Exosomatic Measures

The problem of endosomatic contamination of exosomatic measures is one which plagues the investigator (Lacey, Bateman, & Van Lehn, 1953; Edelberg & Burch, 1962). Any endogenous difference in potential between two skin sites, or any change in this difference, will add algebraically to the exosomatic potential developed by the *constant current* system. Although endosomatic (diffusion) potentials are considerably altered by the application of an external current, they can nevertheless produce a net result which is neither fish nor fowl (Fig. 1.6). Under ordinary circumstances, exosomatic voltage and voltage change, which in the constant current system are proportional to resistance and resistance change, are large enough to mask out endosomatic effects (Fig. 1.6). As resistance falls, however, skin potential and skin potential changes may account for a considerable portion of the total measure, possibly more than half. Furthermore, inactivation of the exosomatic response does not at all imply inactivation of the endosomatic system. If the exosomatic and endosomatic voltages are of the same order and of opposite polarity, an apparent resistance of zero, or even a "negative" resistance, as well as apparent increases of resistance during a GSR, may appear. Lacey et al. (1953) circumvented this problem by reversing polarity every 30 sec and calculating the mean of the two measures.

With a *constant voltage* system, an endosomatic potential, P, will divide itself across the series resistor, R_k, and the subject resistance in the same proportion as the battery voltage, such that the voltage across R_k (Fig. 1.2) is

$$e = \frac{R_k}{R_k + R_s} \cdot P \tag{11}$$

This effect, then, becomes greater as the subject resistance falls. The amount of error will be small if the internal resistance of the subject is high relative to the series resistance. This further reinforces the desirability of keeping the series resistance of the constant voltage measuring system as low as possible. The endosomatic error is also a function of the applied voltage, becoming proportionally smaller as the source voltage becomes larger.

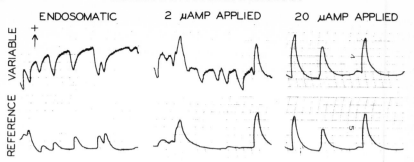

FIG. 1.6. Interaction of skin potential response with exosomatic GSR. Reference is an inactive site. *Lower trace* in each case is the exosomatic trace at 20 μamp applied to site 2cm². Gain of *first two upper traces* is 5 times that of others. (From Edelberg, R., & Burch, N. R. *Archs. gen. Psychiat.*, 1962, 7: 163-169.)

The endosomatic effect can be minimized by the use of two matched active sites. It can be shown that two sites chosen on the same aspect of a single appendage, and separated from each other by not more than 1 or 2 cm, have similar transcutaneous potentials and similar endosomatic responses, resulting in almost complete common mode cancellations of these potentials.

Under some circumstances, for example in simultaneous comparison of two sites for the effect of a variable applied to one of them, it has been practical, because of single-ended amplification, to use a common inactive site which was so large that it made a negligible contribution to the total resistance when paired with the much smaller active sites (Edelberg et al., 1960). The endosomatic contribution was assumed to be relatively similar in each of the compared active sites and therefore to be canceled out in the comparison. Skin potential, however, may in itself be affected by the variable factor and constitute a source of error. Furthermore, although any contribution of the common inactive site is canceled out in the comparison, it serves to dilute the relative effect of the variable. Unforeseen contribution of this common site may also produce a considerable amount of cross-talk. As an over-all practice it is best to avoid such possibilities entirely and to make the use of independent matched pairs of sites standard procedure for all exosomatic measures. This choice has been facilitated by the growing availability of excellent DC amplifiers whose common mode rejection of 60-cps interference from line voltage fields is optimally utilized when both electrodes have the same impedance to ground. An electrode array consisting of two electrodes having balanced input to the amplifier and a system ground on the subject but outside the measuring circuit is most effective.

Polarity Reversal in Exosomatic Systems

After reviewing the literature on electrodes, Landis (1932) expressed doubts that a truly nonpolarizable electrode would ever appear. Relatively high electrode currents, necessary to overcome the limitation in amplification or to avoid endosomatic effects can be calculated to produce at least some degree of polarization. This effect may become accentuated if prolonged use of an anodized silver electrode as the cathode of a pair causes electrolysis of the chloride coating while the other becomes continuously anodized. As one solution to the problem of polarization, Ax (1960) resorted to polarity reversal twice per sec. This method not only tends to reduce polarization, but inadvertently reduces the undesirable biological effects of excess current density. It also serves to allow correction for the contribution of endosomatic potential to base level as in Lacey's method. This switching demands special accessory circuitry but is well worth the added complexity. It carries with it the problem of switching artifacts, however. Such switching circuits are not to be confused with sinusoidal AC measurements which will be treated in a separate section.

Endosomatic Measurement

Two similar skin sites which have a high potential relative to the inside of the body and which undergo large fluctuations in this potential will not show any indication of this activity if they are connected as a pair to a sensitive voltmeter since only the difference in their potential can be measured. Hence, two sites of dissimilar activity must be chosen. For the difference in potential to be interpretable, one of them must be a fixed reference. If, for example, the arm was assumed to be inactive and was paired with the palm, a negative response in the arm would be wrongly interpreted as a positive response from the palm. Unfortunately, it is not true that a region which is inactive in conductance response is also inactive in potential response, and the arm, often used as the "inactive" reference site for potential measurements, can in fact become very active. Examples of the relative endosomatic activity of various skin sites were presented in Table 1.2. These were measured by recording against a site rendered inactive by the skin-drilling method of Shackel (1959), a painless, readily learned technique which removes enough of the epidermis to break through the barrier layer and in effect short-circuits the site to the inside of the body. If there is objection to skin drilling, e.g. with certain types of patients or with young children, certain other sites may be substituted, which though not at zero transcutaneous potential are essentially inactive in terms of skin potential response (Table 1.2). One of these is the inner aspect of the ear lobe. Another is directly over the ulnar bone at a point one-fifth the distance from the elbow to the wrist. A third is directly over the tibia, at a point one-eighth the distance from the foot to the knee. Of the three, the ear lobe is most inactive being essentially as activity free as a skin-drilled site, but its use may introduce an electrocardiograph artifact into the record which is often considerable. The use of the ulnar site as a reference for hand measurement and of the tibial site for foot measurement is preferred despite the danger of a small SPR contribution from the reference. It should be emphasized that the base potential recorded under these circumstances is ambiguous, because these references have a finite transcutaneous potential which can undergo slow drift independently and in accord-

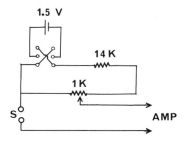

Fig. 1.7. Bucking circuit for use in measuring skin potential response.

ance with change in behavioral state. Skin potential data are therefore generally not comparable from subject to subject or even within a single subject across conditions unless the skin drilling technique is used. This may in part account for the absence of correlation between SPR and SP reported in the literature (Wilcott, 1958b). The use of concentrated brine to eliminate skin potential activity has been reported by Keller (1931) and this method has been adopted by various workers, but I have demonstrated that exposure of a site to concentrated brine (5 M) for as long as 45 min does not appreciably reduce its potential or activity relative to a skin-drilled site.

In recording of SPR, one encounters the same problems found in so many other measures, that of observing small fluctuations in a sizeable base level. The necessity of eliminating the large steady component cannot be dealt with by the bridge methods used for resistance or conductance measures. Instead, one uses a bucking system which consists essentially of a variable voltage source placed between the subject and the amplifier. The circuit in Fig. 1.7 allows cancelation of up to ± 100 mv. The input impedance of the amplifier must be very high relative to the subject resistance, since the endosomatic potential distributes itself across the subject and the amplifier in proportion to their relative impedances. If the input impedance of the amplifier were only four times the subject resistance, for example, potentials and responses would be attenuated 20%. One way to maximize the amplifier-to-subject impedance ratio is to make the endosomatic site as large as possible.

Measurement of Skin Impedance

The impedance of the skin to alternating current is determined by a network represented by the circuit in Fig. 1.8, which is a modification of Cole's model (1933). C_s represents the static, fixed, or structural capacity of the membrane, and P, the polarization element involving a polarization capacity, C_p, and a series polarization resistance, R_p. C_p and R_p are functions of current intensity and frequency. C_p is in fact not a true capacitance but a representation of the energy-storing aspect of membrane structure responsible for the development of the counter-emf (Fricke, 1932; Cole, 1933). The parallel resistance, R_m, is the

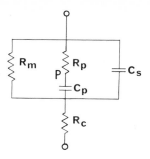

Fig. 1.8. Circuit model of the skin

ohmic resistance of the membrane which corresponds with the hypothesis that the membrane is a leaky capacitor and can in fact conduct a direct current. The series resistance, R_c, represents in part the resistance of the corneum and in part that of the corium and of the internal volume conductor. At extremely low levels of DC, the true ohmic resistance of the membrane can theoretically be determined since polarization at that stage is negligible and the site of C_p acts predominantly as an ohmic conductor. As current strength increases, polarization increases and C_p becomes appreciable. The development of the counter-emf can be observed by the deviation of the shape of the voltage rise curve from an exponential form at about 50 μsec after application of a step voltage (Hozawa, 1928). The behavior of polarized skin is probably best understood if we think of an imaginary battery placed in series in the current path oriented so that it opposes current flow. As higher potentials are applied, the ion flux through the system increases, but so does the strength of the battery which is generated by this flux. Thus only a relatively small fraction of the potential across the cell is of the dissipative IR drop type. The rest is conservative, in the form of the polarization potential. When an alternating current is applied to the skin, the total impedance falls with increase in frequency as does an ordinary RC network (Barnett, 1938), but because of the nature of polarization capacity, which decreases with increase in frequency, reactance maintains a constant relation to resistance and hence phase angle tends to remain relatively constant, over a wide frequency range, reported variously from 55° to 83°. The impedance of human skin and especially the phase angle has been used in dermatological research (Rothman, 1954, Ch. 7) because of its implications with regard to skin structure.

The effect of the neural impulses associated with electrodermal activity is to change the selective permeability of cutaneous membranes and thereby the polarization capacity. Since polarization capacity at high frequencies, i.e. above 10kc becomes relatively small, it can be appreciated that the GSR is almost unobservable at high frequencies. This lays the basis for using very high frequencies, e.g. 50 kc in impedance plethysmography since at this frequency, Z,

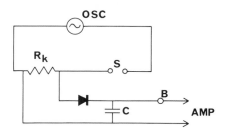

FIG. 1.9. Simple circuit for determining skin impedance. R_k = 50 ohms; C = 2.0 ufd; applied voltage = 0.5 v (RMS). Bucking circuit may be inserted at *Point B*.

reduces to approximately the value of R_c and it becomes fairly certain that the contribution of the skin to any fluctuations in Z is negligible. This is so only if the series ohmic resistance of the skin itself does not change. When the site becomes relatively dry, however, and the series resistance of the corneum appreciable, a sudden episode of sweating may hydrate the corneum and produce an ohmic resistance change which effectively changes impedance. I have been able, by controlling the resting moisture level of the skin, to record GSRs on this basis even at 20 kc. The observation by Forbes and Landis (1935) of GSR activity above 12 kc may perhaps be interpreted on this same basis. At lower frequencies polarization capacity is appreciable, and true GSR may be measured, although with some decrement up to at least 200 cps. Gerstner and Gerbstadt (1949) have used this same frequency to observe the relation of skin resistance to a variety of clinical conditions.

Most of the factors important to the measurement of apparent resistance also apply to skin impedance measurement. However, polarization of electrodes ceases to be a significant problem except at low frequencies provided the imposed voltage is symmetrical about zero. Impedance may be measured in two ways. In one simple method (Fig. 1.9), fixed alternating voltage is applied and the current rectified and measured. A DC bucking voltage may be inserted at *Point B* if one wishes to observe small fluctuations in the total impedance. For a more refined measurement in which the phase angle and equivalent capacitance and ohmic resistance may be obtained for any frequency desired, a commercially available AC bridge in conjunction with an external oscillator may be used. In the absence of a commercial bridge, the circuits of Forbes and Landis (1935), Barnett (1938), Bagno and Liebman (1959), or the one in Fig. 1.10 may be used with care being given to the exclusion of stray capacitance and inductance. Plutchik and Hirsch (1963) used the ellipticity of Lissajous figures on an oscilloscope to calculate phase angle and impedance. This method has the advantage of requiring only an oscillator and oscilloscope to make the determination, but is useful only for determining base level, not response. If a commercial bridge is used either with an external oscillator or with an internal generator, care must be taken to limit the peak voltage through the site. Under optimum

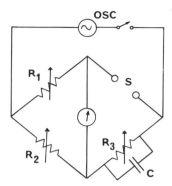

FIG. 1.10. Bridge circuit for determination of skin impedance and phase angle. R_1, R_2, R_3 = 100 K each; C = 0.1 ufd; applied voltage = 0.5 v (RMS). At balance $Z_1/Z_2 = Z_s/Z_{RC}$ and $(X_C)_s/R_s = 1/(2\pi f C R_3)$.

conditions the bridge is symmetrical and the subject receives approximately one-half the bridge voltage. A bridge supply of 0.5 v (RMS) will insure staying within a physiological range. Skin impedance responses recorded with a symmetrical bridge will of course have the same ambiguity discussed under DC measurement.

Amplifier Requirements

The various considerations discussed up to this point enter into the determination of amplification requirements as regards gain, frequency response, input impedance, limit of source impedance, base-line stability, common-mode rejection, and whether input is balanced or single-ended. *Gain* selection requires the greatest consideration.

Skin resistance will, of course, vary over a considerable range and the system chosen should be able to function for sites from 5 K·cm² to 250 K·cm². A site of 1 cm² is convenient in most instances. The resistance of two such sites in series might range from 10 to 500 K (or from 100 to 2 μmho). For a *constant current* system with 10 μamp/cm², the voltage developed would range from 0.1 v to 5 v. Note that this does not change with area if current *density* is maintained constant. Changes in this voltage for typical GSRs would range from negligible changes up to as high as 30%. If one is interested in the relative amplitudes of specific responses, it is useful to set gain as high as the maximum amplitude will allow. If a *count* of GSR is anticipated, one must set certain standards which determine the lower limit of amplitude for inclusion of a given wave in the count. Since the population of response amplitudes decreases continuously to zero (or practically to zero) the count will clearly be influenced by gain setting unless a standard in terms of some meaningful parameter is adopted. The choice of this limit is in part determined by the size of the maximum response expected, which should, ideally, still be "on scale." Experience has shown that for a constant current system, a gain that allows a full scale deflection in the neighborhood of 20% of the base level is suitable. This allows recognition of waves which are 0.2% of base level (i.e. 1% of full scale). Increasing the sensitivity beyond this increases the total GSR count but does not appreciably alter the sum of amplitudes after calibration correction. Furthermore, increasing sensitivity beyond this level increases the representation of ever-present background spontaneous activity and hence may dilute out the effects of a given variable on GSR count. For a current density of 10 μamp/cm² the system should be capable of a maximum gain of 20 mv full scale, to satisfy the above requirements.

In the constant voltage system, the sensitivity required of the amplifier is a function of the size of the current-measuring resistor, as well as area of the site. If the series resistor, R_k, is to be limited to 5% of the resistance of the subject, any increase in the size of the site must be accompanied by a proportional reduction in R_k. This does not imply a decrease in sensitivity, since current flow and current change per response will increase directly with area and will thereby compensate for the reduction in R_k. With this system it is logical to express range requirements in terms of an absolute conductance change, rather than as a fraction of base level. Experience indicates this to be 5 μmho for a pair of 1 cm² sites in series. As indicated previously, such a pair may be expected to have a minimum resistance of 10 K. The series resistor must therefore be 500 ohms or less. By using Equation 9, one finds that with a 1-v source and a 500-ohm series resistor, a full scale sensitivity of 2.5 mv is needed to obtain a range of 5 μmho. This holds for 1 cm² sites . If the sites are made 2 cm², R_k must be reduced to 250 ohms, but range is doubled and amplifier sensitivity therefore remains unchanged. The input impedance requirements of the DC amplifiers have been indicated elsewhere. For the constant voltage system, Z_i should be greater than 50 K and for a constant current system at least 10 megohms, preferably 100.

In AC *impedance measurement*, the amplifier requirements vary according to the nature of the measure. For total impedance at any given frequency when phase angle need not be measured, the circuit in Fig. 1.9 can be used and will produce a rectified voltage of the order of 1% of the applied 0.5 v source, i.e. in the range of 5 mv full scale; a low impedance DC amplifier will suffice. If the bridge circuit in Fig. 1.10 is used, the accuracy of the measurement will depend on the resolution of the null detector, whether it be auditory or visual. Since AC amplification can be used, with its readily available high gain, amplifier sensitivity is not a problem. The output of the AC amplifier can be rectified and fed into a low gain DC amplifier or used to drive a writer directly. As in any symmetrical bridge circuit, if the off-balance signal is to be measured, input impedance of the amplifier or detector should be as high as possible, and at least 10 megohms.

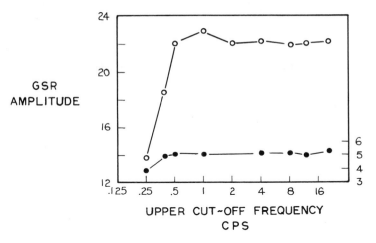

FIG. 1.11. Upper frequency characteristic of the GSR for medium amplitude (O) and small amplitude (●) waves. In each case, a single magnetically taped wave was fed repeatedly through a Krohn-Hite filter at various upper cutoff frequencies.

In general the *skin potential* of an active site, for example on the palm, is about 30 to 50 mv negative with respect to the inside of the body (Edelberg, 1963). Inactive areas are typically about 10 to 15 mv negative with respect to the inside of the body but may go positive. Hence one requires a full scale range of about 50 mv for measurement of base potential without a bucking battery. If SPR is to be measured, a bucking battery is used to allow higher amplification. A sensitivity level which allows the largest responses to be measured and still gives adequate resolution for ease of reading is attained at 10 mv full scale.

The *upper frequency cutoff* of almost any DC amplifier is much higher than necessary to record GSR. There are some rare exceptions, for example, in the case of a few high gain DC voltmeters employing low frequency choppers. By contrast, the frequency response of the pen-writer is in many instances borderline. The frequency response requirements of the GSR may be determined by recording a series of waves on magnetic tape, playing them back through low frequency filters set at various values of upper and lower cutoffs, and comparing amplitudes at each frequency. Figure 1.11 shows a typical example of the results of this evaluation. It indicates that an upper frequency response which is flat to 1 cps is adequate for faithful recording. Some waves have been observed whose frequency requirements ran to 2 cps, but these are relatively uncommon. The lower limit should ideally be DC not only because it is desirable to obtain base level values but because the top of a slow wave may have low frequency components in it which require essentially DC recording capabilities.

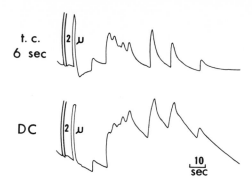

FIG. 1.12. Simultaneous direct-coupled and condenser-coupled recording of GSR from a single site. Time constant (*t.c.*) of condenser circuit is 6 sec.

Condenser-coupled Recording

There are occasions when the investigator may be willing to relinquish stringent low frequency requirements either because he does not have adequate DC amplification or because he would like to eliminate the need for frequent manual adjusting of the base-line position, for example in long term runs. Although there are some GSR instruments having automatic reset features on the market, most available systems require manual balancing. The use of a blocking capacitor can eliminate the need for monitoring since an artificial base line is established to which the recording always returns. Figure 1.12 shows simultaneous DC and condenser-coupled recording from the same site, using a 6-sec time-constant in the AC coupled system (Edelberg et al., 1960). An amplitude comparison shows that each system gives the same amplitude write-out despite the distortion of the recovery limb. Simons and Perez (1965) have superimposed the highly amplified AC write-out upon the DC base resistance trace to obtain both measures on a single channel. If SPR is to be recorded through a condenser-coupled system, a time constant of 15 sec or more should be used to avoid confusion of positive waves with overshoot during recovery.

In some cases it is desirable to write out the GSR on a condenser-coupled polygraph having a lower cutoff in the 1 cps range, e.g. the EKG setting, or even higher (Bloch, 1952). The use of this lower cutoff results in a wave which tends to approach the first derivative of the primary wave. Its amplitude is attenuated and it becomes biphasic. This effect is accentuated as the time constant is shortened further until at a value of 0.05 sec a rather faithful first derivative is obtained. The amplitude of the first derivative happily bears a linear relation to that of the primary wave (Fig. 1.13) and can therefore be used in its place if either relative rather than absolute amplitude data or count alone is desired. It may be this relationship which explains an equally useful observation,

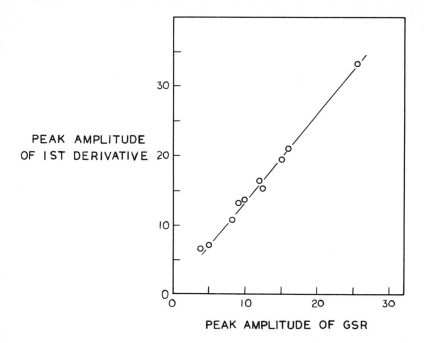

FIG. 1.13. Amplitude of the first derivative of the GSR as a function of the amplitude of the directly coupled primary wave write out. Units are in millimeters of deflection.

namely that the amplitudes of the derivative-like waves obtained through an EKG amplifier are also linearly related to those of the primary wave.

Single-ended versus Balanced Recording

If a differential DC amplifier is available, the common-mode rejection can be utilized for reduction of 60 cps interference from the power mains only if neither electrode is grounded. This feature is most effective when the impedance of each electrode with respect to ground is similar because common-mode rejection is effective only against in-phase voltages of equal amplitude with respect to ground. Pickup of 60 cps is minimized when an indifferent ground site is placed somewhere on the body, preferably near the active electrodes. Often a *single-ended* exosomatic GSR system must be used in conjunction with EEG measures and at such times certain EEG channels may show considerable GSR activity. This may be understood if one recognizes that the differential EEG amplifier usually has an input impedance with respect to ground which is of the order of 1 megohm. The circuitry is shown schematically in Fig. 1.14. R_1 and R_2 represent the skin resistances at the GSR sites. If a constant current system is used for GSR, any activity in R_2 acts as a voltage source for the EEG

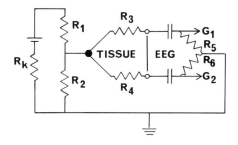

FIG. 1.14. Circuit model showing basis of cross-talk from single-ended GSR system to EEG. Skin resistances, R_1, R_2, R_3, and R_4, have a common point in the tissue and body fluids.

circuit in which R_3 and R_4 are scalp resistances and R_5 and R_6 amplifier input resistances. If R_3 and R_4 are equal, any voltage change developed at R_2 undergoes common-mode cancelation at inputs G_1 and G_2. If R_3 and R_4 are unequal and the voltage change across R_2 is appreciable, a portion of the change will show on the EEG trace. This type of artifact can be minimized by making R_3 and R_4 as equal as possible, or by making R_2 as small as possible, i.e. by using a very large site, e.g. a 15 sq. in. plate on the arm.

Convention in Polarity of Write-out

When one records from a constant current system, the write-out is proportional to resistance which should logically increase in the upward direction. However, because so many biological responses, e.g. the nerve or muscle action potential, have been shown traditionally as upward deflections it is common procedure for those emphasizing GSR to show these waves upward with resistance decreasing upward. On a similar basis it is common practice in endosomatic measures to have negative deflections go upward. Studies which emphasize base resistance levels however usually show resistance increasing upward, causing GSR waves to go downward. In conductivity circuits both base conductance and response increase upward.

Special Problems

Movement Artifact

The sources of artifact due to movement such as flexing an appendage or pressing against some object may arise from four main sources: (1) disturbance of the electrolyte concentration near the solid-liquid electrode interface; (2) change in the intimacy of contact between the electrode and the skin; (3) pressure-induced local change in skin resistance (Ebbecke response); (4) movement of the appendage across an electromagnetic field. Of these the first is a common source of drift and slow wave artifact. It has been successfully dealt with (Kahn & Sattler, 1964) by physically isolating this interface so that movements of the whole electrode relative to the skin do not result in disturbance of the phase boundary. This is accomplished by compressing silver and silver chloride particles under high pressure into a pellet surrounding a silver wire, and shielding this pellet from the skin with a perforated plastic plate. Several modifications of this principle have been successfully used elsewhere. The second source of artifact (change of intimacy of contact) occurs either when an electrode chamber is incompletely filled or when the electrode paste is so dilute that reduction of its depth by pressure on the electrode container produces a significant drop in series resistance. The third is a biological process which can apparently be eliminated only by preventing the movement which elicits it. The electromagnetic field responsible for the last of these, unlike an electrostatic field, is not easily eliminated by shielding. Increasing distance from heavily loaded power lines is most helpful. Use of twisted leads or of cable with a powdered shield has also been found helpful. One of the surest ways to reduce artifact is to prevent flexion of the appendage by splinting. This is especially suitable for finger electrodes because of the ease of splinting the finger with a piece of tongue depressor and two strips of masking tape. Another method is to select a site less apt to be disturbed. For example, in a series of runs on groups engaged in an assigned discussion it was found that nervous drumming on the table top with the finger was a common cause of pressure and flexion artifact. Splinting on the dorsal side helped to reduce this but the most satisfactory results were obtained when the site itself was placed on the dorsal surface of the finger, this site being on the average just as active, and the splint applied to the palmar surface. One related method is to choose the nonpreferred hand for electrode sites since subjects are more apt to use the preferred hand for scratching, picking, rubbing, and wiggling, all of which fall outside the sphere of control of the experimenter. Furthermore the subject feels psychologically more at ease when his preferred hand is free of appurtenances.

If the experimenter wishes to undertake a somewhat more involved routine, he may choose to place his electrodes on the foot over the abductor hallucis muscle as previously described. Recordings from such sites correlate very highly with those from the palm and are on the average as high in amplitude. This site has two disadvantages, one being the greater degree to which the feet are subject to the effects of cold weather, and secondly the greater nuisance involved in removing shoe and stocking.

Long Term Runs

Under some circumstance, for example in studies on sleep, circadian rhythms, or extended isolation, it becomes desirable to leave an electrode in place undisturbed for several days at a time. This immediately presents several knotty problems. For one thing, if the sampling consists of continuous exosomatic recording, there is a progressive de-anodizing of the cathodal electrode and a progressive depression of the skin resistance as reported by Wenger and Gustafson (1962). Another difficulty is the progressive drying out of an unsealed electrode or the gradual buildup of an osmotic pressure in a sealed chamber with a hypertonic electrode paste. Maceration of skin which may occur after long exposure to an aqueous electrode paste poses yet another problem. One may also mention the factor of discomfort, in which pressure or constriction plays a role, as well as the problem of inflammation especially along the edge of the electrode after long term wearing.

The long term electrical effects can be readily dealt with either by the use of intermittent sampling or by the use of polarity reversal or even low frequency AC excitation. The AC methods have not to my knowledge been tested for their advantage in long term recordings, and the success of this approach is at present a matter of conjecture.

The problem of long term effects of the paste and capsule both on activity and comfort demands a somewhat radical departure from common practice. The following has been the method of choice for this author. After much trial and error it was concluded that the problem of affixing to the skin a comfortable, capsule-type electrode which remains suitable for electrodermal measurement for any period beyond 24 hrs is a formidable one, and although it may ultimately be solved, the present state of the art does not indicate an answer immediately forthcoming. The solution appears to be the elimination of the capsule and the cementing by the use of an electrode medium which does not dry out. A solution of 78% glycerol having a total concentration of 0.6% NaCl (i.e. 0.1 M) or one of 90% polyethylene glycol-400 with the same NaCl concentration is found to be in vapor equilibrium with ambient air at 65% relative humidity. It will absorb or release moisture as the humidity changes but can be left on the skin for 10 days or more without drying out. The conductivity of this solution is, however, only 4% of that of the same NaCl concentration in water. For this reason only a very shallow layer can be tolerated between the electrode and the skin without causing an appreciable contribution to the series resistance. In practice one uses an anodized silver cloth electrode, described earlier, provided with a Pliofilm mask having a cut-out of the appropriate area. The skin is dabbed with an excess of the glycerol or polyethylene glycol solution. A sheet of Pliofilm is applied over the electrode extending beyond it ½ in. on each side and the preparation is held in place with nonadhesive elastic bandage. It should be noted that any excess of solution creeping beyond the electrode cut-out is not serious because the low conductivity of this very thin layer of solution results in an extremely high lateral resistance. Tests showed that addition of this solution around the borders of a site that had been prepared carefully to avoid getting any solution beyond the electrode produced a negligible alteration in the resistance of the site. On the other hand, the transverse conductance through this electrode medium is entirely adequate. A layer of the electrode medium 1 cm² in cross-section and 0.5 mm deep would contribute only 150 ohms to the series resistance of the site. With the electrode cloth resting directly on the skin, the maximum distance to the electrical barrier under the corneum would be less than 0.5 mm. Palmar (finger) resistance levels of nine subjects tested after 1 hr of exposure averaged only 8% higher than their control sites in contact with an aqueous paste containing 0.1 NaCl in pure water. After 12 to 14 days of continuous exposure *with replenishment* of the medium, these sites on seven subjects showed resistance averaging 2.1 times that of control sites which were freshly prepared with an aqueous electrode jelly. Their GSR amplitudes initially averaged 96% of control values and after 12 to 14 days were 74% of controls. None showed any cutaneous sensitization reaction.

In another population of eight subjects run *without replenishing* the polyethylene glycol, the conductance after 5 to 6 days averaged 57% of the freshly prepared control site, while GSR amplitude using a constant voltage system averaged 36%. Average levels and activity as percentage of freshly prepared control sites are shown as a function of time in Table 1.3. Skin potentials and skin potential responses were also observed and are tabulated in the same table. Surprisingly, while the positive responses fell progressively over a 12- to 14-day period, negative responses rose to well above control values. The condition of these sites after ultimate removal of the electrode was excellent. In only 2 of the 16 sites was there any inflammation and this a minor skin eruption along the edge of the electrode. For runs of 24 hrs or less the cloth electrode may be backed with sponge rubber but for longer runs it is best to avoid this added thickness under the tape and the possibility of pressure edge effects which are usually the site of any eruptions that may ensue. It should be noted that there was a large difference in the results with and without re-

TABLE 1.3 *Skin conductance and potential measures as a function of time during constant wearing of a long term electrode without replenishment of the medium.*
Values (except SP) are ratios of each measure to that of a freshly prepared control site adjusted to an initial value of 1.

Days Worn	N	Relative Conductance	Relative GSR Amplitude	Skin Potential Difference: Long Term Site Relative to Control Site	Relative Total SPR Activity
0	8	1.00	1.00	0.0	1.00
1	8	0.81	0.87	−11.0	0.94
2	8	0.65	0.74	−13.3	0.88
3	8	0.48	0.60	−10.8	0.71
4	8	0.51	0.50	−10.5	0.57
5	8	0.52	0.40	−19.0	0.53
6	8	0.53	0.31	−13.2	0.57
7	7	0.40	0.17	−10.0	0.60
8	7	0.36	0.15	2.9	0.61
9	5	0.27	0.12	0.0	0.64
10	4	0.26	0.14	−1.7	0.69

plenishment of solution. With replenishment, which can be accomplished *without disturbing the electrode*, the site can apparently last much longer, probably because the unreplenished glycerol or glycol is slowly absorbed or metabolized and the site dries out. Evidence for this was obtained by adding fresh glycol solution to a dry site which had become completely inactive in exosomatic recordings. The conductance of the site doubled and the exosomatic GSR rose to 33% of control level. The drying out effect is predictably more serious with constant voltage than with constant current as discussed earlier. When 9- to 11-day-old sites (five subjects) showing only slight activity in the constant voltage exosomatic recording were changed over to a constant current system, the response rose from 15% of the control site to 60%. At the present state of the art, then, if daily or 48-hr replenishment of this medium is impossible, the constant current system is superior in long term runs for obtaining GSR, although not for base level.

Simultaneous Exosomatic and Endosomatic Recordings from a Single Site

In sleep runs, the problem with the long term effects of continuous direct current through a site have been a source of concern. One solution attempted by Dr. Joe Kamiya* is the use of the endosomatic potential produced by the skin to measure its own resistance. If two skin potential electrodes are suddenly shunted with an external resistor, the potential recorded with a high impedance amplifier will show a drop. The shunt resistance which causes the potential to drop by one-half is equal to the internal resistance of the skin generator (Venables & Sayer, 1963). Given *any* shunt, the amount of drop in potential can be used to calculate the internal resistance by the following equation

$$R = \frac{e_0 - e_s}{e_s} \cdot R_s \tag{12}$$

where e_0 is the original potential reading and e_s the potential reading with the shunt, R_s, applied. If used with an amplifier of high input impedance, this method is feasible but one investigator using it in conjunction with EEG found considerable switching artifact. An alternative method is suggested, based on a rather similar idea. If one interposes between one of the skin potential electrodes and the amplifier a low impedance source of low level, low frequency AC, e.g. 10 mv at 20 cps, this voltage will divide itself between the subject and amplifier in proportion to their impedances. By using capacitance coupling into the AC amplifier with a time constant of 0.05 sec and rectifying the output, the endosomatic base potential contribution will be blocked and the value of the skin conductance can be calculated by Equation 13

$$C_s = \frac{Y_s}{Y_t - Y_s} \cdot C_a \tag{13}$$

---

*J. Kamiya, personal communication.

where C_s, = skin conductance, C_a, = amplifier input conductance, Y_t, the deflection produced by the AC source with the subject leads shorted, and Y_s, the deflection with the subject in series. It should be recognized that this is in fact a method of obtaining the skin impedance with a very low voltage source.

Another practice in long term runs which has been successful for avoiding operator fatigue or loss of data due to lapse of operator vigilance has been the recording of electrodermal responses with the condensor coupling previously described. If base levels are still desired, they can be observed on a parallel DC channel adjusted for relatively low sensitivity (Edelberg et al., 1960) or by the method of Simons and Perez (1965).

Group GSR

When electrodermal measures are recorded from a group of interacting individuals, it is sometimes desirable to obtain a composite recording of their conductance changes on a single channel. This can be readily accomplished by a modification of the single conductance circuit as shown in Fig. 1.15. If the electrodes are 1/4 in. in diameter, a basic individual series resistance of 1000 ohms is appropriate. The series resistor chosen, R_k, should be adjusted for the number of subjects, N, such that

$$R_k = \frac{1000 \text{ ohms}}{N}$$

Average conductance, $C\Sigma/N$, can then be obtained by

$$\frac{C\Sigma}{N} = \overline{C} = \frac{E_k}{1000} \tag{14}$$

where E_k is the measured potential. Alternatively, calibration may be accomplished by switching in a shunt of a suitable value with the subjects out of the circuit. If group responses are desired as well as group conductance, the DC component can be canceled out by one of the methods previously discussed, namely by capacitance coupling to a second amplifier as shown, or by interposing a bucking system between R_k and the amplifier as discussed under measurement of skin potential.

Potential Measures with Solutions

There have been a number of studies reporting the effect of specific electrolytes or pharmacological agents on electrodermal activity and these have frequently included simultaneous measurements made on two sites. If the control solution and experimental solution are at different effective concentration there will develop between the two electrodes immersed in these solutions a concentration potential which may be confused with the biological effect. This problem has commonly been encountered in electrochemical or electrophysiological studies and is generally solved by the use of salt bridges (Hitchcock, 1945). Each

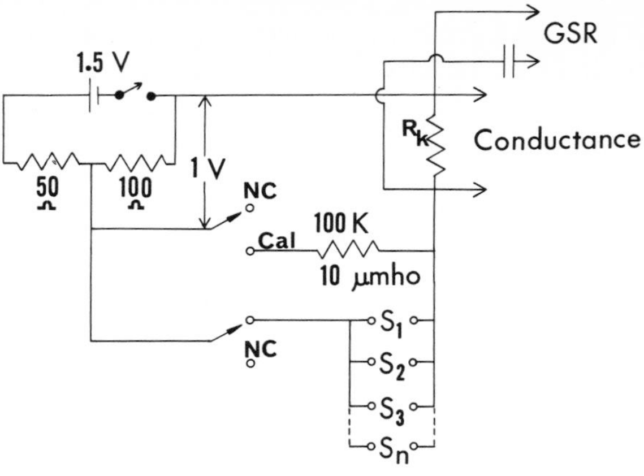

FIG. 1.15. Constant voltage system for measuring total conductance of a group of subjects.

electrode is immersed in an identical solution, e.g. 1 M KCl and connection to the control and experimental solutions made with an agar-KCl salt bridge. At times it may be that two different pastes are being tested and it is not feasible to use salt bridges. In such a case, each member of the pair of electrodes may be dipped into a puddle of the paste on a glass slide, and one of the puddles spread until it touches the other. The potential difference is measured and a properly oriented bucking voltage of this value inserted between the amplifier and one of the leads.

Data Treatment
General Considerations
GSR. If a subject is seated at rest and a loud bell sounded, there will generally occur in the electrodermal trace a wave which is considerably larger than any background activity with a well defined latency of 1.5 to 2 sec. There is no difficulty in relating this response to the specific stimulus which caused it, and such waves have for this reason been termed by Burch and Greiner (1958) *specific* responses. On a similar basis they have lumped all other responses, both those occurring spontaneously and those elicited by some unidentified external stimulus as *nonspecific*. Because the nonspecific waves, in a low level external stimulus field, are predominantly *spontaneous*, i.e. responses to internally generated neural events, it is to be expected that these will constitute a measure of different significance than do the specific responses. This difference has been demonstrated by Burch and Greiner in the response to stimulant and depressant drugs. The count, i.e. the frequency of occurrence, of nonspecific waves increases with increasing central activation, while the amplitude of specific responses to an electrical shock shows a bell-shaped curve with a maximum at a level they

term "alert." The count of specific responses will obviously be determined by the frequency of stimulus presentations and is a useless measure, unless one wishes to measure the frequency of "no response." The count of nonspecific responses on the other hand has proved to be a useful measure in numerous behavioral experiments (e.g. Silverman, Cohen, & Shmavonian, 1959; McDonald, Johnson, & Hord, 1964), but it has the disadvantage that its frequency may be influenced by uncontrolled variables in the stimulus field. GSR count has, for example, been a convenient measure in studies of group interaction (Kaplan, Burch, Bloom, & Edelberg, 1963). In such a situation the nonspecific frequency is dominated by responses to unidentified stimuli, namely the context and affectual content of the verbal material. This imposes a degree of ambiguity on the measure, since it is difficult to separate out that aspect of each subject's activity which is a function of his nonspecific internal activation and that which represents a response to the external stimulus field. Total amplitude per unit of time is also an ambiguous hybrid measure since a high frequency of low amplitude responses and a low frequency of high amplitude responses offer the same value but clearly have very different behavioral significance. One measure which has shown some promise in resolving these difficulties is the use of average amplitude together with count. The interpretation of these two in conjunction may allow relatively high discrimination of the quality of activation.

Base levels. Analysis of base levels of conductance or resistance has been preferred by many investigators instead of GSR measures. Until recently very little use has been made of *base potential* but the development of stable DC amplifiers and the possible advantages of this method in avoiding the deleterious effect of current in long term runs, has led to some interest in examining this measure (Leiderman & Shapiro, 1964).

While the commonest measure in this category is base-line level as sampled at standardized times or its change from one state to another, the time rate of change of base level in a given state may be a better indicator of activity in that state than is a measure GSR amplitude or frequency. It is necessary, however, to correct this slope for base level effect (Martin & Edelberg, 1963).

Rickles (1964) has discussed the desirability of expressing base levels in terms of specific resistance or specific conductance, a practice which is clearly desirable for facilitating comparison of data from different laboratories. These should be expressed in terms of the value for a single 1 cm² site. If two sites each 1 cm² are measured in series, the specific resistance would be one-half that measured for the pair and the specific conductance would be twice that measured for the pair.

Analysis of GSR and SPR

Single wave amplitudes. The analysis of a single GSR in terms of amplitude appears to be a simple matter but is in fact fraught with the necessity for numerous decisions. If a subject at rest with a level base line has a single response (Fig. 1.16a), there is no difficulty in determining its amplitude, i.e. peak level

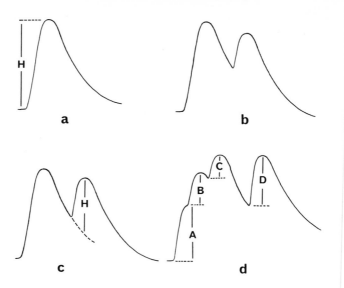

Fig. 1.16. Criteria for measurement of GSR amplitude (H). *Method d* is preferred over *Method c* for treatment of compound responses.

minus base-line level. Suppose, however, this wave occurs during recovery from a previous one (Fig. 1.16*b*); should one then correct base-line level by extending the recovery slope of the previous wave to a point below the peak of the second wave (Fig. 1.16*c*). To the extent that the amplitude of the wave is considered an index of the intensity of the neural volley which generated it this question can be answered from animal experiments. The plantar nerve of a cat was sectioned and the distal stump stimulated with two standard volleys such that the response to the second fell on the recovery slope of the first. Except for a very localized region of reduced activity lasting 1.5 sec after the peak of the first wave, the amplitude of the second wave was the same as that of the first (Fig. 1.17). This was also true for the ascending portion. When the two volleys were only ½ sec apart, the resulting amplitude was twice that of a single wave. On the basis of these observations, the total amplitude, ΣH represented in Fig. 16*d* would be: $A + B + C + D$. Of these the value given to amplitude C is somewhat less than the relative neural activity it represents and a more accurate total for this group would be: $A + B + 1.3 C + D$. For practical reasons, however, it seems appropriate to adopt the simpler summation as standard procedure. Summation of many waves can be accomplished rapidly by accumulating their individual amplitudes with pencil marks along the edge of a paper sheet and finally measuring the total length of the edge delineated.

If a constant voltage circuit is used, the measurement of conductance change is simple and direct and amplitudes may be appropriately summed. With a con-

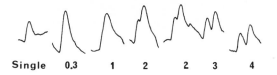

Single 0.3 1 2 2 3 4

Intershock Interval ··· Seconds

FIG. 1.17. Effect of intershock interval on amplitude of a second GSR closely following a first one. Each response is produced by stimulation of the lumbar sympathetic trunk of the cat with a single 0.5 msec 1-v pulse. Note that a response falling shortly after start of recovery limb is attenuated.

stant current system, a problem is posed in summing response amplitudes if there is to be an ultimate transformation to conductance units. An approximate transformation can be made by using an average base resistance value in the solution. Thus

$$\Delta C = \frac{\Delta R_1}{R_1{}^2} + \frac{\Delta R_2}{R_2{}^2} \cdots + \frac{\Delta R_n}{R_n{}^2} \approx \frac{\Sigma(\Delta R)}{(\Sigma R/n)^2} \approx \frac{\Sigma(\Delta R)}{(\bar{R})^2} \tag{15}$$

In measurement of single responses, one normally applies a correction for base level, for example by using "per cent change in resistance," "log resistance change," or other transformations (Lacey, 1956). It is worth noting that in the constant voltage system there may be no need to express the change in terms of base level, since a resistance correction is already an intrinsic part of the conductance change notation. The nature of this may be appreciated by examination of Equations 2 and 3. From Equation 3,

$$\Delta C \approx - \frac{\Delta R}{R^2}$$

conductance change can in one sense be viewed as the resistancce change corrected for base-line effect by dividing by the square of the base resistance. Carrying this one step further, the conductance change can be shown to be equal to the fractional change in resistance times base conductance.

A potentially useful relation can be derived from Equation 3, namely

$$- \frac{\Delta C}{\Delta R} = \frac{1}{R^2} = C^2$$

Using absolute values for ΔC and ΔR to eliminate the negative sign,

$$C = \sqrt{\frac{|\Delta C|}{|\Delta R|}} \tag{16}$$

indicating that base conductance can be obtained from amplitude measures on two condenser-coupled systems, one constant voltage, the other constant current.

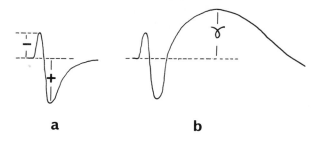

a   b

Fig. 1.18. Criteria for measurement of amplitude of the negative and positive waves and of the γ wave of the skin potential response.

Another derivative of Equation 3

$$\frac{\Delta C}{C} = - \frac{\Delta R}{R} \tag{17}$$

indicates that the fractional change in conductance is the same as the fractional change in resistance.

Counting. The above findings have implications with regard to the counting of GSRs. The animal studies showed that any second wave superimposed upon a first during its rising phase produced no easily observed inflection in the wave unless it came near the peak (i.e. after rounding off of the first wave had started). Consequently in counting at this laboratory, any point of inflection of the ascending limb is arbitrarily considered the starting point of a second wave and all amplitude change from inflection point to peak is assigned to the second wave (Fig. 1.16*d*). Waves occurring as inflections on the downward slope are not considered in the count unless they are (1) inflections of *any* size which occur within 1.5 sec after peak or (2) clearly defined waves which reach the assigned threshold of amplitude rise from inflection to peak. When a wave overlaps two time periods, the period in which it started should be given credit for this wave, since it must have contained the initiating stimulus.

Endosomatic waves. The analysis of endosomatic waves presents a problem which has not been adequately met, namely the treatment of a wave containing positive and negative components. A study by Holmquest and Edelberg (1964) has demonstrated the great ambiguity which occurs when one adds positive and negative waves which are slightly out of phase and which may vary in amplitude. One of the most disturbing facts is that a large negative wave, compounded with a positive wave of moderate size may show no positive component at all, only a change in wave shape. Furthermore, a positive wave may start considerably before the wave crosses the base line in the positive direction. For the present, the most common procedure is to take the peak negative deflection minus starting base-line level as the negative wave, and peak positive deflection from the same base line as the positive wave (Fig. 1.18a). This is admittedly an invalid designation of the relative size of the two components, but it has for the present the advantage of being relatively standard. There frequently appears, following a truly unipolar biphasic SPR, a third negative deflection of considerably slower dominant frequency, the γ wave (Fig. 1.18b). When observation of this wave is included, again for the sake of general agreement, its assigned amplitude may be considered the peak reached by the γ wave minus the original base-line level prior to initiation of the entire complex. Some strides have been made toward arriving at a more rational basis for separation of these waves but an operational system is not yet available.

Electronic Aids in Data Reduction

One of the simplest measures to facilitate data reduction by electronic intervention is the use of the first derivative or an approximation of it. The exaggeration of inflection points which this produces aids greatly in the recognition of compound waves, especially on the ascending limb. Further, it makes base line adjustment unnecessary. The first derivative has been put to great use by Burch and Childers (1963) in the development of their automatic analyzer. Conversion of the primary wave to its first derivative allows the use of the positive- and negative-going base line cross of the derived function for obtaining the onset-to-peak interval, both as a counting event and as a measure of rise time. They have also used the area circumscribed by the first derivative and base line as a useful measure closely related to amplitude. This electronic system has been made all the more convenient by their inclusion of a digital write-out of GSR count, total GSR rise time per unit time, and total first derivative area per unit time.

Latency Measures

Electrodermal responses have a long latency of the order of 1 ½ to 2 sec, of which about 10 to 20% is devoted to slow conduction down sympathetic fibers (Gildemeister, 1923; Bloch, 1952) and about 25 to 50% to the release and diffusion of acetylcholine from the nerve endings to the effector. This last process can be greatly extended to as long as 5 sec by cooling (Maulsby & Edelberg, 1960). About 50% of the latency depends on central delay. When a behavioral scientist uses latency as a measure, he is usually interested in changes in latency attributable to changes in central processing and must therefore work with changes in a component which in itself represents only a fraction of the total latency. It is, therefore, of utmost importance to maintain the peripheral component of total delay as constant as possible; hence, surface temperature must be carefully controlled. Moreover, since the variable portion is frequently less than 50% of the total, the delay between stimulus and onset of response must be measured with precision. An electrodermal response unfortunately does not rise precipitously but has a somewhat gradual start which confounds the point of origin. The use of a first derivative write-out helps greatly to locate this point; the second derivative is even more effective but is useable only with a very clean signal.

Conclusions

The number of compromises alluded to in this chapter, "pending further data," may be regarded as an indicant of the unfinished state of the art. Much remains to be done in the area of selecting a standard voltage or current density or in developing a system which obviates the need for these. The technique for long term monitoring of electrodermal activity, although improved, is an area still calling for determined effort. The relative information content of skin conductance, skin impedance, and skin potential, and of their base levels versus their fluctuations must be determined in order to provide a basis for selection of the most appropriate method. In the absence of this, a potpourri of measurements and techniques has been presented. It is hoped that the experienced investigator may be able to enhance his appreciation of the choices available to him, and that the intrepid neophyte entering this area will be to some extent guided around the many pitfalls strewn across his path.

Acknowledgment

Special thanks are due to Dr. Neil R. Burch who first acquainted me with the galvanic skin response.

REFERENCES

Ax, A. F. Comment on conductance measurement. *Psychophysiol. Newsltr.* 1960, *6*: 12–13.
Bagno, S., & Liebman, F. M. Impedance measurements. *Electronics*, 1959, *32*: 62–63.
Barnett, A. The phase angle of normal human skin. *J. Physiol., Lond.*, 1938, *93*: 349–366.
Blank, I. H., & Finesinger, J. E. Electrical resistance of the skin. *Archs. Neurol. Psychiat., Chicago*, 1946, 56: 544–557.
Bloch, V. Nouveaux aspects de la méthode psychogalvanique ou électrodermographique (EDG) comme critere des tensions affectives. *Année psychol.*, 1952, *52*: 329–362.
Burch, N. R., & Childers, H. E. Automatic GSR analyzer. *USAF School of Aerospace Medicine Tech. Doc. Rep. 63–74*, 1963.
Burch, N. R., & Greiner, T. H. Drugs and human fatigue: GSR parameters. *J. Psychol.*, 1958, *45*: 3–10.
Clark, L. C. Jr., & Lacey, J. I. An improved skin electrode. *J. Lab. clin. Med.*, 1950, *35*: 786–787.
Cole, K. S. Electric conductance of biological systems. *Cold Spring Harb. Symp. quant. Biol.*, 1933, *1*: 107–116.
Costiloe, P., & Schneider, R. A. Seasonal variations in autonomic measurements. Paper presented at the meeting of the Society for Psychophysiological Research, Washington, D. C., 1964.

Darrow, C. W. The galvanic skin-reflex and finger volume changes. *Am. J. Physiol.*, 1929, 88: 219–229.

Darrow, C. W. Uniform current for continuous standard unit resistance records. *J. gen. Psychol.*, 1932, 6: 471–473.

Davis, R. C. The effect of varying current on the galvanic reflex. In J. M. Cattell (Ed.), *Proc. IX Int. Congr. Psychol., New Haven, 1929.* Princeton, N. J.: Psychological Review Company, 1930. Pp. 140–141. (a)

Davis, R. C. A vacuum tube for stabilizing the current during measurements of the galvanic reflex. *Am. J. Psychol.*, 1929, 41: 474–475. (b)

Day, J. L., & Lippitt, M. W., Jr. A long-term electrode system for electrocardiography and impedance pneumography. *Psychophysiology.*, 1964, 1: 174–182.

Ebbecke, U. Die lokale galvanische Reaktion der Haut. Über die Beziehung zwischen lokaler Reizung und elektrischer Leitfähigkeit. *Pflügers Arch. ges. Physiol.*, 1921, 190: 230-269.

Edelberg, R. Microelectrode study of the galvanic skin response. *Fedn Proc. Fedn Am. Socs exp. Biol.*, 1961, 20: 326.

Edelberg, R. Electrophysiologic characteristics and interpretation of skin potentials. *USAF School of Aerospace Medicine Tech. Doc. Rep. 63-95*, 1963.

Edelberg, R. Independence of galvanic skin response amplitude and sweat production. *J. invest. Derm.*, 1964, 42: 443–448. (a)

Edelberg, R. Effect of vasoconstriction on galvanic skin response amplitude. *J. appl. Physiol.*, 1964, 19: 427–430. (b)

Edelberg, R. Response of cutaneous water barrier to ideational stimulation: a GSR component. *J. comp. physiol. Psychol.*, 1966, 61: 28–33.

Edelberg, R., & Burch, N. R. Skin resistance and galvanic skin response. *Archs gen. Psychiat.*, 1962, 7: 163–169.

Edelberg, R., Greiner, T., & Burch, N. R. Some membrane properties of the effector in the galvanic skin response. *J. appl. Physiol.*, 1960, 15: 691–696.

Edelberg, R., & Wright, D. J. Two galvanic skin response effector organs and their stimulus specificity. *Psychophysiology*, 1964, 1: 39–47.

Féré, C. Note sur les modifications de la résistance électrique sous l'influence des excitations sensorielles et des émotions. *C. r. Séanc. Soc. Biol.*, 1888, 40: 217–219.

Forbes, T. W., & Landis, C. The limiting AC frequency for the exhibition of the galvanic skin ("psychogalvanic") response. *J. gen. Psychol.*, 1935, 13: 188–193.

Forbes, T. W. Problems in measurement of electrodermal phenomena—choice of method and phenomena—potential, impedance, resistance. *Psychophysiology*, 1964, 1: 26–30.

Fricke, H. The theory of electrolytic polarization. *Phil. Mag.*, 1932, 14: 310–318.

Fries, J. F., & Richter, C. P. Lung cancer: detection by use of electrical skin resistance method. *Archs intern. Med.*, 1964, 113: 624–634.

Gerstner, H., & Gerbstadt, H. Über Wechselstromwiderstand der menschlichen Haut. *Pflügers Arch. ges. Physiol.*, 1949, 252: 111–122.

Gildemeister, M. Zur Physiologie der menschlichen Haut. *Pflügers Arch. ges. Physiol.*, 1923, 200: 251–284.

Gougerot, L. Recherches sur l'impédance cutanée en courant alternatif de basse fréquence au cours de différent dermatoses. *Annls Derm. Syph.*, 1947, 7: 101–111.

Grings, W. W. Methodological considerations underlying electrodermal measurement. *J. Psychol.*, 1953, 35: 271–282.

Hagfors, C. Two conductance bridges for galvanic response measurements. *Rep. Dep. Psychol., Univ. Jyväskylä, Finl.*, 1964, 60: 1–20.

Hitchcock, D. Electromotive forces. In R. Höber, (Ed.), *Physical chemistry of cells and tissues*, Philadelphia: Blakiston, 1945, Pp. 64–65.

Holmquest, D., & Edelberg, R. Problems in the analysis of the endosomatic galvanic skin response. *Psychophysiology*, 1964, 1: 48–54.

Hozawa, S. Studien über die Polarisation der Haut. I. Die "Anfangszacke" des elektrischen Stromes durch den Menschenkörper, betrachtet als Ladungsersheinung der Polarisationskapasität der Haut. II. Uber oszillatorische Ladung de Polarizationskapazität der menschlichen Haut. *Pflügers Arch. ges. Physiol.*, 1928, 219: 111–158.

Hozawa, S. Zur Theorie über die Polarisation und die Diffusionkapazität lebender Zelle, insbesondere der Haut. *Z. Biol.*, 1931, *91*: 297–314.

Janz, G. J., & Taniguchi, H. The silver-silver halide electrodes. *Chem. Rev.*, 1953, 53: 397–437.

Kahn, A.R., & Sattler, F. P. Origin of steaming potentials and motion artifacts in biological electrodes. In R. Plonsey (Ed.), *Proceedings of the 17th Annual Conference on Engineering in Medicine and Biology, Vol. 6.* Cleveland: The Conference Committee for the 17th Annual Conference on Engineering in Medicine & Biology, Publisher, 1964. P. 6.

Kaplan, H. B., Burch, N. R., Bloom, S. W., & Edelberg, R. Affective orientation and physiological activity (GSR) in small peer groups. *Psychosom. Med.*, 1963, *25*: 245–252.

Keller, P. Grund- und Tonuspotentiale der menschlichen Haut. *Arch. Derm. Syph.*, 1931, *162*: 582–610.

Kennedy, J. L., & Travis, R. C. Surface electrodes for recording bioelectric potentials. *Science*, 1948, *108*: 103.

Lacey, J. I. The evaluation of autonomic responses: Toward a general solution. *Ann. N.Y. Acad. Sci.*, 1956, *67*: 123–164.

Lacey, J. I., Bateman, D. E., & Van Lehn, R. Autonomic response specificity, an experimental study. *Psychosom. Med.*, 1953, *15*: 8–21.

Lader, M. H., & Montagu, J. D. The psycho-galvanic reflex: a pharmacological study of the peripheral mechanism. *J. Neurol. Neurosurg Psychiat.*, 1962, *25*: 126–133.

Landis, C. Electrical phenomena of the skin. *Psychol. Bull.*, 1932, *29*: 693–752.

Landis, C., & DeWick, H. N. The electrical phenomena of the skin (psycho-galvanic reflex). *Psychol. Bull.*, 1929, *26*: 64–119.

Leiderman, P. H., & Shapiro, D. Studies on the galvanic skin potential level: some behavioral correlates. *J. psychosom. Res.*, 1964, *7*: 277–281.

Lykken, D. T. Properties of electrodes used in electrodermal measurement. *J. comp. physiol. Psychol.*, 1959, *52*: 629–634.

Lykken, D. T., & Rose, R. A rat-holder with electrodes for GSR measurement. *Am. J. Psychol.*, 1959, *72*: 621–622.

Lykken, D. T., & Roth, N. Continuous direct measurement of apparent skin conductance. *Am. J. Psychol.*, 1961, *74*: 293–297.

McCleary, R. A. The nature of the galvanic skin response. *Psychol. Bull.*, 1950, *47*: 97–117.

McDonald, D. G., Johnson, L. C., & Hord, D. J. Habituation of the orienting response in alert and drowsy subjects. *Psychophysiology*, 1964, *2*: 163–173.

McDowall, R. J. S. The physiology of the psychogalvanic reflex. *Q. Jl exp. Physiol.*, 1933, *23*: 277–285.

Martin, R. D., & Edelberg, R. The relationship of skin resistance changes to receptivity. *J. psychosom. Res.*, 1963, *7*: 173–179.

Maulsby, R. L., & Edelberg, R. The interrelationship between the galvanic skin response, basal resistance and temperature. *J. comp. physiol. Psychol.*, 1960, *53*: 475–479.

Montagu, J. D. The psycho-galvanic reflex: a comparison of DC and AC methods of measurement. *J. psychosom. Res.*, 1964, *8*: 49–65.

Morrison, N. K. Development of conductive cloth plantar electrode for use in measuring skin resistance. *USAF Wright Air Development Center TN-58-284*, 1958.

O'Connell, D. N., & Tursky, B. Silver-silver chloride sponge electrodes for skin potential recording. *Am. J. Psychol.*, 1960, *73*: 302–304.

O'Connell, D. N., Tursky, B., & Orne, M. T. Electrodes for the recording of skin potential. *Archs gen. Psychiat.*, 1960, *3*: 252–258.

Perry, D. J., Wright, E.T., Mount, G. E., & Leland, C. M. An observation in acrosclerosis using the galvanic skin response. *J. invest. Derm.*, 1958, *30*: 173–176.

Plutchik, R., & Hirsch, H. R. Skin impedance and phase angle as a function of frequency and current. *Science*, 1963, *141*: 927–928.

Prideaux, E. The psycho-galvanic reflex: a review. *Brain*, 1920, *43*: 50–71.

Rein, H. Die Elektrophysiologie der Haut. In J. Jadassohn (Ed.), *Handbuch der haut-und geschlechtskrankheiten, Vol. 1.* Berlin: J. Springer, 1929. Pp. 43–91. Cited by S. Rothman, *Physiology and biochemistry of the skin.* Chicago: Univ. Chicago Press, 1954.

Richter, C. P. A study of the electric skin resistance and psychogalvanic reflex in a case of unilateral sweating. *Brain*, 1927, *50*: 216–235.

Richter, C. P. Physiological factors involved in the electrical resistance of the skin. *Am. J. Physiol.*, 1929, *88*: 596–615.

Rickles, W. H., Jr. Engineering considerations in GSR research. *USAF School of Aerospace Medicine, Aeromedical Reviews, No. 4-64*, 1964.

Rothman, S. *Physiology and biochemistry of the skin.* Chicago: Univer. Chicago Press, 1954.

Shackel, B. Skin-drilling: a method of diminishing galvanic skin-potentials. *Am. J. Psychol.*, 1959, *72*: 114–121.

Silverman, A. J., Cohen, S. I., & Shmavonian, B. M. Investigation of psychophysiologic relationships with skin resistance measures. *J. psychosom. Res.*, 1959, *4*: 65–87.

Simons, D. G., & Perez, R. E. The B/GSR module: A combined recording to present base skin resistance and galvanic skin reflex activity patterns. *Psychophysiology*, 1965, *2*: 116–124.

Tarchanoff, J. Über die galvanischen erscheinungen an der Haut des Menschen bei Reizung der Sinnesorgane und bie verschiedenen Formen der psychischen Tätigkeit. *Pflügers Arch. ges. Physiol.*, 1890, *46*: 46-55.

Venables, P. H., & Sayer, E. On the measurement of the level of skin potential. *Br. J. Psychol.*, 1963; *54*: 251–260.

Veraguth, O. *Das psychogalvanische Reflex-phänomen,* Berlin: Karger, 1909.

Vigouroux, R. Sur le rôle de la résistance électrique des tissus dans l'électrodiagnostic. *C. r. Séanc. Soc. Biol.*, 1879, *31*: 336–339.

Wang, G. H. The galvanic skin reflex: a review of old and recent works from a physiologic point of view. *Am. J. phys. Med.*, 1957, *36*: 295–320: 1958, *37*: 35–57.

Wenger, M. A. Seasonal variations in some physiologic variables. *J. Lab. clin. Med.*, 1943, *28*: 1101–1108.

Wenger, M. A., & Cullen, T. D. Some problems in psychophysiological research. Part III. The effects of uncontrolled variables. In R. Roessler & N. S. Greenfield (Eds.), *Physiological correlates of psychological disorder,* Wisconsin: Univ. Wisconsin Press, 1962.

Wenger, M. A., & Gustafson, L. A. Some problems in psychophysiological research. Part II. Effects of continuous current on measurements of electrical skin resistance. In R. Roessler & N. S. Greenfield (Eds.). *Physiological correlates of psychological disorder.* Wisconsin: Univ. Wisconsin Press, 1962.

Wilcott, R. C. Effects of local blood removal on skin resistance and potential. *J. comp. physiol. Psychol.*, 1958, *51*: 295–300. (a)

Wilcott, R. C. Correlation of skin resistance and potential. *J. comp. physiol. Psychol.*, 1958, *51*: 691–696. (b)

Withers, W. C. R. A simple psycho-galvanometer. *Electron. Engng*, 1956, *28*: 36–37.

Yokota, T., Takahashi, T., Kondo, M., & Fujimori, B. Studies on the diphasic wave form of the galvanic skin reflex. *Electroenceph. clin. Neurophysiology*, 1959, *11*: 687–696.

2

The Techniques of Plethysmography

CLINTON C. BROWN, PH.D.

Theoretical Considerations

Plethysmography is a generic term describing various techniques used to measure or reflect the volume changes of a limb or a tissue segment resulting from local vascular activity. The term is derived from the Greek root, "ple thysmos" which means literally, "an enlargement." As a psychophysiological response measurement, plethysmography has had as lengthy a history as that of the electrical skin phenomena. In fact, many of the early investigators felt quite strongly that there was a causal relationship between vascular changes in a tissue segment and changes in its electrical characteristics. Vigoroux quoted by Darrow (1929), stated in 1879 that the reductions he observed in the electrical resistance of the skin (GSR) were due to vasodilation and a consequent easy flow of blood through the cutaneous capillaries. Féré (1888), the co-discoverer of the electrical skin phenomena, explained the fall of tissue resistance as the result of increased irrigation of the tissues by an enhanced blood flow. Sticker in 1897 suggested that decreases in skin resistance were due to vasodilation and that increases were the result of vasoconstriction. Another explanation of the presumed mutual influence of cutaneous vascular and electrical phenomena was provided by Radecki in 1911 who stated that skin resistance changes were due to changes in CO_2 concentration of the blood, which was in turn a function of vasodilation and blood pressure. Perhaps the most ingenious explanation was that offered by Densham and Wells (1927) who described the GSR as a "skin restrictor reflex," i.e. the result of local vasomotor activity which made the skin taut or loose and thus changed its electrical resistance. Darrow's early experiment (1929) was crucial in resolving this matter and pointed out the clear independence of the two phenomena. His simultaneous measurements of electrical resistance and physical volume of two adjacent fingers showed that that stimuli which produced volume changes did not necessarily induce resistance changes. He concluded that the

GSR and digital volume were functions of a common stimulating condition, i.e. different aspects of autonomic nervous system arousal.

The literature on the use of plethysmographic measures in psychological and psychiatric problems is spotty in the past 50 years. Its relative lack of popularity was probably due to the instrumental difficulties inherent in older methods, the restraint it imposed upon the subject, and the somewhat contradictory results obtained in equivalent situations by one or another method of measurement. Recent improvements in technique have eliminated most of the above objections and the response which is measured by contemporary means is only tenuously related to that obtained in the remote literature. Despite significant differences between methods, the fact that all of the methods provide a reflection of what is at its basis a vasomotor phenomena justifies the continued use of the term plethysmography.

Apart from the fact that the plethysmograph provides a unique measure of autonomically induced reactivity, certain of its characteristics meet the necessary criteria for an important and valid psychophysiological response measure. First, the plethysmogram is an extremely sensitive measure of internally and externally induced changes, surpassing even the electrical skin phenomena in this respect. Second, the response may be elicited from human subjects of all ages and from subhuman mammalian species as well (although the significance of the response is different in the latter). Third, the response may be elicited from numerous body sites and the very fact that its nervous control is probably regional permits interesting comparison and combination of area responses (Sokolov, 1963). Fourth, the plethysmographic response exhibits an unusual persistence, i.e. resistance to adaptation and disappearance with the passage of time and repeated stimulation. Plethysmographic responses persist after the electrodermal and heart rate changes have become extinct. In fact, unlike other psychophysiological responses, there is evidence that the plethysmographic response persists in sleep (Ackner & Pampliglione, 1955; Magnussen, 1939; Darrow, 1929). There is a yet undeveloped potential for its use in the measurement of the depth of sleep. Fifth, the plethysmographic response is autonomically based and reflects almost purely the activity of the sympathetic nervous system. Finally, the instrumentation required for more recently devised methods, e.g. impedance and photoelectrical devices, is of comparable simplicity to that required for the measurement of the electrical skin phenomena. These advantages recommend the measurement of the plethysmographic response not only as a monitor of vascular activity but for potentially unique information which it can yield.

Major measurement methods.   The basic physical phenomenon of plethysmography, that of a change in the volume of a limb or tissue segment, is a fairly simple matter. The devices which have been used to transduce this change into measurable or graphic form have ranged from the crude to the complex. They may be divided into three main types of devices: (1) hydraulic or pneumatic systems which use various fluids or air to detect a volume change in the observed part and to convey it to a recording-measuring device (2) electrical impedance devices which reflect changes in the impedance afforded by the interposed tissue to the passage of a high frequency alternating current, and (3) optical or photoelectrical transducers which register variations in the intensity of light transmitted through a tissue segment and intensity modulated by variations in the total bulk of opaque blood in the tissue from moment to moment. A fourth technique, that of the measurement of emitted energy in the infrared and adjacent regions is emerging as a laboratory tool and is yet too new to receive other than brief mention.

General Characteristics of the Plethysmographic Response

Tracings derived from all of the above techniques are continuous records which depict the plethysmogram in a form shown in Fig. 2.1A. There is considerable similarity between this tracing and that depicting continuous blood pressure measures derived by cannulation of a vessel. The rising front of the pulse wave form reflects the systolic inflow to the part and its apex represents the peak volume systole (*P*). The amplitude of this peak, measured from the preceding trough, is termed the pulse volume (PV). *Prior to* the time of the peak volume systole, the inflow and outflow are equal and maximum. After peaking, the curve declines, depicting the rate of outflow without inflow until the diastolic trough (*T*) is reached. At this point, inflow and outflow are again equal, but are minimal. Another cardiac cycle then begins and the events are repeated.

The notch which frequently but not consistently appears on the falling portion of the curve is the dicrotic notch (*D*) which marks the end point of the volume systole. It is produced by the closure of the aortic valve. The appearance of the dicrotic notch on a tracing is a function of both instrumental and physiological factors. An inadequate high frequency response of the measuring system or hysteresis in registry will interfere with its recording. On the other hand, the physiology of the subject, his posture, and the position of the part under measurement also influence the appearance of the dicrotic notch.

A less rapidly changing aspect of the plethysmogram is the blood volume (BV). This is a reflection of the "absolute volume" of the part, representing a level of blood content upon which the blood volume pulses are superimposed. Figure 2.1B shows a section of a tracing in which blood volume and the blood volume pulse are simultaneously registered. The stimulus presented at *S* produces vasoconstriction which is evidenced both by a diminution of the blood volume pulse (BVP) and of a downward movement of the whole tracing (lowering of BV). In the electrical methods, this type of tracing is produced by DC coupling the transducer output to the recorder.

Since pulse amplitude and the absolute blood volume in the part are closely

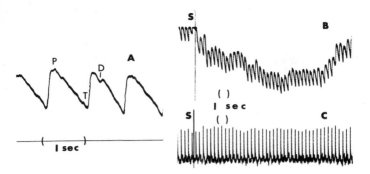

FIG. 2.1.   *Tracing A* is an amplified section of a digital recording made with a photoplethysmograph. The systolic peak occurs at *P*, the diastolic trough at *T*, and the dicrotic notch at *D*. *Tracing B* is recorded with the input circuitry direct coupled to the amplifier and represents the blood volume. A stimulus administered at *S* has caused vasoconstriction producing a downward deflection in the whole tracing. The record shown in *C* was recorded in parallel with *B* but with AC coupling (time constant of 0.01 sec). Note the slight variations in blood volume pulse which are not evident in *Tracing B*.

correlated under certain conditions, it is sometimes desirable to record only changes in the BVP amplitude and wave form. This is shown in Fig. 2.1*C* which was recorded in parallel with tracing 2.1*B* but which was AC-coupled with a time constant of 0.01 sec. Note that a line drawn through the midpoints of the pulse waves is reasonably straight. In this type of recording, the measures of BV are not available.

For most cases, the preferable method of recording is that shown in 2.1*B*. A major difficulty however is that when sufficient amplification is used to produce measurable BVP amplitudes, changes in BV resulting from stimulation are much greater in magnitude and will drive the tracing off the recording limits. A somewhat costly means for preserving both BV and BVP data is that of parallel recording in two channels, one AC-coupled and set at an amplification sufficient to produce good pulse recordings and the other DC-coupled and set at a much lower level of amplification.

Measurable Aspects of the Plethysmogram

The data derived from the plethysmogram vary with the instrumental method used and with the purposes of the experiment. In the volume displacement methods, the actual volume of the part can be determined and both BV and BVP displacements calculated in terms of volume change per cubic measure of the area under study. In the impedance and photoelectrical devices, the values obtained are relative ones and the significance of the measurements lies in the observed *differences* between control and experimental conditions, e.g. pre- and poststimuli, etc. BV changes are most frequently assessed from equivalent points on the wave form, i.e. peak (control) to peak (experimental). BVP amplitudes are usually measured from diastolic trough to systolic peak at different points on the record. Neither the appearance of the dicrotic notch nor the general shape of the wave form have received serious quantification when the plethysmogram has been used for psychological reasons.

External Factors Affecting Plethysmography

Postural changes of the subject during recording produces marked changes in the tracing. Lowering the part under measurement increases the venous pressure, makes the pulse amplitude less, enhances the dicrotic notch, and may make accessory waves appear. Raising the part reduces the distension of the veins, causes an increase in the pulse amplitude, and may cause the dicrotic notch to disappear. In either case, *the actual blood flow through the part is not significantly changed* (Ackner, 1956, a and b).

There is an indirect relationship between the changes in blood flow and volume changes in a *limb*. This is due to the fact that arterioles control the flow of blood but are of small volume while capillary and venous beds are more distensible and thus produce the largest changes in volume. All other things equal, the volume pulsation with each heart beat is the best approximation of peripheral blood flow although changes in venous pressure, by producing more or less resistance, may produce changes in pulse amplitude.

Stimuli which cause a rise in blood pressure regularly diminish blood flow through the hand when measured by the venous occlusion method (Ackner, 1956a), while blood flow through the forearm is unaffected. In the finger, blood pressure changes and pulse volume changes are usually in the opposite direction while sympathectomy reverses this relationship. Traube-Hering waves may be accompanied by finger volume changes in the upright, but not in the recumbent, subject. In general, blood pressure changes are not importantly involved in the plethysmographic response in the finger (Burch & De Pasquale, 1960).

Nervous Control of the Plethysmographic Response

The blood flow in the skin serves two main functions; the regulation of body temperature and nourishment of the skin. Investigations of the regulation of the blood flow have been made by means of direct or indirect thermal stimulation, by drugs which simulate nervous system transmitters, by pharmacological blockage of nervous supply, etc. Animal studies are not relevant because their skin possesses only vasoconstrictor fibers and lacks eccrine glands, thus sweating is absent.

Cutaneous blood flow in regional areas reacts differently and is apparently innervated differently (Best & Taylor, 1961). Cutaneous vessels of the hand and foot are regulated by the sympathetic nervous system; no parasympathetic fibers have been demonstrated. The forehead skin is believed to have a weak or absent vasoconstrictor nerve supply and it has been suggested that cholinergic sympathetic fibers maintain vasomotor tone in these areas but the experimental evidence for this is indirect. On the skin of the trunk, face, arms, and legs, the dominant innervation appears to be vasodilator while the arterial tone in the palm and sole is mainly the result of arterioconstrictor innervation (Hertzman, 1950). Hertzman has also stated that blushing in the face may be controlled by arteriodilator fibers reaching the face via the facial nerve through which they pass to the meningeal and cerebral arteries (Hertzman & Roth, 1942). Whole limb plethysmography involves changes produced in both cutaneous and muscle tissue. This creates a considerable complexity in interpretation since the effects of a stimulus are frequently opposed in these two types of tissues. Adrenaline dilates muscle and constricts skin vessels (Ackner, 1956); heating produces increased blood flow in the skin while exercise increases muscle blood flow. The total volume change recorded by volume or girth plethysmography is frequently the algebraic summation of opposed changes.

The changing capacity of subcutaneous veins adds another dimension of variability. According to Hertzman (1950), there is a "functionally effective venomotor innervation of the skin, at least of the principal subcutaneous veins which probably account for most of the blood capacity of the skin. This veno-constrictor innervation appears to be much more potent than the cutaneous arterioconstrictor supply in most regions, excepting the hands and feet." Only an arterioconstrictor supply has been identified in the hand.

According to Ackner (1956), the ascending pathway for the vasomotor response for *somatic* stimulation in man is the spinothalamic tract and the vasomotor reflex arc is complete in the brain stem below the level of the sensory thalamus. In addition, these reflexes are usually segmentally or regionally arranged (Best & Taylor, 1961).

Skin color is an important clue to the type of circulation present. An intense scarlet color of the skin indicates a normal or increased blood flow and dilated vessels; a deep blue color accompanies slowed blood flow and dilated vessels, while pallor or a light pink color of the skin is seen when the vessels are moderately constricted and the blood flow is normal or rapid (Best & Taylor, 1961). The color of the skin is not dependent normally upon the most superficial vessels but upon the subpapillary venous plexus. These are parallel to the skin surface and present a greater area than the capillary loops which are at right angles to the skin surface.

Studies of human hemidecorticates show equal vasomotor responsiveness of both sides, leading to the general conclusion that the vasomotor responses have no cortical cell station in man.

Fluid displacement methods. Historically, the fluid displacement technique is the oldest means for registering the plethysmographic response and dates from the work done in 1890 by Sewall and Sanford (1890) on the activity of vasomotor mechanisms excited by electrical stimulation. Three main types of fluid displacement instruments are found in the literature; volume displacement measures, girth-measuring techniques, and rheoplethysmographic devices which are a modification of the volumetric technique used mainly for the quantification of absolute blood flow in the digit.

In volume displacement plethysmography, the finger, hand, arm, or leg is placed within a closed rigid container and sealed tightly by various means so that the remainder of the space may be filled with an incompressible, low viscosity fluid such as water. Tubing filled with the same fluid connects the plethysmograph chamber to a suitable recording device such as a pressure bellows, modified optical manometer or strain gauge pressure transducer (Whitney, 1954). Part volumes are registered by the fluid displaced from the container at various times in the recording and pulse volumes show up as oscillations superimposed upon this curve (Burch, 1954).

While most of the older work has been done with this type of apparatus, there are a number of inherent and unique sources of error and artifact. The weight of the fluid filling the system, the impedance presented to brief transient changes in volume presented by the connecting tubing, and relatively inelastic pressure recording devices attenuate and limit the full fidelity of recording. The sealing of the surrounding bulb or vessel to the limb is critical, it must be fluid tight and inelastic yet it cannot constrict the limb. The fluid filling the chamber must be of a constant temperature, e.g. body temperature, or it will serve as a stimulus to vasomotor changes. The enclosures are large, heavy, and constrain the subject excessively. Finally, and most importantly, it is highly probable that the results obtained from limb plethysmography are not at all comparable with those obtained by other means and on other portions of the limb, e.g. the fingers or toes. The bulk of the tissue encompassed in limb volume plethysmography is muscle, while in the fingers and toes the blood supply is mainly to the skin. Muscle and skin circulatory responses may be quite different in direction and extent, as indicated previously.

On the other hand, only volume and electrical impedance techniques may be used to encompass large areas such as the limbs, trunk, or whole body. The instrumentation is relatively simple and inexpensive. If proper attention is paid to the elimination of movement artifact, the control of environmental variables such as temperature, noise, and the placement of the limb with respect to heart level, useful measures may be derived from volume plethysmographic methods.

Girth plethysmography. Girth plethysmographic methods take advantage of the simple geometric relationship between length, circumference, and the total volume of a cylindrical solid. When the length of the part is unchanged and the circumference (girth) monitored, the changes observed are related to volume changes. The girth transducer commonly takes the form of a highly elastic, small gauge latex or silicone rubber tube which is filled with a fluid-conducting substance (electrode paste, mercury, colloidal graphite, powdered carbon) with metallic electrodes stoppering each end. A critique of this technique is to be found in Whitney (1954). It has been demonstrated that although he stress-strain curve of such a device is nonlinear, the relationship between changes in length and changes in gauge resistance is remarkably linear. A lat frequency response can be produced from DC to 150 cps of repetitive, inear gauge displacement (Lawton & Collins, 1959).

The girth devices are less susceptible to movement artifact than the volume methods except when muscles under the measured site are contracting. Most luid-filled gauges are difficult to maintain, either electrolysis of the filling substance or seepage through the tube wall eventually causes a bubble to appear and destroys the gauge. Devices which are filled with powdered carbon do not show this but the powder tends to clump and then must be tapped sharply to produce an even dispersion and restore sensitivity.

The input circuitry for the girth type transducer is commonly a bridge configuration excited by either AC or DC currents. If AC excitation is used there s less electrolysis and electrode destruction but the signal must then be demodulated to produce useful information.

Rheoplethysmography. This technique, modified by Burch (1954) from an older technique by Brody and Russell, is a variation of the volume device. It is illustrated in Fig. 2.2. The cup surrounds a fingertip and the changes in digital volume are transmitted by the surrounding fluid to a suitable recording device. Immediately proximal to the cup is an encircling cuff which is inflated to a level above the venous occlusion pressure (60 mm Hg), but below arterial occlusion pressure. The blood thus continues to flow into the fingertip but its outflow is prevented by the cuff. According to Burch, the trace of increasing volume is a Cartesian plot of the time course of the volume change in the digit. From this he obtains the first derivatives of the volume curves for inflow, outflow, and the difference between these two rates.

For optimum results, the influx of blood following venous occlusion should create a relatively large change in volume without producing a significant change in pressure, i.e. the veins should be in their normally constricted state at the time of occlusion. Measurement, when the venous tone is high, when the veins are full, or when the walls are rigid, will produce error.

There are a number of reports of the effects of such variables as heat and humidity, local cooling and heating, elevation and lowering of the limb, states of reactive hyperemia, hyperventilation, etc., on the rheoplethysmogram (Burch, 1954).

Electrical Impedance Methods

Since the original work with plethysmography was concerned with the relation of volume change produced by various stimuli, both the techniques of impedance and photoelectrical plethysmography represent such major modifications in procedure that there is some reservation about designating them as plethysmogram. However, since the signals produced by both volume plethysmography and either impedance or photoelectrical methods are related to the

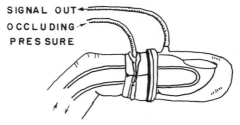

SIGNAL OUT
OCCLUDING
PRESSURE

FIG. 2.2. Basic transducer for rheoplethysmography. The cup surrounding the fingertip is rigid and the entire system including the tubing connecting the cup to the recording device is filled with fluid. The occluding cuff is pneumatically inflated from a separate source to a point above the venous occlusion pressure.

quantity of blood in the measured site, they may be rightfully considered under this general heading. While volume plethysmography produces data which may be quantified in terms of the number of cubic centimeters of change in volume per unit of volume of the measured part, the impedance and photoelectrical methods can provide only *relative* measures representing a magnitude of change from basal or resting conditions.

Impedance plethysmography is based upon the phenomena that biological tissues are moderately good conductors of alternating electrical current and that they show a characteristic impedance (the alternating current equivalent of electrical resistance) to the passage of such a current. A portion of this impedance is fixed and is determined by such factors as the volume and type of tissue between the measuring electrodes. Another portion of the impedance is variable in the sense that it is a function of the quantity of blood in the interposed tissues from moment to moment. Changes in the total observed impedance therefore reflect a change in the ratio of the blood to tissue or in the quantity of blood alone (Geddes & Hoff, 1964).

The transducers for impedance plethysmography consist of metallic electrodes in the form of "finger rings" or flat metal plates of aluminum, copper, stainless steel, or brass attached to the digit, limb, or portion of the trunk to be measured. This flexibility of location is very advantageous in comparison to the volume methods, since measurements can be made from innumerable sites other than the limbs or extremities.

The tissue and blood exhibit both capacitive and resistive components (Nyboer, 1959). For numerous reasons it is desirable to eliminate the capacitive effects. Their contribution is minimal when the frequency of the applied current is in the range of 100 to 200 kHz.

The apparatus required is somewhat complex although it is essentially a full bridge arrangement. Nyboer (1955) uses a Kelvin double bridge arrangement which isolates the electrode pairs used for applying the current from the measurement pair. Polarization problems normally encountered in skin resistance measurements (see Chapter 1) are entirely eliminated. The output signal is amplified, demodulated, and recorded. A derivation of the rationale for measurement and details of the tracings are given in Brown et al. (1965).

Impedance plethysmography is possibly the least prone to movement artifact of all of the methods. However, the absolute magnitude of the impedance measured is dependent upon the amount of current applied to the tissue. Current or current density should always be specified when it is necessary to rigorously define the impedance. Another objection to the electrical impedance procedure is that measurement is made at a site some distance removed from the source of the phenomena (the exact current paths through the intervening tissues cannot be defined) and the results are therefore somewhat of a compromised average. An excellent review of the topic of impedance measurement may be found in Geddes and Hoff (1964), Nyboer (1959), and Schwann (1955).

Photoelectrical Plethysmography

Photoelectrical plethysmography originated in the work of Bonsmann (1934) in Germany and of Hertzman (1938) in this country. Recent advances in electronics, mainly in the development of new photosensitive materials, have added to the precision and sensitivity of the technique without altering the basic methods.

Photoplethysmography is made possible by the fact that living tissue is transparent to red and infrared radiation (7000 to 9000 Å) while nonhemolyzed blood is relatively opaque in this same region (Zijlstra, 1953). It may be seen that by the choice of a photodetector of suitable size and spectral sensitivity and the use of a light source rich in the 7000 to 9000 Å region that the interposition of living tissue between the light and the cell will create a modulation of the cell output which is a function of the concentration of blood in the area. Such cells are now commercially available and tungsten lamps are rich in this spectral region. Three methods for accomplishing this are shown in Fig. 2.3.

If one assumes a linear relationship between the intensity of light striking the cell and its electrical output (usually a resistance change), the light intensity may be determined by the use of a derivative of the Lambert-Beer equation; $I = I_0 e^{-Ad}$, where I_0 is the intensity of the incident light, I is the intensity of the emerging light, A is the average absorption coefficient of the interposed tissue-blood complex, and d is the thickness of the interposed tissue. The exponent, $-Ad$, represents the absorption coefficient of both blood and tissue as well as the quantity of tissue. Since both the quantity of tissue and its absorption coefficient are well controlled by a fixed placement of the transducer; I, representing the modulated output signal, is a function of both the color of the blood (which determines its absorption coefficient) and quantity of blood from moment to moment.

The modulation of cell output due to blood may be further partitioned into two components, a residual component which represents the relatively constant

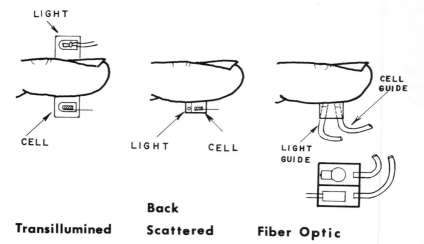

Back

Transillumined   Scattered   Fiber Optic

FIG. 2.3. Three different methods for applying the photoplethysmograph. The transillumi-
nation method requires a higher intensity light source and reveals the vascular changes in
deeper lying as well as cutaneous tissue, but it is more bulky and difficult to use on subjects
with pigmented skin. The backscattering technique permits the use of a lower level light source
and avoids many of the problems associated with heating the skin. Changes are measured
in the superficial cutaneous area only. The use of fiber optics permits the use of higher intensity light sources and avoids the heating problem because of the attenuation offered by the
light guide. Although this technique is shown applied to the fingertip, it may be used on
many other body areas, e.g. the dental gingiva.

amount of blood in the tissue, the blood volume (BV), and a variable component due to changes induced by the pulse pressure wave, the blood volume
pulse (BVP). With the cell placed in a full bridge arrangement and provided
with a steady source of DC, a direct recording displays both components
simultaneously. If only the pulse pressure wave is of interest, the bridge may be
AC-coupled with a suitable time constant (e.g. 0.03 sec) and only the pulse
pressure wave will appear.

    Both the BV and BVP are relative rather than absolute measures. The abso-
lute value of each of these is dependent upon the pressure of application of the
transducer, the elevation of the part from heart level, etc. At the present stage
of the art, it is not possible to provide an absolute measure for the photoelectrical plethysmograph, i.e. one in which the tracing may be defined in absolute
units.

Physical Requirements of the Photoelectric Plethysmograph
    Weinman, Bircher, and Levy (1960) and Weinman and Manoach (1962) have
provided an excellent theoretical discussion of the physical basis for photoplethysmography. The general requirements for both sensitive and artifact-free
recordings are as follows. (1) The light source and photocell must be held in a

fixed spatial relationship to one another and to the tissue under observation or a type of "motion" artifact will be generated (Brown et al., 1965). (2) Some provision must be made for shielding the tissue from heat generated by the lamp used as a light source. This may be accomplished by using a fiber optic light tube as shown in Fig. 2.3, a "cold" light source such as a neon tube or electroluminescent element, or by the use of subminiature, low power lamps such as the L12-3 (Kay Electric Company, Pinegrove, New Jersey) which consumes less than 4 milliwatts of power and produces 10 millilumens of light in a case size of 0.030 × 0.080 in. Heat from the light source will produce reflex vasomotor activity and prohibit accurate measurement. (3) The light source must be fed from a *constant* source of DC power such as a battery. Fluctuations in light intensity will be indistinguishable from vasomotor activity. (4) The transducer must be mounted in such a way as to provide a *light* constant pressure on the tissue; lateral movements must be avoided. Studies are needed to determine the effects on the plethysmogram of different pressure to provide good recordings. (5) The plethysmograph pickup should be mounted on the fingertip, and the arm should be maintained at approximate heart level for either the seated or reclining subject. Any movement of the limb will produce vasomotor changes.

Types of Photoplethysmograph Transducers

The three general means for transilluminating the tissue have been shown in Fig. 2.3 above. Hertzman (1938), Weinman et al. (1960, 1962), and Rawson (1959) have used transmitted or backscattered light. A significant innovation in transducer design was made by Giddon et al. (1963) who employed fiber optics both to direct light upon the tissue from a remote source and to transmit the incident light from the tissue to the photocell.

The fiber optic light guide is made up of a bundle of very tiny (50 μ in diameter) fibers of one type of glass each of which are "clad" with glass of a different refractive index to enforce longitudinal transmission and transverse reflection. A number are gathered together, bundled tightly, and the ends squared and polished. The resulting assembly, which is very flexible, will transmit about 50% of incident light from one end to another and will inhibit the transmission of both ultraviolet and infrared rays. The least inexpensive light guides are "noncoherent," i.e. the location of an individual fiber within the array varies randomly from one end to another, but are quite adequate for this application. Reviews of the physical properties of fiber optics are to be found in Siegmund (1962) and Hicks and Kiritsy (1962).

Fabrication of the Photoplethysmographic Transducer

Most commercial transducers are unsatisfactory for reason of bulk or excessive heat produced by the light source. I fabricate transducers by using the Kay light mentioned above and a Clairex 404 SL cell which is modified by the removal of the glass case (Fig. 2.4). A third lead is added for one terminal of the lamp and the other terminal is soldered to one of the cell leads. Three wires serve to connect the transducer to the recorder. The finished assembly i potted in clear Castolite resin to a finished size of ³/₈ in. in diameter by ¹/₈ in in thickness. Care must be taken to sink the light bulb envelope below the fac of the active surface of the cell so that the cell does not "see" the light directly. The cell mentioned is a "side-on" view unit so that the wires emerge parallel to the skin.*

The material of the cell is cadmium selenide which has a peak spectral response of 6900 A. The action of the cell is photoresistive, i.e. increasing light causes a decreasing resistance. It is a very sensitive material, reaching a value of 250 ohms at only 2 footcandles of illumination and exhibiting a 220% change in conductance for a change in illumination of between 1 and 0.01 footcandle. The "L" in the type number indicates that it is a low resistance device produced by a manufacturing process which creates a large area of sensitive material.

The schematic diagram shown in Fig. 2.4 is that of a full bridge with the photocell as the unknown leg and a potentiometer used for initial balancing. The lamp shares a ground lead with the cell and the variable resistor inserted in the lamp circuit provides for reducing its level of illumination. With the device attached to the finger and the lamp at full brilliance and the output of the cell AC-coupled to the recorder, increasing the value of this resistance will produce a lowering of illumination, but at some point less than full brilliance the pulse height will peak. It has not been determined why this is true although it is probably related to the change in the spectral content of the light as a function of filament temperature.

In use, the photoplethysmograph is attached to the dorsal surface of the fingertip by means of a strip of masking tape. Power is applied to both the bridge and light circuits and with the recorder direct coupled, the bridge is balanced by means of the 50 K variable resistor. The recorder should then be switched to AC coupling. The tracing may then be run without further adjustment of the bridge balance if the BVP only is required. Since the changes in BV are in excess of those in the BVP, when both measures are desired it is necessary to increase the gain to the point where the BVP is of the desired amplitude and either (1) rebalance the bridge when major BV changes occur, or (2) record in two channels simultaneously, one at lower amplification and DC-coupled (BV), the second at a higher amplification and AC-coupled (BVP). Major changes in BV will not affect the recording of the BVP in the first chan-

---

*The manufacturer has recently discontinued production of the side mounted cell described in the text. The Clairex 704-L is essentially similar electrically and may be adapted for use by bending the two leads into a sharp 90° turn at the point where they exit from the sealed, metal case. The resulting assembly will be slightly larger than that described but the cell need not be demounted. Cells produced by other manufacturers which display similar spectral response and electrical characteristics may also be substituted.

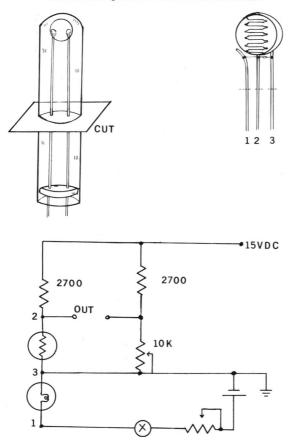

FIG. 2.4. Steps in the construction of a miniature photoplethysmograph. The tubular glass enclosure is cut and discarded and the cell area promptly dipped in a transparent coating such as clear Insul-X, E 33. The cell leads are scraped bright close to the cell and *lead 3* is bent into a loop to form *lead 1*. The Pinlite leads are first wrapped and then soldered around *leads 1* and *3* close to the cell. The hook shape shown on *lead 1* provides anchorage and resistance to twist. The unit is then potted in clear Castolite. When this is set, the leads are trimmed close to the unit, connecting wires are attached, and the rear and side surfaces are painted opaque black. The bridge circuit shown beneath may be mounted in a blank Offner coupler and powered by the internal voltages.

nel and a record of the BV changes at an appropriately lower amplification will be available in the second channel.

Applications of Plethysmography

Evidence from literature, folk lore, and clinical observation (the observation of the red face of rage and the pale countenance of fear or anguish) indicate the powerful effects upon circulation produced by emotions. Vasocon-striction of the cutaneous vessels on an emotional basis is part of a bodily alerting reaction to stress which serves the function of diverting the bulk of the blood supply to those areas which are necessary for mobilization for either offense or defense. Yet the experimental demonstration of this fact is made difficult by the essential artificiality of laboratory devised situations to produce "stress," "fear," or "anger" and the inability to monitor reliably an individual who is in the throes of a real emotional experience. It is not surprising therefore to find the most of the studies of the status of vascular skin reactions in emo-tion have dealt with the neurotic and the psychotic.

Mosso in 1881 first demonstrated the effects of emotion on the plethysmo-graph by showing that a decrease in volume accompanied acute psychic stimuli. A number of investigators have confirmed this finding with the use of such stimuli as a pinch, cold, heat, electric shock, difficult arithmetic problems, noise, light, and a threat. Yet is has also been demonstrated by Hallion and Comte in 1895 and more recently by Ungar (1964) that a continued repetition of an adequate stimulus leads eventually to an adaptation resulting in the extinction of the vasoconstrictor response. If the vasoconstriction was only a reflex produced by an adequate stimulus, extinction would not occur. It would seem, therefore, that the vasoconstrictive reaction is not produced by the mere sensory aspects of the stimulus, but is generated by a more complex "psychical" state which it arouses. Tests carried out on hypnotized normal subjects (Doupe, Miller, & Keller, 1939) show that hypnosis per se does not alter the state of the cutaneous blood vessels, but that the suggestion that a limb was analgesic produced a diminution of the vasoconstrictive response to such stimuli as pin pricks and ice water. Hypnotic suggestions to a subject who was actually chilled to the effect that he was hot or suggestions that the subject was experiencing either pain or cold did not produce vasoconstrictive responses. It would seem that the plethysmogram reflected changes in feeling tone which accompanied the actual awareness of the stimulus.

Sleep is a state of altered consciousness, similar in some respects to hypnosis but differing in the respect that stimuli of normal intensity are apparently not perceived. Yet a number of studies have confirmed Mosso's original observa-tions that plethysmographic responsiveness to noise, cold, and heat is main-tained during sleep. Ackner's study (Ackner & Pampliglione, 1955) has shown that plethysmographic responses persist at depths of sleep where other indices such as skin resistance, respiration, and heart rate fail to show either spontan-eous changes or responsiveness to stimuli.

The consensus of opinion seems to be that the cutaneous vasoconstriction response is the reflection of an arousal or alerting reaction (Ackner, 1956) while Sokolov and other Russian workers contend that the pattern of vasoconstric-tion in the digit accompanied by vasodilation in the forehead precisely and exclusively defines the orienting response (Sokolov, 1963; Vinogradova &

Sokolov, 1957). The Russian investigators have defined two other types of vascular reflexes in addition to the above mentioned pattern which is presumed specific to the orienting reaction. These are : (1) a thermoregulatory reflex which produces vasoconstriction in both the hand and forehead in response to cold and vasodilation in response to heat and is not accompanied by change in the palmar skin resistance, and (2) a defense reflex appearing to a variety of stimuli when they are of high intensity, i.e. painful, which consists of vaso-constriction in both the forehead and hand accompanied by a fall in palmar skin resistance.

The Russian workers have attached great significance to the measurement of forehead cutaneous vascular activity in the area of the bifurcation of the temporal and frontal arteries. They claim that these recordings are "closely comparable with those recorded directly from cerebral vessels in cases with skull defects. Cerebral vasodilatation also coincided with a similar change in the retina, associated with increased cerebral supply" (Sokolov, 1963, p. 39). The significance of this response is that it serves to "strengthen the action of strong, painful stimuli and . . . to weaken the action of stimuli of low or medium intensity . . ." (p. 66) and by this modification to focus the perception on important and dangerous events and to assist in creating a disregard of the unimportant. There is much need for further investigation along these lines by American investigators.

At least one study reports that both the temperature and volume of the fingers were modified by the mere act of directing the subject's attention to these areas (Li Chao-i, Len Yuan-lien, & Wang, 1964). Combined EEG and plethysmographic studies in individuals with abnormal EEG recordings showed that those individuals with the most grossly disturbed patterns of pulse wave activity showed abnormal EEG responses to hyperventilation (Lhamon, 1949).

The Plethysmographic Response as a Psychophysiologic Measure
A number of studies (Acker & Edwards, 1964; Luria & Vinogradova, 1959; Lang et al., 1963) have employed the plethysmographic response as an unconditional response, usually in studies of semantic conditioning or semantic generalization. This technique has proved to be quite productive, especially in the hands of Russian workers. That the response is a sensitive indicator is shown by its spread to word stimuli only semantically related to the experimental word which was conditioned to shock or sound.

Plethysmographic Responsiveness in Neurotic and Psychotic Subjects
The observation that mental patients, particularly severe schizophrenics, suffered from cold hands and feet has often been made by nurses and ward personnel. The most striking examples of this condition exhibit acrocyanosis (a deep blue color of the extremities of the body) which is apparently associated with profound disturbances in circulation. An early note on this condition (Minski,

1937) attempted to explain this condition on the basis of a fundamental disturbance in the physical side in schizophrenia which consisted of a "clumsiness of adaptive responses to changed conditions" and to an "inadequate autonomic nervous system." The condition of acrocyanosis was observed in other varities of psychotics (Stern, 1937) and a study of 52 patients with various diagnoses showed that there was diminished blood flow in the hand, forearm, and legs of these individuals which was restored to normal levels by heating the subject (Abramson, Schloven, & Katzenstein, 1941). These investigators concluded that there was "no lesion of the arterial tree in schizophrenics." Essentially the same findings had been reported by Jung and Carmichael (1937). It is concluded by Ackner (1956) that this type of circulatory disturbance in the severe psychotic is not the consequence of emotional disturbance, but since it is seen most commonly in the severely withdrawn and inactive patients, that it represents the action of the normal physiological mechanism for preserving body heat.

Another set of conclusions was reached by Henshel, Brozek, and Keys (1951) who used both normal control subjects and schizophrenic patients. They measured both the photoelectric plethysmogram on the finger and skin temperatures on both the finger and cheek. Measuring the time relationships of the BVP curve to reflex dilation of the finger produced by placing the feet in hot water, they found that while the profile of the curve of adaptive change to heat was almost identical in both schizophrenic and normal patients, that the adjustment took significantly longer for the schizophrenic than the normal (25.5 min versus 16.2 min). An analysis of the measure, "crest time percentage of cycle length" showed no significant differences between control and schizophrenic groups thus demonstrating that there was no organic vascular damage in the schizophrenic group, e.g. open arterioventricular shunts. They conclude that while there is no evidence of basic abnormality in the peripheral skin circulation in schizophrenics, there is probably either (1) an exceptionally high and persistent state of tonus in skin vessels, or (2) an abnormally high temperature threshold for temperature regulating centers in the hypothalamus. It would appear that this question has not yet been completely resolved.

A very ingenious study of plethysmographic reactivity in states of anxiety was performed by Ackner (1956). Reasoning that emotional arousal is accompanied by peripheral vasoconstriction, but recognizing that the measurement of absolute differences between anxious and control subjects would be obscured by differences due to physiological individuality and not related to the factor of anxiety, he arranged his study to compare *changes* in peripheral circulation in both types of subjects from waking to sleep states. Ackner did not depend upon nocturnal sleep which would be contaminated by individual differences in habits, degree of fatigue, etc., but induced sleep by means of Seconal. The drug was administered to anxious patients, nonanxious patients, and normal controls in the morning hours. Plethysmograms, EEG, skin resistance, and pulse rate measures were taken throughout the drug session as well as during several waking control sessions held at the same time of day. His results showed that the three groups differed significantly (1) in the size of the BVP during the resting control state and (2) in the amount of increase in pulse volume from resting to sleep states. Pulse rates did not significantly differentiate the groups although there was considerable within-subject variability, a factor which in itself deserves further study. Ackner's study is significant not only for the finding that peripheral cutaneous vasoconstriction is found in anxious subjects but also as a demonstration of a technique which permits measurements of relative change between two controllable states of consciousness, sleep and waking.

Van der Merwe and Theron (1947) used both physical and psychological stimuli to produce peripheral cutaneous changes in a group of subjects. By using heat, cold, and mental arithmetic and measuring the plethysmographic response, they found that the total volume displacement (stimulus induced BV change times duration of change) produced by these stimuli was significantly correlated with the subject's scores on the Bell Adjustment Inventory. Theron (1948) continued this line of investigation with normal subjects and found a similar significant correlation between the Bell scores expressive of emotional stability and the rate of change of finger volume. A factor analysis of the data yielded three factors: (1) emotional stability-lability, (2) a measure of basic emotional tension, and (3) a specific factor.

Application of this technique to a group of neurotics and normal controls (Van der Merwe, 1948 and 1950) further supported the pulse volume measure as an indicator of emotional tension and revealed significant differences between normals, anxious patients, and a patient group described as hysteric-neurasthenic. Van der Merwe reported lowered BVP and other signs of sympathetic dominance in the anxious group and indications of dilation and parasympathetic dominance in the hysterics and neurasthenics; a finding which is unique in the literature.

Unstimulated deflections in finger pulse volumes which occur spontaneously in normals were observed by Burch, Cohn, and Neumann (1942) and Neumann et al. (1944) to be relatively small with little variation in size of deflection in individuals who were observed to be phlegmatic and emotionally stable. Those subjects who showed considerable variation in the size of the deflections tended to be excitable and subject to mood swings.

The above studies suggest that the measurement of peripheral cutaneous vasoconstriction provides a means for assessing the physiological differences between various of the psychiatric groups and normals. There also seems to be some possibility for determining rather minor fluctuations in emotional arousal in normal subjects in laboratory situations provided sufficient controls are exerted and a reasonable attempt is made to produce a realistic emotion-provoking situation. A matter of particular interest is the observations that valuable information may be obtained from the plethysmogram during normal and drug-induced sleep.

Retrospectively, however, it would appear that the contemporary techniques, particularly the photoelectrical plethysmograph transducer, which are sensitive to changes in the vascular contents of the superficial cutaneous tissue, are only indirectly related to the older volume methods which reflected gross changes in the volume of muscle tissue. The contemporary techniques seem to represent an evolved measurement which may be only superficially related to the techniques of the older, limb-volume plethysmograph. It is therefore suggested that a new term may be appropriate to designate the phenomena which the optical plethysmograph now monitors, the term "peripheral vascular response." It also seems necessary to free oneself from the customary ways of thinking about the immediate and remote causes of this reaction and to explore new hypotheses concerning the role of the peripheral vascular response in transient and persistent modifications of affect and mood. If a major emotional arousal is accompanied by a gross redistribution of circulating blood from tissues where it serves as a maintenance function to internal organs and tissues where there is the need for emergency support on a defensive or offensive organismic basis, then it would be important to monitor simultaneously the changes in both types of tissues.

The peripheral vascular response measure deserves an increasing use in studies of the physiological changes in altered states of consciousness produced by sleep, chemical agents, or the hallucinogenic drugs; in the analysis of changed status of anxious or depressed psychiatric patients; in the assessment of mood and emotional responsiveness in normals; and, potentially, in the delineation of physiological reaction types who might show differing susceptibility to physical and psychosomatic disorder.

REFERENCES

Abramson, D.I., Schloven, N., & Katzenstein, K. H. Peripheral blood flow in schizophrenia and other abnormal mental states. *Archs Neurol. Psychiat., Chicago*, 1941, *45*: 973.
Acker, L. E., & Edwards, A. E. Transfer of vasoconstriction over a bipolar meaning dimension. *J. exp. Psychol.*, 1964, *67*: 1-6.
Ackner, B. Emotions and the peripheral vasomotor system. *J. psychosom. Res.*, 1956, *1*: 3-20. (a)
Ackner, B. The relationship between anxiety and the level of peripheral vasomotor activity. *J. psychosom. Res.*, 1956, *1*: 21-48. (b)
Ackner, B., & Pampliglione, G. Combined EEG, plethysmographic, respiratory and skin resistance studies during sleep. *Electroenceph. clin. Neurophysiol.*, 1955, 7: 153.
Best, C. H., & Taylor, N. B. *The physiological basis of medical practice.* Baltimore: Williams & Wilkins, 1961.
Bonsmann, M. R. Blutdruckversuche an der maus und ratte mittels photozelle. *Arch. exp. Path. Pharmak.*, 1934, *176*: 460–482.

Brown, C. C., Giddon, D. B., & Dean, E. D. Techniques of plethysmography. *Psychophysiology*, 1965, *1*: 253–266.

Burch, G. E. *Digital plethysmography*. New York: Grune & Stratton, 1954.

Burch, G. E., Cohn, A. E., & Neumann, C. Rheopneumoplethysmography, alpha and beta waves. *Am. J. Physiol.*, 1942, *136*: 433.

Burch, G. N., & De Pasquale, N. Relation of arterial pressure to spontaneous variations in digital volume. *J. appl. Physiol.*, 1960, *15*: 23–24.

Darrow, C. W. The galvanic skin reflex and finger volume changes. *Am. J. Physiol.*, 1929, *88*: 219–229.

Densham, H. B., & Wells, H. M. The mechanism by which the electrical resistance of the skin is altered. *Q. Jl. exp. Physiol.*, 1927, *18:* 175.

Doupe, J., Miller, W. R., & Keller, W. K. Vasomotor reactions in the hypnotic state. *J. Neurol. Psychiat.*, 1939, *2*: 97.

Féré, C. Note sur des modification de la resistance electrique sous l'influence des excitations sensorielles et des emotions. *C. r. Séanc. Soc. Biol.*, 1888, 217.

Geddes, L. A., & Hoff, H. E. The measurement of physiologic events by electrical impedance. *Am. J. med. Electron.*, 1964, *3*: 16–27.

Giddon, D. B., Goldhaber, P., Kushnir, H., & Gustafson, L. A. Photoelectric monitoring of gingival vascular reactions. *Int. Ass. Dent. Res.*, 1963, *41*: 76.

Henshel, A., Brozek, J., & Keys, A. Indirect vasodilatation in normal man and in schizophrenic patients. *J. appl. Physiol.*, 1951, *4*: 340–344.

Hertzman, A. B. The blood supply of various skin areas as estimated by the photoelectric plethysmograph. *Am. J. Physiol.*, 1938, *124*: 328.

Hertzman, A. B., Vasomotor regulation of cutaneous circulation. *Physiol. Rev.*, 1950, *39*: 280–306.

Hertzman, A. B., & Roth, L. S. Absence of vasoconstriction reflexes in forehead circulation. Effects of cold. *Am. J. Physiol.*, 1942, *136*: 692–697.

Hicks, J., & Kiritsy, P. Fiber optics. *Glass Ind.*, 1962, *44*: 193–196, 208–211.

Jung, R., & Carmichael, E. A. Uber vasomotorische reaktionen und warnsregulation im katatonen stupor. *Arch. Psychiat. Nervkrankh.*, 1937, *107*: 107–300.

Lang P. J., Geer, J., & Hnatiow, M. Semantic generalization of conditioned autonomic responses. *J. exp. Psychol.*, 1963, *65*: 552–558.

Lawton, R. W., & Collins, C. C. Calibration of an aortic circumference gauge. *J. appl. Physiol.*, 1959, *14*: 456–467.

Lhamon, W. T. Relation between certain finger volume changes, electroencephalographically manifested brain activity and psychopathological reactions. *Psychosom. Med.*, 1949, *11*: 113.

Li Chao-i, Lin Yuan-lien, & Wang, S. Influence of attention on the state of the dermal vessels. *Acta psychol. Sinica*, 1964, *3*: 298–302.

Luria, A. R., & Vinogradova, O. S. An objective investigation of the dynamics of semantic systems. *Br. J. Psychol.*, 1959, *50*: 89–105.

Magnussen, G. Vasomotor changes in the extremities during sleep. *Acta psychiat. neurol. scand.*, 1939, *14*: 39–54.

Minski, L. A note on some vasomotor disturbances in schizophrenia. *J. ment. Sci.*, 1937, *83*: 437.

Neumann, C., Lhamon, W., & Cohn, A. A study of factors (emotional) responsible for changes in the pattern of spontaneous rhythmic fluctuations in the volume of the vascular bed of the finger tip. *J. clin. Invest.* 1944, *23*: 1.

Nyboer, J. Electronic impedance plethysmograph. *I.R.E. Trans. med. Electron.*, 1955, *3*: 55.

Nyboer, J. *Electrical impedance plethysmography*. Springfield, Ill.: Charles C Thomas, 1959.

Radecki, W. Les phenomenes psychoelectriques. *Archs Psychol. Suisse romande*, 1911, *11*: 209.

Rawson, R. O. A highly sensitive, miniaturized photoelectric plethysmograph. *J. appl. Physiol.*, 1959, *14*: 1049–1050.

Schwann, H. P. Electrical properties of body tissues and impedance plethysmography. *I.R.E. Trans. med. Electron.*, 1955, *3*: 32.

Sewall, H., & Sanford, E. Plethysmographic studies of the human vasomotor mechanism when excited by electrical stimulation. *J. Physiol., Lond.*, 1890, *11*: 179–207.

Siegmund, W. P. Fiber optics: principles, properties and design considerations. Paper presented at 6th Annual Meeting, Avionics Panel AGARD (NATO), Paris, France, July 1962.

Sokolov, E. N. *Perception and the conditioned reflex* (Translated by S. W. Waydenfeld). New York: Pergamon Press, 1963.

Stern, E. S. Acrocyanosis. *J. ment. Sci.*, 1937, *83*: 408.

Theron, P. A. Peripheral vasomotor reactions as indices of basic emotional tension and liability. *Psychosom. Med.*, 1948, *10*: 335.

Ungar, S. M. Habituation of the vasoconstrictive orienting reaction. *J. exp. Psychol.*, 1964, *1*: 11–18.

Van der Merwe, A. B. Diagnostic value of peripheral vasomotor reactions in psychoneuroses. *Psychosom. Med.*, 1948, *10*: 347–354.

Van der Merwe, A. B. The value of the finger plethysmograph in diagnosing neurotic cases. *Proc. S. Afr. psychol. Ass.*, 1950, *1*: 10–12.

Van der Merwe, A. B. & Theron, P. A. A new method of measuring emotional stability. *J. gen. Psychol.*, 1947, *37*: 109–123.

Vinogradova, O. S., & Sokolov, E. N. A study of the reactions of the blood vessels of the hand and head as components of certain unconditioned reflexes. *J. Physiol., Russ.*, 1957, *42*: 57–67.

Weinman, J., Bicher, C., & Levy, D. Application of a photoconductive cell to the study of peripheral circulation in limbs of animals and man. *J. appl. Physiol.*, 1960, *15*: 317–230.

Weinman, J., & Manoach, M. A photoelectric approach in the study of peripheral circulation. *Am. Heart J.*, 1962, *62*: 219–231.

Whitney, R. J. The electrical strain gauge method for measurement of peripheral circulation in man. In G. E. W. Wolstenholme (Ed.). *Peripheral circulation in man*. Boston: Little, Brown & Co., 1954, P. 45.

Zijlstra, W. A. *Fundamentals and applications of clinical oximetry*. Ossen, Netherlands: Van Gorcum, 1953. P. 24.

3

The Measurement of Respiration

MARVIN STEIN, M.D., AND THOMAS J. LUPARELLO, M.D.

Respiration is a complex process which provides oxygen to the cells and removes carbon dioxide from them. From the earliest moments of life the respiratory system is associated with a variety of behavioral activities which have considerable emotional significance. As the infant feeds, for example, there is coordination of sucking, swallowing, and breathing, and respiration is thereby involved in the earliest significant relationships that the individual has with other people. Throughout the life of an individual respiratory processes have a marked affective and symbolic significance and provide a means of expressing emotional reactions and needs. It is an everyday observation that breathing is an integral part of emotional expression, e.g. laughter and crying.

Respiratory function is regulated by the central nervous system (CNS) by means of respiratory centers in the pons and medulla. These centers receive information from many receptors and have connections with areas in the cortex, hypothalamus, and the reticular activating system. Respiration is further regulated by a group of respiratory reflexes from the lungs, heart, and great vessels. These reflexes are mediated primarily by the vagus, and there is some evidence that sympathetic pathways may also be involved in a few of the reflexes. There are several recent reviews of the regulation of respiration and the respiratory reflexes (Comroe, 1965; Widdicombe, 1963 and 1964).

The close association of the respiratory system with emotional processes and with the autonomic nervous system has led a number of investigators to a consideration of the psychophysiology of respiration, and to the use of measures of respiration as an index of autonomic activity. A variety of approaches have been used, and for the purpose of presentation these will be reviewed under four major headings: (1) emotions and respiration; (2) personality types and respiration; (3) conditioning techniques and respiration; and (4) respiratory psychophysiological disorders. Following this review, the measurement of the various aspects of respiration will be considered.

Emotions and Respiration

A number of investigators have attempted to correlate respiratory changes with specific emotions. One of the earliest reports was by Lehman (1905) who investigated the differential effect of pleasure and displeasure on respiration and found that the feeling of pleasure was accompanied by a rapid respiratory rate. Feleky (1916) reported a study in which the subjects were asked to recall six primary emotions, i.e. pleasure, pain, anger, disgust, wonder, and fear, while a pneumographic record was obtained. He found specific inspiratory-expiratory (I/E) ratios for the various emotions. Stevenson and Ripley (1952) have correlated respiratory patterns with changes in the emotional state of subjects during interviews.

Studies dealing with the influence of emotions on metabolic rate and respiration were stimulated to a great extent by accidental observations made during the determination of basal metabolic rates on apprehensive or emotionally disturbed subjects. It has been rather common to find that the metabolic rate is higher during an initial test, when the subject is somewhat apprehensive, than on later occasions. Ziegler and Levine (1925) found an increase in metabolic rate and a slight change in the rate and amplitude of respiration in a group of psychoneurotic patients when the subjects were asked to recall specific emotional events in their lives. A marked increase in metabolic rate and an irregularity of respiration during hypnotically induced anxiety and apprehension has also been reported (Whitehorn, Lundholm, & Gardner, 1929).

Finesinger (1939) investigated the effect of the recall of pleasant and unpleasant ideas on the respiratory response of normal and neurotic subjects. Of the respiratory functions studied, the minute volume, i.e. ventilation per min or tidal volume × rate, showed the greatest consistency of deviation in relation to changes in ideational stimulation. Most phobic patients and those with anxiety neuroses, as well as the majority of control subjects, showed a considerable increase in minute volume during unpleasant periods as compared with pleasant ones. Essentially similar changes were found by Finesinger and Mazick (1940) in an analogous population during the actual administration of painful stimuli and again during subsequent recall of the experience.

Other investigators have been interested in the relationship of psychodynamic patterns and respiration. Alexander and Saul (1940), for example, analyzed respiratory tracings with special reference to psychological correlations and found suggestive evidence of a relation between emotional themes having to do with the ingestion, retention, and elimination of food and certain characteristics of the spirogram.

Several studies have been concerned with the effect of emotions on the physiology of the diaphragm. Faulkner (1941, a and b) found during fluoroscopic examinations that the discussion of pleasant life situations caused an increased amplitude of diaphragmatic movement while unpleasant situations restricted it. Wolf (1947) observed during the discussion of conflicts that the inspiratory excursion of the diaphragm exceeded that found during expiration. When an adequate inspiratory excursion of the diaphragm was no longer possible as a result of changes in its contractile state, dyspnea developed.

Lovett-Doust and Schneider (1955) analyzed changes in capillary blood oxygen saturation in relation to emotional stimuli. They found that stressful stimuli with specific emotional meaning to a subject produced a significant anoxemic reaction.

It has been reported that there is increased ventilation and oxygen consumption following the hypnotic suggestion of situations eliciting anxiety and anger. Hypnotic suggestion of depression was not followed by a change in the respiratory variables in the same subjects (Dudley, Holmes, Martin, & Ripley, 1964).

Personality Types and Respiration

A number of investigators have attempted to correlate personality or constitutional types with respiration. Romer (1924) reported that the different personality types could be identified by their respiratory patterns. Nielsen and Roth (1929) stated that it is possible to classify individuals on the basis of their spirograms into essentially nine basic types. It was their opinion that the respiratory types were hereditary and that the occurrence of a specific type of breathing presages certain predispositions in the individual. For example, a characteristic respiratory pattern was found to be associated with endocrine disturbances while another type of spirogram occurred more frequently in neurotic and psychotic states. The evidence for the specific types, however, is not convincing.

A body plethysmograph was used by Golla and Antonovitch (1929) in their studies of respiration and thought. They found two types of habitual respiration among their subjects. The regular pattern of respiration occurred in subjects who utilized predominantly visual imagery, while the irregular type of breathing was found in subjects with predominantly auditory imagery. Wittkower (1935) has reported, however, that the two types of breathing are evenly distributed among a normal population.

Conditioning Techniques and Respiration

A considerable number of conditioning paradigms have utilized respiration. Several investigators have used electric shock as the unconditional stimulus (US), and various respiratory measures as the unconditioned (UR) and conditioned response (CR). Upton (1929) reported a conditioned increase in the amplitude of respiration in the guinea pig after several hundred combined stimulations by a tone and an electric shock to the hind limbs. Sharp inspirations were conditioned in rats to a buzzer which had been followed by a shock to the right forelimb. The conditioning of respiration was observed to be sooner established and later extinguished than concurrently conditioned limb movement of avoidance (Kappanf & Schlosberg, 1937). Walker and Kellog (1939), utilizing a buzzer preceding a shock, observed in dogs a conditioned response characterized by a decrease in amplitude and rate of respiration. The conditioned respiratory response was also established earlier and extinguished later than the concomitant conditioned flexor reflex. Freedman (1951) observed in dogs a conditioned respiratory response accompanying the conditioning of an avoidance flexion of a shock stimulus. The respiratory CR consisted of inspiratory gasps with or without hyperpnea or polypnea. Conditioning of respiration with a buzzer and shock has also been demonstrated in humans in the waking state and under hypnosis (Konradi & Bebeschina, 1957).

Changes in the composition of the inspired air have been utilized by other investigators in conditioning studies. Konradi and Bebeschina (1957) used the sound of a metronome as a conditional stimulus (CS) and the inhalation of a mixture of air with 7% of carbon dioxide as the US in humans. They found after 15 conditioning trials a marked conditioned increase in ventilation. In another experiment the same authors had a small group of subjects spend 8 hours in an air-tight chamber in which the concentration of the accumulated exhaled carbon dioxide produced a marked rise in pulmonary ventilation. After a few trials a conditioned increase in ventilation was observed during the first minutes after the subjects entered the chamber. Britvan (1957) produced periodic rhythmic respirations by exposing dogs to the inhalation of oxygen every 2 min. After a series of trials the experimental situation alone was found to produce the same changes of respiration as those which had characterized the exposure to oxygen.

Conditioned disturbances of respiration have been noted in experimental neurosis produced in a variety of animals exposed to conflict situations. Gantt (1941) observed in one of his dogs, following the onset of an experimental neurosis, an "asthma-like pattern" characterized by raucous respiration and slow labored breathing. This respiratory pattern continued for several years and appeared every time the dog was taken to the experimental box in which he was conditioned. Lidell (1951) demonstrated that chronic respiratory dysfunctions characterized by increased rates, gasping, labored, and irregular respirations inevitably accompanied experimental neurosis in the sheep and goat.

Several authors, based on clinical observations, have discussed the role of a conditioned mechanism as a possible determinant in the development and precipitation of asthmatic attacks. Recently, several investigators have reported that a respiratory response similar to asthma can be conditioned in the guinea pig (Ottenberg, Stein, Lewis, & Hamilton, 1958; Noelpp & Noelpp-Eschenhagen, 1951). Dekker, Pelser, and Groen (1957) produced attacks of asthma experimentally by exposing two asthmatic patients to the inhalation of the appropriate allergen. After a series of exposures, inhalation of a neutral solvent alone precipitated attacks characterized by a progressive decrease in vital capacity. These phenomena were interpreted as a result of conditioning by the simultaneous exposure of the patient to the inhalation of the allergen and to the experimental situation.

Respiratory Psychophysiological Disorders

Although considerable attention has been devoted to the experimental induction of asthmatic attacks by allergens or other physical means, relatively few studies have attempted to test experimentally the hypothesis that emotions are related to the development and precipitation of asthmatic attacks. Ziegler and Elliot (1926) were among the first investigators who tried to evaluate experimentally the effect of emotions on the respiration of asthmatic patients. Three asthmatic subjects in whom psychological factors were considered to be important were asked to think about emotion-producing events of their life while a pneumographic record was taken. They showed considerable alteration in the regularity of the respiratory curves and a prolongation of the expiratory phase. In another group of three patients in whom the asthma was primarily allergic, the alterations in respiration were not observed.

Stevenson and Ripley (1952) also used a pneumographic technique in order to evaluate the respiratory response of asthmatic patients with anxiety states. Records were taken during the course of interviews in which significant events and interpersonal relations were discussed. The authors found that discussion of emotional conflicts known to be associated with respiratory symptoms (dyspnea and chest discomfort) evoked the symptoms in more than half of the patients. A prolongation of respiration during periods of emotional disturbance was found in a higher proportion of patients with asthma than in those with anxiety. Treuting and Ripley (1948) exposed five pollen-sensitive patients to the appropriate pollen without the subjects' awareness and in no instance did asthma develop. Asthmatic symptoms such as wheezing often appeared, however, during the discussion of problems relevant to the patient's life situation.

The interrelationship between emotions, life situations, and anoxemia in asthmatic patients was investigated by Lovett-Doust and Leigh (1953). They studied 25 patients and measured arterial oxygen saturation by means of a spectroscopic oximetry technique during the course of a psychiatric interview. A marked reduction in arterial oxygen saturation accompanied the discussion of significant interpersonal relationships. No changes in oxygen saturation values were observed, however, during periods of spontaneous asthmatic breathing which occurred in the course of the interview.

Dekker and Groen (1956) exposed a number of asthmatic patients to specific emotional stimuli, such as pictures and odors which were known to precipitate asthmatic attacks. A number of the patients responded to the stimuli with a decrease in vital capacity associated in some cases with typical asthmatic attacks.

The basic pathophysiological change in asthma is bronchiolar obstruction and several investigators have studied the effect of emotions on bronchiolar physiology. These studies are of considerable importance since changes in respiratory movements, including clinical symptoms resembling asthma, may occur without evidence of bronchiolar obstruction. Faulkner (1941b) has observed bronchoscopically, bronchiolar constriction when unpleasant topics were discussed. Stein (1962), utilizing a technique for measuring airway resistance as an index of bronchiolar obstruction, found in several asthmatic patients the emotional stress produced by the experimental situation was itself provocative of asthmatic symptoms accompanied by a marked increase in airway resistance.

Measurement of Respiration

Although the psychophysiology of respiration has been explored by a variety of approaches, there has been relatively little recent work in this area. In the past 25 years the four journals* in which a majority of the psychophysiological studies are reported have published less than 25 articles primarily concerned with respiration. By contrast, during the same period these journals have published several hundred reports in which cardiovascular variables or the galvanic skin response (GSR) were investigated. In general, the respiratory studies have utilized small numbers of subjects and relatively few of the investigations have been replicated. It is also clear from the above review that the majority of the studies have been concerned primarily with breathing. Pulmonary gas exchange is achieved, however, by a number of processes and includes more than the external aspects of respiration. A large enough volume of inspired air must reach and be distributed every minute to the many alveoli in the lungs. This process is known as ventilation. The second process involved in respiration is the passage by diffusion of oxygen and carbon dioxide across the alveolocapillary membranes. There must be an adequate pulmonary capillary blood flow to permit the venous blood to be distributed to the ventilated alveoli for the uptake of the necessary amount of oxygen and elimination of carbon dioxide. In addition to these components of respiration, the mechanical factors involved in breathing are of considerable importance in providing adequate pulmonary gas exchange.

In the present chapter the various processes involved in respiration will be considered along with examples of some of the techniques that may be used to measure them. In addition, the advantages and limitations of some of the methods will be considered.

Ventilation

The metabolic processes of the body require oxygen and produce carbon

---

*The four journals are: *Psychosomatic Medicine, Journal of Psychosomatic Research, Journal of Abnormal and Social Psychology,* and *Journal of Comparative and Physiological Psychology.*

dioxide. Oxygen is obtained from the capillary blood to which is added the excess carbon dioxide. This capillary gas exchange lowers the partial pressure of oxygen (PO_2) of venous blood below that of the arterial blood and raises its partial pressure of carbon dioxide (PCO_2). The primary function of the respiratory system is to keep the arterial blood at constant levels of PO_2 and PCO_2. This is accomplished by supplying the alveoli with the amount of oxygen utilized by the tissues, and removing from the alveoli the excess of CO_2 added to the blood. The optimal levels of PO_2 and PCO_2 in the pulmonary alveoli are maintained by the process of ventilation in which fresh air is inspired and an equal volume, in most instances, is expired.

Air passes through a conducting airway from the nose and mouth to the alveoli. Since there is relatively no exchange between oxygen and carbon dioxide and blood in the conducting airway, this space is referred to as the anatomical dead space. Most psychological studies will not be concerned with the measurement of the anatomical dead space. It is difficult to measure in most laboratories but can be accomplished by means of continuous, rapid electrical gas analyzers. It has been noted that in adults the anatomical dead space in milliliters is equal to the ideal weight of the subject in pounds (Comroe, Forster, Dubois, Briscoe, & Carlsen, 1962).

The quantitative measure of the depth of breathing is the tidal volume or the total volume of each breath. The tidal volume in adults is approximately 400 to 600 ml, but there is a considerable range. Variables such as body size and weight, exercise or other factors which alter oxygen requirements, or carbon dioxide tension are associated with changes in tidal volume.

The majority of psychophysiological studies will be concerned with the total ventilation or the volume of air entering the nose and mouth each breath or each minute. The alveolar ventilation is the volume of air entering the alveoli each breath or minute and is always less than the total ventilation. The amount by which it is less depends upon the volume of the anatomical dead space, tidal volume, and rate of breathing.

Two types of methods for the measurement of pulmonary ventilation have been employed. One depends on changes in the girth of the chest and abdomen, and the other on the measurement of the volume of the inspired and expired air. With the girth method a thoracic pneumograph has been chiefly used. A distensible air-filled tube is placed around the chest and connected to a pressure transducer and the signal amplified and recorded. In addition to the traditional pneumograph, a variety of strain gauges have been used and changes in the circumference of the thorax recorded as changes in the resistance of the strain gauge. One approach has been to use wire, crystal, or ceramic strain gauges and measure the change in force exerted by the stretched elastic material. Other investigators have measured the change in the electrical resistance of a conducting fluid in an elastic cylindrical tube as its length changed. Carbon black and copper sulfate solution have been used and it has been noted that they are both reliable for measuring respiratory rate, but neither are useful in measuring amplitude. Recently a light rubber tube filled with mercury has been used as a gauge to measure the circumference of the chest but the results cannot be expressed in terms of volume of air (Ackner, 1956).

The second major approach to the measurement of ventilation is by measuring the volume of inspired and expired air by simple volume recorders. An ordinary basal metabolism apparatus may be utilized to record a spirogram from which tidal volume and the frequency of respiration can be determined. The bell or bellows may be filled with air and the apparatus used as a closed system with rebreathing for a few breaths. Usually this does not produce significant anoxemia or carbon dioxide accumulation. The basal metabolism apparatus can be used as an open system by having the valves arranged so that the subject breathes directly either from or into the bell or bellows. The capacity of most bells or bellows is about 4.5 to 6.0 L and, therefore, a continuous record is possible for only 30 to 60 sec. A recording for a longer period of time can be obtained by using a series of valves which permit the subject to inspire air from a bag containing 50 to 100 L of air, and to expire air into an air-tight box which surrounds the bag (Fig. 3.1).

Psychophysiological investigations have primarily used the girth techniques which provide measures of amplitude, rate, pattern, and the I/E ratio or the I fraction (duration of the inspiratory period divided by the time of the total breath). The amplitude measures are relative and can be used within the same subject, but not as reliable intrasubject data. This limitation of the amplitude measures has forced most investigators using pneumographs to rely upon rate as a respiratory variable. Respiratory frequency is not an entirely valid measure of ventilation since either fast or slow rates may be associated with hypo- or hyperventilation. As can be seen in Fig. 3.2, it is possible to have the same amount of total ventilation per min (minute volume) with variations in frequency and tidal volume (Comroe et al., 1962).

The girth method and the techniques used for measuring volumes may give different results. Sheer and Kroeger (1961) investigated the effect of an intravenous injection of serotonin in the intact anesthetized dog and measured respiration by simultaneous recordings from a spirometer, thoracic pneumograph, and an oximeter. Following the injection, the spirogram revealed an increase in the rate and depth of respiration for a few seconds and then a period of apnea. The apnea coincided with a fall in the oxygen saturation. The pneumographic recording, in contrast to the spirogram, showed deep and rapid chest movements even during the cessation of tidal movements (Fig. 3.3).

These limitations of the pneumographic techniques and the requirement of face masks, mouth piece, or nose clamp with the absolute volume methods has led investigators to develop other methods which give reliable and valid volume measures. Shapiro and Cohen (1965) have recently described a method which relates thoracic and abdominal movements to volume. An analogue

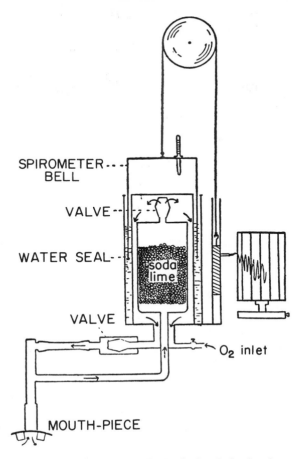

SPIROMETER---
BELL

VALVE--

WATER SEAL--- soda lime

VALVE

O₂ inlet

MOUTH-PIECE

Fig. 3.1. Schematic diagram of the Benedict-Roth closed circuit spirometer. (From Best, C. H., & Taylor, N. B. *The physiological basis of medical practice.* Baltimore: Williams & Wilkins, 1961.)

computer is used to determine the volume of air from changes in the electrical resistance of mercury capillary length gauges on the chest and abdomen. Preliminary results show a substantial correlation with spirometric measures.

Recently there has been considerable interest in the use of electrical impedance measurements in the determination of respiratory rate and volume. Impedance pneumography is based upon a functional relationship between transthoracic impedance and the volume of respired air. Geddes and Hoff (1964) have reviewed the use of the electrical impedance method in recording respiratory phenomena. A two-terminal constant current, direct-coupled impedance pneumograph has been described and is shown in Fig. 3.4 (Baker, Geddes, &

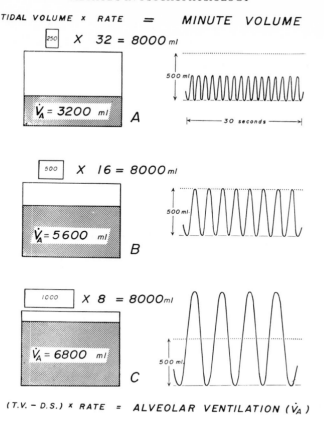

FIG. 3.2. *Left,* area of each small block represents tidal volume (250, 500 or 1,000 ml). Total area of each large block (*shaded + unshaded*) – minute volume. *Shaded area of each block* represents volume of alveolar ventilation per min. *Right,* spirographic tracings. (From Comroe, J. H., Jr., Forster, R. E., II, Dubois, A. B., Briscoe, W. A., & Carlsen, E. *The lung.* Chicago: Yearbook Medical Publisher, 1962.)

Hoff, 1965). The output variations are due to the voltage obtained from the transthoracic impedance change during breathing. The type and placement of the electrode bear special consideration in impedance pneumography. A variety of electrodes have been used and most work indicates that electrodes which have a small surface area and good skin contact provide the most satisfactory measurement of tidal volume. A number of reports have shown that values of tidal volume measured by impedance pneumography closely approximate those simultaneously obtained on a spirometer over a portion of the useful tidal range. Impedance pneumography at present is still limited to studies in which a minimum of apparatus can be attached to a subject, and more reliable and valid instrumentation cannot be used.

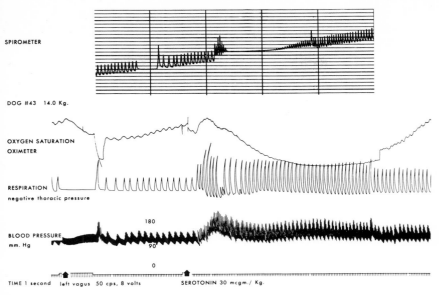

SPIROMETER

DOG #43   14.0 Kg.

OXYGEN SATURATION
OXIMETER

RESPIRATION
negative thoracic pressure

BLOOD PRESSURE
mm. Hg

180

90

0

TIME 1 second   left vagus 50 cps, 8 volts   SEROTONIN 30 mcgm./ Kg.

FIG. 3.3. Different effects produced on the spirometer and thoracic pneumograph measures
of respiration with intravenous injection of serotonin in the intact anesthetized dog. Note the
loss of tidal air volumes which coincides with a fall in carotid artery oxygen saturation in spite
of continued rapid thoracic respiratory movements. (From Sheer D. E., & Kroeger, D. C.
In D. Sheer (Ed.), *Electrical stimulation of the brain*. Austin: Univ. Texas Press, 1961.)

Ventilatory Measures in Animals

The animals most often used in respiratory studies are the cat and dog. The
measurement of ventilatory variables in these species has been accomplished by
a variety of techniques. Although most of the techniques are variations of the
spirometric and chest pneumographic methods used with human subjects, mention will be made of a few of the more commonly employed.

The spirometer is perhaps the most frequently used apparatus and is often
attached to the anesthetized animal by a tracheostomy tube. The use of soda
lime cannisters for absorbing CO_2 and a large reservoir allow prolonged measurements in a closed system. Otherwise, as with human subjects, a series of
valves can be used with a bag and box unit, or with an open system.

The chest pneumograph is utilized primarily for measuring respiratory rate.
It is based on the same principle as with humans and has the same limitations.
Thermal sensors can also be used for measuring respiratory rate. The thermal
sensor is simply a sensitive thermocouple placed in such a position that as the
animal breathes the alternating temperature change between cool inspired air
and warm expired air is recorded as inspiration and expiration.

In many of the animal studies of respiration, an automatic pump system is
employed to deliver a predetermined volume at a constant rate. This procedure

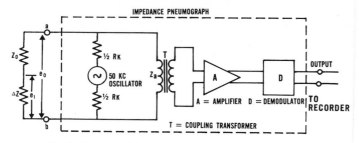

Block diagram of Impedance pneumograph.

Z_o = Transthoracic impedance at resting expiratory level

ΔZ = Change in transthoracic impedance with respiration

R_k = Added resistance to make oscillator approximate a constant current source = 200K

Z_a = Input impedance of amplifier = 50K

FIG. 3.4. Impedance pneymograph. (From Baker, L. E., Geddes, L. A., & Hoff, H. E. *Am. J. med. Electron.*, 1965, 4: 73–77.)

is often required since in the majority of studies the animals are anesthetized, and it also permits the control of ventilation in order that other respiratory variables may be studied.

Pulmonary Circulation and Diffusion

As reviewed in the preceding section, the function of ventilation is to maintain optimal levels of PO_2 and PCO_2 in the pulmonary alveoli. The pulmonary circulation enables an essential amount of O_2 to be added to the tissue capillaries and an essential amount of CO_2 to be removed. This function is carried out by a distributing system composed of the right ventricle, pulmonary arteries and arterioles, and a collecting system for the pulmonary capillary bed. The gas exchange of O_2 and CO_2 takes place by diffusion between the alveolar air and the pulmonary capillary bed. The passage of O_2 and CO_2 is entirely passive without any secretory or active transport processes.

Most psychophysiological studies will not be concerned with the measurement of functions of the pulmonary circulation or of pulmonary gas diffusion. Physiologists have developed a number of methods for studying these aspects of respiration and some of these will be mentioned for future reference. There are techniques for the measurement of pressures, blood flow, vascular resistance, and the distribution of blood flow in the pulmonary circulation (Comroe et al., 1962). Diffusion can be measured by determining the pulmonary diffusing capacity. A gas which has greater solubility in blood than in the alveolar capillary membranes is required. Oxygen and carbon monoxide both meet this requirement, and methods are available with the use of carbon monoxide or O_2 for measuring the pulmonary diffusing capacity (Comroe et al., 1962).

lood Gases

It is possible to determine the effectiveness of the respiratory processes in
1aintaining the optimal levels of PO_2 and PCO_2 in the pulmonary alveoli and
apillaries by studying the arterial blood O_2 and CO_2 content and pressure.
ome oxygen goes directly into solution in the plasma, while other molecules
f oxygen are transported in the blood by chemical combination with hemo-
lobin (Hb). Carbon dioxide is carried in solution and chemical combination
y the venous blood from the tissues to the lungs where it is eliminated.

Several investigations of the relationship between emotions and respiration
ave used measures of the blood gases. Most psychophysiological laboratories
ill not be set up for such techniques, however, a few techniques will be briefly
escribed here since they may be of importance in some studies.

There are several methods for measuring blood O_2. The arterial blood oxy-
en saturation is the relation of the actual O_2 content of arterial blood to the
apacity of the blood for holding O_2.

'ercentage saturation of Hb with O_2 =

$$100 \times \left(\frac{\text{ml } O_2 \text{ combined with Hb}}{\text{maximum ml } O_2 \text{ capable of combining with } O_2} \right)$$

'he saturation of arterial blood can be measured by a manometric technique
'hich determines the O_2 content before and after exposure to atmospheric O_2
Comroe et al. 1962). A spectrophotometric method can also be used but has
1e disadvantage of not being able to determine during the procedure the arteri-
l blood CO_2. It is possible by means of an oximeter to estimate continuously
rterial oxygen saturation without the withdrawal of blood. The oximeter con-
ists of a filter photometer which is attached to the ear. The oximetric technique
, less accurate than the other procedures, but it may be useful in psychophysio-
)gical studies requiring constant monitoring of changes in arterial oxygen satu-
ation. A very sensitive measure of blood O_2 is that of the actual arterial O_2
ension. This can be determined directly and continuously by an oxygen elec-
rode and analyzer.

Several approaches are available for measuring blood CO_2. One is the direct
etermination of CO_2 content of arterial blood which can be accomplished by
bubble method (Riley, Campbell, & Shepard, 1957), or by the use of a CO_2
lectrode (Severinghaus & Bradley, 1958). Since gas and blood PCO_2 are
ssumed to be equal across the alveolar membranes, alveolar PCO_2 is frequent-
y used as a measure of arterial blood PCO_2. Alveolar PCO_2 can be meas-
red continuously from breath to breath by means of an infrared analyzer
Dubois, Fowler, Soffer, & Fenn, 1952).

Mechanical Properties of the Lungs

As mentioned earlier, another important aspect of respiration is the mechani-
al factors involved in breathing. These specifically are concerned with the

forces that cause inspiration and expiration, and the resistances to the flow ⟨ gas in and out of the lungs. In order for air to move into the alveoli, the alveol. pressure during inspiration must be less than atmospheric pressure. This accomplished by active contraction of the inspiratory muscles which enlar₃ the thorax and decrease intrathoracic pressure. The alveoli enlarge with tł lowering of intrathoracic pressure and the total alveolar pressure is lowered ⟨ less than atmospheric with air flowing into the alveoli. The contraction of tł inspiratory muscles produces the force necessary to overcome (1) the elast recoil of the lungs and thorax, (2) the tissue resistance of the lungs and thora and (3) the resistance to air flow through the airways of the tracheobronchi tree.

Following relaxation of the inspiratory muscles, the elastic tissues of the lun₃ and thorax recoil. This recoil is usually adequate to return the lungs and thor≀ to the resting expiratory level. Expiration is a passive process except when tł resistances to the elastic recoil are exceptionally great. At that time contractio of the expiratory muscles may be required.

A number of sensitive techniques are available for measuring the mechani⟨ of breathing. The methods for measuring the elasticity of the lungs and tł resistance to air flow will be briefly reviewed. It is possible to determine tł pulmonary tissue resistance, but this will not have much application in psych⟨ physiological studies.

Compliance

The lungs and thorax are elastic tissues which are stretched during inspiratio and recoil to their resting position during expiration. The measurement of tł elasticity of the lungs and thorax is based upon the relation between pressur and volume. This relationship is expressed in terms of the volume change pɛ unit of pressure change and is known as compliance. In man, compliance ⁚ expressed as liters per cm of H_2O.

The measurement of lung compliance requires the determination of tł transpulmonary pressure or the pressure differential between the pleural spac and the mouth. An adequate approximation of intrapleural pressure can b made by means of an esophageal balloon. A pressure-volume curve can b constructed by having a subject with an esophageal balloon inspire differer volumes of air. Following each inspiration the subject is asked to hold hi breath and the intraesophageal pressure is measured. The pressure and volum₁ are plotted and the compliance computed as slope of the line.

There are several other techniques available for measuring compliance (Con₁ roe et al., 1962). It is also possible to determine compliance while the subject ⁚ breathing and not under static conditions as described above. Comroe (1965 however, has pointed out that a determination made during rapid breathin may not be a true measure of compliance.

Airway Resistance

The respiratory muscles primarily overcome the elastic recoil of the lungs and thorax. There is also resistance to air flow in the upper and lower airways. This resistance is referred to as airway resistance and is calculated as the ratio between the transairway pressure (mouth pressure minus alveolar pressure) and the air flow. Airway resistance is expressed in man as centimeters of $H_2O/L/$ sec, with normal values ranging from 0.05 to 1.5 cm of $H_2O/L/sec.$

In order to calculate airway resistance, it is necessary to measure simultaneously atmospheric pressure, alveolar pressure, and instantaneous air flow. Alveolar pressure is measured by means of recording pressure changes while the subject sits in an air-tight box or body plethysmograph. The technique permits the determination of the alveolar pressure at any time during the respiratory cycle (Dubois, Botelho, & Comroe, 1956). It is also possible to measure alveolar pressure by means of an interrupter technique. In this procedure, air flow is briefly stopped by a shutter and the mouth pressure is assumed to equal alveolar pressure. The interrupter procedure is not as valid an approach as is the use of a body plethysmograph.

Spirometers are ideal for measuring tidal volume, respiratory rate, and lung volume subdivisions. They fail, however, to give precise information about air flow. Fleisch (1925) designed the pneumotachograph specifically for the registration of air flow. It is essentially a face mask which contains a fine mesh Monel wire screen. The pressure drop across the screen as the subject breathes is a direct function of the air flow. A differential pressure transducer is used to monitor the pressure drop and amplification and recording of the signal provides a record of instantaneous air flow during breathing. It should be pointed out that integration of the air flow provides another means of measuring tidal volume. With the simultaneous measurement of air flow and alveolar pressure it is possible to calculate airway resistance.

Most psychophysiological laboratories will not have the specialized apparatus required for measuring the mechanics of breathing in man. It is possible to obtain information about the resistance of the airways with only a spirometer and a recorder. A series of pulmonary function tests has been developed which provides indirect methods of evaluating the mechanical properties. Maximal mid-expiratory flow and maximal breathing capacity correlate highly with airway resistance, and the procedure for these determinations are readily available in most physiology textbooks.

Mechanics of Breathing in Animals

In recent years, methods have become available for measuring compliance and airway resistance in animals. Compliance can be measured in an anesthetized animal with an open thorax and tracheal cannula. Measured volumes of air are pumped into the trachea and following each volume the trachea is closed

and the static pressure of the lung recoil recorded. It is also possible to inflat
the lungs with different pressures and record the volume changes. In either cas
a pressure-volume curve is plotted, and the slope of the line is a measure o
compliance.

With the simultaneous measurement of intrapleural pressure, tidal volume
and air flow, airway resistance and compliance can be determined. The intra
pleural pressure can be measured directly from the intrapleural space. In larg
animals, such as the dog and cat, flow and volume may be determined b
the use of a pneumotachograph. In the guinea pig, a body plethysmograph pro
vides a means of measuring tidal volume, and the flow can be obtained b
electric differentiation of the volume signal with respect to time.

By relating the volume and flow rate to intrapleural pressure at specific point
during the respiratory cycle, data can be obtained on the mechanical propertie
of the lungs. The intrapleural pressure has an elastic component and a flow resis
tive component. Amdur and Mead (1958) have described a procedure fo
evaluating the elastic component and the flow resistive component separately
and thereby permitting the calculation of resistance and compliance. A tech
nique is also available in which the signals for tidal volume, intrapleural pres
sure, and rate of air flow are fed into an oscilloscope which displays th
pressure-flow and pressure-volume loops (Mead & Whittenberger, 1953). Th
compliance pressure component and the resistive pressure component may b
electronically subtracted from the appropriate loop and compliance and resis
tance determined. This technique permits rapid repeated measures and i
especially useful in monitoring changes in resistance and compliance durin;
an experiment.

Mechanical Properties of the Lungs and Psychophysiological Studies

The measurement of the mechanical properties of the lungs is especially sig
nificant for the psychophysiological investigation of respiration since it has bee
shown that the determination of resistance and compliance provides an inde>
of airway caliber. Although the nerve supply to the airways of the tracheo
bronchial tree is extensive, little research has been concerned with the CN{
and autonomic nervous system control of airway size. This is evident from ɛ
recent review of the regulation of tracheobronchial smooth muscle (Widdicombe, 1963). There has also been a relatively meager amount of work in the
area of the effect of emotions on airway caliber.

Airway caliber has special significance to psychophysiological studies since it
is independent of voluntary control. As indicated in the review at the beginning
of this chapter, most psychological studies concerned with respiration have involved ventilation (rate, tidal volume, minute volume) which can be modifiec
voluntarily. A consideration of airway size is also of special importance in the
psychophysiological investigation of bronchial asthma. The primary pulmonary
change in bronchial asthma is bronchiolar obstruction which produces the
signs and symptoms. Schiavi, Stein, and Sethi (1961) recently demonstratec

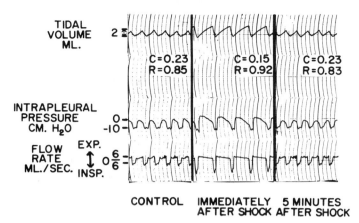

TIDAL
VOLUME
ML.

C=0.23
R=0.85

C=0.15
R=0.92

C=0.23
R=0.83

INTRAPLEURAL
PRESSURE
CM. H₂0

FLOW   EXP.
RATE
ML./SEC. INSP.

CONTROL   IMMEDIATELY   5 MINUTES
AFTER SHOCK AFTER SHOCK

FIG. 3.5. Sample tracing of guinea pig respiration after exposure of animal to electrical shock. The three records were taken from the same animal. Note the shortened inspiration and prolonged expiratory phase immediately following shock without changes in resistance (R) or compliance (C) (Schiavi et al., 1961).

that it is possible to produce in the guinea pig, in response to a pain-fear stimulus, an asthmatic-like respiratory pattern (shortened inspiration and prolonged expiration) without evidence of bronchiolar obstruction as reflected in the mechanical properties of the lungs (Fig. 3.5). This was in contrast to the finding of an identical respiratory pattern which was accompanied by an increase in airway resistance and decrease in compliance in experimental allergic asthma in the guinea pig (Fig. 3.6). Schiavi, Stein, and Sethi found that the asthmatic-like respiratory pattern following the pain-fear stimulation was related to the screeching of the animals and not obstruction of the bronchioles. Humans may also develop an asthmatic-like respiratory pattern without concomitant changes in bronchiolar physiology. The above findings suggest that it is important to define asthma in terms of bronchiolar function as well as the usual ventilatory variables. Such respiratory criteria will permit precise evaluation of psychological factors which may play a role in bronchial asthma.

The availability of techniques for measuring the mechanical properties of the lungs provides the opportunity for quantitative research on the effect of emotions on, and the nervous regulation of airway caliber.

Summary

A close relationship exists between the respiratory system and emotional processes. Respiration is regulated by the CNS and the autonomic nervous system. Respiration is an area of research particularly suited to psychophysiological investigation. A review of the literature reveals, however, relatively few reports of psychophysiological studies in which respiration has been the major area of interest. Respiration is a complex function which includes ventilation, gas diffusion, pulmonary circulation, and gas transport in the blood as well as

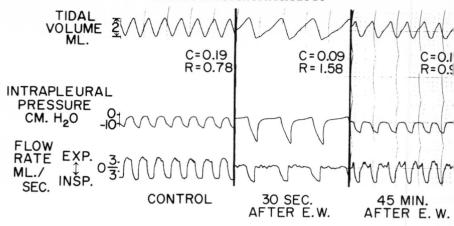

FIG. 3.6. Sample tracings of guinea pig respiration. The tracing at the *left* is for a control period: the *middle tracing* is from the same sensitized animal 30 sec after exposure to egg white spray; and the tracing on the *right* was recorded 45 min after exposure. Note the decrease in compliance (*C*) and increase in resistance (*R*) following exposure (Schiavi et al., 1961).

the mechanics of breathing. It may be that it is this complexity which has resulted in the relative neglect of respiration as an area of psychophysiological investigation. Techniques are now available for the study of all aspects of respiration and many are applicable to psychophysiological research. Further knowledge derived from such studies is greatly needed and will increase vastly the scope of psychophysiology.

REFERENCES

Ackner, B. A simple method of recording respiration. *J. psychosom. Res.*, 1956, *1*: 144–146.
Alexander, F., & Saul, L. J. Respiration and personality, a preliminary report. *Psychosom. Med.*, 1940, *2*: 110–118.
Amdur, M. D., & Mead, J. Mechanics of respiration in unanesthetized guinea pigs. *Am. J. Physiol.*, 1958, *192*: 364–368.
Baker, L. E., Geddes, L. A., & Hoff, H. E. Quantitative evaluation of impedance spirometry in man. *Am. J. med. Electron.*, 1965, *4*: 73–77.
Britvan, R. Effect of conditional reflexes on the respiratory motor centers. In K. Bykov, (Ed.), *The cerebral cortex and the internal organs.* New York: Chemical Publishing Company, 1957.
Comroe, J. H., Jr. *Physiology of respiration.* Chicago: Yearbook Medical Publishers, 1965.
Comroe, J. H., Jr., Forster, R. E., II, Dubois, A. B., Briscoe, W. A., & Carlsen, E. *The Lung.* Chicago: Yearbook Medical Publishers, 1962.
Dekker, E., & Groen, J. Reproducible psychogenic attacks of asthma. A laboratory study. *J. psychosom. Res.*, 1956, *1*: 58–67.
Dekker, E., Pelser, H. E., & Groen, J. Conditioning as a cause of asthmatic attacks. *J. psychosom. Res.*, 1957, *2*: 97–108.

Dubois, A. B., Botelho, S. Y., & Comroe, J. H., Jr. A new method for measuring airway resistance in man using a body plethysmograph: values in normal subjects and in patients with respiratory disease. *J. clin. Invest.*, 1956, *35*: 327–335.

Dubois, A. B., Fowler, R. C., Soffer, A., & Fenn, W. D. Alveolar CO_2 measured by expiration into the rapid infrared gas analyzer. *J. appl. Physiol.*, 1952, *4*: 526–534.

Dudley, D. L., Holmes, T. H., Martin, C. J., & Ripley, H. S. Changes in respiration associated with hypnotically induced emotion, pain and exercise. *Psychosom. Med.*, 1964, *26*: 46–57.

Faulkner, W. B. The effects of emotions on diaphragmatic function. *Psychosom. Med.*, 1941, *3*: 187–189. (a)

Faulkner, W. B. The influence of suggestions on the size of bronchial lumen. *N. W. Med.*, *Seattle,* 1941, *40*: 367–369. (b)

Feleky, A. The influence of emotions on respiration. *J. exp. Psychol.*, 1916, *1*: 218–222.

Finesinger, J. E. Effect of pleasant and unpleasant ideas on respiration in psychoneurotic patients. *Archs Neurol. Psychiat., Chicago,* 1939, *42*: 425–490.

Finesinger, J. E., & Mazick, S. G. The effect of a painful stimulus and its recall upon respiration in psychoneurotic patients. *Psychosom. Med.*, 1940, *2*: 331–368.

Fleisch, A. Der pneumotachograph; ein apparat zur geschwindigkertsregistrierung der atemluft. *Pflügers Arch. ges. Physiol.*, 1925, *209*: 713–722.

Freedman, B. Conditioning of respiration and its psychosomatic inplications. *J. nerv. ment. Dis.*, 1951, *113*: 1–19.

Gantt, W. H. Experimental basis for neurotic behavior. *Psychosom. Med. Monogr. Suppl.*, 1941, *3*: Nos. 3 and 4.

Geddes, L. A., & Hoff, H. E. The measurement of physiologic events by electrical impedance. A review. *Am. J. med. Electron.*, 1964, *3*: 16–27.

Golla, F. L., & Antonovitch, S. The respiratory rhythm in its relation to the mechanism of thought. *Brain*, 1929, *52*: 491–509.

Kappanf, W. E., & Schlosberg, H. Conditioned responses in the white rat. III. Conditioning as a function of the length of the period of delay. *J. genet. Psychol.*, 1937, *50*: 27–45.

Konradi, G. P., and Bebeschina, Z. V. Effect of conditional reflexes on the respiratory motor neurons. In K. Bykov, (Ed.), *The cerebral cortex and the internal organs.* New York: Chemical Publishing Company, 1957.

Lehman, A. *Die korperlichen ausserungen psychischer zustand.* Leipzig: Reisland, 1905.

Lidell, H. The influence of experimental neuroses on respiratory function. In H. Abramson, (Ed.), *Treatment of asthma.* Baltimore: Williams & Wilkins, 1951.

Lovett-Doust, J. W., & Leigh, D. Studies on the physiology of awareness. The interrelationships of emotions, life situations and anoxemia in patients with bronchial asthma. *Psychosom. Med.*, 1953, *15*: 292–311.

Lovett-Doust, J. W., & Schneider, R. Studies in the physiology of awareness: an oximetrically monitored controlled stress test. *Can. J. Psychol.*, 1955, *9*: 67–78.

Mead, J. & Whittenberger, J. L. Physical properties of human lungs measured during spontaneous respiration. *J. appl. Physiol.*, 1953, *5*: 779–796.

Nielsen, J., & Roth, P. Clinical spirography. *Archs intern. Med.*, 1929, *43*: 132–138.

Noelpp, B., & Noelpp-Eschenhagen, I. Experimental investigation of the pathogenesis of bronchial asthma. *Helv. med. acta*, 1951, *18*: 142–158.

Ottenberg, P., Stein, M., Lewis, J., & Hamilton, C. Learned asthma in the guinea pig. *Psychosom. Med.*, 1958, *20*: 395–400.

Riley, R. L., Campbell, E. J. M., & Shepard, R. H. A bubble method for estimation of PCO_2 and PO_2 in whole blood. *J. appl. Physiol.*, 1957, *11*: 245–249.

Romer, C. Beitrage zur behandlung der psychoneurosen. *Klin. Wschr.*, 1924, *3*: 354–358.

Schiavi, R., Stein, M., & Sethi, B. B. Respiratory variables in response to a pain-fear stimulus in experimental asthma. *Psychosom. Med.*, 1961, *23*: 485–492.

Severinghaus, J. W., & Bradley, A. F. Electrodes for blood PO_2 and PCO_2 determination. *J. appl. Physiol.*, 1958, *13*: 515–520.

Shapiro, A., & Cohen, H. D. The use of mercury capillary length gauges for the measurement of the volume of thoracic and diaphragmatic components of human respiration: a theoretical analysis and a practical method. *Trans. N. Y. Acad. Sci.*, 1965, *27*: 634–649.

Sheer, D. E., & Kroeger, D. C. Recording autonomic responses as an index of stimulation effects. In D. Sheer (Ed.), *Electrical stimulation of the brain*, Austin: Univ. Texas Press, 1961.

Stein, M. Etiology and mechanisms in the development of asthma. In J. H. Nodine & J. H. Moyer (Ed.), *Psychosomatic medicine*. Philadelphia: Lea & Febiger, 1962. Pp. 149–156.

Stevenson, I., & Ripley, H. Variations in respiration and in respiratory symptoms during changes in emotions. *Psychosom. Med.*, 1952, *14*: 476–490.

Treuting, T., & Ripley, H. Life situations, emotions, and bronchial asthma. *J. Nerv. ment. Dis.*, 1948, *108*: 380–398.

Upton, M. The auditory sensitivity of guinea pigs. *Am. J. Psychol.*, 1929, *41*: 412–421.

Walker, E. L., & Kellog, W. N. Conditioned respiration and the conditioned flexion response in dogs. *J. comp. Psychol.*, 1939, *27*: 393–409.

Whitehorn, J. C., Lundholm, H. & Gardner, G. E. The metabolic rate in emotional moods induced by suggestions in hypnosis. *Am. J. Psychiat.*, 1929, *9*: 661–666.

Widdicombe, J. G. Regulation of tracheobronchial smooth muscle. *Physiol. Rev.*, 1963, *43*: 1–37.

Widdicombe, J. G. Respiratory reflexes. In W. O. Fenn & H. Rahn (Ed.), *Handbook of physiology, Section 3, Vol. I.* Washington, D. C.: American Physiological Society, 1964. Pp. 585–630.

Wittkower, E. Studies on the influence of emotions on the functions of organs. *J. ment. Sci.*, 1935, *81*: 533–682.

Wolf, S. Sustained contraction of the diaphragm, the mechanism of a common type of dyspnea and precordial pain. *J. clin. Invest.*, 1947, *26*: 1201.

Ziegler, L. H., & Elliot, D. The effect of emotion on certain cases of asthma. *Am. J. med. Sci.*, 1926, *172*: 860–865.

Ziegler, L. H., & Levine, B. S. The influence of emotional reaction on basal metabolism. *Am. J. med. Sci.*, 1925, *169*: 68–76.

4
The Measurement of Biological Temperatures

HARDY W. TROLANDER, B.S.

The temperature of a body, according to Maxwell, is its "thermal state considered with reference to communicate heat to other bodies." These words of definition provide an appropriate introduction to an examination of the means of monitoring biological temperatures, for they convey several implications pertinent to an understanding and evaluation of present day instrumentation and techniques.

Heat from a body under observation may be communicated to a sensor of temperature by conduction, convection, and radiation. If the communication is good, the sensor's report of what it senses will be accurate provided that the sensor is both a competent observer and communicator of its state.

Since many living organisms include means for the maintenance of a high order of temperature regulation, a biological temperature sensor ought to be capable of distinguishing subtle changes of level over relatively restricted spans of temperature. Biological measurements, however, occur through a spectrum which extends somewhat beyond those limits of environment within which organisms survive. Hence, many biological temperature sensors are routinely exposed to, and must accurately report, temperatures ranging from the vicinity of $-50°C$ to that of $+125°C$.

Currently most thermometrical means depend upon conduction to communicate heat between the biological organism and the sensor of its temperature. This mechanical contact between body and sensor establishes a clear and direct channel of communication. However, such sensors must be of adequate substance to resist the equally direct stresses of the biological environment and hence may influence as well as sense.

The desire to avoid mechanical contact has spurred the development of temperature measuring devices dependent upon radiation between body and sensor. However, environment is then interposed, body and sensor must communicate through an additional interface, and it is axiomatic that some of the communication will be lost.

95

In many applications the term "monitoring" is synonymous with recording and a temperature sensor, as for example a glass thermometer, may not be applicable when its means of communicating state is not in acceptable form for easy recording.

An electrical signal, such as a voltage proportional to temperature, is readily recorded, but may be nonlinear and consequently lose resolution and accuracy over one or more sectors of its range. Some sensors, while generally linear in their response to temperature, produce extremely modest signals which lose significance in the "noise" of their environment. Thus, thermocouples, while accurately sensing the temperature state, may not be able to communicate this information through a background caused by parasitics arising at points of inhomogeneity within their circuits.

It seems likely that emphasis will continue to be placed on automatic recording of data, and that a growing requirement that such data be provided in digital form or in a form which is readily convertible thereto will influence the choice of sensors and favor the development of certain types over others of equal accuracy.

Temperature Scales

The Kelvin scale is recognized as the absolute thermodynamic scale to which all temperatures should be ultimately referred. In 1954, the Tenth General Conference on Weights and Measures defined this scale by means of a single fixed point, the triple point of water, to which was assigned the temperature 273.16°K exactly (Swindells, 1958). In 1948, the Ninth General Conference decided to give the degree of temperature the designation of degrees Celcius in place of Centigrade in the interest of international uniformity. Although this scale, in use throughout the scientific world, is now the Celcius scale, and its zero point is defined to be the temperature 0.01°C below that of the triple point of water, it should be understood that a thermometer accurate in centigrade degrees needs no corrections or scale factors to read in Celcius degrees.

Although thermometers graduated on the Fahrenheit scale are in routine clinical use, in the interest of uniformity all temperatures herein will be stated in degrees Celcius.

The international standard for the range of biological temperatures is the standard resistance thermometer, and temperatures are defined in terms of the resistance of its platinum resistor.

Liquid-in-Glass Thermometers

The liquid-in-glass thermometers common to the measurement of biological temperatures are generally based on the expansion of mercury with increasing temperature. Mercury maintains a uniform coefficient of expansion and remains in the liquid state from $-38.87°$ to $356.9°C$. Several types of these thermometers, each with distinctive characteristics, are widely used.

Total immersion thermometers. Total immersion mercury thermometers must be completely surrounded by the medium under observation in order to achieve their maximum accuracy of measurement. Although this is a limitation which usually prevents their use (with accuracy) on the biological preparation, such thermometers are valuable as laboratory standards, and with proper care may serve to calibrate other temperature measuring devices to accuracies on the order of ±0.02° to ±0.05°C over the range −35° to +150°C. This is generally adequate accuracy for most applications. Although it is stated that there is gradual change in the volume of the bulbs of glass thermometers, with better grades of thermometer glass readings will not be shifted by as much as 0.1°C in many years (Swindells, 1958). Since precision mercury-in-glass thermometers with Bureau of Standards certification are modest in cost, it may be expected that they will continue to be used as biological laboratory standards.

Partial immersion thermometers. Partial immersion thermometers are similar in construction to those calibrated for total immersion. Stem corrections must be applied to their readings, however, when the immersed portion is at a different temperature than the ambient surrounding the emergent stem.

It is generally difficult to make accurate corrections. The temperature of the media surrounding the stem may or may not be the temperature of the stem itself. Drafts are often present and may be significant. Therefore, the better grades of partial immersion thermometers should not be expected to yield measurements beyond accuracies of 0.1° to 0.5°C.

Clinical thermometers. Clinical thermometers, used to determine the body temperature of humans and animals, are maximum reading thermometers covering at least the range 36° to 41°C (Busse, 1943). The mercury must expand out of its bulb through a constriction formed at the bottom of the capillary tubing of the stem. Upon contraction, the mercury column separates at the constriction and remains in the stem until shaken down. In this manner the thermometer provides a memory of the maximum temperature to which it has been exposed. The bulbs of clinical thermometers are made small to minimize heat capacity, but the stem must be graduated and readable in increments of 0.1°C. Hence, the bore diameter of the capillary is limited and difficult to read. This is partly overcome by molding into the tubing a lens front which magnifies the width of the column.

Clinical thermometers manufactured to accepted standards and given normal care will be correct to 0.1° from 36.5° to 39°C.

Thermoelectrical Thermometry

Thermocouples. Thermoelectrical thermometry evolved from the discovery of Thomas Johann Seeback in 1821 that if two dissimilar metals are joined in a circuit consisting of two junctions at different temperatures, then a current will flow through the circuit. Heat is converted directly into electrical energy, and the electromotive force (emf) thus generated provides a convenient and accurate measurement of the temperature difference existing between the two junctions. However, if one of the junctions is maintained at a known constant temperature (reference junction), say at 0°C, the resulting emf is proportional to the absolute temperature of the second junction. From here it is a simple step to calibrate a voltage measuring device to read in units of temperature.

Although thermoelectrical effects have been usefully employed in temperature measurement for over a hundred years, there has been no satisfactory explanation for the mechanism wherein heat is converted to electrical energy or the manner in which the electromotive force varies with temperature. Hundreds of combinations of dissimilar metals have been investigated, and differences on the order of a thousand to one or more have been found to exist in their electromotive forces. A very strong hint is therefore provided that minute differences in the purity of these metals will result in substantial variations of their resultant emfs with temperature.

Recent efforts at developing new forms of thermocouples have been spurred by requirements to measure very high temperatures. It may be that these programs will provide new and useful tools for measurement over the more modest and restricted range of biological temperatures, but until that occurs it is likely that this region will be served by long established and well understood couples such as Copper-Constantan. Over many years these relatively high output thermocouples (42 μv/°C at 37°C) have proven to be stable and reproducible. Their virtues and drawbacks are representative of the application of thermocouples as a class to the measurement of biological temperatures. Their characteristics are well understood and may be referenced to well defined standards.

As an aid to specificity the ensuing discussion will be based exclusively on couples of Copper-Constantan. It should be understood, however, that most of the comments are generally applicable to any of the couples in common usage over this particular temperature range. For convenience and consistency, all references to thermocouple emf versus temperature will assume that the reference junction is at 0°C or is compensated to 0°C unless otherwise specified.

The emf of Copper-Constantan (Table 4.1) increases rather uniformly with temperature and over the range of 0° to 100°C follows the expression

$$e = at + 0.04^2$$

where e is the emf in microvolts, t is the temperature in degrees Celcius, and a is a constant determined by measurement of the emf at 100°C (Roeser, 1961). From the above relationship or the emf values of Table 4.1 an increase in sensitivity with increasing temperature is noted.

Thermocouples provide their own output signal (emf), and for certain appli-

TABLE 4.1. *Typical Temperature-emf values for Copper-Constantan thermocouple reference junction at 0°C.*

Temperature	Electromotive force	Temperature	Electromotive force	Temperature	Electromotive force
°C	mv	°C	mv	°C	mv
0	0.000	35	1.401	70	2.909
5	0.193	40	1.610	75	3.132
10	0.389	45	1.821	80	3.358
15	0.587	50	2.034	85	3.584
20	0.787	55	2.250	90	3.814
25	0.990	60	2.468	95	4.044
30	1.195	65	2.688	100	4.277

cations this is an advantage over the other commonly used electrical temperature transducers such as platinum, nickel, and thermistor resistance elements which must be provided with an excitation source such as a battery or power supply. When accurate measurements are required, regulation of this source of excitation may be critical. In addition, Copper-Constantan thermocouples are obtainable in small diameter wire sizes, commonly 0.001 in. to 0.010 in., hence they are readily capable of "point" measurements and are easily adapted to surface or mass temperature measurement.

However, three inherent characteristics of these thermocouples continue to impede their general application to the monitoring of biological temperatures. Inspection of Table 4.1 reveals that the total change in output voltage over the range of 0° to 100°C is 4.28 mv, hence a change of 0.1°C in the vicinity of 37°C will result in a change in the output of the couple of approximately 4 μv. This is a very small signal, and existing DC amplifiers capable of discretely amplifying at this voltage level with adequate stability for monitoring over periods of several hours or more are expensive. Secondly, accepted practice requires that the temperature of the reference junction must be held constant during this period to the order of 0.02°C or less if the 0.1°C at the measuring junction is to remain significant. The third characteristic is somewhat more obscure; variations in the homogeneity of the material of the thermocouple leads are equivalent to junctions of dissimilar metals and are likely to produce spurious signals. When the thermocouple leads are not exposed to temperature gradients no such signals will be introduced, but where leads pass through the walls of cold chambers or incubators, for example, severe gradients may exist. These spurious components of the resultant output voltage are often significant, and it is difficult to compensate for their effect. Hence suppliers place limits of error of 0.5°C for special (close) tolerance thermocouples over the range of $-13°$ to 52°C in recognition of factors beyond the simple reproducibility of the junctions, the bulk purity of the metals and alloys of metals, and the control of the reference junctions.

Thermocouple Indicators

Mirror or light beam galvanometers. The classical light beam galvanometer remains a basic tool for the measurement of small potentials. The best of modern amplifying techniques through solid state electronics will approach, but not equal, the sensitivity of these time proven devices. A light weight mirror attached to the moving coil of the galvanometer reflects a light beam from a fixed source onto a ground glass scale. The light beam is often folded via additional mirrors to increase the effective optical arm of the system. This results in an indicator capable of reading out thermocouples to a precision on the order of 0.1°C.

However, the light beam galvanometer displays several basic shortcomings which interfere with its widespread application to many of the routine problems of temperature measurement. The long optical arm required for high sensitivity falls prey to sources of vibration since unwanted deflections of the sensitive coil are equivalently multiplied. It is usually necessary to read these instruments head on and in shade due to loss of brightness along the successive stages of the optical path. When moved the instrument must usually be re-zeroed since the restoring torque of the suspension is small in proportion to the effective radius (optical arm) of the coil.

Potentiometers. The emf or voltage of a thermocouple may be measured very accurately by comparing it with a stable known emf. The scheme of Fig. 4.1 illustrates a simple form of potentiometer. The stable emf is provided by the standard cell which, being of limited capacity, is used only for purposes of calibration. In operation, the switch is placed in Position 1 and $R2$ adjusted for zero deflection of the galvanometer, thus providing an emf across $R1$ derived from the service cell but equal to that of the standard cell. With the switch in Position 2, $R1$ is adjusted for zero deflection of the galvanometer at•which point the emf appearing between *Points A* and *B* of the potentiometer $(R1)$ is equal to that of the thermocouple. $R1$ may be calibrated in emf (millivolts) or in temperature.

Millivoltmeters. Although used extensively in pyrometry, pointer-type millivoltmeters are not widely employed in the measurement of biological temperatures. Their usual sensitivity is on the order of 10 mv or more for full scale deflection; reference to Table 4.1 indicates that this translates to approximately 235°C full scale. Millivoltmeters therefore tend to be applicable only to those relatively few requirements for wide range measurements involving resolution to no better than several degrees Celcius.

Resistance Thermometry

Resistance thermometry based on conducting metals. The beginnings of modern resistance thermometry may be found in the publications of H. L. Callendar which date to 1887. Callendar was aware that the electrical resistance of pure metals was a function of temperature, and recognized that this char-

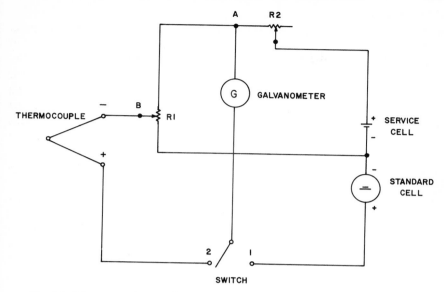

Fig. 4.1. Thermocouple potentiometer. Basic scheme of potentiometer indicator for thermocouple thermometer.

acteristic had practical application to thermal instrumentation. The Callendar equations remain a fundamental part of the art of precision platinum resistance thermometry.

The change in the resistance of most pure metals with temperature is positive and falls between 0.2 and 0.6% degree in the region of 25°C. Coils of platinum, nickel, or copper wire of sufficient resistance to be readily measured are the accepted thermometric elements of this form of resistance thermometry. These metals are available in fine wire of high purity and, within the range of biological temperatures, are stable, reproducible, and display a generally linear resistance-temperature characteristic.

Nickel elements are more widely used in industrial process control than in biological measurements. Nickel displays somewhat greater sensitivity (roughly 0.6%/°C versus 0.4%/°C) than platinum, and its temperature coefficient increases markedly with temperature. It is not as linear as platinum or copper in this respect. However, this apparent deficiency is sometimes turned to advantage in counteracting the nonlinear output characteristic of the Wheatstone Bridge (Grant & Hickes, 1962). The linearity of this combination may be made quite high, the output of such a system being suitable for direct readout by digital voltmeter.

Pure copper has the most linear relationship of resistance to temperature of any of the common metals. Its stability is adequate for the measurement of biological temperatures, but its application has been limited in comparison with that of nickel and platinum. The sensitivity of a copper resistance element is very close to that of a similar element of platinum at room temperature, and cost clearly favors copper. However, the low resistivity of copper results in sensors either bulky or fragile and thus tends to preclude its widespread application.

The characteristic of strain-free, fully annealed pure platinum wire is particularly stable, and has been adopted as the international standard for temperature measurements between $-183°$ and $630°C$. An example of platinum resistance-temperature values is given in Table 4.2. The very uniform characteristic

TABLE 4.2. *Temperature-resistance values for platinum temperature sensor*

Temperature	Resistance	Temperature	Resistance	Temperature	Resistance
°C	ohms	°C	ohms	°C	ohms
0	1000	35	1139	70	1276
5	1020	40	1158	75	1295
10	1040	45	1178	80	1315
15	1060	50	1198	85	1334
20	1079	55	1218	90	1354
25	1099	60	1237	95	1373
30	1119	65	1256	100	1393

must be inspected in $15°$-segments to observe the modest decrease in the change of resistance with increasing temperature. The size of platinum sensors has seriously restricted their general application to the measurement of biological temperatures. Recent progress in the development of platinum films deposited on inert substrates might alleviate this problem, for there is promise that this technique may yield small stable sensors of known resistance-temperature relationships which are rugged enough for many of the common applications.

When platinum sensors are remotely located, the resistance of the lead wires must be stringently accounted for. The temperature coefficient of copper is equal to that of platinum, and the addition of a modest amount of copper wire lead resistance may change calibration by a degree or more, and this will vary with lead temperature. Three-lead systems and balanced-bridge readouts obviate this problem but introduce additional restrictions on system flexibility.

The cost of closely interchangeable platinum sensors is appreciable, and in circumstances where they cannot be protected attrition is inevitable. However, when it is necessary to make measurements of absolute temperature significant to a few hundredths of a degree or better, platinum resistance thermometry is proven and accepted.

Resistance thermometry based on semiconductors. Semiconductors were identified by Faraday as early as 1834, but for many years their properties were little understood. The sheer number of possible combinations of these materials tended to prevent either an ordered development of their characteristics or an adequate descriptive theory of their behavior. A century lapsed before enough understanding and sufficient manufacturing techniques emerged to enable the fabrication of useful electrical devices from semiconducting materials. Thermistors were among the first of these (Becker, Green, & Pearson, 1946).

Commonly, thermistors are composed of the oxides of nickel, manganese, cobalt, and iron. However, the technology continues to advance rapidly and recently other elements, principally germanium and silicon, are finding application.

Thermistors, very sensitive, small in size, and low in cost, are among the most widely used electrical sensors of temperature. Recent techniques which yield thermistors interchangeable in their resistance-temperature characteristics to within 0.1°C have broadened their use in biological applications. Since the art is relatively new, it may be expected that further improvements in thermistors will be forthcoming. Thermistors are available in a wide variety of resistance values and thus permit matching of the characteristics of the sensor to those of the readout instrumentation. Their resistance level and sensitivity allow lead resistance to be disregarded in most biological applications.

Thermistors display many of the physical properties of ceramics. They are very hard, and will usually withstand extremes of pressure without measurable change in their resistance-temperature characteristics. The resistance of most thermistors used for the monitoring of biological temperatures decreases as their temperature increases. This change in resistance (sensitivity) is between 1.0 and 5%/ degree C. Sensitivity also decreases with increasing temperature, and typically, a thermistor with a sensitivity of 5%/ degree at 0°C will change on the order of 3%/ degree at 100°C. A resistance-temperature curve is given in Fig. 4.2; its shape is typical of many types of thermistors (Table 4.3).

TABLE 4.3. *Typical temperature-resistance values for thermistor temperature sensor*

Temperature	Resistance	Temperature	Resistance	Temperature	Resistance
°C	Ohms	°C	Ohms	°C	Ohms
0	19,592	35	3,918	70	1,051
5	15,236	40	3,196	75	888.0
10	11,942	45	2,620	80	753.8
15	9,428	50	2,162	85	642.4
20	7,496	55	1,792	90	549.8
25	6,000	60	1,493	95	472.4
30	4,834	65	1,249	100	407.6

The high sensitivity of thermistors makes them applicable to the measurement of small temperature changes, and relatively simple systems are capable of resolving temperatures to 0.001°C for short periods. Although the stability of thermistors is not yet as well understood as platinum resistance or mercury-in-glass thermometers, many of the better grades will maintain their calibration within 0.02°C for periods of a year or more when temperatures do not exceed 100°C.

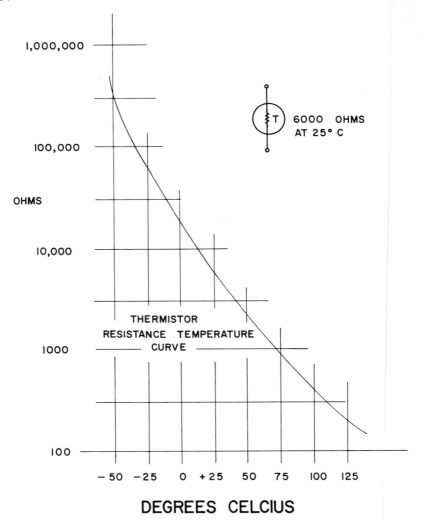

FIG. 4.2. Thermistor resistance characteristic. Typical example of thermistor response over biological temperature range.

The large temperature coefficient of many thermistors is usually a disadvantage when a wide range of temperatures must be covered within a single measurement range. The resistance of a thermistor at −50°C may be 2000 times the resistance of the same thermistor at 125°C. The typical Wheatstone Bridge of resistance thermometry, whether operated at null or not, is not at its best when it must encompass a change of this magnitude in a single range. Additionally the change in sensitivity of thermistors with temperature is a complication, but as has been noted in the case of nickel, may be worked to advantage under certain conditions.

For single spans of 50°C or less it is possible to apply combinations of series and parallel resistors to thermistors and achieve acceptable linearity for many applications. For wider spans these techniques tend to result in very substantially reduced sensitivity for marginal improvement in linearity and are not widely applicable.

A network employing two thermistors of different resistance values may be made to display a linear characteristic over a substantial temperature range (Trolander & Harruff, 1965). The two forms of such a network which are illustrated in Fig. 4.3 provide a constant numerical change of resistance or alternatively a linear output voltage with temperature. The two thermistors may be combined into one composite thermistor to maintain small size and ensure temperature equilibration between sections.

Typical combined tolerance of absolute accuracy and thermistor-to-thermistor interchangeability remains within ±0.15°C from −30° to +100°C. In the voltage divider configuration of Fig. 4.3, the output voltage linearity with temperature remains within ±0.2% over the stated range. By suitable choice of E_b the network will provide output voltage in direct numerical coincidence with temperature provided that it is biased, as in a bridge circuit, to yield 0 v at 0°C, and may be readout directly by digital voltmeter.

It is noted that the values of the components of both networks are the same, and that either a constant change of resistance or a linear output voltage is obtained by simple network transformation.

Composite thermistors are the sensors of the automatic multipoint scanning and recording thermometer described at a later point in this chapter. In this instance the fixed resistances of the network are located within the instrument and are time-shared from sensor to sensor.

Resistance Thermometry Temperature Indicators

Almost all of the indicators for biological temperature sensors which produce a change in electrical resistance with temperature employ forms of bridge circuits, each of which stems from the classical Wheatstone Bridge. The variation between instruments is a function of type of resistance sensor employed and the form of readout or display included within the indicator.

The significant differences between indicators relative to their means of display may be treated by identifying them within the following three categories: (1) direct readout on an electrical meter calibrated in the units of temperature; (2) direct in-line digital display in temperature; and (3) null indicators in conjunction with calibrated nulling dial.

Meter readout instruments. Direct readout on an electrical meter is accomplished when a meter, such as a microammeter, is connected to the output of a fixed-balance bridge circuit. The bridge, including the sensor, is in balance at

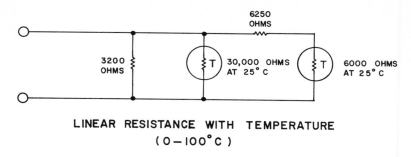

LINEAR RESISTANCE WITH TEMPERATURE
(0 − 100° C)

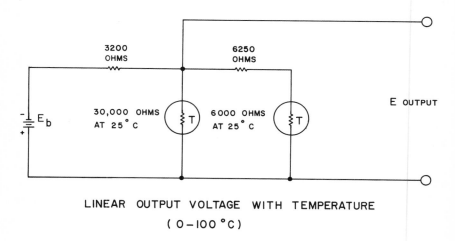

LINEAR OUTPUT VOLTAGE WITH TEMPERATURE
(0 − 100 °C)

FIG. 4.3. Linear thermistor networks. Use of two thermistors (or thermistor composite) to linearize response over wide temperature range.

only one sensor temperature. This is the point of zero meter deflection, the point to which the meter returns when the instrument is not in operation. The meter is calibrated to the degree of unbalance caused by the change in resistance of the sensor over the calibrated range of the instrument.

The diagram of Fig. 4.4 is representative of such an indicator for use with thermistor sensors. In this example the selector switch, *SW-1*, alternatively connects each of the four thermistor probes into the indicator. The fifth position introduces a calibrating resistor, *R4*, as a check on the state of the battery powering the indicator. *R9* provides a range of adjustment for changes in the voltage of the battery.

Given that *R6* and *R7* are of equal resistance, the bridge will be in balance when the thermistor probes are equal in resistance to the value of *R3*. This occurs at the lowest temperature on the meter scale. Since this indicator is in-

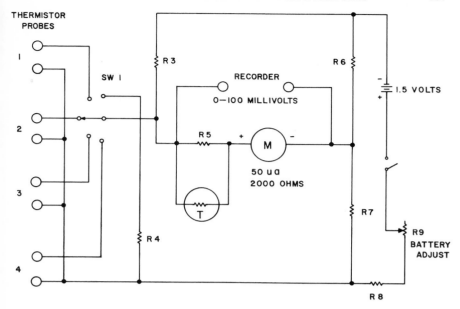

FIG. 4.4. Thermistor bridge. Thermistor bridge circuit typical of commercial thermistor thermometers, and basically similar to bridges employing platinum, nickel, or other types of resistance sensors. (Courtesy of Yellow Springs Instrument Company, Inc.)

tended for use with negative coefficient thermistors the meter deflects in the direction of increasing temperature as the bridge unbalances from decreasing thermistor resistance. When the resistance of the sensor is a known function of temperature the meter dial may be directly calibrated in the units of temperature.

The resistance of the coil of the meter movement may in itself be on the order of 1000 or 2000 ohms, and being copper its resistance increases on the order of 0.4%/degree Celcius. Therefore, another negative coefficient thermistor, T, in parallel with a fixed resistance, $R5$, may be included in the meter circuit as compensation for the change in meter resistance with temperature. Hence, the output of the bridge is developed across a constant load and the current flowing through the meter is independent of its coil temperature.

The accuracy of these instruments is often that of the meter movement itself. A 1% meter is accurate to 1% of its full scale deflection, and, for example, if it is calibrated in temperature for the range 30° to 50°C in a single linear range, it should be regarded as being no more accurate than ±0.2°C.

Meter readout instruments are widely accepted for the monitoring of biological temperatures since they are simple, reliable, and require a minimum of care and understanding on the part of the user.

Digital instruments. The block diagram of Fig. 4.5 illustrates the functional

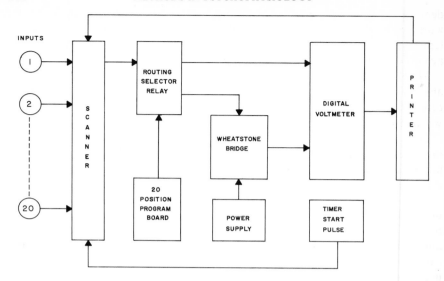

FIG. 4.5. Multichannel digital indicating and recording indicator. Chart indicating major functions and routings within digital temperature monitoring system.

relationships of the major subassemblies of a digital indicating and recording thermometer. In addition to temperature, this instrument may monitor other parameters. The program board is so arranged as to allow either direct entry into the digital voltmeter or entry of temperature information via the Wheatstone Bridge or any desired intermixture thereof.

The timer provides a start command to the scanner on a predetermined time cycle, for instance, 1/min. Since this establishes the number of readings per channel per unit of time, often these systems provide a choice of time base to match the required frequency of measurement.

Upon command from the timer, the scanner successively connects each of the inputs, as for example thermistor probes, to the routing selector relay. If all twenty are thermistor or platinum temperature sensors, the program board will be arranged to connect them in turn to the Wheatstone Bridge. The remaining resistive elements of the bridge are fixed, hence the digital voltmeter reads the output voltage of the bridge. This value is then recorded on paper by the printer. Additionally, channel identification is imprinted on the paper adjacent to the temperature information. The system is interlocked to prevent the scanner from advancing until the printer has concluded its cycle of the operation.

The Wheatstone Bridge of this instrument is basically similar to the bridge circuit discussed and illustrated previously (Fig. 4.4). The values of $R6$ and $R7$ are determined by the condition that the bridge be balanced and hence provide zero output at 0°C. The two additional conditions which are imposed by the requirement that the digital voltmeter readout in direct numerical coincidence with temperature are that the output voltage of the bridge must be linear with temperature, and maintain a direct decimal relationship with the units of temperature. The former is a function of the bridge and sensors, the latter is achieved by proper choice of bridge supply voltage.

Metallic resistance temperature sensors and composite thermistors are suitable for use with digital systems covering the broad range of biological temperatures. Single thermistor sensors are particularly suitable for those digital systems which must resolve to 0.01°C or better over a narrow range of temperatures.

Digital indicators are generally more complex than meter readout instruments and are perhaps best suited to requirements for the collection of large amounts of data which must be stored in a form which permits ready access to a computer.

Manual-null indicators. Manual-null indicators generally employ a single uncalibrated meter as an indicator of bridge balance. One of the resistances of the bridge, as for instance $R3$ (Fig. 4.4) is made variable and provided with a dial calibrated in temperature. The accuracy of such an indicator is primarily a function of the calibration and stability of the variable resistance. Since measurements are taken with the bridge in balance, relatively large changes in battery potential have little effect on accuracy.

Manual-null indicators are capable of providing equal accuracy at lower cost than other types, and are generally simple and reliable. However, they are usually not as convenient to use and do not permit recording.

Examples of Electrical Temperature Sensors for Biological Applications

Biological temperature measurements are made at many diverse sites by a large number of discretely different types of sensors. The thermistor probes of Fig. 4.6 are representative of styles which have been developed specifically for biological applications.

The probe of Fig. 4.6a is a general purpose esophageal rectal probe for humans and larger animals. The outer covering of the sensing tip and the lead wire is of vinyl; the probe is therefore quite flexible. The outer covering is smooth, relatively slippery, and soft, yet resists the actions of body fluids. It is intended for use in locations of slowly changing temperature since the plastic protective covering reduces speed of response.

The surface temperature probe of Fig. 4.6b is characterized by high surface to mass and front to back thermal conduction ratios. The contacting surface is a thin section of stainless steel with an epoxy coating covering the thermistor and back surface. This construction results in rapid response in addition to relatively low thermal mass. Even so, if the surface being measured is a thermal insulator, some sophistication of technique is required for accurate measurements.

Certain applications require probes to be particularly rugged and reliable under stressful conditions. The style illustrated in Fig. 4.6c is commonly used

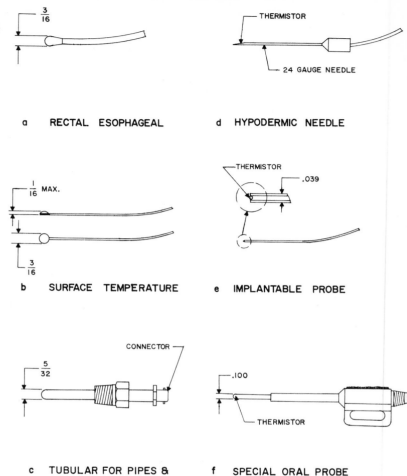

a   RECTAL ESOPHAGEAL   d   HYPODERMIC NEEDLE

b   SURFACE TEMPERATURE   e   IMPLANTABLE PROBE

c   TUBULAR FOR PIPES &   f   SPECIAL ORAL PROBE
    CLOSED VESSELS

FIG. 4.6. Thermistor probes for biological applications. A few of the many specialized types routinely employed in the monitoring of biological temperatures. (Courtesy of Yellow Springs Instrument Company, Inc.)

to monitor and control the temperature of the blood as it is being circulated within an artificial heart-lung. A waterproof connector allows the lead wire to be disconnected since this probe is frequently autoclaved in service.

Embedded in the tip of a fine gauge hypodermic needle, the thermistor of the probe shown in Fig. 4.6d is less than 0.01 in. in diameter. When such probes are given the care needed to avoid bending or breaking the needle, they are otherwise rugged and long lived. Many of these types will measure safely to 150° C and may be autoclaved repeatedly.

A very thin layer of insulation covers the otherwise partly exposed thermistor in the implantation probe of Fig. 4.6e. Time constants on the order of 0.1 sec may be achieved in this manner.

The oral temperature probe of Fig. 4.6f has been included as a typical example of the many highly specialized requirements found in the monitoring of biological temperatures. It is employed to monitor oral temperatures during space flights, and is small and light, yet may be maneuvered into position by gloved hands.

Radiometry

Deep body temperature is generally stable and well controlled, but surface temperature, as for example skin temperature, responds to external influences and often varies over a wider temperature range. The skin is a thermal insulator of relatively limited heat capacity. Thus its surface temperature may be primarily a function of either internal or external influences depending upon both the temperature and nature of its immediate external environment.

Temperature measuring means which depend upon direct thermal conduction and the transfer of a finite amount of thermal energy between the skin and the sensor are often a significant external influence upon the temperature being measured. A means of avoiding this difficulty may be provided through measurement of the radiant energy which is emitted from every body in an amount proportional to its absolute temperature. Radiometers have been devised for this purpose and are capable of measuring very discrete changes in skin temperature. Often these employ thermistors as sensors of the radiant energy (Stoll & Hardy, 1960).

However, complications are introduced since the sensor, unless at absolute zero, is also a body emitting radiant energy. A simplifying assumption that both the skin and the sensor are near perfect "black bodies" allows the use of an expression for blackbody radiant energy exchange.

$$R = S_0 (T_1^4 - T_0^4)$$

where R is the energy, S_0 is a constant, and T_1 and T_0 are the temperatures (degrees Kelvin) of the skin and the ambient at the sensor (reference temperature). Thus the reference temperature must be known in order to determine the temperature of the body being measured. Additionally it is noted that the energy exchange is a function of the level of the absolute temperatures of the two bodies. Although neither of these complications present unsolvable difficulties, existing instrumentation requires care and a great deal of understanding on the part of its users. Consequently this means of monitoring biological temperatures has not yet achieved widespread use.

Thermography. Thermal topograms of biological systems are often developed from the information of a multiplicity of discrete temperature sensors or from a single sensor scanning the surface under observation. The usual scanning method utilizes a radiometric instrument which employs a detector of infrared radiation as its sensor (Barnes, 1963).

When the surface consists of a large area of limited heat capacity and displays irregular temperature gradients, direct contact sensors may modify its temperature, and may or may not detect all of the significant gradients. These difficulties may be avoided through the use of a scanning radiometer provided that the surface is nontransparent and nonreflective to the wave lengths received and measured by the sensor of its radiation.

Human skin is considered to be a blackbody which is nonreflective and nontransparent to the longer infrared wave lengths. With suitable filtering a sensor such as a thermistor will only respond to these wave lengths and will provide an accurate thermal topogram of the area under observation. Since the significance of the topogram is generally in its ability to resolve differences in temperature within the area being scanned (rather than to determine absolute temperature), some of the difficulties of radiometric measurements are minimized.

However, ambient radiation and temperature must be controlled and the surface immobilized during the scanning period. Unfortunately these are typical of the constraints characteristically associated with, and generally restricting, radiometric means for the monitoring of biological temperatures.

Quartz Crystal Thermometry

Quartz crystals of various orientations display sharply resonant characteristics which are temperature dependent while otherwise stable. The electrical signal from such a resonator which varies in frequency, rather than level, with temperature may be readout in digital form through the use of electronic counting and timing techniques (Hammond & Benjaminson, 1965).

The recent development of crystal "cuts" or orientations which are linear in frequency with temperature is a major contribution to this form of thermometry. These crystal sensors are capable of a high order of resolution, typically 0.0001°C, throughout the biological temperature spectrum. Although stability is not yet well established, it appears that the accuracy of crystal sensors may be made to approach 0.01°C or better for many routine measurements.

Quartz sensors are likely to remain bulky in comparison with similar thermistor and thermocouple types. Additional complications arise when measurements must be made from remote locations since its oscillator circuitry is normally required to be within a few feet of the crystal sensor.

Practical quartz crystal thermometry is a recent development, hence it is necessary to speculate concerning its biological applications. The present drawbacks with regard to bulk and remote-site measurements may prove to be permanent deficiencies. However the recognized virtues of quartz in either natural or artificial form as a very stable material will spur additional developments in this form of thermometry. At a minimum it is likely that quartz thermometers will become accepted laboratory standards for the checking and calibration of other biological temperature sensors.

Summary

Requirements for data obtainable only from sites heretofore regarded as awkward or obscure, and the application of the computer have accelerated the development of a variety of temperature measuring means. Emphasis on new forms and refinement of older forms of electrical temperature sensors is a natural result of the high stage of development of the electricity-based communication art. However, it appears likely that the bulk of biological temperature monitoring will continue to be performed by liquid-in-glass thermometers and thermistor-based systems, and that the quartz thermometer may become a particularly suitable standard within the range of biological temperatures.

Radiometric instruments have been touched upon briefly, and a host of specialized instruments have been omitted in entirety. This should not imply depreciation of their abilities within the constraints of their particular applications. Indeed, insofar as they fill the requirements of diagnostics, the instruments of thermography are likely to exercise far greater influence on the actions of clinicians, for example, than those of platinum resistance thermometry. However, it is probable that generally applicable means of measurement will remain as the working tools of the trade, and that knowledge obtained through their use will continue to define the points of departure and establish the new requirements of specialization.

REFERENCES

Barnes, R. B. Thermography of human body. *Science, N.Y.*, 1963, *140*: 870–878.
Becker, J. A., Green, C. B., & Pearson, G. L. Properties and uses of thermistors. *Electl Engng, N.Y.*, 1946, *65*: 711.
Busse, J. Thermometry. *Med. Phys.*, 1943, *1*: 1555.
Grant, D. A., & Hickes, W. F. Industrial temperature measurement with nickel resistance thermometers. In C. M. Herzfeld (Ed.), *Temperature, its measurement and control in science and industry*, Vol 3. New York: Reinhold, 1962.
Hammond, D. L., & Benjaminson, A. Linear quartz thermometer. *Instrums Control Syst.* 1965, *38*: 115–119.
Roeser, W. F., & Lonberger, S. T. Methods of testing thermocouples and thermocouple materials. *Natn. Bur. Stand. Handbk 77*, 1961, *2*: 88.
Stoll, A. M., & Hardy, J. D. Thermistor radiometer. *Med. Phys.*, 1960, *3*: 659.
Swindells, J. F. Calibration of liquid in glass thermometers. *Natn. Bur. Stand. Circ. 600*, 1958.
Trolander, H. W., & Harruff, R. W. A wide range linear output thermistor sensor for biological temperatures. In Y. Iwai (Ed.), *Digest of the Sixth International Conference on Medical Electronics and Biological Engineering, Tokyo, 1965*. Tokyo: Okumura Printing Co., 1965.

5

Interarea Electroencephalographic Phase Relationships

CHESTER W. DARROW, Ph.D.

Wherever rhythmic effects occur, in whatever media, information concerning the phase relationship between rhythms may extend the parameters of knowledge. Most impressive, perhaps, is the interplay of the earth's diurnal cycle with the lunar cycle. With the help of the reflected light of the sun as transducer, we are able to read the "phases" of the moon, and we behold in the timing of the tides the dynamic, world moving effect of phase relations between earthly and lunar cycles. The increased visibility of microscopic structure obtained by the introduction of phase-sensitive polarization in the microscope is but one of the examples in the case of light. The way in which phase differences between sounds are detected in the ears and contribute to the acuity of direction perception is an example from the world of sound. The heterodyning of high frequencies from the broadcast band against a fixed frequency to derive meaningful signals at auditory frequency is a further example, which, as we shall see, may be pertinent to the understanding of certain mechanisms of the electroencephalogram (EEG).* We need not be surprised, therefore, to find that phase relationships between EEG waves of different brain areas provide measures of cerebral function of great lability which contribute both to psychophysiological function and to our understanding.

We were first convinced of the importance of interarea EEG relationships when we began to compare the potential differences between EEG tracings of adjacent brain areas. And when we attempted to collate patterns of different

---

*A possible example of the devasting effect on communications of a lapse in built-in phase-linked synchrony is the great northeastern electrical blackout (see *New York Times* headline November 11, 1965).

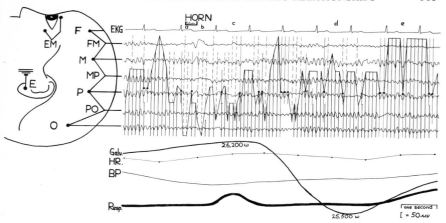

Fig. 5.1. Monopolar (scalp to ear lobes) recordings of frontal, motor, parietal, and occipital areas were made with bipolar potential-difference tracings interpolated between adjacent pairs which provided a comparison of the relative magnitudes of their waves. In this chart, *solid ordinates* beginning in or near occipital monopolar valleys (positive) extend upward through all coincident monopolar positive valleys and through all coincident upward pointing bipolar peaks as an indication of the relative strength of occipital change or "dominance." Decreased posterior or increased anterior dominance is seen to follow the stimulus and to precede and attend the galvanic response. Following stimulation, coincidences in anterior areas (as traced by the *dotted ordinates*) are seen to precede solid occipital ordinates. *EM*, eye movement electrodes; *E*, ear electrode; *F, M, P,* and *O*, monopolar (to ear lobe) recording; *FM, MP,* and *PO*, bipolar interarea recording; *Galv.*, palmar galvanic record; *HR.*, heart rate; *EKG*, electrocardiogram; *BP.*, blood pressure; *Resp.*, respiration. *Solid ordinates*, occipital "dominance;" *dotted ordinates*, anterior coincident monopolar valleys; *contour*, spread of "occipital dominance."

areas by drawing ordinates through approximately simultaneous peaks or valleys the shifting temporal differences between areas became impressive. An early attempt of the kind is shown in Fig. 5.1. There is interesting similarity to the frequently seen "anterior leading" following stimulation now often observed during automatic EEG phase recording.

History of EEG Phase Analysis

There have been many methods, as elaborated by Burch (1959), for analyzing, correlating, and scoring the electroencephalogram. Only a few of these have been directly concerned with the relative time or phase comparison of activities in different brain areas. Among the first to make such comparisons was Cohn (1942), who employed an optomechanical instrument, the cycloscope, a tool of astronomy, to study intracerebral wave patterns.

The temporal variability among simultaneously occurring events in the brain as shown by the electroencephalograph was also studied by Sonneman and Kennard (1947) in their interphase analyzer. The authors converted the push-pull alternating voltages from their EEG preamplifiers to "single-ended operation" by inverting one side of the output and averaging it through a 0.5 megohm divider with the un-inverted half of the output. Differences between "converted" patterns of different areas were registered by push-pull comparison.

Another elaborate instrumental development was Goodwin and Stein's "brain wave correlator" (1948) which transformed the conventional EEG into square wave patterns which were independent of the wave form or amplitude of the unmodified EEG record. The proportion of overlap of square waves from different brain areas was appraised by integrating voltages from the compared areas over time to obtain an index of the in-phase correspondence.

Obviously, the in-phase relationship is but one of the spectra of EEG phase relations. Furthermore, techniques involving integration and requiring the averaging of results over appreciable periods of time represent only mean tendencies. The limitation imposed by averaging is inherent in most of the early approaches to phase recording because effects which occur transiently and rapidly among the networks of the nervous system are averaged out. Any truly satisfactory phase analysis technique must permit sensitive detection and display of both the moment-to-moment relationships and the long time tendencies.

Another method using square waves for purposes of "period analysis" should be considered because of its promise of possible automatic handling of EEG data. The instrument is said to provide information on the degree of similarity between contiguous and homologous activities which can be evaluated with reliability (Burch & Childers, 1963). With modifications which would permit monopolar common reference recording and allow separate scoring for the negative-going and the positive-going "periods" the instrument might be adaptable for automatic phase comparisons.

A method for topographic recording involving simultaneous sampling of the EEG voltages of compared brain areas has been developed by Rémond and Offner (1952). With a sampling rate of 60/sec the EEGs are closely monitored and isoelectric voltage contour lines characteristic of different areas are recorded. Variations in the contours for successive EEG cycles provide a display of phase from many areas.

Methods offering possibility for both short time evaluation and for long time averaging are the display systems, which permit one to observe patterns of illumination by an array of lights over an area, corresponding to the movement of spreading peak voltages over a region of cortex. Displays of this type have been developed by Cohn (1950) and by Lilly (1949 and 1958). The rapidity of changing patterns makes rapid photography requisite to the study of such displays.

Somewhat more elaborately, Walter and Shipton (1951) have presented by their toposcope an array of spacially arranged cathode ray tubes (CRT) corresponding to 22 electrode positions on the head. Light intensity in the CRT is maximum at the peak voltages of the respective EEG traces. The timing of respective patterns is read relative to the 12 o'clock position as the images on the tubes are caused to rotate radar-fashion at a determined rate. Varying displacements of the bright areas in the various CRT reveal the phase relations between areas; or, in order to read phase directly from individual scopes, one brain area may determine the over-all rotation rate for all of the scopes while EEG peak voltage in the respective brain areas controls points of illumination of the respective CRT. Cinematic preservation of the complex patterns permits study of the elaborately detailed interrelationships.

Similar in some ways but simpler in operation than the Walter-Shipton instrument is the Petsche and Marko toposcope (1955, a&b). Here again the peak voltages of the EEGs determine the illumination in the CRT traces. Here there are eight electrode positions portrayed, and eight CRT traces, all in line on the face of a single scope. A photo-sensitive strip moving across the scope face preserves a record of transcribed events. Displacements of peak intensity of traces in different brain areas relative to one another provide clues to phase relationship. Areas of high voltage are easily seen to move sequentially through the brain. Evaluations of shifts in peak intensity from trace to trace and from moment to moment are more difficult, and the temporal relations between the peak intensities of successive waves may be correspondingly hard to follow. The instrument has been extensively used in the evaluation of relative timing of high voltage bursts in subcortical structures where the timing of shifts in over-all amplitude appears clear and significant. These findings will be elaborated later.

In the instruments described above which depend upon the relative brightness of traces for the identification of *peak* voltage, the valleys between the peaks are ignored, and the fact that the conventional EEG averages the recorded voltage above and below an instrumentally determined isoelectric base line presents little difficulty. In voltage determined evaluations, however, where both the negative and the positive halves of the EEG pattern are participating in the comparison this is not so simple. The well balanced EEG where one-half of the deflection appears above the isoelectric base line and the other half below is, of course, an instrumental artifact. It is a product of the use of condenser coupling between the scalp or cortical electrodes and the EEG preamplifiers and of the electronic engineers clever use of feedbacks to provide the most stable, easily handled and beautifully symmetrical tracings of the EEG. The actual patterns occurring in the brain, as seen by examination of DC recordings, for example those by Goldring and O'Leary (1954 and 1957) and Motokizawa and Fujimori (1964), tend to consist of negative or positive displacements completely above or below zero potential. Both negative and positive components seldom appear together in a single wave.

These considerations were brought home to us in the early days when we first began drawing ordinates through the peaks or the valleys of well aligned EEGs for evaluation of phase. It became evident that profitable numerical treatment of data could be obtained only if the positive and the negative halves of the EEG configuration were treated in separate comparisons. And it became evident that any automatic electronic evaluation would succeed best if it too treated negative and positive halves of the EEG patterns separately. Accordingly in the development of an instrument for phase comparison either the positive or the negative half of the EEG, the part either above or below the base line, was eliminated by a rectifying filter. The fact that the rectified EEG wave pattern thus obtained appear more nearly the analogues of the directionally oriented DC potentials emitted by the brain than are the diphasic, beautifully balanced patterns of the conventional electroencephalogram is further basis for hope that the derivations obtained by this type of phase analysis may represent in some respects fundamentals of cerebral function.

Institute for Juvenile Research (I.J.R.) Phase Analyzer

Initial efforts at obtaining a unit for clean cut interarea phase comparison were handicapped by the necessity of making the write-out by means of a condenser-coupled power amplifier (Darrow & Arnott, 1953). When a DC write-out was obtained, although it involved a revision of high voltage to low voltage pen-driver operation, it permitted the differentiation to become stable and clear. With the simplest and most elementary of techniques, when the rectified positive (or negative) half waves to be compared were fed into opposite sides of a push-pull power amplifier, we were now given the clear time and amplitude differentiations produced by the EEG phase indicator (Darrow Wilcott, Siegel, Stroup, & Aarons, 1956) shown in Fig. 5.2. As is generally well known, two waves of like polarity and equal amplitude fed for comparison into opposite sides of a push-pull amplifier will balance and cancel. If they are in-phase, but one of higher voltage than the other, a deflection is produced which is in the direction of the larger. And, if one wave leads or is ahead of the other in time, the comparison record makes an unbroken transition of the base line which slopes from the earlier toward the later occurring deflection And, if the compared waves are of exactly opposite polarity, they result in a bipolar diphasic pattern in which first one then the other is leading. A simpler and more elemental depiction of temporal-amplitude-polarity relationships is hard to conceive. However, these phase indicator tracings still require manual scoring and counting for evaluation. They are a far cry from automation. To facilitate the accumulation of extensive data, a phase scorer was developed as is also illustrated in Fig. 5.2 (Darrow & Smith, 1964). This transformed the leading and lagging indications of the phase indicator into simple, instrumentally countable and scoreable pips above and below the base line. In-phase comparisons, which score zero on the phase indicator, are independently scored by another pen on the basis of simultaneous base line crossings. An additional important phase variable, the occurrence of rapid diphasic phase reversal between cortical areas during psychologically crucial situations (Darrow & Hicks, 1965), has also been provided an automatic readout and will be described later. With automatic counters and printers which will soon be available along with the adaptation of our output for registration on the Computer

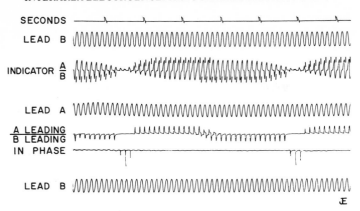

FIG. 5.2. Phase relations involving "beating" between two frequencies: *A*, at 8.0/sec, , at 7.5/sec. Whereas the phase indicator shows leading and lagging by unbroken transi- ons of the base line (*marked by accents*) the phase scorer shows the same changes by upward nd downward pips of the phase scorer record. The in-phase scorer tracing indicates simul- neity of *A* and *B*. See text for details. (From Darrow, C. W., & Hicks, R. *Psychophysiology*, 965, *1*: 337–346.)

f Average Transients ("CAT"), numerical and statistical evaluations will hortly be available. Preliminary illustrations and evaluation of the technique s offered by Darrow and Hicks (1965). Figure 5.3 from Darrow and Hicks llustrates the effects of a small attention-getting alerting stimulus in producing ome of the described effects.

ogical Interpretations Derived from Phase Relationships

For a rational understanding of these phenomena we may consider the re- ults from several different angles. By the logic of the situation, *in-phase* effects ndicate common causes and identity of conduction times. Thus, when frontal 4 to 18/ sec spindles in different areas occur in-phase with one another, one is nclined to suspect a common origin, possibly in the thalamus. In occipital nd lateral occipital, *LO-LOT*, leads in Fig. 5.3, for example, in-phase suggests ommon origins and similar function.

Sequential effects, *leading* or lagging, are suggestive of cause and effect re- ations or of processes of conduction in the nervous system. One of the most ommon leading effects of this kind is seen when central brain areas lead more occipital ones following arousal and are subsequently followed by a period of nterior lagging (or occipital leading) during recovery, as in comparisons M/LP and LP/LC in Fig. 5.4. Anterior and posterior effects of this kind have reviously been referred to by Darrow, Wilson, Vieth, and Maller (1960) as 'acceleration" and "momentum." These surface sequential relations may have leep lying origins involving the order in which anteriorly located motor and utonomic cortical projections are followed by proprioceptive and sensory con- equences as aftereffects of stimulation. The effects may involve those thalamic

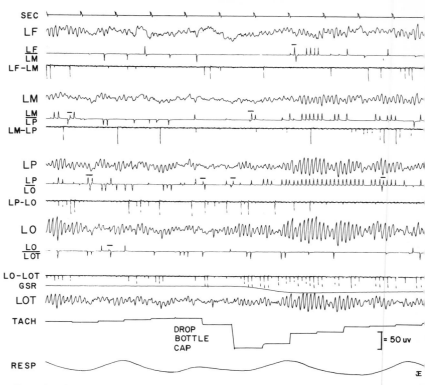

FIG. 5.3. Phase comparison of left frontal (LF), left motor (LM), left parietal (LP), l occipital (LO), and left occipital-temporal (LOT) areas before and after an alerting stimul (dropping of a bottle cap). The scorer record shows increased anterior leading between fron and motor, motor and parietal, and parietal and occipital areas. The in-phase scorer show following the stimulus, increased in-phase activity between occipital and occipital-tempo areas. Rapid interarea phase reversals are overscored. GSR, palmar galvanic response; TAC cardiotachometer; RESP, respiration. (From Darrow, C. W., & Hicks, R. Psychophysiolog 1965, 1: 337–346.)

reticular mechanisms in which Jasper (1949), Hanberry, Ajmone-Marsan, a Dilworth (1954), and Jasper, Naquet, and King (1955) demonstrated th stimulation of the medioventral portions of the nonspecific thalamic nucl produce responses of the shortest latency in the anterior portions of the corte whereas stimulation of dorsolateral portions of these nuclei occasions priori of response in parietal and occipital cortical areas.

A further phase-generated effect of possible direct neural and psychophysi logical significance is the occurrence of rapid diphasic reversals of phase su gestive of feedback between areas or reverberation and intercortical interactio This is seen accompanying attention-getting stimuli calling for perceptual eva uation. It is increased by meaningful stimuli, especially verbal ideational stimu

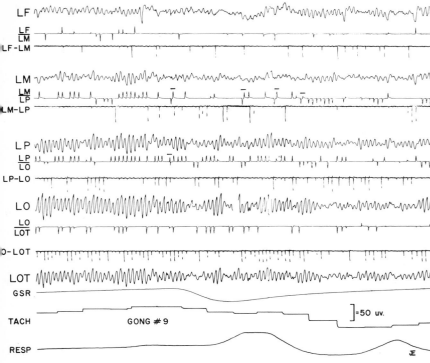

FIG. 5.4. The same measures as in Fig. 5.3. Motor-parietal and parietal-occipital phase comparisons show initial anterior leading (upward pips) in anticipation of and reaction to the ninth in a series of loud gongs, and occipital leading (downward pips) is shown as a delayed aftereffect possibly attributable to processes of perseveration or relaxation and recovery.

uch as the word "pregnancy" in Fig. 5.5. The effect can be conditioned and it s eliminated by adaptation (see Darrow & Hicks, 1965). Diphasic phase reversal effects occur so frequently in conditions of psychological stimulation (see Fig. 5.5) that we have come to postulate that this type of reaction may represent part of the mechanism of excitation by meaningful stimuli and involve intercortical effects. In fact, an entire theory regarding the role played by the cortex can be built around the interactive phenomena of phase. This will be elaborated later.

Diphasic EEG feedback effects attributable to sheer hyperirritability of tissue, such as following strychnine, penicillin, or excessive sensory or other excitation, also have to be taken into account. It is frequently seen in association with hyperactivity in children. Disturbed behavior problem children with dysrhythmic EEGs tend to show a superabundance of generalized diphasic interarea phase reversal activity. In this same connection, we have an impression

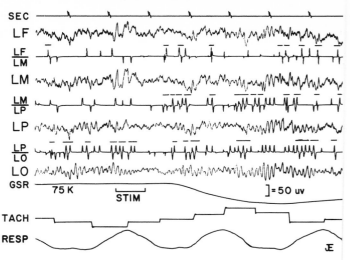

that poorly cooperating aggressive individuals are likely to show a prevalence of anterior leading whereas friendly cooperative easygoing or passive individuals more frequently show occipital leading. Strong interarea phase reversal or interaction between motor and parietal and between parietal and occipital areas seems to characterize individuals with a high level of controlled sensori-motor reactivity. These are now matters for systematic investigation.

Applications and Potentialities of Phase
Cortex

What, if any, information has been contributed by the use of phase which is not available to us by direct inspection of EEGs? Time relationship of causal significance may be included in this evaluation.

The interphase analyzer of Sonneman and Kennard (1947) is reported as having served mainly to provide refinements of observation in the clinical evaluation of EEG records. They note, "In many instances in which the EEG suggests a focus which is indefinite and in which phase reversals may be present only temporarily, clear delineation by the use of the analyzer is often possible." Baggchi (1957) has used phase differences derived by the photographic overlay of patterns for a similar purpose.

The Goodwin correlator shows an increase of in-phase activity with increase of frequency in animals (Hennman, Goodwin, & Toll, 1949). CO_2 increases the in-phase score, barbiturate anaesthesia decreases it.

For any who think that the resources of information contained in the EEG have approached exhaustion, the Walter-Shipton toposcope (1951) may demonstrate the immense amount of new detail carried by an EEG during routine examinations, both in normal and in pathological cases. Details of timing, asymmetry, and wave spread tax to capacity both the memory and imagination of the observer.

The fact that the "spontaneous" or casual cortical activity is related to the amplitude and pattern of evoked responses, particularly in the case of sensory afferent evoked potential (Landau, Bishop, & Clare, 1961), and that cortical responses evoked by optic nerve stimulation vary with the phase of spontaneous and poststimulatory slow waves (Bishop, 1933) indicates something of the extent of cortical involvement. Brazier and Casby (1949) have well emphasized the complications attributable to the competition of waves of different frequencies and different origins.

Subcortical Mechanisms

The possibilities of phase recording technique for exploring neural function in subcortical structures have been demonstrated by Petsche and Stumpf (1960) in rabbits. There is evidence for facilitation of high voltage slow activity in the hippocampus simultaneously with low voltage fast "activation" effects in the cortex, and the rhythms of the cortex (unipolar recording) are generally nearly 180° out of phase with those of the hippocampus and hypothalamus. The basic rhythm was found to originate in the septum, to reach greatest amplitude in the hippocampus, thence to go to hypothalamic and other structures.

Adey, Dunlop, and Hendrix (1960) found out of phase relations (bipolar recording) between dorsal and ventral hippocampal areas with increased 6/sec hippocampal slow waves while cats were learning a food-getting procedure. By digitalizing the data on cards and feeding it to a computer they obtained cross-correlations showing the high average inherent rhythmicity of the 6/sec bursts in entorhinal and dorsal hippocampal records during the approach performance. Phase shift from dorsal hippocampal leading to entorhinal leading characterized the apparent intention to make a learned movement.

Phase and Frequency

It became apparent early that a normally changing phase pattern in the cortex depends upon the presence of adequate cortical rhythm, or, possibly, that the function of the cortical rhythm, teleologically speaking, is to provide a *carrier wave* for adequate elaboration of phase relations (see "Phase and Cortical Function").

How fine should an attempted phase analysis of the EEG be? Would anything be gained by the elaboration of 360° of phase angle? Such a measure, we would venture, is practically precluded by the sometimes amorphous and often nonsinusoidal and nonrepetitive character of the EEG wave pattern. If obtained, it would possibly only de-emphasize those aspects of interarea timing which are now recordable and appear important. The question is, perhaps, what are the interarea timing variables intrinsic to the nervous system?

With the development of techniques capable of demonstrating changes in single wave-by-wave relationships the possibility of single wave interchannel potential reinforcements or inhibitions becomes open for investigation. Even the concept of phase may need to be broadened from one involving only repetitive numerically countable oscillations and interactions at adjacent frequencies.

Laterality of Cerebral Function

If we are interested in pursuing an explanation of the organic basis of symbolic verbal function, phase analysis offers a ready tool. Laterality differences related to verbal and manipulative behavior in the majority of the population are well documented. Sensitive temporal comparisons are afforded by phase, and preliminary explorations indicate a relation of EEG and phase to laterality preference.

Cornil and Gastaut (1947) demonstrated a tendency toward lower amplitude of a on the dominant side, and Sugar (1947) attributed the effect to an improvement in cortical circulation on the more active side. Wilson, Vieth, and Darrow (1957), in predominantly right-handed subjects, compared the effect of a loud gong stimulus with the effect of writing simple words first with one hand and then with the other. No reliable difference between a activity of the two sides was notable with the gong, but during writing greater blocking of a occurred in the left hemisphere regardless of hand used.

A systematic phase comparison of right and left leading during inactivity was made by Giannitrapani, Sorkin, and Enenstein (1965) in 10 right-handed and 10 left-handed individuals, asleep and awake. Half of each group were children, and half adults, but only the adults showed significant phase differences related to handedness. There was significantly more occipital and parietal left leading, under waking conditions in the right-handed group; more occipital and parietal right leading under similar conditions in the left-handed group. A unique finding was that during sleep anterior areas showed homolateral rather than contralateral leading, a reversal so consistent that a formula based on EEG leading could be derived having 0.96 predictive value for the handedness of individuals within the group.

Phase and Cortical Function

If the cortex is a screen on which is projected *in microcosm* the world without and within the organism, the question is still, how does it work? Is it a super telephone switchboard? Is it a sophisticated computer partly digital and partly analogue in operation? Or do we disdain all electromechanical models and retreat behind a mathematical screen? The EEG rhythms of the cortex have long since been largely delegated to vegetative, unspecific, and regulatory functions. Sophisticated symposia have even asked, "What good is alpha?" Probably no one of moment would still entertain the suggestion that brain waves are something to *sense* and *think with*, but such an hypothesis is here a possible by-product of phase.

To account for the apparent diphasic interaction effects which are characteristic of many stimulating situations, we have postulated that specific behaviorally meaningful impulses carrying information, both from without and from within the body, project to their specific receptors in the cortex where they may affect the local EEG. Although the effects projected are too small for easy observation, these changes are nevertheless, adequate to shift the patterns of local waves and to alter their relationships to the same but unmodified waves in surrounding areas. Thus, a locally modulated unspecific EEG rhythm may heterodyne with its unmodified neighbor to trigger diphasic phase effects which will register in the phase recorder, and also, possibly, differentially excite local cortical receptors.

How a slightly modulated rhythm may heterodyne or interact with its own unmodulated pattern and generate a signal has been experimentally demonstrated in Fig. 5.6. A single oscillator-generated frequency of 9 cps was here arranged to control two pen-writer amplifier channels which were, therefore, in-phase. When the time relation of inputs to either of these pen outputs was slightly modified by switching in a small capacitor, the effect on either of the two pen writeouts might escape notice, but that there were effects is demonstrated by the diphasic patterns generated in the phase comparison record. Thus, the familiar Morse code signal, S-O-S, could be transmitted by key via *one* of the 9 cycle rhythms and picked up as a signal by the phase recorder with practically no observable distortion of either of the original 9 cycle patterns. It was further demonstrated that a rhythmic sinusoidal (*a*-like) rhythm was unnecessary as a carrier wave. Transmission of the signal was obtainable even with a single, very irregular, nonrhythmic, EEG-like pattern as carrier (*C* and *D* of Fig. 5.6).

These observations suggest that either *a* rhythm or the widespread diffuse, unspecific, relatively irregular oscillatory activity of the EEG over the surface of the head may contribute as a carrier wave in normally alert motor-autonomic and sensory projection function. Local cortical interaction such as this may provide a mechanism by which the waking *a* rhythm monitors for *significant evidence of change* the barrage of incoming information projected on the cortex. Any *new* stimulus which produces a local cortical effect induces a local difference and, is therefore an effective stimulus. With local cortical function thus open to domination by any transient novelty, problematical new and threatening situations will necessarily receive cortical-subcortical assessment. This may be associated with widespread "blocking" or "activation" of the EEG and may even trigger learned effects or activities which have been found appropriate in meeting the situation.

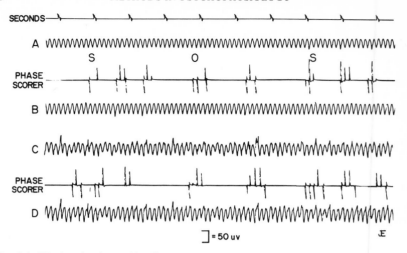

FIG. 5.6. The barely observable effect on timing of shifting a small capacitor from one to another of two channels recording the same frequency is clearly registered by the phase scorer. The signal is picked up and may be transmitted as a familiar code signal equally well whether the sinusoidal rhythm *A* and *B* or the irregular pattern *C* and *D* is the basis of self comparison.

Summary

What then may we say of interarea EEG phase relations as agents of cerebral function? We have had, it would seem, pinpointed for us three interrelated modalities of phase-involved cerebral function which may be clearly observed and discriminated in different contexts. At the electrophysiological level we have conditions of anterior and posterior leading and of diphasic interarea interaction or phase reversal. At the neurophysiological level these phenomena involve the motor and autonomic projection areas anteriorly and the somesthetic and sensory projection areas posteriorly with the possible importance of reverberatory interarea interaction processes as a third parameter. And at the psychophysiological and behavioral levels there are still other intimately related anterior versus posterior and interactive functions regarding which we await the results of further research. Enormous areas in neurophysiology, both cortical and subcortical, and in psychophysiology, psychology, and psychopathology contain phase-related phenomena now open to study regarding the roles of temporal relationships in the nervous system.

Acknowledgements

I would like to express my indebtedness to many colleagues: Dr. Noël Jenkin, Dr. Jerome Cohen, Dr. Duilio Giannitrapani, Dr. Stanley Lorens, Richard Vieth, Bernard Rosenberg, Allen Sorkin, Jerry Enenstein, Mrs. Katie Dunston, John Czarnik, and Mrs. Gail Kaliss.

REFERENCES

Adey, W. R., Dunlop, C. W., & Hendrix, C. E. Hippocampal slow waves; distribution and phase relations in the course of approach learning. *Archs Neurol., Chicago*, 1960, *3*: 74–90.

Baggchi, B. K. Superimposed oscillographic traces as a qualitative method to determine inter-channel phase and other differences in EEG. *Electroenceph. clin. Neurophysiol.*, 1957, *9*: 175.

Bishop, G. H. Cyclic changes in excitability of the optic pathway of the rabbit. *Am. J. Physiol.*, 1933, *103*: 213–224.

Brazier, M. A., & Casby, J. A study of the electrical fields at the surface of the head. *Rapports du 2e Congres de l'Electroencephalographie, Paris, Septembre, 1949.*

Burch, N. R. Automatic analysis of the electroencephalogram: a review and classification of systems. *Electroenceph. clin. Neurophysiol.*, 1959, *11*: 827–834.

Burch, N. R., & Childers, H. E. Information processing in the time domain. In W. S. Fields & W. Abbott (Eds.), *Information storage and neural control.* Springfield, Ill.: Charles C Thomas, 1963.

Cohn, R. A cycloscopic study of the human electroencephalogram. *J. gen. Physiol.*, 1942, *25*: 517–522.

Cohn, R. A simple method for cerebral toposcopy. *Electroenceph. clin. Neurophysiol.*, 1950, *2*: 97–98.

Cornil, L., & Gastaut, H. Données electroencéphalographiques sur la dominance hémisphérique. *Rev. neurol.*, 1947, *79*: 207.

Darrow, C. W., & Arnott, G. P. A device for simultaneous comparison of variable EEG brain patterns. *Proceedings of Eighth National Instrument Conference, Chicago, 1953.*

Darrow, C. W., & Hicks, R. Interarea EEG phase relationships following sensory and ideational stimuli. *Psychophysiology*, 1965, *1*: 337–346.

Darrow, C. W., & Smith, H. F. An instrument for automatic scoring of EEG phase relationships. *Electroenceph. clin. Neurophysiol.*, 1964, *16*: 614–616.

Darrow, C. W., Wilcott, R. C., Siegel, A., Stroup, M., & Aarons, L. Instrumental evaluation of EEG phase relationships. *Electroenceph. clin. Neurophysiol.*, 1956, *8*: 333–336.

Darrow, C. W., Wilson, J. P., Vieth, R. N., & Maller, J. M. Acceleration and momentum in cerebral function reflected in EEG phase relations. In J. Wortis (Ed.), *Recent advances in biological psychiatry*. New York: Grune & Stratton, 1960. Pp. 51–59.

Giannitrapani, D., Sorkin, A., & Enenstein, J. Laterality preference of children and adults as related to interhemispheric phase activity. *J. neurol. Sci.*, 1966, *3*: 139–150.

Goldring, S., & O'Leary, J. L. Correlation between steady transcortical potential and evoked response. I. Alterations in somatic receiving area induced by veratrine, strychnine, KCl, and novocaine. II. Effect of veratrine and strychnine upon the responsiveness of visual cortex. *Electroenceph. clin. Neurophysiol.*, 1954, *6*: 189–212.

Goldring, S., & O'Leary, J. L. Cortical DC changes incident to midline thalamic stimulation. *Electroenceph. clin. Neurophysiol.*, 1957, *9*: 577–584.

Goodwin, C. W., & Stein, S. N. A brain wave "correlator." *Science, N.Y.*, 1948, *108*: 507.

Hanberry, J., Ajmone-Marsan, C., & Dilworth, M. Pathways of nonspecific thalamocortical projection system. *Electroenceph. clin. Neurophysiol.*, 1954, *6*: 193–198.

Hennman, E., Goodwin, C., & Toll, K. Correlation studies on animals. *Electroenceph. clin. Neurophysiol.*, 1949, *1*: 521.

Jasper, H. Diffuse projection systems: the integrative action of the thalamic reticular system. *Electroenceph. clin. Neurophysiol.*, 1949, *1*: 405–420.

Jasper, H., Naquet, R., & King, E. A. Thalamic cortical recruiting responses in sensory receiving areas in the cat. *Electroenceph. clin. Neurophysiol.*, 1955, *7*: 99–114.

Landau, W. M., Bishop, G. H., & Clare, M. H. The interactions of several varieties of evoked response in visual and association cortex of the cat. *Electroenceph. clin. Neurophysiol.*, 1961, *13*: 43–53.

Lilly, J. C. A 25-channel potential field recorder. *Proceedings Second Annual Joint IRE-AIEE Conference on Electronic Instrumentation in Nucleonics and Medicine, New York, 1949.*

Lilly, J. C. Correlations between neurophysiological activity in the cortex and short-term behavior in the monkey. In H. F. Harlow & C. N. Woolsey (Eds.), *Biological and bi* *chemical bases of behavior.* Wisconsin: University of Wisconsin Press, 1958. Pp. 83–10

Motokizawa, F., & Fujimori, B. Fast activities and DC potential changes of the cerebral co tex during EEG arousal response. *Electroenceph. clin. Neurophysiol.*, 1964, *17*: 630–63

Petsche, H., & Marko, A. Toposkopische Untersuchungen zur Ausbreitung des Alpharhyt mus. *Wien. Z. NervHeilk.*, 1955, *12*: 87–100. (a)

Petsche, H., & Marko, A. Über die Ausbreitung der Makrorhythmen am Gehirn des Me schen und Kaninchens auf Grund Toposkopischer Untersuchungen. *Arch. Psychia* *NervKrankh*, 1955, *193*: 177–198. (b)

Petsche, H., & Stumpf, C. Topographic and toposcopic study of origin and spread of t regular synchronized arousal pattern in the rabbit. *Electroenceph. clin. Neurophysio* 1960, *12*: 589–600.

Rémond, A., & Offner, F. Etudes topographiques de l'activité EEG de la region occipital *Rev. neurol.*, 1952, *87*: 182–189.

Sonneman, H., & Kennard, M. A. An interphase analyzer of the electroencephalogra *Science, N. Y.*, 1947, *105*: 437–438.

Sugar, O. Asymmetry in occipital electroencephalograms. *Dis. nerv. Syst.*, 1947, *8*: 141–15

Walter, W. G., & Shipton, H. W. A new toposcopic display system. *Electroenceph. cli* *Neurophysiol.*, 1951, *3*: 281–292.

Wilson, J., Vieth, R., & Darrow, C. W. Activation and automation in right and left hemi pheres. *Electroenceph. clin. Neurophysiol.*, 1957, *9*: 570–571.

6
Rheoencephalography, A Diagnostic Method for the Study of Cerebral Circulation Dynamics: Principles and Application

S. A. RADVAN-ZIEMNOWICZ, M.D.

Various ingenious and complex methods for measuring transient and steady state factors of blood flow have been employed.

Transient changes in blood flow and vascular volume in humans and animals are accompanied by pulsation; this pulsation is characteristic of most living tissues and organs. The measures which have been used to monitor these fluctuations are: pressure, temperature, pH, relative concentration of dyes, gases, or ionizing compounds in the blood, and penetration by, or transmission of, various types of energy such as electric and magnetic currents, ultrasonic and sound fields. A frequently used technique is cannulization where the blood is metered by a sensing device inside the artery or vein or both. Attempts to measure blood volume changes by means of extravascular flowmeters on intact vessels have met with serious problems because of the limits in size and weight of the apparatus, influences of body temperature, polarization, and foreign body reactions. The most difficult problems in use are the requirements for stability, sensitivity, and a reliable determination of both the zero reference and the calibration for absolute quantitative measurements of blood flow. For these reasons, intravascular and extravascular flowmeters are still considered to be in the experimental stage of development. Such methods as those described above are frequently unreliable because results are difficult to replicate in experimental or clinical application due to the interference of many factors (which often cause deleterious effects on the blood, the surrounding tissues, and the organism itself) introduced by the methods themselves. The many techniques of recording changes in a single vessel only cannot reflect total limb or organ pulsations.

Studies have been made using macro-, micro-, and cinephotomicrography; such optical methods have met with limited success, again because of the difficulties in calibration and in reproducibility. Metabolic techniques registering fluctuations in blood flow have been enhanced by the use of surface cortical electrodes which give quantitative and, recently, continuous recordings of partial pressure of oxygen (PO_2), pH, and partial pressure of carbon dioxide (PCO_2). Isotopes have been used for study of cerebral circulation in experimental and clinical research and give fair accuracy. However, the method is rather complicated, expensive, and technically difficult. It is impossible to use such a technique for the study of circulatory dynamics during prolonged observations or to make many controlled repetitions. The scanning method is seldom used and the prospects for its wider application do not seem favorable.

Alternating current has been used to register the changes in electrical conductivity caused by fluctuations in tissue impedance with each pulsation of blood. This method has been called "electrical impedance plethysmography" by American authors; it is termed "electroplethysmography" (EPG) by the Russians; "diagraphy" and "electrocapacitography" (ECPB) by the Japanese; and "rheography" by European investigators.

In the field of general biology, such terms as biorheology, hemorheology, and rheometry are in use to describe the deformation and flow of biological systems or materials derived from living organisms. The similarity of these terms should not be confused with those describing rheography.

A relatively new and promising approach to the measurement of vascular dynamics uses high frequency alternating current applied across a tissue segment to produce an output signal which reflects the impedance (the AC equivalent to resistance) of the segment. The total impedance thus measured represents the fairly constant contributions provided by tissue and a variable factor representing the quantity of the blood in the current pathways in the field created in the vicinity of applied electrodes. This latter factor is variable since it is dependent upon the quantity of blood present which in turn reflects the changing hemodynamic status of the examined segment. Such vascular factors account for only 0.05 to 0.1% of the total impedance but these small signals, with proper procedures and interpretation, can yield valuable information. The rheographic method permits the recording and comparison of blood flow in symmetrical parts of the body without cannulization or surgical exposure of vessels. The use of alternating current avoids the electrolytic action of direct current and the influence of changing values in skin resistance. Many different frequencies of alternating current, 9, 10, 20, 30, 45, 175, and even 300 kc, have been applied. Various detection and amplification circuits and all manner of recording techniques are in use. One group of investigators is of the opinion that, with the use of alternating current, the monitored changes are in tissue impedance, and use the term, impedance plethysomodiagraphy. Another group describes the observed changes as variations in capacitance and applies the term, capacitography.

The first observations of fluctuations in the electrical properties of living tissue were published by Cremer (1907, a and b); an isolated frog's heart was placed between the plates of a condenser and a string galvanometer was used to register the cardiac rhythm. This "dielectrography" or "radiocardiography" has been further elaborated by Aetzler and Lehmann (1932) who registered changes in pulse and heart volume. More studies on dielectrographic pictures of the heart and on pulse were conducted by Rosa (1940, a and b), Matsuno (1935), Schmitz and Schaefer (1935), Mann (1937 and 1954), and Dulbecco and Palomba (1938). Nyboer (1959 and 1960) described measurements of resistance in relation to the filling of vessels of the extremities with the use of electrical impedance plethysmography with high frequency (175 kc) current. The impedance method has been accepted by several cardiovascular centers for the study of variations in blood volume and form of pulse wave.

The frequency of alternating current falls in the range of 9 to 100 kc. For studies on extremities and heart, Polzer, Schuhfried, and Heeger (1960) used 20 to 30 kc. For cranial rheography Jenkner (1962, a and b) used a frequency around 20 kc. Schwan considered the best frequency to be around 1 kc. The same frequency was used by Soulairac and Gougerot and Marstal (1960) in their work on cerebral atherosclerosis. For circulatory studies on limbs, Schmitt (1957) used 30 kc, while Bagno introduced a 50 kc transistorized impedance plethysmograph in his work with Nyboer and collaborators. Recently, Lechner, Jenkner, Rodler, & Heppner (1961) applied 9 kc of current through the head. Frequencies lower than 10 kc can produce disagreeable sensations. Moskalenko and Naumenko (1959), in their study on the movement of the blood and its relation to changes in conductivity, used AC current of various frequencies between 20 and 500 kc. In the majority of their studies an alternating current of 300 kc was used. In a recent publication, these authors considered the best frequency for intracranial circulatory studies to be 15 to 30 kc but in the same paper they wrote that the frequencies of 80 to 100 kc appear to be optimal for intracranial recording in man and for other parts of the body. They utilized also the method of ultrahigh frequency with radio waves 30 to 50 cm in length through the head.

The use of alternating current techniques in research on cerebral circulation has been much delayed because the vessels in the extremities and the heart have been the main targets for circulatory work. Alternating current was used for the first time for diagnostic purposes on intracranial tumors by Meyer and Schlueter in 1921 and by Grant in 1923 and Polenow in 1934. This new method was called brain rheometry to localize brain tumors by determining the impedance of the growth and surrounding tissue. A probe was introduced into the brain through the trephined skull and the tissue impedance was measured on the scale simultaneously with an acoustic signal modulated parallel to the impedance and serving as a monitor for the surgeon. Alternating current of about 1 kc was used. Physiological salt solution and cerebrospinal fluid gave values of about 80 ohms and the sound signal of minimal intensity; blood gave about 150 ohms; normal brain gave an impedance of about 600 ohms and the strongest acoustic signal; and brain tumors gave readings of about 300 ohms. Pauli and Redwitz (1925) and Lihotsky (1926) also applied brain rheometry to the localization of brain tumors. Lihotsky was the first investigator to observe convulsions during this diagnostic use of alternating current when the probe was placed too close to the motor cortex or to the internal capsule. Grant (1923) reported that cerebral rheometry was used in 75 cases in which a tumor was found and that this method was of special value in detecting diffuse subcortical gliomas. Grant was further able to substantiate his assertions on gliomatous tumors. In every case in his series, either on the operating table or at post mortem, glioma tissue gave electrical resistance values from 1/2 to 2/3 lower than that of the surrounding normal brain. The method did not attract as much attention as the then new diagnostic techniques of ventriculography, pneumoencephalography, and arteriography.

The further use of rheography for diagnostic purposes was neglected for about 25 years. Sufficiently precise and reliable instrumentation was lacking. Moreover the appearance of an impressive method of encephalography and ventriculography caused, according to Grant,* a neglect of cerebral impedance studies. The principle of an alternating current bridge was applied by Mann (1954) to the study of peripheral circulation, and a so-called "capacigraph" was used for measuring cardiac output. Rosendal (1940) investigated the conductivity of human tissue to alternating current. Morioka (1937) reported on normal so-called dielectrosphygmogram of the head monitored by the use of an alternating current bridge. Gangler (1937) reported an experimental study of brain resistance in traumatic cerebral concussion and compression. The work of Spiegel, Henny, Wycis, and Spiegel (1945) describing the high and low frequency impedance changes in the brain following a concussion, and the reports of Merrem and Niebeling (1953) and Niebeling and Thieme (1953) describing the measurements of resistance in brain tissue should be cited. These studies represent disconnected attempts at the determination of cerebral vascular dynamics in this period.

Progress in technology has resulted in better instrumentation for the measurement and registration of the conductivity of tissues for alternating current. Simultaneous recording from two symmetrical vascular areas has been a great advance in rheography. Holzer, Polzer, and Marko (1945) and later Kaindl, Polzer, and Schuhfried (1959, a and b) reported the use of middle frequency (15 kc and later 20 to 30 kc) paired signal generators with two calibrated

---

*F. C. Grant, personal communication.

Wheatstone Bridges adjustable for both resistance and capacitance. This was the first application of symmetrical recordings simultaneously in the left and right extremity. In cranial rheography it was possible to assess simultaneously the circulatory changes in the left and right hemisphere. This apparatus has enabled much more extensive studies of the heart and the peripheral circulation including the brain. In the constant fluctuating circulation influenced by many factors, e.g. cardiac, vascular, and tissue metabolism, it is essential to compare each pulsation in symmetrical parts of the body. When the tracings are taken separately it is wrong to attempt an evaluation of circulatory changes by super-imposing recordings taken at different times.

The study of the cerebral circulation by this method was conducted some-what earlier. Kaufman, Nims, Nyboer, and Somberg (1944) described an ex-periment with the use of impedance plethysmography for examination of circu-latory changes in the brain. The extradurally placed electrodes were used in an anesthetized dog. The partial obliteration of the pulse volume was accom-plished by inflating a cuff to a pressure of 100 and 200 mm Hg around the dog's neck. They did not continue to publish on the subject of cerebral circu-lation. Donzelot, Meyer, Heine, Milovanovich, and Dreyfus (1951) reported on the application of the method in humans and called it "transcranial diag-raphy." Polzer and Schuhfried (1950), Auinger, Kaindl, and Neumayr (1953), and Merlen (1955) used rheography of the skull for evaluation of changes in vessels in the head. Rheographic examination was performed by Kaindl, Kraus, and Praetan (1955) during a ligation of the human carotid artery.

The general terms "rheograph" and "rheogram" were introduced by Holzer and Polzer (1946) with "rheocardiogram" being proposed for rheographic tracings of the heart. Jenkner (1957), who focussed his study on cerebral cir-culation, proposed the term "rheoencephalography," his tracings paralleled the pulse waves and blood flow in the human hemispheres. He considered that recordings taken from the scalp arose almost entirely from changes in the sup-ply of the internal carotid artery.

Cardiovascular centers in several countries are studying rheography of the heart and of the peripheral circulation in both upper and lower extremities, in jugular veins, liver, kidneys, and recently of the uterus. Rheographic exami-nation of the head is less accepted.

Contrary to the more numerous favorable reports which consider rheoen-cephalography as a valuable method in brain studies, there are a number of papers reporting inconclusive or negative results. One of the main problems encountered is the difficulty in determining if the recording is of intracranial, i.e. cerebral origin, or if it is mainly a tracing of extracranial, i.e. external carotid artery, circulation. Another difficulty, besides differences in technical specification and recording, is the lack of an optimum method for interpreta-tion of registered data. DuBois and Nims (1945) used a special impedance plethysmograph with alternating current of 175 kc and observed the peripheral circulation of patients breathing under low and high atmospheric pressure.

They did not obtain any conclusive results. Friedmann (1955) investigated cases of carotid artery occlusion and subdural hematoma but could not obtain any conclusive diagnostic results. In his opinion this method chiefly registers the extracranial circulation. Spunda (1955) concluded from his experience with cases of unilateral extensive intracranial hemangioma, following stellate blockade changes, and after the use of vasodilating drugs injected into the external and internal carotid artery, that he was unable to monitor adequately the events in intracranial circulation. He considered the tracings to be the results of circulatory fluctuations outside the bony skull. Spunda (1955) employed 300 kc for measuring pulsations and denied any value to such observations for cerebral diagnosis. Simonson (1961) took forehead impedance plethysmograms in a group of subjects using a modification of Schmitt's apparatus and 25 kc currents. He studied the effects of hypoxia before and after 7 min of breathing a mixture of 10% O_2 and 90% N_2. He concluded that he recorded essentially extracranial circulation because of the high electrical resistance of the bony skull, "but some contamination with cerebral circulation cannot be excluded."

Dobner (1958) and Posteli, Garbini, and Picchio (1957) considered the rheograms of the head as a tracing of both the intracranial and extracranial circulation with equal participation of both.

However, rheographic tracings from the head are considered by the majority of authors as intracranial in origin and as registering the changes in cerebral blood flow. A list of primarily European publications may be found in the monographs of Kedrov and Naumenko (1954), Garbini and Picchio (1958), Kaindl, Polzer, and Schuhfried (1959a), and Jenkner (1959).

Rheography of the head is still in the early stage of development according to Garbini and Gastaut, Rodler, Lechner, Bostem, and Naquet (1960), Gougerot and Marstal (1960), Hatakeyama (1959), Hatakeyama and Aizawa (1962), Schuhfried (1961), Jenkner (1962b), Ziemnowicz (1963, a to e), and Ziemnowicz and Masucci (1962). There is evidence that much remains to be done in rheoencephalography. The equipment is not yet standardized and many different frequencies, circuits, and methods of amplification and calibration are in use. Electrodes differ in material, shape, size, and placement. There is no standard form of registration or rate of tracing. The interpretation of rheoencephalographic data is also far from uniform.

Methodology
Instrumentation
    Several authors expressed their belief that the rheographic method is still in its pioneering stage. Kunert (1961b) wrote that we are only in the beginning of research work in this field. Naumenko[†] stated that after 20 years, most of the

---

†A. I. Naumenko, personal communication.

problems of the method are as yet insufficiently investigated and concluded that there is still an insufficient collaboration between investigators in different specialities. Cardiovascular centers in several countries accepted rheography as one of the methods for studying the circulation in extremities. Cranial rheographic examination is much less widely accepted.

In the course of the last 5 years I experimented with several apparatuses but the rheograph of Schuhfried proved to be the most reliable. Uncritical application of unreliable equipment can cause doubtful and inconclusive results. In the United States, rheoencephalography recently became a subject of controversy. Close collaboration of experimental and clinical investigators with physicists and electronic engineers is necessary in order to build adequate instrumentation for these studies and obtain reliable and reproducible results.

Schuhfried's double rheograph contains two Wheatstone Bridges, each with its own oscillator supplying alternating current of slightly differing frequencies of approximately 30 kc and about 10 ma. Each bridge can be used independently or both may be employed simultaneously for comparison of symmetrical parts of the body, e.g. of two halves of the head. The patient constitutes the unknown arm of each bridge through two pairs of scalp electrodes. The part of the head through which the alternating current flows contributes electrically a combination of both resistance and capacitance. Both bridges of the rheograph have calibrated resistor and condensor dials for measuring and nulling the unknown values for each pair of electrodes and for the volume of conducting tissue. During the equilibration of a bridge connected with the patient, it is necessary to short circuit a standardized small resistance which when normally added to the circuit causes the unbalance of each of the Wheatstone Bridges. The slightly untuned bridge is more sensitive and yields a voltage which is modulated by the conductivity fluctuations in the measuring range.

The rhythmic pulse waves in cerebral circulation induce only very small changes in the AC impedance of tissue. These variations are of approximately 0.05 to 0.1% or less of the over-all impedance. These very small ranges of variation must be amplified and recorded by a sensitive and reliable apparatus. The recent advances in electronic instrumentation permit an adequate amplification of the rheographic output free from interference or noise.

Experimental work indicates that the capacitative component of the observed changes is minimal, often less than 5% and that the impedance fluctuations are parallel to the blood flow fluctuations in the tissue. The blood in a tissue segment has the lowest specific resistance to direct current. This resistance will be further reduced when an alternating current is applied, e.g. from 3,000 or 10,000 ohms (at DC) to 300 ohms or less. The frequencies below 10 kc cause some disagreeable sensations for the examined person. Alternating current of 20 to 90 kc frequencies seems to be optimal at the present time for rheographic circulatory studies. These frequencies do not produce disagreeable sensations to the subject and at the same time the apparatus is more sensitive to vascular changes.

The double rheograph has additional controls which permit finer calibration by adding a resistance which increases the conductivity and causes an upward deflection of calibration tracing. The value of a routine calibration is 0.1 ohm (100 milliohms) for 10 mm of pen deflection. For recordings with very high amplitudes, it is advisable to use 0.5 ohm for a 10-mm deflection. When the amplitude of the rheogram is very low, it is possible to calibrate 0.05 ohm for 10-mm signal deflection. The calibration can be repeated during the recording and it will appear as a sharp curve (preferably on the decline) superimposed on the tracing. Rheoencephalography uses the standard neurophysiological convention of polarity. The calibrating signal is recorded as an upward deflection of the tracing with a sharp return to the base line and subsequently a mirror like curve below the base line, i.e. a diphasic spike wave form. The influx of blood on each pulse causes a decrease of impedance for alternating current flowing through the tissue segment resulting in an elevation of rheographic curve above the base line. The rheograph of Schuhfried permits recording of the first derivative of the REG curves. These tracings are usually placed next to the corresponding REG channel. Such recordings of the first derivative are read in millimeters of amplitude and correspond to the greatest angle of inclination of each rising arm of the rheogram. This supplementary graphic analysis displays quantitatively the steepness of the incline which is an important criterion for diagnostic interpretation.

The output signal from each of the Wheatstone Bridges is amplified, rectified, demodulated, and presented at the output of the rheograph for tracing by a recorder with a sufficient sensitivity and frequency response. A standard EEG machine or a good polygraph is best for registration. The recorder is calibrated on 50 μv input signal deflection. The amplification for the direct writing oscillographs is about 50 times lower than for a routine EEG, or is in the range of an EKG monitoring for longitudinal (hemispherical) REG, and is sufficient also for regional REG tracings.

The standard rheoencephalographic examination in this laboratory consists of a simultaneously recorded EKG tracing and the REG monitoring taken from two symmetrical areas of the head. The same recordings are duplicated once or twice on different channels for better critical evaluation of any abnormalities in timing, form, and amplitude. Paper speed is usually 30 or 25 mm/sec; for prolonged observation 15 or 10 mm/sec. Occasionally when greater detail is desired, 50, 60, or 100 mm/sec speed of chart drive is used.

The encephalograph as a recorder has the additional advantage of permitting the increase or reduction of amplification simultaneously for all channels. When a polygraph is used, it is convenient to have a means of simultaneous calibration by an accessory electrode selector panel which also facilitates the multiple channel input selection. Since the rheograph applies a high frequency alternating current to the patient, this signal may sometimes appear on the EKG leads or on other electrodes and cause interference. This has been a particular problem with equipment using chopper amplifiers. For these instruments, it is necessary to add a filtering network to bypass the high frequency signals from other inputs.

An electrocardiogram is included in all tracings to identify the cardiac cycle, changes in heart force and timing, and to diagnose any cardiac abnormalities which might affect the cerebral circulation. The synchronous monitoring of EKG with REG is considered by the author as obligatory for proper interpretation of rheoencephalographic data.

A pneumogram is taken in all polygraphic tracing to study the influence of normal and abnormal respiration (hyperventilation, dyspnea, CO_2 and O_2 inhalation) on the functional state of cerebral vessels and on the cardiac action.

An example of an eight-channel electroencephalograph used for rheoencephalographic tracing is as follows: Channel 1, EKG; Channel 2, right REG; Channel 3, first derivative of the right REG (or left REG); Channel 4, right REG (repeated); Channel 5, left REG; Channel 6, first derivative of the left REG (or right REG); Channel 7, left REG (repeated); and Channel 8, EKG (repeated).

A six-channel polygraph is used for rheoencephalographic study in the following manner: Channel 1, pneumogram; Channel 2, EKG; Channel 3, left REG; Channel 4, right REG; Channel 5, left REG (repetition or first derivative); Channel 6, right REG (repetition or first derivative).

Many different electrode shapes, sizes, and materials are in use. I have obtained satisfactory recordings by the use of such diverse electrodes as the large (30 mm x 25 mm x 5 mm or 15 mm x 15 mm x 5 mm) aluminum blocks for clinical REG or the standard EKG electrodes cut to various sizes. Silver mesh electrodes embedded in rubber or the silver discs for routine EEG were used with good results as well as electrocorticographic electrodes, and even stainless steel or silver-platinum alloy needles (25 to 30 gauge) inserted subcutaneously for experimental REG and for studies on eye circulation, so-called "rheo-ophthalmography" (ROG) described in 1962 (Ziemnowicz, 1962). Proper calibration and adjustment of amplification is a constant requirement.

Since the REG depends upon the detection of very small changes in alternating current flow due to the circulatory fluctuations in impedance, it is essential that a stable low resistance contact be made with the patient. The total impedance of electrodes and the adjacent tissue should be as small as possible. Any good electrode jelly or paste may be used. Most of those available commercially are satisfactory and contain sufficient conducting materials and water. These jellies may give a higher resistance than does a piece of cotton or absorbent paper saturated in saline solution. However, a fast drying contact material does not permit prolonged recording. Measurement of resistance after bilateral symmetrical placement of electrodes allows one to check the amount of base-line resistance to test if it is identical on both sides. When it is higher on one side it is necessary to improve the contact between electrodes and skin. Perforated rubber strips can hold the electrodes to the scalp, but it is very difficult to maintain identical distances between the electrodes. I have devised a special adjustable plastic carrier which fits over the head. This cranial electrode holder is adjustable for head size and permits more precise and easily reproducible placement of spring loaded scalp (REG) and eye (ROG) electrodes (Ziemnowicz, 1962). For regional tracings, electrodes pasted on thick rubber bands were found very useful.

Electrode placement. Despite the number of investigators who are clinically using rheoencephalography, it is evident that this method is still in the early stages of development. There is, for instance, a lack of accepted standards for electrode placement. The most often used configuration is that of the fronto-retromastoid or longitudinal placement of electrodes in pairs, each pair on one side of the head (Fig. 6.1). The electrodes must be placed symmetrically at equivalent positions and interelectrode distances as exactly as possible. Asymmetrical placement of electrodes results in differences in amplitude and in other artifacts which may cause errors in evaluation and may make an interpretation of such a tracing impossible. More detailed technical descriptions of longitudinal or hemispherical REG have been published (Kaindl, Polzer, & Schuhfried, 1959a; Jenkner, 1957; Garbini & Picchio, 1958; Kedrov & Naumenko, 1951).

The longitudinal REG permits registration of pulsations from each brain hemisphere individually and enables a localization of circulatory disturbances in the left or right sides or in both hemispheres. This appears to suffice for the majority of investigators. Very few authors have tried to differentiate between the circulation arising from the carotid arteries and that arising from the vertebral-basilar system or between the branches of internal carotid artery or the left and right side of the vertebral-basilar supply (Hatakeyama & Aizawa, 1962; Kunert, 1959; Fasano, Angelino, Braguzzi, & Braggi, 1961; Martin, Karbowski, & Vaney, 1963; Lechner et al., 1961). One group uses transverse REG recordings from frontal, temporal, and occipital areas with one electrode on each side of the examined region (Fig. 6.2). In the transverse REG it is difficult to compare the circulation between each pair of electrodes because the interelectrode distances vary as does the amount of blood in each monitored tissue volume. The relationship between the tracings can only be vaguely surmised. Using this diagonal placement it is important to realize that a unilateral deficit in one region may be masked by the normal or compensatory increased circulation in the opposite side, since this placement sums both sides. The transverse REG cannot localize a deficit in one or the other hemisphere.

The cerebral circulation should be viewed as a summation of normal (average), increased, or decreased circulation. The constant dynamic fluctuations are due to changes in the functional conditions, e.g. increase or decrease in local nerve tissue metabolism. When a deficit occurs it may be hidden in a whole cerebral hemisphere by compensatory increase of blood inflow or by

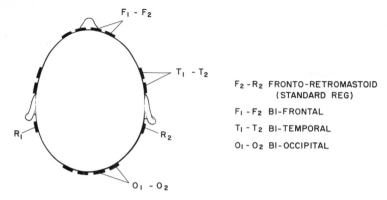

$F_2 - R_2$ FRONTO-RETROMASTOID
(STANDARD REG)

$F_1 - F_2$ BI-FRONTAL

$T_1 - T_2$ BI-TEMPORAL

$O_1 - O_2$ BI-OCCIPITAL

FIG. 6.1. Placement of electrodes for rheoencephalography. Fronto-retromastoid position is for hemispherical standard REG. Regional REG is recorded from bifrontal, bitemporal, biparietal, and bioccipital derivation. Eye rheographic electrodes (ROG) are not shown here.

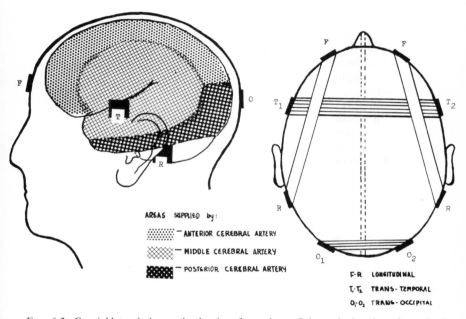

AREAS SUPPLIED by:

░░░░ — ANTERIOR CEREBRAL ARTERY

▒▒▒▒ — MIDDLE CEREBRAL ARTERY

████ — POSTERIOR CEREBRAL ARTERY

F-R   LONGITUDINAL

T_1-T_2 TRANS-TEMPORAL

O_1-O_2 TRANS-OCCIPITAL

FIG. 6.2. Cranial lateral view and calvarium from above. Schematic drawing of standard, generally applied longitudinal hemispherical derivation (FR). Transversal temporal (T_1-T_2), and transversal occipital (O_1-O_2) derivations as well as transversal frontal are not accepted.

the bulk of predominantly normal circulation. The appearance of a deficit in hemispherical circulation might represent a massive occlusion or compression or a restriction of arterial inflow with failure in compensatory mechanisms.

In order to localize circulatory lesions more accurately to smaller regions of the brain, I have developed a method which is termed "regional rheoencephalography" (Ziemnowicz, 1962, 1963). In the various papers this new method is described in detail with physical, experimental, and clinical data and further reports are in preparation. Our goal is to register separately the circulatory variations in the anterior, in the middle cerebral artery, and in the right and left sides of the vertebral-basilar system of supply in a manner that will give a useful tracing with minimal participation from the neighboring arterial branches. Regional rheoencephalography consists of simultaneous bipolar and bilateral recordings taken from adjacent pairs of active electrodes (generating and receiving) placed symmetrically over the proper regions of the head. The regional REG allows a discrimination of disturbances in blood flow separately in the frontal, temporal, and occipital areas of the brain. This attempt has been successful also in the regional rheographic tracing from the ophthalmic artery of the eye.

In regional rheoencephalography the patient remains in the same reclining position with slightly elevated head and shoulders as for longitudinal (hemispherical) rheoencephalographic recording. For a frontal regional REG tracing (Fig. 6.1 and 6.3) the medial electrodes of each pair are located on the forehead over the eyebrows parasagittally 10 mm from the middle line. The lateral electrodes are applied to the frontal area 20 mm behind the rostral electrode. For temporal tracing the placement of the more lateral electrode is above the ear with the anterior edge in the prolongation of the most anterior point of

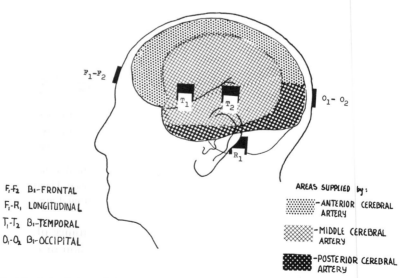

F_1-F_2 B_1-FRONTAL
F_1-R_1 LONGITUDINAL
T_1-T_2 B_1-TEMPORAL
O_1-O_2 B_1-OCCIPITAL

AREAS SUPPLIED by:
-ANTERIOR CEREBRAL ARTERY
-MIDDLE CEREBRAL ARTERY
-POSTERIOR CEREBRAL ARTERY

FIG. 6.3. Lateral view of electrode placement for hemispherical or longitudinal standard REG and for regional REG derivations. The parietal pair of electrodes are not shown here. The drawing shows the areas supplied by anterior, middle, and posterior cerebral arteries.

the upper ear attachment, and the more rostral electrodes of each pair are 20 mm in front of the supraauricular electrodes. For occipital derivation the electrodes are placed similarly to the frontal tracing 20 mm from each other and the medial electrodes are 10 mm from the middle line above the occipital protuberance. The above described method of standard, hemispherical, and regional rheoencephalography permits standardization and reliable repetition. The simultaneously recorded electrocardiogram gives information regarding normal or disturbed cardiac function.

Physiopathological Significance of the Craniocerebral Rheogram

The scalp rheogram includes the changes in electrical impedance to an alternating current of that portion of the head between and in vicinity of the electrodes. In comparison to the brain, the soft superficial tissues and the skull receive only a small fraction of the blood supply to the head as a whole. Therefore the pericranial and cranial circulation *a priori* might be expected to play a negligible role in comparison to the intracranial cerebral blood flow. Studies on the superior jugular vein have indicated that the blood from extracerebral sources amounts on the average to 2.7% of the total volume with a range from 0.0 to 6.6% (Kety & Schmidt, 1948, a and b). Electric impedance, measured in ohms, is the total opposition that a circuit represents to an alternating current. It includes resistance, inductive reactance, and capacitive reactance. Osseous tissue does not have an increased impedance to alternating current of middle frequencies; but, the skin shows a marked impedance (Horton & Van Ravenswaay, 1935).

Using the same amplification, transcutaneous tracings show lower amplitudes than similar recordings taken with the electrodes lying on the bone or on the dura mater. The findings of Kaindl and Jenkner were confirmed by our experimental studies†† using superficial scalp electrodes, needles applied through the skin reaching the calvarium, and with the application of epidural, subdural, and intracerebral electrodes. The rheoencephalographic tracings taken in this laboratory from electrodes placed on the intact scalp have lower amplitude in comparison to the simultaneously recorded REG from the symmetrically contralateral side of the head where the electrodes have been placed directly on the exposed cranial bones. The amplitude of the REG increases after a wide decompression of one hemisphere by the removal of a part of calvarium. Resection of a part of cerebral hemisphere, e.g. a frontal lobectomy, reduces the transcutaneous longitudinal REG in a way similar to that described after hemispherectomy where the rheogram on the side of the defect may be very flat. Experiments, done mostly on cats, were also done on dogs, rabbits, and monkeys.

Besides experimental operations, some significant observations on REG tracings have been made during neurosurgical operations on humans. An operation

††Paper in preparation.

was performed in two cases on very large unilateral arteriovenous malformations of the brain. The procedure consisted of producing an artificial embolization in the malformed area of internal carotid artery supply through a partially ligated external carotid artery (Luessenhop,, Gibbs, & Velasquez, 1962). The rheographic curves observed on an oscillographic screen did not change significantly or measurably during the clamping off or after the ligation of the external carotid artery. The recorded tracing also did not show any significant difference after such elimination of the external carotid artery inflow. In contrast to these observations, very distinct variations of cranial REG on the side of the operation were induced by procedures on the neck involving the internal carotid artery. A fast and forced injection of x-ray contrast medium or other fluids intraarterially or manipulations of the surgically exposed vessel produced sudden irregular high voltage waves. Temporary clamping of the internal carotid artery caused abrupt low voltage curves. The intraarterial introduction of artificial emboli caused changes in the REG as did the introduction of an arterial catheter with an inflatable tip. These results, in our opinion, are sufficient proof to justify the term "rheoencephalography" denoting a flow measurement (REG) for rheography of the head.

Rheoencephalographic curves are distinctive and reflect immediately the changes in cerebral blood flow induced by either cardiac or vascular factors of extracranial or intracranial origin. These tracings may demonstrate a separate or a combined cardiac and peripheral vascular pathology with unilateral or bilateral disturbances. The method is very sensitive due to the fact that the changes in conductivity for alternating current are 3.4 times as great as those in blood volume (Schwan, 1955). In general it is necessary to emphasize that it is quite frequently difficult to obtain a bilaterally symmetrical REG tracing even in normal individuals, especially in older age groups.

The correlation of rheoencephalographic data with heart activity and with the anatomical and functional status of vessels is obvious. The rheograms of brain circulation are phasic, synchronous with cerebral pulsations, and they regularly follow the cardiac systole with a delay of about 250 msec. Rheoencephalography is a very sensitive method for recording cerebral circulatory changes induced by disturbances of cardiac origin. Not only will heart arrest be immediately manifested in the REG, but also one abnormal systole in a cardiac arrhythmia will produce an abnormal REG curve (Fig. 6.4).

Rheographic tracings permit the observation of changes in both cerebral hemispheres during hyperventilation or subsequent to an increase CO_2 or a decreased oxygen tension. In selected cases, monitoring of REG may give important information during and after the changes in position of the neck (Fig. 6.5) and of the whole body, and during and after a compression test of the left and the right carotid arteries (Fig. 6.6). The carotid artery compression hypoxic test may induce cardiac fibrillation and even cardiac arrest with an acute cerebral circulatory insufficiently as demonstrated in our cases having an

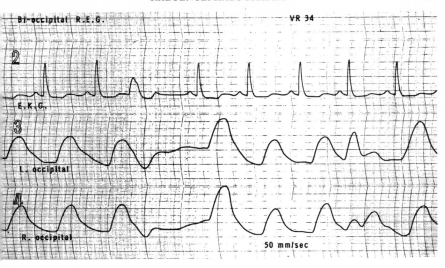

FIG. 6.4. Disturbances in cerebral circulation, cardiac in origin. This 65-year-old woman came to be examined as a healthy volunteer. The very marked cardiac inotropic arrhythmia with frustrated cardiac systole and occasional extrasystole is well reflected in cerebral arterial rheograms. The bioccipital REG, which represents the vertebral-basilar system, shows a missing pulsation related to cardiac abnormality with compensatory increase caused by the normal heart beat which follows.

extensive arteriosclerosis. This danger has been emphasized by us in a discussion on hypoxic EEG tests during the International Advanced Courses in EEG in Marseilles and the International Congress of Neurophysiology in Rome in 1961.

Continuous REG monitoring of long duration does not disturb the patient. It may be performed during therapeutic procedures such as brain surgery and during the diagnostic tests such as carotid or basilar arteriography. The results of rheoencephalographic studies used in diagnosis and prognosis of various conditions are discussed in more detail in the following sections.

Interpretation of Rheoencephalographic Tracings

The REG tracings are evaluated for (1) amplitude, (2) form, and (3) timing in a manner similar to that used in the observation of pulses in peripheral vessels in the extremities or in the neck.

The physical basis and the aspects of quantitative measurements will be discussed in a future publication. It should be noted here that the changes in tissue impedance are mainly a function of the extracellular electrolytes. This method is used also for intracerebral microelectrode studies on consciousness, sleep, and memory (Adey, Kado, & Didio, 1962; Ranck, 1964; Birzis & Tachibana, 1964). The rheoencephalographic changes in impedance occur

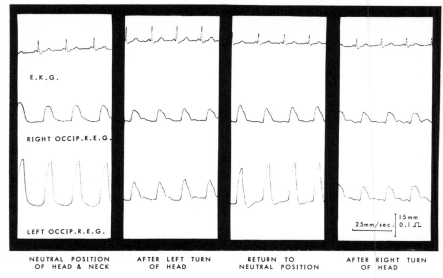

NEUTRAL POSITION   AFTER LEFT TURN   RETURN TO   AFTER RIGHT TURN
OF HEAD & NECK   OF HEAD   NEUTRAL POSITION   OF HEAD

FIG. 6.5. Disturbances in cerebral circulation, vascular in origin, in the area of the right side of the vertebral-basilar system with compensatory increase on the left side of this system. The deficit in posterior circulation is more marked when the head is in horizontal, dorsally hyperextended position and after right and left head turns. Head rotation reduces the already deficient right side circulation and lowers to about 50% the left compensatory increase. The head in neutral position and when bent forward 45° restores the previous values. Subjective signs of dizziness were produced 14 sec after the instantaneous changes induced by head rotation. The case illustrates the sensitivity and reproducibility of the method for hemodynamic studies. The extracranial factor of cerebral circulatory pathology is thus demonstrated. The 53-year-old man, neurologically negative, was involved in a severe automobile accident 6 weeks before the examination.

synchronously with variations of the filling of cerebral vessels and are caused by greater conductivity of blood than brain tissue. As mentioned before, our tracings obtained during extra- and intracranial operations support the views of Jenkner and other authors that the standard fronto-retromastoid (REG) represents almost entirely the pulsations in the internal carotid arterly supply to the left and right hemisphere in man. A decrease in quantity of blood supplied to a volume of tissue creates diminished conductivity for alternating current. This results in lower amplitude of tracing.

Our experience with regional REG permits the consideration of the bipolar, bifrontal derivation as an indication of circulatory changes in the left and right anterior cerebral artery area of supply. The bipolar-bitemporal tracing represents the pulsations in the volume of tissue supplied by the left and right medial cerebral artery. The occipital bipolar tracing records the changes in the region supplied by the left and the right side of the vertebral-basilar system. In my opinion, bilateral and simultaneous registration of longitudinal and subse-

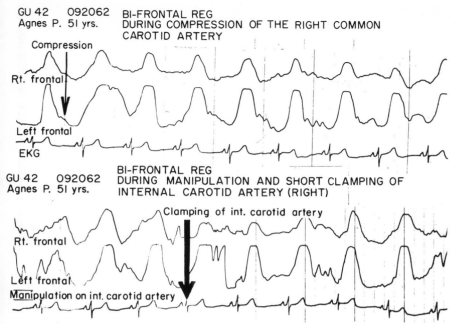

GU 42 092062 BI-FRONTAL REG
Agnes P. 5l yrs. DURING COMPRESSION OF THE RIGHT COMMON
CAROTID ARTERY
Compression

Rt. frontal

Left frontal

EKG

GU 42 092062 BI-FRONTAL REG
Agnes P. 5l yrs. DURING MANIPULATION AND SHORT CLAMPING OF
INTERNAL CAROTID ARTERY (RIGHT)

Clamping of int. carotid artery

Rt. frontal

Left frontal

Manipulation on int. carotid artery

FIG. 6.6. Digital compression of the right common carotid artery on the neck does not change markedly the already lowered circulation in the right anterior cerebral artery. In contrast to clamping of the interior carotid artery which reduced the right side circulation and also influenced the left side circulation.

quently all regional derivations enables a more exact localization of disturbances in the cerebrovascular system. The problems of quantifying the REG with respect to the three parameters noted above will now be discussed in detail.

Evaluation of REG amplitude. Rheoencephalographic amplitude is measured from the base line to the height of the greatest elevation of the curve, e.g. at the point of the first peak. Amplitudes are comparable on account of calibration, which is usually set at 10 mm/100 milliohms (0.1 ohm). The normal range of amplitude varies at this sensitivity level between 100 and 150 milliohms. Normal variations in blood flow through the internal carotid artery on one side may cause a lowered amplitude record in that side and consequent asymmetry. Only the differences of more than 10% between the symmetrical areas on the left and right side are considered as significant of pathology. Pulsatory deficit caused by heart malfunction reduces the amplitude in tracings from both carotid arteries and the vertebral-basilar system. If the decrease is of vascular origin the tracings are asymmetrical. The cardiac origin of circulatory disturbances in the brain, particularly during cardiac arrhythmias, can be demonstrated by the occurrence of symmetrical variations in form, timing, and amplitude of the REG tracing (Fig. 6.4). A combination of cerebrovascular and cardiac pathology makes evaluation of the rheoencephalographic abnormalities more difficult.

Regional REG tracings sometimes have lower amplitude. Occipital derivations are occasionally reduced to one-half of the longitudinal hemispherical tracing. When the deficit in circulation is pronounced, it is often necessary to increase the amplification in all recording channels to allow an easier interpretation of details. Unilateral lowering of amplitude may be caused not only by extracranial or intracranial pathology in the wall of the vessel or its lumen but may also occur when the normal cerebral vessels are compressed by hematoma (extradural, subdural, intracerebral) or other accumulation of fluid or air. The cerebral compression results in lower amplitude, smaller angle of incline, and less details of the tracing. The diagnosis of bilateral lesion, vascular or extravascular in origin, is more difficult. Even more difficult are the cases when the compression is combined with cerebral contusion. The cerebral contusion causing brain edema or swelling or both induces an increase in amplitude and a steeper incline. The differentiation may also be difficult between cerebrovascular occlusion and cerebral hemorrhage. In such cases, the pharmacological test (e.g. with amyl nitrite) is indicated. The carotid artery compressive test may be dangerous and its results are often questionable.

Evaluation of REG form. The form of the REG tracing is important in the evaluation of cardiac efficiency, patency of vessels, and changes in blood vessel tonus. The rheoencephalogram is similar in many respects to the extracranial internal carotid artery rheogram or to any peripheral arterial rheogram or plethysmogram. It is also similar in form to a flowmeter record. The cranial rheogram REG has lower amplitude of pulsations than peripheral tracings, a steeper incline, and a slightly different form with two rounded peaks. The morphological difference between cerebral and peripheral rheograms is due to the additional factors such as venous intracranial pressure and incompressible but movable cerebrospinal fluid. A unilateral decompressive craniotomy increases the REG amplitude and increases the steepness of the incline. The incline or the ascending branch of each curve is normally steep and fast and should not be longer than 15 to 20% of the total duration of the pulse cycle. The inclination starts normally from the base line, becomes higher and steeper, then flattens out just before the first peak or the maximum amplitude of the rheogram is reached. At the first peak the decline begins, the curve dips and descends more gradually than the incline, with minor oscillations to the base line. Then a new cyclic phase begins, signaled and preceded by the systolic complex of EKG. In many normal tracings, especially in young subjects, the second peak is indistinguishable when the first is high and sharp. As a rule, the decline is longer than the incline and depends mainly on the rate of outflow of blood. In aged subjects the elevation changes into a plateau-like formation in advanced arteriosclerosis and then the second peak is also indistinguishable.

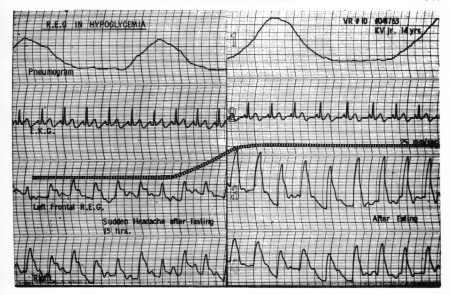

FIG. 6.7. Normal rheoencephalographic tracings have been disturbed by progressive reduction of amplitude and variation in form. Violent headache forced interruption of examination. Food intake relieved pain and brought normalization of respiration, heart function, and first cerebral circulation (earlier on the left).

In the interpretation of the REG tracing the steepness of the incline is important. Measurements of the angle of incline are difficult. Application of the first derivative tracing permits an instantaneous comparison of the angles. The height of the first derivative is directly proportional to the greatest angle of incline in all rheographic curves. The rheograph with two circuits for registration of the first derivative on each side is of value in the interpretation of the tracing. A marked decrease in steepness of the incline occurs in a number of conditions in which there is a deficit in blood pulsation, e.g. a compression of the brain by intracranial hematoma, hygroma, hemorrhage, cerebral cyst, abscess, poorly vascularized brain tumors, or by an intracranial accumulation of air. In advanced arteriosclerosis the first peak is low; a plateau formation makes it impossible to distinguish the second peak and the decline is smooth without any details. An arteriosclerotic patient with high blood pressure may demonstrate only a slight decrease in the steepness of the incline. The extracranial occlusion of the internal or common carotid artery may be accompanied by a smaller amplitude with a slowly rising incline and by a delay in timing of the first peak on the side of occlusion. An arteriovenous malformation may cause a faster appearance of the first peak, but the nearby brain tissue may have a reduced arterial blood inflow and consequently also a lower amplitude. In this condition the pulse wave will arrive sooner on the involved side rather than on the normal side. It will also be drained sooner by th venous shunt of malformation.

Repeated and prolonged recording may sometimes reveal a pattern whicl is characteristic for the individual patient.

Evaluation of REG timing. In addition to evaluating the amplitude an form of the tracings, an analysis of timing (from peak to peak) is included i the interpretation of rheograms. The speed of the cerebral pulse wave can b approximately measured on the EKG and REG tracings when they are recordec simultaneously. Between the systolic complex of heart action and the first peal of the REG curve, there is a time lapse of about 250 msec (0.25 sec). This delay may be prolonged in older individuals especially when the incline is less steef and the elevated part of the curve is of a plateau type as is frequently seen ir an advanced arteriosclerosis. The time factor in the rheographic tracing is very important in the evaluation of cardiac arrhythmia, arteriovenous malformation aneurysm, and intracranial and extracranial carotid or basilar occlusion or stenosis. In cardiac arrhythmia, each extrasystole and compensatory pause immediately induces rheographic variation by producing synchronous disturb- ances in timing and a deficit or surplus in the pulse volume.

The evaluation of the cerebral circulation requires at least 5 min for each derivation when one uses a paper speed of 15 or 25 and 30 or 50 mm/sec in performing the tracing. For the analysis of details, e.g. small additional waves, a paper speed of 60 or 100 mm/sec is required. In subjects demonstrating occasional cardiac abnormality, it is necessary to prolong the examination. Rotation of the head and hyperextension of the neck was applied by me for the diagnosis of extracranial pathological changes in the vertebral arteries (e.g. arteriosclerosis) or in their vicinity (e.g. cervical spondylosis).

Experimental studies with simultaneous recordings of rheoencephalogram, rheography of the extracranial internal and common carotid arteries, EKG and EEG tracings involving a series of different procedures on blood vessels on the brain and its coverings, in the cat, dog, rabbit, and monkey have been performed and the findings are to be published shortly.

Applications

Rheoencephalography may find wider application in the evaluation of the dynamics of the normal cerebral circulation in humans at rest, during various activities, or undergoing stress. Rheoencephalographic changes have been ob- served without any abnormal clinical signs. This method will record the actual circulatory status of normal individuals who may have asymmetry in cerebral blood supply or who may possess a borderline circulatory compensation. When such people are submitted to stress as in flying, diving, or racing, they may demonstrate sudden temporary insufficiency in the cerebral circulation. This may explain the pathology of accidents in which the factor of speed was involved.

Rheography of the cerebral circulation is a supplement to the clinical study and is especially valuable in the hands of those familiar with the physiology and pathophysiology (as far as it is known) of cerebral hemodynamics. By supplementing other examinations, rheoencephalography is useful in differentiation of such conditions which may not be readily diagnosed. Cerebral hemodynamics are not always affected by neurological disorders and in these cases the rheographic method is not helpful, but many times the REG information is useful in clarifying the pathology, diagnosis, and sometimes even the neurological prognosis of clinical cases.

The rheographic tracings can be easily misinterpreted. Technical errors may also cause misleading recordings. The asymmetrical curves and differences in amplitude can be induced by a nonsymmetrical placement of electrodes, poor contact of electrodes with the skin, or improper contacts anywhere within the circuit. It is also necessary to detect and eliminate outside electrical interference and any defects in the amplifying and recording apparatus. In rheoencephalography we apply a comparatively strong signal and it requires less amplification and therefore a less important role is played by the physiological artifacts such as muscle potential, sweating, eye movements, and heart potentials.

Even when proper techniques are employed, rheoencephalographic tracings can be difficult to evaluate. An asymmetrical REG is frequently observed in normal individuals despite a lack of any clinical or even transient pathological signs. This may be explained by the fact that there is a great "normal" variability of vessels in the circle of Willis and beyond; by the effects of anatomical asymmetry, perinatal trauma, and by the effects of functional variations. Sometimes we may find a paradoxical lateralization of circulatory changes when the REG abnormality and the clinical signs are not located in the same hemisphere or in the same region. Such a situation may occur when the vascular lesion (arteriosclerotic occlusion, hemorrhage) is comparatively small but located in a strategically important area (e.g. striate artery). A small damage in an important region or a deeply located area can induce a massive or a distinctive neurological deficit. Simultaneously the opposite hemisphere may demonstrate a greater deficit in blood supply than the side containing an acute small vascular lesion. The opposite hemisphere can show a more generalized and diffuse occlusive arterial pathology.

An old circulatory asymmetry may be difficult to interpret when a small but important deficit occurs on the side which formerly had more abundant blood flow. Diagnostic problems arise in transient circulatory disturbances and after recanalization or removal of vascular occlusion or compression. There are also cases with a persistent neurological deficit, but with recovery or return of cerebral blood supply to more normal condition. A slowly progressing deficiency or a slight deficit in cerebral circulation may be hidden by the collateral compensatory supply on the same side or from the opposite side in the case of a frontal or occipital deficit.

Great caution should be used in interpretation of single and short tracings Repeated examinations and the application of the method of regional REG are helpful toward more correct conclusions.

The advantages of the rheographic method applied to cerebrovascular research are in my opinion, obvious. The patients do not have more discomfort than in a routine EEG and EKG examination, except for the need to change the position of electrodes or connections on the head and on the special electrode panel for regional REG derivations. The present technique is in a process of constant improvement. The REG method studies the variations in impedance and conductivity for alternating current being sent through the living tissue and is not an investigation of much weaker bioelectrical potentials as in the EEG. Despite this essential difference, the rheoencephalographic tracings are often difficult to interpret. It is necessary to fulfill all technical requirements and to know the limitations of the rheographic method.

Rheoencephalography may serve as a screening method for individuals who are subjected during the performance of their duties to abnormal volume and pressure changes in their cerebral vessels produced by sudden acceleration and deceleration.

Repeated serial rheoencephalographic examinations can supply information on the dynamics of ischemic disorders of the brain. This may be of some value in the interpretation of cardiac or vascular functional and anatomical pathology or both.

With the process of aging there is a progressive increase of arteriosclerosis in the blood vessels supplying the brain. These changes frequently do not parallel the chronological age of an individual. If one accepts the fact that the brain is a complicated organ with numerous vital functions of the greatest significance for a useful human life, one would have to conclude that the evaluation of cerebral biological age is a very important determination. Rheoencephalography may permit one to determine the biological age of the cerebral circulation.

The most valuable data are obtained by serial recordings repeated when there is any change in objective or subjective signs. This method may supply information on the effects of therapy. It may also be of great value in the prognosis of circulatory disorders of the brain.

Rheoencephalography may be of assistance in the diagnosis of disturbances in cerebral circulation caused by the following conditions.

1. Anatomical changes in vessels caused by atherosclerosis, vascular occlusion with thrombosis or embolism, and by aneurysm or arteriovenous malformation.

2. Pathological disorders that are found to be of cardiac or aortic origin

3. The influences of hemicrania on cerebral circulation.

4. Cerebral edema, e.g., after contusion, and late results of brain injury

5. Compression of the brain and its vascular supply by extradural, subdural

or intracerebral hematoma, cyst, expanding tumor, or by hygroma, an abscess, or accumulation of air.

6. The influences of narcosis, surgical procedures, and various drugs (amyl nitrite, histamine, papaverine, adrenaline, acetylcholine, and others), and oxygen or carbon dioxide.

7. The influences of the sympathetic nervous system, carotid sinus, and of changes in position as they affect circulation in the brain.

8. The influences of aura and of focal and generalized epileptic seizures.

9. The consequences of inflammatory and degenerative disorders of the brain.

10. The effect that a specific type of sensory stimulation (e.g. acoustic, visual) can have on brain circulation.

11. Consequences of mental disorders, especially during specific hallucinations.

12. The effects on the circulation of drugs applied in psychiatry.

13. The effects of drugs used for inducing experimental psychosis or specific hallucinations.

14. The influence of isolated psychological testing with elimination of additional stimulation.

15. Correlation between the biological and chronological age and memory and performance of subjects.

The rheographic method may also be used, as shown by our pilot studies, for monitoring the changes in the cerebral tissue between the intracerebral electrodes. This technique may demonstrate the functional circulatory variations in a small area inside the brain.

Rheoencephalography, especially the regional method described above, may supplement other clinical and neurophysiological data and can help in their interpretation and possibly their explanation.

REFERENCES

Adey, W. R., Kado, R. T., & Didio, J. Impedance measurements in brain tissue of animals using microvolt signals. *Expl. Neurol.,* 1962, *5*: 47–66.

Atzler, E., & Lehmann, G. Ueber ein neues Verfahren zur Darstellung der Herztaetigkeit (Dielektrographie). *Arbeitsphysiologie,* 1932, *5*: 536–680.

Auinger, W., Kaindl, F., & Neumayr, A. Ueber die Brauchbarkeit der Schaedelreographie am Menschen insbesondere zur Beurteilung des Effektes therapeutischer Massnahmen auf das Verhalten der Gefaesse. *Z. Kreislaufforsch.,* 1953, *42*: 104–116.

Birzis, L., & Tachibana, S. Local cerebral impedance and blood flow during sleep and arousal. *Expl. Neurol.,* 1964, *9*: 269–285.

Cremer, M. Uber die Registrierung mechanischer Vorgange auf electrischen Wege speziell mit Hilfe des Saitengalvanometers und Saitenelektrometers. *Münch. med. Wschr.,* 1907, *54*: 1629. (a)

Cremer, M. Ueber das Saitenelektrometer und seine Anwendung in der Electrophysiologie *Münch. med. Wschr.*, 1907, *54*: 505–507. (b)

Dobner, E. Die Schaedelrheographie als Methode zur Diagnose orthostatischer Kreislauf stoerungen. *Elektro-Med.*, 1958, *3*: 169–174.

Donzelot, E., Meyer-Heine, S. Milovanovich, J. B., & Dreyfus, B. L'etude de la circu lation cerebrale par la diagraphie transcranienne. *Archs Mal. Coeur*, 1951, *44*: 219–225

DuBois, D., & Nims, L. F. An improved impedance plethysmograph. *NRC Committee Aviat Med. Rep.*, 1945, No. 439, 1–4.

Dulbecco, R., & Palomba, G. Osservazioni su di una curva di volume del cuore umano: a pletismodiagramma. *Cuore Circul.*, 1938, *22*: 86, 153.

Fasano, V. H., Angelino, P. F., Braguzzi, E., & Braggi, G. Considerations sur le rheographi cranienne. *Neuro-Chirurgie*, 1961, *7*: 202–209.

Friedmann, G. Der Wert der Schaedelrheographie. *Arzneimittel. Wschr.*, 1955, *24*: 553–556

Gangler, J. Experimentelle Unterschungen ueber den elektrischen Widerstand der Hirnsub stanz bei Commotio und Compressio Cerebri. *Dt. Z. Chir.*, 1937, *299*: 508–528.

Garbini, G. C., & Picchio, A. A. *La Reografia.* Bologna: Bologna Medica, 1958.

Gastaut, H., Rodler, R., Lechner, H., Bostem, F., & Naquet, R. A propos d'une nouvelle methode de rheoencephalographie. In *Medical electronics*. London: Ileffe and Sons, Ltd. 1960. Pp. 160–168.

Gougerot, L., & Marstal, N. Rheoencephalographie en cercle pointe. *C. r. Séanc. Soc. Biol.* 1960, *154*: 2190–2191.

Grant, F. C. Localization of brain tumors by determination of the electrical resistance of the growth. *J. Am. med. Ass.*, 1923, *81*: 2169–2171.

Hatakeyama, I. Electrocapacitography. A method for recording changes in volume of body and organs. *Jap. J. Physiol.*, 1959, *9*: 387–393.

Hatakeyama, I., & Aizawa, H. Electrocapacitographical studies on the blood circulation of human head. *Yokohama med. Bull.*, 1962, *13*: 1–8.

Holzer, W., & Polzer, K. Methodik der Rheocardiographie. *Wien. med. Wschr.*, 1946, *96*: 316–319.

Holzer, W., Polzer, K., & Marko, H. *Rheokardiographie.* Wien: Maudrich, 1945.

Horton, J. W., & Van Ravenswaay, A. C. Electrical impedance of the human body. *J. Frank-lin Inst.*, 1935, *220*: 557–572.

Jenkner, F. L. Ueber den Wert des Schaedelrheogrammes fuer die Diagnose cerebraler Ge-faesstoerungen. *Wien. klin. Wschr.*, 1957, *69*: 619–620.

Jenkner, F. L. Rheoencephalography. A method for diagnosing cerebrovascular changes. *Confinia neurol.*, 1959, *19*: 1–20.

Jenkner, F. L. *Rheoencephalography.* Springfield, Ill.: Charles C Thomas, 1962. (a)

Jenkner, F. L. Ergebnisse der fortlaufenden Beobachtungen der Hirndurchblutung mittels Rheoencephalographie. *Neurochirurgia*, 1962, *5*: 19–38. (b)

Kaindl, F., Kraus, H., & Praetan, J. Rheographische Durchblutungskontrolle des Schaedels bei Eingriffen an der Arteria carotis. *Zentbl. Neurochir.*, 1955, *15*: 6–11.

Kaindl, F., Polzer, K., & Schuhfried, F. *Rheographie (Eine Methode zur Beurteilung peri-pherer Gefaesse).* Darmstadt: D. Steinkopff, 1959. (a)

Kaindl, F., Polzer, K., & Schuhfried, F. Die Amplitudenauswertung des Rheogramms. *Wien. Z. inn. Med.* 1959, *40*: 175–178. (b)

Kaufman, S. S., Nims, L. F., Nyboer, J., & Somberg, H. M. New application of the im-pedance plethysmograph. *NRC Committee Aviat. Med. Rep.*, 1944.

Kedrov, A. A., & Naumenko, A. L. Certain peculiarities of the regulation of intracrania circulation. *Fiziol. Zh. SSSR*, 1951, *37*: 431–438.

Kedrov, A. A., & Naumenko, A. L. *Physiological problems of the intracranial circulation with their clinical interpretation.* Moscow: Medgiz, 1954.

Kety, S. S., & Schmidt, C. F. The effects of altered arterial tensions of carbon dioxide and oxygen on cerebral blood flow and cerebral oxygen consumption of normal young man *J. clin. Invest.*, 1948, *27*: 484–492. (a)

Kety, S. S., & Schmidt, C. F. The nitrous oxide method for the quantitative determination of cerebral blood flow in man; theory, procedure and normal values. *J. clin. Invest.*, 1948 *27*: 476–483. (b)

Kunert, W. Ueber die Grundlagen der Schaedelrheographie. *Z. klin. Med.*, 1959, *156*: 94–116

Kunert, W. Fortschritte der Schaedelrheographie. *Z. Kreislaufforsch.*, 1961, *50*: 572–580.

Lechner, H., Jenkner, F. L., Rodler, H., & Heppner, F. A new method of rheoencephalography. In J. S. Meyer & H. Gastaut (Eds.), *Cerebral anoxia and electroencephalogram.* Springfield, Ill.: Charles C Thomas, 1961. Pp. 214–222.

Lihotsky. Weitere Erfahrungen der Hirn-Rheometrie nach. *Zentbl. Chir.*, 1926, *153*: 452–458.

Luessenhop, A. J., Gibbs, M., & Velasquez, A. C. Cerebrovascular response to emboli. *Archs Neurol.*, *Chicago*, 1962, *7*: 264–274.

Mann, H. Study of peripheral circulation by means of alternating current bridge. *Proc. Soc. exp. Biol. Med.*, 1937, *36*: 670–673.

Mann, H. The capacigraph, instrument for recording cardiac output. *J. Mt Sinai Hosp.*, 1954, *20*: 360–364.

Martin, F., Karbowski, K., & Vaney, P. Rheoencephalography. II. A polygraphic study of some changes in cardiac rhythm. *Schweiz. Arch. Neurol. Psychiat.*, 1963, *92*: 93–104.

Matsuno, K. Dieektrographische Untersuchungen ueber die Herzwirkung der Kohleusaure. *Arbeitsphysiologie*, 1935, *8*: 610–615.

Merlen, J. F. Exploracion de las arterias cerebrales por la reografia. *Angiología*, 1955, *7*: 298–305.

Merrem, G., & Niebeling, H. G. Ergebnisse der Hirngewebswiderstandsmessung. *Zentbl. Neurochir.*, 1953, *13*: 193–206.

Meyer, A. W., & Schlueter, D. Apparat zur Bestimmung des elektrischen Widerstandes im Gehirn. *Zentbl. Neurochir.*, 1924, *48*: 1824-1827.

Morioka, Y. Etudes sur les dielectrogrammes. *Nippon junk. Gak.*, 1937, *1*: 397–399.

Moskalenko, Y. E., & Naumenko. A. I. changes of the electrical conductivity of blood during its movement. *Bull. exp. Biol. Med. U.S.S.R.*, 1959 2: 77-81.

Moskalenko, Y. E., & Naumenko, A. I. Hemodynamics of cerebral circulation. In E. Simonson, & T. H. McGavack (Eds.), *Cerebral ischemia.* Springfield, Ill.: Charles C Thomas, 1964. Pp. 21-61.

Niebeling, H. G. & Thieme, M. Technik der Hirngewebswinderstandsmessung. *Zentbl. Neurochir.*, 1953, *13:* 206-211.

Nyboer, J. *Electrical impedance plethysmography.* Springfield, Ill.: Charles C Thomas, 1959.

Nyboer, J. Plethysmography: impedance. Electrical impedance plethysmograph. In O. Glasser (Ed.), *Medical physics, Vol. 3.* Chicago: Yearbook Publishers, 1960. Pp. 459-471.

Pauli, W. E., & Redwitz, E. Bemerkungen zur Konstruktion und Verwendung der Meyer Schluetterschen Sonde. *Dt. Z. Chir.*, 1925, *193*: 343-348.

Polzer, K., & Schuhfried, F. Rheographische Untersuchungen am Schaedel. *Wien Z. NervHeilk.*, 1950, *3*: 395-399.

Polzer, K., Schuhfried, F., & Heeger, H. Rheography. *Br. Heart J.*, 1960, *22*: 140-148.

Posteli, T., Garbini, G. C., & Picchio, A. A. Angiological exploration of a new clinical significance: peripheral and visceral photoplethysmography and rheography. *Minerva med. mediterr.*, 1957, *48*: 2297-2301.

Ranck, J. B. Specific impedance of the cerebral cortex during spreading depression. *Expl Neurol.*, 1964, *9*: 1–16.

Rosa, L. Beitraege zur Kreislaufdynamik auf Grund radiocardiographischer Untersuchungen. *Z. Kreislaufforsch.*, 1940, *32*: 377. (a)

Rosa, L. Diagnostische Anwendung des Kurzwellenfeldes in der Herz und Kreislaufpathologie: Radiocardiography. *Z. Kreislaufforsch.*, 1940, *32*: 118. (b)

Rosendal, T. *The conducting properties of the human organism to alternating current.* These, Copenhague: J. Jorgensen & Co., 1940, Pp. 1–192.

Schmitt, O. H. Lead vectors and transfer impedance. *Ann. N.Y. Acad. Sci.*, 1957, *65*: 1092–1109.

Schmitz, W., & Schaefer, H. Die zeitlichen Beziehungen der Taetigkeitsaenderungen des Herzens. *Z. Kreislaufforsch.*, 1935, *27*: 513–522, 550–569.

Schufried, F. Rheographie. *Aztl. Forsch.*, 1961, *15*: 455–462.

Schwan, H. P. Electrical properties of body tissues and impedance plethysmography. *I.R.E. Trans. med. Electron.*, 1955, *3*: 31–46.

Simonson, E. Effect of age on the changes of extracranial circulation during hypoxia. *Circulation Res.*, 1961, *9*: 18–22.

Spiegel, E. A., Henny, G. S., Wycis, H. T., & Spiegel, A. M. Impedance changes in cerebrum following concussion. *Proc. Soc. exp. Biol. Med.*, 1945, *60*: 237–238.

Spunda, C. H. Ueber Wert und Anwendung der Schaedelreographie. *Wien. klin. Wschr.* 1955, *67*: 788–792.

Ziemnowicz, S. A. R. The rheographic method applied for research on ocular circulation *Invest. Ophthal.*, 1962, *1*: 428.

Ziemnowicz, S. A. R. The differential rheoencephalography for study of regional circulation in cerebrovascular disease. *Neurology meeting abstract, Neurology, Minneap.*, 1963 *13*: 348. (a)

Ziemnowicz, S. A. R. Techniques of differential rheograms for monitoring the regional circulation in the brain and in the eye. *Conference Internationale d'Electronique Medicale Liege, July 22-26, 1963*. In F. Bostem (Ed.), *Medical electronics*. Liege: Desoer, 1965.(b

Ziemnowicz, S. A. R. Rheographic differential method for evaluation of cerebral and ocula circulation in cardiac and cerebrovascular disease. *Excerpta Medica Int. Congress Series No. 57, Copenhagen, August 11-16, 1963*. (c)

Ziemnowicz, S. A. R. Technics of regional rheography for monitoring the circulation in the brain and in the eye. *Proc. Conf. Med. Biol., Baltimore*, 1963, *16*: 96–97. (d)

Ziemnowicz, S.A.R. Diagnostic value of rheographic studies in cardiac and cerebrovascula diseases. *Proceedings abstract of The American College of Physicians, First Sectiona Meeting (Midwest) Detroit, Michigan, November 21-23, 1963*. (e)

Ziemnowicz, S. A. R. Rheographic regional method for evaluation of cerebral and ocula circulation in cardiac and cerebrovascular disease. *J. Am. Geriat. Soc.*, 1964, *13*: 35-43

Ziemnowicz, S. A. R. The present status of standard and regional rheoencephalography (REG). In C. H. Millikan, R. G. Siekert, & J. P. Whisnant (Eds.), *Cerebral vascula diseases— Fourth Conference, 1964*, New York: Grune & Stratton, 1965, Pp. 74-80 83-85, 111, 126.

Ziemnowicz, S. A. R., & Masucci, E. F. Evaluation of cerebrovascular disease by rheoenceph-alography, *Va med. Res. Conf.* 1962, 135.

ADDITIONAL READING

Adey, W. R., Kado, R. T., Didio, J., & Schlindler, W. J. Impedance changes in cerebral tissue accompanying a learned discriminative performance in the cat. *Expl. Neurol.*, 1963, 7 259-281.

Aetzler, E., & Lehmann, G. Eine neue Methode der Plethysmographie am Menschen. Bemer-kungen zur der Arbeit von L. Asher and E. Hopf. *Klin. Wschr.*, 1935, *14*: 1581.

Aizawa, H. On the electrocapacitogram of head. *Jap. J. Physiol.*, 1959, *21*: 652.

Aizawa, T., & Hamaya, S. Cerebral sclerosis and cerebral circulation. *Jap. Heart J.*, 1961 *2*: 133-146.

Aizawa, T., Tazaki, Y., & Gotoh, F. Cerebral circulation in cerebrovascular disease. *Wlc Neurol.*, 1961, *2*: 635-640.

Asher, L., & Hopf, E. Eine neue Methode der Plethysmographie am Menschen. *Klin. Wschr.* 1935, *14*: 1365.

Beer, V. O., Schlegel, H. J., & Schley, W. Die Messung durchblutungsabhaengiger Scheinleit wertsaenderungen in menschlichen Schaedel. (The measurements of changes in the a.c conductance in the human skull that depend on the degree of blood perfusion). *Natur wissenschaften*, 1956, *43*: 49–51.

Bertha, H., Heppner, F., Jenkner, F. L., Lechner, H., Rodler, R. Zur deutung des Schaed-elrheogrammes (Investigation of the value of skull rheograms). *Zentbl. Neurochir.* 1955, *15*: 257–266.

Brobeil, A., Härter, O., Herrmann, E., & Nilsson, N. J. Messungen von cerebralen Kreis-laufzeiten am Menschen und ihre Beziehung zur Gehirndurchblutung. *Acta physiol scand.*, 1957, *40*: 121–129.

Burch, G. E. Digital rheoplethysmography. *Circulation*, 1956, *13*: 641–653.

Curro, D. B., & Pavoni, M. Rheoencephalographic findings in patients affected by cerebrovas-cular diseases. *Riv. Neurobiol.*, 1963, *9*: 815–837.

Czernik, A. Badania reograficzne narzadu krazenia Postepy. *Kardiol. pol.*, 1957, *5*: 108–133.

Esposito, A. The cerebral rheogram in the newborn. *Clin. Obstet. Gynec.*, 1963, *65*: 357–366.

Forbes, H. S., & Wolf, H. G. Cerebral circulation: vasomotor control of cerebral vessels. *Archs Neurol. Psychiat.*, 1928, *19*: 1057–1068.

Gastaut, H., Rodler, R., Lechner, H., Bostem, F., & Naquet, R. Premiers resultats cliniques obtenus avec une methode perfectionnée de rheoencephalography. *Path. Biol., Paris*, 1959, *7*: 1–10.

Geddes, L. A., & Hoff, H. E. The measurement of physiologic events by electrical impedance: a review. *Am. J. Med. Electron.*, 1964, *3*: 16–27.

Geddes, L. A., et al. Rheoencephalography. *Cardiovasc. Res. Center Bull.*, 1964, *2*: 00.

Gougerot, L., Foncin, J. F., & Marstal, N. La validite de la rheoencephalographie. In *Medical electronics*, London: Ileffe and Sons, Ltd., 1960. Pp. 109–176.

Gurdjian, E. S., & Webster, J. E. Digital carotid artery compression with occlusion of the anterior cerebral artery. *Neurology, Minneap.*, 1957, *7*: 635–640.

Gurdjian, E. S., Webster, J. E., Hardy, W. G., & Lindner, D. W. Nonexistence of the so-called cerebral from of carotid sinus syncope. *Neurology, Minneap.*, 1958, *8*: 818.

Horton, J. W., Van Ravenswaay, A. C., Hertz, S., & Thorn, G. W. The clinical significance of electrical impedance determination in thyroid disorders. *Endocrinology*, 1936, *20*: 72–80.

Ingvar, D. H., & Soderberg, U. A new method for measuring cerebral blood flow in relation to the electroencephalogram. *Electroenceph. clin. Neurophysiol.*, 1956, *8*: 403–412.

Ingvar, D. H., & Soderberg, U. Direct method for the measurement of cerebral blood flow. *Nature*, 1956, *340*: 177–339.

Jenkner, F. L. Das Rheoencephalogram: ein wertvolles Hilfsmittel fuer die Diagnosestellung bei akutem und chronischem Subduralhaematom. *Wien. med. Wschr.*, 1958, *37*; 764–767.

Jochweds, B., Czernik, A., & Serzysko, W. Studies on the effect of euphyllin on cranial rheogram in patients with cerebral atherosclerosis. *Polskie Archwm Med. wewn.*, 1960, *30*: 816–817.

Jochweds, B., Czernik, A., Serzysko, W. Z., Niszczynska, M. Studies on diagnostic value of cranial rheography in the detection of vascular changes in the so-called primary diabetis in young subjects. *Polskie Archwm Med. wewn.*, 1960, *30*: 920–921.

Kaindl, F. Rheographic peripherer Arterien. Eine neue Methode zur Beurteilung arterieller Gefaesse. *Arch. Kreislaufforsch.*, 1954, *20*: 247–286.

Kedrov, A. A., & Naumenko, A. L. Attempt at a quantitative evaluation of central and peripheral circulation by an electrometric method. *Klin. Med. Wien.*, 1948, *26*: 5–32.

Kedrov, A. A., & Naumenko, A. I. Some characteristics of the regulation of intracranial circulation. *NASA tech. transl.*, 1963, F–161.

Kedrov, A. A., & Naumenko, A. I. The mechanism of intracranial circulation. *NASA tech. transl.*, 1963, F–159.

Kety, S. S. Circulation and metabolism of human brain in health and disease. *Am. J. Med.*, 1950, *8*: 205–217.

Kety, S. S. The cerebral circulation. In R. McDowall (Ed.), *The control of the circulation of the blood*. London: Wm. Dawson and Sons, 1956.

Kety, S. S. The general metabolism of the brain in vivo. In W. D. Richter (Ed.), *Metabolism of the nervous system*. New York: Pergamon Press, 1957.

Kety, S. S. The cerebral circulation. In J. Field, & H. W. Magoun (Eds.), *Handbook of physiology, Section 1, Vol. 3*. Washington, D. C.: American Physiological Society, 1960. Pp. 1751–1760.

Krygicz, H. Diagnostische Moglichkeiten der Rheoangiographie. *Wien. Z. inn. Med.*, 1960, *41*: 281–290.

Kunert, W. Rheographische Messungen in Vertebralis-stromgebiet. *Nervenarzt*, 1961, *32*: 34–38.

Lassen, N. A. Cerebral blood flow and oxygen consumption in man determined by the inert gas diffusion method. Copenhagen: Christtreus Bogtrykkeri, 1958.

Lassen, N. A., & Ingvar, D. H. Regional blood flow measurement in man. *Archs Neurol., Chicago*, 1963, *9*: 615–622.

Lifshitz, K. Rheoencephalography with the use of averaging techniques. *Proc. Conf. on Eng. Med. Biol. Baltimore*, 1963, *16*: 98–99.

Lifshitz, K. Rheoencephalography. *J. nerv. ment. Dis.*, 1963, *136*: 388–389; *137*: 285–296.

McDonald, D. H. *Blood flow in arteries*. Baltimore: Williams & Wilkins, 1960, P. 39.

McHenry, L. C. Rheoencephalography: a clinical appraisal. *Neurology, Minneap.*, 1965, *15*: 507–517.

Martin, F., Vaney, P., & Karbowski, K. Rheoencephalography. I. A preliminary note on an original 6-channel apparatus. *Schweiz. Arch. Neurol. Psychiat.*, 1963, *91*: 446–457.

Matsumoto, H., & Marson, A. C. Cortical cellular phenomena in experimental epilepsy: ictal manifestations. *Expl Neurol.*, 1964, *9*: 305–326.

Meyer, A. W. Methodezum Auffinden von Hirntumoren bei der Trepanation durch elektrische Widerstandsmessung. *Zentbl. Chir.*, *48*: 1824–1826.

Meyer, A. W. Hirn-Rheometrie, eine Methode zum Auffinden von Hirntumoren. *Dt. med. Wschr.*, 1928, *54*: 1366–1367.

Meyer, J. S. Changes in cerebral blood flow resulting from vascular occlusion. In W. S. Fields (Ed.), *Pathogenesis and treatment of cerebrovascular disease*. Springfield, Ill.: Charles C Thomas, 1961.

Meyer, J. S., & Gastaut, H. *Cerebral anoxia and the electroencephalogram*. Springfield, Ill.: Charles C Thomas, 1961.

Meyer, J. S., Gotoh, F., Tazaki, Y., Hamaguchi, K., Ishikawa, S., Nouailhat, F., & Simon, L. Regional cerebral blood flow and metabolism in vivo. Effects of anoxia, hypoglycemia, ischemia, acidosis, alkalosis, and alterations of blood PCO_2. *Archs Neurol., Chicago*, 1962, *7*: 560–581.

Novack, P., Shenkin, H. A., Bortin, L., Goluboff, B., & Soffe, A. M. The effects of carbon dioxide inhalation upon the cerebral blood flow and cerebral oxygen consumption in vascular disease. *J. clin. Invest.*, 1953, *32*: 696–702.

Nyboer, J. Electrical impedance plethysmography; physical and physiologic approach to peripheral vascular study. *Circulation*, 1950, *2*: 811–821.

Nyboer, J. D., Bagno, S., Barnett, A., & Helsey, R. Radiocardiograms: Electrical impedance changes of the heart in relation to electrocardiograms and heart sounds. *J. clin. Invest.*, 1960, *19*: 773–963.

Nyboer, J., & Watson, T. R. Constant mass displacement ballistocardiography and electrical impedance plethysmography. *J. Lab. clin. Med.*, 1955, *46*: 270–284.

Obrist, W. D., & Henry, C. E. Relation of EEG to cerebral blood flow and metabolism in old age. *Electroenceph. clin. Neurophysiol.*, 1963, *15*: 610–619.

Orlandi, G., Garbini, G. C., & Gentili, G. Differential diagnosis of vascular from neoplastic affections of the brain, as resulting from rheographic studies. *Minerva med. mediterr.*, 1957, *48*: 3225–3228.

Perez-Borja, C., & Meyer, J. S. A critical evaluation of rheoencephalography in control subjects and in proven cases of cerebrovascular disease. *J. Neurol. Neurosurg Psychiat.*, 1964, *27*: 66–72.

Pratesi, F., Nuti, A., & Sciagra, A. Cranial rheography: functional test in the diagnosis of vascular disorders of the brain. *Minerva med. mediterr.*, 1957, *48*: 3223–3224.

Ranck, J. B. Specific impedance of rabbit cerebral cortex. *Expl Neurol.*, 1963, *7*: 144–174.

Report AD 429 848 U.S. Naval Missile Center, Point Magu, California. On electrical impedance plethysmograph. Experimental results are included to show that the device can provide an indirect index of systolic pressures, changes in vascular volume, heart rate and rhythm and respiratory cycles.

Robinson, B. W., & Tompkins, H. E. Impedance method for localizing brain structures. *Archs Neurol., Chicago*, 1964, *10*: 563–574.

Schaeffer, H. *Elektrophysiologie*, Vols. 1 and 2. Wien: Deuticke 1940, 1942.

Scheinberg, P. Application of blood flow measurements to future investigations. In C. H. Millikan, R. G. Siekert, & J. P. Whisnant (Eds.), *Cerebral vascular diseases—Third Conference*. New York: Grune & Stratton, 1961.

Schmitt, O. H. The cerebral circulation: some gerontological considerations. In E. Simonson & T. H. McGavack (Eds.), *Cerebral ischemia*. Springfield, Ill.: Charles C. Thomas, 1964. Pp. 5–21.

Schwan, H. P. Electrode polarization and its influence on the determination of dielectric properties of solutions and biological material. *Z. Naturf.*, 1951, *3*: 121.

Schwan, H. P., & Kay, C. F. Specific resistance of body tissues. *Circulation Res.*, 1956, *4*: 666–670.

Schwan, H. P., & Sittel, K. Wheatstone Bridge for admittance determination of highly conducting materials at low frequencies. *Trans. A.I.E.F. (Communications and Electronics)*, 1953. 114.

Seipel, J. H., Ziemnowicz, S. A. R., & O'Doherty, D. C. Cranial impedance plethysmography as a method of detection of cerebrovascular disease. In E. Simonson & T. H. McGavack (Eds.), *Cerebral ischemia*. Springfield, Ill.: Charles C. Thomas, 1964. Pp. 162–180.

Serra, P., & Urso, L. Osservazioni rheografiche sulla circulazione cerebrale in corso di narcosi *Minerva anest.*, 1956, *22*: 86–90.

Sigman, E., Kolin, A., Katz, L. N., & Jachnin, K. Effect of motion on electrical conductivity of the blood. *Am. J. Physiol.*, 1937, *118*: 708–719.

Simonson, E. In E. Simonson & T. H. McGavack (Eds.), *Cerebral ischemia*. Springfield, Ill.: Charles C Thomas, 1964.

Sokoloff, L. Factors regulating the total regional circulation of the brain. *Proc. 3rd Microcirculatory Conf.*, 1958, Pp. 89–88.

Sokoloff, L. The action of drugs on cerebral circulation. *Pharmac. Rev.*, 1959, *11*: 1–85.

Sokoloff, L. Metabolism of the central nervous system in vivo. In J. Field & H. W. Magoun (Eds.), *Handbook of physiology, Section 1, Vol. 3*. Washington, D. C.: American Physiological Society, 1960. Pp. 1843–1864.

Soulairsc, A., Gougerot, L., & Marstal, N. Intérêt de la rhéoencéphalographie dans l'étude des affections mentales artériopathigenes. *Annls méd. psychol.*, 1961, *119*: 352–366.

Van Harreveld, A. I. Water and electrolyte distribution in central nervous tissue. *Fedn Proc. Fedn Am. Socs exp. Biol.*, 1962, *21*:

Van Harreveld, A. I., Hooper, N. K., & Ausick, J. T. Brain electrolytes and cortical impedance. *Am. J. Physiol.*, 1961, *201*: 139–193.

Van Harreveld, A. I., & Schade, J. P. Changes in the electrical conductivity of cerebral cortex during seizure activity. *Expl Neurol.*, 1962, *5*: 383–400.

Viciu, E., Safirescu, T., & Bulandra, C. The clinical value of rheography. *Medna internă*, 1962, *14*: 241–254.

Ziemnowicz, S. A. R. Regional rheoencephalography (R.R.E.G.) applied in aeromedical selection and as an early warning device. Preprints *13th Internat. Cong. Aviation & Space Med., Dublin, Ireland (1-4) 1964*.

Ziemnowicz, S. A. R. Rheoencephalographic study after craniocerebral trauma; diagnostic and prognostic evaluation. *Proc. 8th Internat. Cong. Neurol. Vienna, Austria. Excerpta Med.*, 1965, *94:* 72.

Ziemnowicz, S. A. R. Cerebral and cardiovascular aging studied by the new method of regional rheoencephalography. *Proc. 7th Internat. Congr. Gerontology, Vienna, Austria*, 1966, *7:* 166–167.

Ziemnowicz, S. A. R. From pilot selection to stroke prevention. *Internat. Meeting on Aerospace Medicine, Sydney, Australia, 1966*.

Ziemnowicz, S. A. R., McWilliams, J., Jr., & Kucharski, W. E. Remarks on electrical field distribution in standard, hemispherical REG and in regional rheoencephalography (RREG). *Proc. 17th Conf. Eng. Med. & Biol., Cleveland, Ohio*, 1964, *17*: 29.

Ziemnowicz, S. A. R., McWilliams, J., Jr., & Kucharski, W. E. Conductivity versus frequency in human and feline cerebrospinal fluid. *Proc. Conf. Eng. Med. & Biol., Cleveland, Ohio*, 1964, *17*: 108.

7
Measurement of Blood Flow and Blood Pressure

FREDERICK OLMSTED, B.A.

History of the measurement of blood pressure extends to at least the first experiment of Curate Stephen Hales in 1711 (1733). Hales' experiment consisted of having "caused a mare to be tied down—neither very lean, not yet lusty; having laid open the crural artery about three inches from her belly, I inserted into it a brass pipe—fixed to a glass tube nine feet in length—," and blood was allowed to rise in the tube "eight feet three inches," a mean pressure of about 200 mm Hg, which is hypertensive, but the experiment was not quite physiological, to say nothing of its value in relation to psychology. The early experiments on blood flow, beyond the drastic and self-defeating method of exsanguination into a calibrated container, were conducted in anesthetized animals, again under hardly natural conditions.

It is not the intention of this chapter to present a complete or detailed history and enumeration of techniques, but rather to trace the development and describe the status of methods that now seem to be useful in the determination of arterial pressure and blood flow in man and animals that could be of value in conscious subjects. This implies, in the ideal situation, the absence of anesthesia (except local), pain, awkward or restrained postures, sedation, and as far as possible, lack of awareness by the subject of the process of measurement.

Present methods fall into two categories; the intermittent, such as the Riva-Rocci cuff, Korotkoff sound determination of arterial pressure, and the dye dilution technique of blood flow measurement, in contrast to continuous measurement by intra-arterial catheter and implanted blood flow probe, the last limited to animals. The latter two techniques are quite satisfactory, because they do not disturb the subject physically.

Measurement of arterial pressure became more practical with Poiseuille's invention of the U tube mercury manometer in 1826 (1828). Over the next century the frequency response of recording methods was improved, reaching a satisfactory level in the optical, stiff membrane manometer of Hamilton,

Brewer, and Brotman (1934). Diaphragm displacement was small enough to produce frequencies of over 100 cps. However, this required surgery, rigid cannulae, anesthesia, photographic recording in darkness, and was generally inconvenient. The modern age of blood pressure determination came with Lambert and Wood's (1947) use of the unbonded strain gauge transducer and carrier wave electronic amplification. It was then possible, because of still smaller diaphragm displacement, to use smaller needles and small bore tubing to work with simple vascular punctures and record graphically in daylight, and to have the subject connected by only a light, flexible electric cable.

There are several varieties of contemporary direct pressure transducers, the most common being the unbonded strain gauge bridge (Statham) and the variable reactance transducer (Sanborn). These are connected to blood vessels by needles or semirigid miniature tubing introduced through a special thin wall needle which can be withdrawn over the tubing or which splits in half when removed from the vessel. These transducers can also be connected to intravascular and intracardiac catheters. The most comfortable of the direct methods is that of the semirigid tubing and a small transducer attached to one arm. Long cables allow considerable freedom of movement.

A third design of the pressure transducer is the capacitance type in which pressure moves a very rigid diaphragm that is one side of a condenser in a radio frequency bridge. One version (Lilly, Legallais, & Cherry, 1947) has the smallest displacement of all such manometers, and consequently the highest frequency response. It can be used with very small bore needles and tubing, but is somewhat unstable as to base line because of a thermal effect on the spacing of the measuring capacitor.

Indirect methods that are automatic are based on the inflatable arm cuff and some device to detect arterial pulsations distal to the cuff. This transducer, in the more reliable machines, is a microphone held over the brachial artery to sense Korotkoff sounds. Other machines use a finger pulse transducer, usually satisfactory with the normal subject, but not for the patient in a precarious cardiovascular state, for the first thing that disappears in shock is the peripheral pulse. The general principle of the automatic indirect blood pressure machine is that arm cuff pressure is recorded during gradual cuff deflation along with the first systolic sounds and the disappearance of the diastolic ones. The finger pulse appearance may substitute for the systolic sounds, and time of maximum pulsation as the diastolic end point, although this technique is not nearly as accurate as that using a microphone.

Several automatic indirect arterial blood pressure machines have been constructed and have even appeared on the market, but most now gather dust in some back room. A promising and practical recent device was reported by Hinman, Engel, and Bickford (1962). This is a portable device worn by the subject and includes a miniature tape recorder for preservation of determinations. The subject's only task is to inflate an arm cuff above systolic pressure.

The tape recorder turns on automatically and records cuff pressure and the changing Korotkoff sounds. The cuff deflates automatically in linear fashion, and the tape recorder turns off when pressure falls to 50 mm Hg. Several periods of recording in humans in their daily routine have shown rather wide variations in arterial pressure with various levels of activity.

Although the electrocardiogram is often telemetered (Sperry, Gadsen, Rodriquez, & Bach, 1961), only the beginnings of this have taken place in arterial pressure (blood flow telemetry is more advanced). Arterial pressures have been transmitted from baboons in a large exercise compound. The transducer was a miniature capsule containing a solid state strain gauge bridge. The entire pressure gauge was implanted in the distal arch of the aorta, and wires brought out under the skin to the top of the head. A plastic helmet worn by the animal contained an FM transmitter for both arterial pressure and flow which will be described later.

The unbonded strain gauge pressure transducers and the reactance transducers now available are very reliable, demonstrating no noticeable base-line drift or sensitivity change over many hours use. This reliability depends not only on the transducer itself but also on the carrier wave preamplifier and recorder driver amplifier. The Statham gauge and Sanborn recorder have been known to be within 1% of original settings for days at a time. The only care that must be taken is to avoid bubbles of air when filling these manometers. As a precaution, these gauges should be calibrated once a day against a mercury manometer or an aneroid manometer of proven accuracy.

The pressure transducers operate by being energized (excited) by an alternating current of from 600 to 2400 cps. The small changes in resistance or reactance brought about by fluctuations in blood pressure can then be conveniently amplified by an AC amplifier, and then demodulated and filtered (the carrier excitation wave removed) to a DC physiological signal for recording. The electronic carrier wave preamplifier for the pressure gauge is furnished at least by the two recording companies. Sanborn has its own pressure transducer (reactance type) and a special carrier amplifier for use with it that is somewhat less in price than their standard carrier wave preamplifier for use with strain gauge transducers.

Measurements of Blood Flow

Some of the earliest determinations of blood flow were also made by Curate Stephen Hales who used the calibrated exsanguination bucket, a self-defeating procedure since the method of measurement seriously affects the flow itself. Ludwig's (1861) strohmur was the first scientific and productive measuring instrument for determination of blood flow. Blood was displaced hydraulically at a rate proportional to flow velocity. This device was never highly popular because of clotting problems and questions as to its accuracy. Recently a highly improved apparatus was devised by Mellander and Rushmer (1960) which consists of a small thermistor heated by a minute resistance coil. A feedback circuit controlled the heating coil to maintain the thermistor bead at a constant temperature; thus heating coil current (power) was exponentially proportional to flow rate. Even more recently an ultrasonic Doppler effect transducer has been placed on a catheter tip (McLeod, 1964). All of these methods require some means of measuring the diameter of the blood vessel, they sample only a point of the flow cross section, and must be positioned in the vessel's center. The strohmur and the thermistor devices have been on the shelf for some time, while the Doppler effect probe on a catheter tip is still in the laboratory. Each of these methods, with catheterization, would be satisfactory for measuring changes of blood flow or cardiac output in conscious subjects if the technique were in further stages of development.

Measurement of Cardiac Output

The first useful indirect (nondestructive but intermittent) measurements of cardiac output were by the Fick method (1870). This technique depends on the arteriovenous (A-V) differences in oxygen or carbon dioxide levels, and the respiratory consumption of O_2 or output of CO_2. Venous blood must be mixed. Arterial blood, with the subjects breathing O_2, is assumed saturated at 95%. The formula is as follows.

$$\text{Cardiac output} = -\frac{O_2 \text{ Consumption (ml)}}{\text{A-V } O_2 \text{ difference (ml \%)}} \times 100 = \text{L/min}$$

It is obvious that the amount of blood moved is proportional to oxygen consumed and oxygen lost from the bloodstream. The technique is somewhat distracting, as respiration is from a spirometer, and the right auricle should be catheterized to obtain mixed venous blood.

More modern is the Stewart-Hamilton dye dilution method (Hamilton, Moore, Kinsman, & Spurling, 1928). This depends on measurement of the arterial dye concentration curve over a known time; the dye is injected intravenously or ideally into the right auricle for complete mixing. The arterial concentration is determined photometrically by drawing arterial blood through a cuvette illuminated by a particular wave length of light (that absorbed by the dye) directed onto a photodetector (photomultiplier tube). The resultant curve is recorded and planimetered by hand or by computer to give the mean arterial dye concentration. Then cardiac output is represented by the amount of dye dilution and the time of the mean concentration curve.

$$\text{Cardiac output} = \frac{\text{injected dye}}{\text{mean arterial dye concentration} \times \text{time of arterial curve}}$$

An alternate to direct sampling is the curve recorded by a photoelectric ear piece (ear oximeter) in which a red filter and an infrared filter are used with separate photocells connected in opposition, so that ear thickness has no effect, but the passage of a blue dye does. Dyes more suitable than the original Evans blue are those which are quickly metabolized or excreted, such as Fox green or Cardiogreen. Thus the dye dilution techniques, coupled with a soft, indwelling catheter, can be made quite comfortable for the human subject, but measurements of cardiac output are necessarily intermittent.

Another intermittent method of blood flow determination is limb plethysmography. An arm or leg is enclosed in a water- or airtight chamber, and an occlusive cuff applied proximal to the chamber. Fine rubber tubing filled with mercury (Whitney gauges) (Whitney, 1953) can be wrapped around the limb in place of the chamber. When pressure in a proximal occluding cuff is raised above venous return pressure, the limb increases in size in proportion to arterial inflow but for a limited time only, and this can be measured as volumetric displacement in the chamber or by changes in gauge resistance. To repeat the determination, the cuff must be deflated and normal inflow-outflow balance attained in the limb.

Arterial pressure can be measured continuously in the conscious human, but not blood flow or cardiac output, except incidentally during surgical procedures. It is only in animals that continuous measures can be made, and excellent techniques have recently been developed so that the complete hemodynamic function in large to medium sized conscious animals can be recorded continuously, beat to beat. These methods are somewhat complex, but certainly deserve description.

Blood Flow Measurements

There are two types of perivascular, noncannulating electromagnetic flowmeters in current use, the sine wave (Kolin & Kado, 1959) and square wave (Denison, Spencer, & Green, 1955) devices. There are two types of ultrasonic flowmeter (Franklin, Watson, & Van Citters, 1964) of which the probes can be implanted: pulsed transit time and Doppler effect. The latter has been adapted to telemetry. The sine wave flowmeter is slightly more popular than the square wave flowmeter since the sensing elements can be made smaller. These have even been constructed for implantation on the ascending aorta of the rat (Ledingham & Cohen, 1963).

Figure 7.1 shows the basic principles of all the devices. The electromagnetic flowmeter is based on the principle of the Faraday monopolar generator (Fig. 7.1, 1, 2, and 3). Briefly, a moving electrical conductor (iron, mercury, or blood, which is 1% salt and as such, conducting) cutting the lines of force of a magnetic field at right angles to it generates electricity proportional to the speed of its motion or flow. This electrical potential is sensed by electrodes at right angles to both the magnetic field and direction of flow. Flow is integrated across the diameter of the artery. If a DC magnetic field is used, the electrodes will rapidly polarize and signal drift will take place unless the electrodes are salt half bridges. To avoid this difficulty, the magnetic field is reversed several hundred times a second by either a sine wave or square wave exciting current. The resulting electrical signals picked up by the sensing electrodes are in microvolts, can be amplified by an AC amplifier, and are the final flow signal obtained by rectification and filtering. The sine wave flowmeter has the disadvantage that the magnetic field directly induces a relatively large background signal in wires carrying the flow signal. This artifact can be avoided by sensing flow only at the peaks of the sine wave when the magnetic field is changing the least or very little. This is called the "gated" sine wave method (Kolin & Kado, 1959) since the amplifier is turned off except during the wave peaks. A fairly good zero reference line is obtained by turning off the magnet if the gating position has been properly established. Another version of the gated sine wave is available (Khouri & Gregg, 1963). It has been used to measure coronary artery flow and cardiac output simultaneously.

In the square wave electromagnetic flowmeter (Denison et al., 1955), the magnetic field is created by a flat topped exciting wave, hence "square." At the time of the field reversal, there are very large ringing current surges in the magnet coil, thus the amplifier is gated off at this time and turned on only toward the end of the cycle when the magnetic field is stable. A moderately reliable zero reference is obtained by turning off the magnet. The probes are larger than those of the sine wave flowmeter. However, most experiments in the past have employed this flowmeter, because it was the first reliable one available commercially. Work with the square wave flowmeter has been done mainly during acute experiments and more or less extensive surgery is required during experiments.

Another version of the sine wave design is the "phase shift" flowmeter (Olmsted, 1962, a and b). This is based on the principle that the flow signal wave form, *Curve A*, and that of the background, *Curve B*, are approximately 90° out of phase. Their vector sum curve is, however, a single sine wave. When blood flows this wave increases in amplitude but must also shift in phase (Fig. 7.2). The electronic circuit uses the principle of frequency modulation to limit the amplitude changes and remove them, thus leaving only the phase changes which are turned into useful flow signals by a phase-sensitive detector. Zero is obtained by reference to a separate phase standard control. This flowmeter is immune to electrical interference from fluorescent lights, motors, or even an electrocautery nearby.

Sources of Error in Flowmeters

Flowmeters are comparatively new devices and for many reasons possess an inherent absolute error of about 10%. Although from day to day in the same animal, some implanted transducers have a relative drift of only about ±2%

$$E = D_{cm} \cdot h_g \cdot V_{cm/sec} \cdot 10^{-8}$$

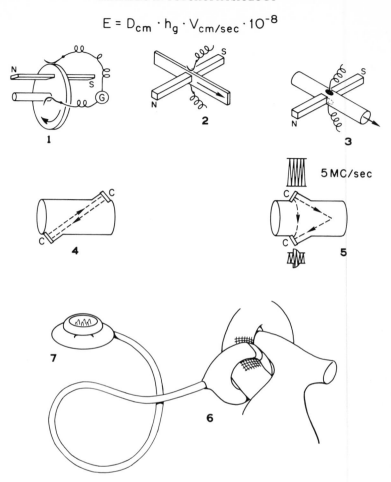

FIG. 7.1 The *top drawings* show the principle of the electromagnetic flowmeter. *1* is the Faraday monopolar generator. On the rotation of the metal disc in the magnetic field a current flows between rim and axle through the galvanometer, its potential proportional to speed of the disc. In *2* the disc has been replaced by a metal strip, but the principle is the same. In *3* the strip has been replaced by a conducting fluid in a pipe. With the high input impedance of modern amplifiers, the conducting fluid can be blood. The formula shows the potential generated. It is small, usually in the order of 10 to 100 μ v. *D* is diameter in centimeters, *h* is magnetic field in gauss, *v* is average velocity of flow, and 10^{-8} is a constant. *4* is the pulsed transit time ultrasonic flow probe. Sound travels diagonally across the blood stream, first one way, and then the other, reversing 400 time/sec, from the barium titanate crystals (*C*). The upstream, downstream time difference (a few microseconds) represents speed of flow. *5* is the Doppler effect ultrasonic flow probe. A 5 megacycle/sec signal is transmitted continuously at an angle along the flowstream. Particulate matter (red cells) reflect sound back to the other crystal which is lower in frequency if down-

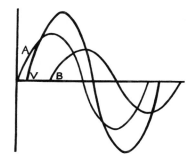

FIG. 7.2. This shows the component wave forms of the sine wave flow transducer. Let *A* be a constant background (transformer effect in signal leads) and *B* the flow signal. The only real wave present is *V*, the vector sum of *A* and *B*. If flow signal *B* increases, *V* becomes larger and shifts to the right; if *B* becomes smaller, so does *V*, and shifts to the left. This is phase shift information. The amplitude changes are removed by squaring and limiting circuits as in FM, thus producing a quiet flow signal. (From Olmsted, F., & Aldrich, F. D. *J. appl. Physiol.*, 1961, *16*: 197–201.)

about a mean. The sources of error are both in the application of the flow probes and the electronic units themselves. In the electromagnetic types, the greatest source of drift and error is in the electrical contact of the electrodes with the vessel wall. In acute experiments, the probes must fit snugly, and in the case of the phase shift flowmeter, be very clean; this seems true for the gated sine wave device also. In chronic implants, tissue growth between probe and vessel promotes good electrical connection and the probes then become very stable.

Movement of the probes relative to the vessel causes a decrease in signal as the angle of the electrodes and magnetic field shifts from 90°. The error is not serious for moderate movement as it equals the cosine of the angle of shift. Metal objects such as hemostats near the probes distort the magnetic field and can cause large errors and electrical unbalance in both sine wave and square wave probes.

Zero base line is a constant source of typically small errors. In the gated sine wave machine, this point is located by tuning the gate position for point of minimum or no pulsations of the output when the probes are on arteries. The gate is then shifted 90° to record; zero base line is obtained by turning off the

---

stream and higher if upstream. A large received signal is at the original frequency; mixed with this is the flow signal which forms a beat frequency at flow velocity. The 5 megacycle signal is discarded by demodulation, leaving the flow signal alone. *6* is a phase-shift probe installed on the ascending aorta. The gap filler is in place. Dacron mesh can be seen under the probe. A double layer of the mesh extends half way around the artery. *7* is the exterior connection; a skin button containing a multiple electrical connector. The button is passed under the skin to between the scapulae. An incision is made just large enough to get the smaller part of the skin button outside.

magnet. This base line may drift somewhat since the flowmeter is sensitive to line frequency interference and electrocautery radiations at some distance. The square wave flowmeter is also sensitive to this sort of interference, and its electrical zero is subject to some drift.

The phase-shift flowmeter has no electrical zero. It is assumed to be at the end diastolic level when recording from the pulmonary artery or ascending aorta. Otherwise the vessel must be occluded distal to the probe for zero, or zero found in saline before placing the probe, and referred to a separate phase standard.

The square wave flowmeter calibrations are sensitive to hematocrit levels up to and over 10% of saline calibration values. This is because the erythrocytes act as partial insulators or capacitors in the DC magnetic field. The AC, or sine wave flowmeters, are relatively insensitive to this error since the AC signal potential is carried as well in a capacitive medium as in serum electrolyte solution.

Ultrasonic Blood Flow Methods

The ultrasonic flowmeters operate on two different physical principles. One is the pulsed transit time flowmeter (Franklin, Baker, & Rushmer, 1962). Two piezoelectric barium titanate crystals are mounted opposite each other on the two ends of a plastic sleeve surrounding a blood vessel (see Fig. 7.1, *Part 4*). Each crystal is excited alternately with a strong pulse of electricity, while the unexcited crystal acts as a receiver. Each crystal is alternately a transmitter and receiver, the reversals taking place 400 times a second. On excitation and reception, the crystals "ring" briefly at about 5 megacycles/sec. Since each alternate pulse is upstream in the blood vessel, and the others downstream, the speed of blood flow is subtracted from the upstream transmission time and added to the downstream transmission time. The difference is a few parts in a million, but this differential velocity is directly related to blood flow. The probes are light and need not touch the blood vessel directly as sound coupling to the crystals takes place through fluid and tissue (filling in between probe and vessel) within a week after surgery. The electronics are complex, and also somewhat complex to operate, especially if more than one probe is used at a time, and the device is not at present commercially available, although much excellent basic research on cardiodynamics in exercising dogs has been done with it (Franklin, Van Citters, & Rushmer, 1962).

The other ultrasonic flowmeter is based on the Doppler effect (Franklin et al., 1964). Two piezoelectric crystals are opposite each other, but on the same end of the sleeve of the flow probe, faced in toward the center of the flow stream at an angle of about 45 to 60° (Fig. 7.1, *Part 5*). One crystal continuously acts as a transmitter at 5 megacycles/sec. Some of the ultrasound from it is reflected back to the other crystal which acts continuously as a receiver. If blood is going away from the crystals, its velocity is subtracted from the sound waves from the transmitter, and the sound reflected back to the receiver will be at a slightly lower frequency than that sent from the transmitter. Likewise, if blood is moving toward the crystals, the received sound will be slightly higher in frequency than that transmitted. This change in frequency is directly proportional to speed of flow and creates a beat frequency with the main sound wave which is detected and demodulated to give a flow pattern.

During the past few decades, a number of flow measuring devices have been used in acute experiments by direct intervention in the blood stream. This of course involves surgery and more or less disturbance of the circulation. Such things are the bubble flowmeter, the rotameter (often recording), the turbinometer, the bristle flowmeter (Brecher & Praglin, 1953), and so on. There was no hope of any natural method of measuring blood flow continuously and fairly accurately until Kolin's noncannulating AC electromagnetic flowmeter was devised in 1936 and Wetterer's DC electromagnetic flowmeter almost simultaneously in 1937. Nevertheless, it was not until 1958 that Kolin developed a flow probe suitable for chronic implantation around blood vessels (Kolin & Kado, 1959). In the meantime the rather complex pulsed ultrasonic transit time flowmeter had been in use by Rushmer and his group (Franklin et al., 1962), but this method was too intricate for the investigator without a staff of electronic engineers. In the meantime, Denison, Spencer, and Green (1955) had also combined the principles of Kolin and Wetterer into the square wave flowmeter; this was rapidly developed, and for many years was the most reliable (and still may be) of the instruments of this type available to investigators. The contour and weight of the probes were not particularly suitable for chronic studies, and almost all of the work done with this flowmeter was during acute experiments.

However, in 1958 Spencer, Johnston, and Denison implanted a flow probe on a dog's ascending aorta and measured cardiac output (less coronary artery flow) in the conscious animal for the first time with an electromagnetic flowmeter. This has since been repeated many times by others with the gated sine wave meter and the phase detection method of Olmsted and Page (1965) and again with the pulsed and Doppler effect ultrasonic flowmeters.

Technique of Implantation

The methods used in our laboratories are concerned with measuring arterial pressure and cardiac output in unanesthetized, trained dogs. They have been used in several pharmacological studies and in the study of hypertension. Over several years the techniques developed have enabled us to carry out prolonged and complex experiments, such as month-long infusions or continuous 48-hr recordings.

The flow probes are placed around the ascending aorta. The surgical technique has been described elsewhere (Olmsted, 1962 a), but it is worth reviewing with the addition of latest improvements. Formerly a rounded edge, gapped probe was used, and a piece of boiled compressed polyvinyl sponge placed under the top arm of the probe to protect the aorta. The bottom section (see Fig. 7.1, *Part 6*) could not be so treated because of an electrode that must make contact with the vessel wall. Within a few weeks the back of the aorta was eroded through. The probes now used have a filler piece and make a complete ring when in place. The segment of the ascending aorta next to the pulmonary artery and most of its top area under the probe are covered by a double layer of 100% Dacron mesh as illustrated in Fig. 7.1. Electrical contact through the Dacron mesh is good. One end of this mesh is attached to the lower arm of the probe, and the free end is pulled around the aorta by a piece of umbilical tape when the probe is placed.

The surgical approach is through the fourth left interspace. The pericardium is incised an inch medial to the phrenic nerve from over the right ventricular outflow tract to as far down as can be reached over the aorta. The heart is suspended in a pericardial basket, leaving access to the lower side of the aorta. The fat pad on the ascending aorta is removed, and this vessel and the pulmonary artery lifted from beneath. A point is seen where these vessels are not in immediate contact; the edge of the ascending aorta can be seen. A finger is placed beneath this point and the tissue dissected through to it. This sharp dissection is carried out in both directions between the aorta and pulmonary artery until the finger can be introduced easily between the two vessels. The flow probe is placed around the ascending aorta by pulling the vessel in with a piece of umbilical tape around it. The Dacron mesh is arranged and the gap filler put in place.

For measurement of arterial pressure, the left subclavian artery is dissected free from the aortic arch to the internal thoracic artery and sectioned between ligatures at this site. A piece of arterial prosthesis (Dacron or Teflon) is placed around the arterial catheter which is then put into the clamped subclavian artery. The catheter is tied semitight in place with umbilical tape, the clamp removed, and the catheter advanced 1 or 2 cm into the aortic arch and tied firmly. The arterial graft prosthesis, previously beveled and cut long enough to reach from the aorta to beyond the segment of subclavian artery, is slipped over the artery and sutured to the aorta with 0000 a-traumatic silk. The distal end of the graft is sewed shut and the ends of this suture tied around the catheter, thus effectively joining the catheter to the aortic arch. The subclavian artery under the tie necroses in a few days. A small tube may also be placed in the vena cava superior (for injections) by way of an external jugular vein in which it is fixed with a purse string suture. Catheters and the flow probe terminal end in skin buttons which are placed at the back of the neck. The arterial button contains a stopcock with the handle removed. The venous tube button has a needle hub and a luer-lok fitting plug, and the probe cable button contains a multiple electric connector. Alternately the two tubes may be simply brought out the skin without buttons. They are filled with heparin (50 mg/ml) and the distal ends plugged before surgery.

The recording laboratory is equipped with a 6-channel graphic recorder* of adequate frequency response, flowmeters of the phase shift design (Olmsted, 1962 b), and a manifold of operational amplifiers† for deriving various functions from pressure and flow (Olmsted, 1962 a). The flow signal represents velocity of blood flow in the aortic arch, and must be converted to stroke volume and cardiac output. Mean arterial pressure is taken as the integral of pulsatile pressure. Heart rate is derived from the flow signal. Peripheral resistance is the quotient of mean arterial pressure divided by cardiac output at 4-sec intervals. In addition to this equipment there are power supplies, cathode ray oscilloscopes, and soft pads for the dogs to lie on. Wires connecting the dogs to the bank of apparatus are suspended from a track on the ceiling, so that the dogs are free to move about the room.

Important requisites in obtaining valid data from animals are that they be in good health, fully recovered from surgical procedures, and thoroughly accustomed to the recording techniques. Therefore the dogs are allowed a week of kennel rest to recover from the operation of implanting the probe and catheter. After this they are taken to the laboratory and allowed to explore it for several minutes. They are then connected to the recording machine. This is done by having them wear a shoulder harness or jacket to which a long spring can be attached. The spring is connected at the other end to a ceiling track, and the cables for the flowmeter and a pressure gauge parallel the spring to the dog. The dogs undergo these sessions before data are taken from them.

The pressure transducer we have found most satisfactory as to size and weight, ruggedness, accuracy, and frequency response is the Statham P23d. It is filled with silicone oil, and cleaned only if blood leaks into it. Beyond the gauge is a 3-way stopcock and several inches of medium stiff catheter which terminates in a male luer connector to fit the arterial skin button. The gauge is attached at heart level to the harness or jacket, and the male fitting placed in the skin button stopcock, which is opened with a small screwdriver fitting the slot left by removal of the stopcock handle. All catheters, when not recording, are filled with heparin, 50 mg/ml, to prevent clotting, and the arterial stopcock is specially ground and lubricated with heavy vacuum grease to prevent any reflux of blood into the catheter tip. The concentrated heparin is removed via the 3-way stopcock on the gauge and the catheters filled with dilute heparin. Also recommended for filling catheters when not in use is a mixture of 6% Dextran and 10% heparin. It is ascertained that there are no

---

*Sanborn 150 series, now discontinued.
†Philbrick 6009.

bubbles in the catheters or gauge, which is open to air, and calibrated and the recorder set at zero. Arterial pressure can then be recorded by turning the 3-way stopcock to connect the gauge to the artery.

When the connector to the flowmeter is plugged in, the flowmeter is balanced, and sensitivity set by introducing a predetermined amount of background signal to mix with the flow signal. The probes and flowmeter are calibrated with saline before implantation. Figure 7.3 shows a sample recording from a trained dog lying quietly. The factors derived from the analogue circuits are below the recordings of flow and pressure.

Several satisfactory recording machines are available, the two most medically oriented firms being Sanborn (Hewlett Packard) and Offner (Beckman), although Electronics for Medicine has a good photographic recording system. Usually the investigator wants to see the record as it appears, beat to beat, and prefers a heat or ink stylus in a rectilinear system. The Grass recorder is curvilinear. The two most popular flowmeters are the Medicon (Statham) gated sine wave design and the Carolina Medical Electronics square wave device. The former is probably more suitable for chronic, implanted preparations; the latter slightly more stable and accurate. Frequency responses are adequate.

Finally, when working with unanesthetized, unrestrained animals, the importance of comfort, a natural environment, and thorough training during recording procedures cannot be emphasized too much. Base-line values in cardiac output and arterial pressure or any flow values will be too high, usually because of an unnaturally high heart rate, unless the animals are completely accustomed to laboratory procedures and personnel.

Obviously, the development of telemetry of blood flow and blood pressure in a reliable form holds promise of a near perfect method of observing, in animals at least, these two physiological factors under the most natural conditions possible, or under any test conditions the investigator wishes to impose. In this way the significant beat to beat changes may be recorded under a variety of situations. The flowmeter is already available, but it is not yet directional, nor has it been commercially designed to incorporate the additional modulation in its telemetry signal for blood pressure transmission. The units for exciting the flow probe and telemetry are about the size of medium flash light batteries, and can easily be carried by dogs and even the smaller primates.

REFERENCES

Brecher, G. A., & Praglin, J. A modified bristle flowmeter for measuring phasic blood flow. *Proc. Soc. exp. Bio. Med.*, 1953, *83*: 155.
Denison, A. B., Jr., Spencer, M. P., & Green, H. D. A square wave electromagnetic flowmeter for application to intact blood vessels. *Circulation Res.*, 1955, *3*: 39–46.

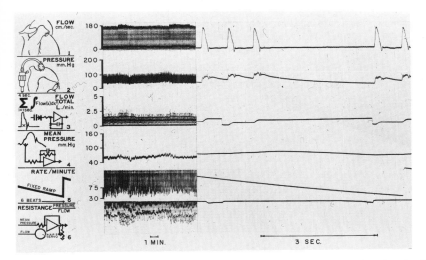

Fig. 7.3. Multiple channel recording from a resting, trained dog. *Channel 1*, flow in the ascending aorta; *2*, pulsatile pressure in the aortic arch; *3*, stroke volume (each step) and cardiac output at 4-sec intervals from integration of *Channel 1*; *4*, mean arterial pressure from integration of *Channel 2*; *5*, heart rate; and *6*, peripheral resistance from division of mean pressure by cardiac output. Arterial pressure, cardiac output, and heart rate are considerably lower in the trained dog than in one that is connected to the machine for the first time. The fast part of the tracing shows a diastolic interval of 3 sec.

Fick, A. Veber die messungdes blut-quantums in der herzventriklin. *Sber. phys.-med. Ges. Würzb.*, 1870, *1*: 16.

Franklin, D. L., Baker, D. W., & Rushmer, R. F. Pulsed ultrasonic transit time flowmaster. *I.R.E. Trans. med. Electron.*, 1962, 9: 44–49.

Franklin, D. L., Van Citters, R. L., & Rushmer, R. F. Left ventricular function described in physical terms. *Circulation Res.*, 1962, *11*: 702–711.

Franklin, D. L., Watson, N. W., & Van Citters, R. L. A miniaturized doppler ultrasonic blood flowmeter—telemetry system. *Proc. a. Conf. Engng Med. Biol.*, 1964, 78.

Hales, S. *Statistical essays*. London: Physiological Society, 1733.

Hamilton, W. F., Brewer, G., & Brotman, I. Pressure pulse contours in the intact animal. *Am. J. Physiol.*, 1934, *107*: 427–440.

Hamilton, W. F., Moore, J. W., Kinsman, J. M, & Spurling, R. G. Simultaneous determination of the pulmonary and systemic circulation times in man and of a figure related to the cardiac output. *Am. J. Physiol.*, 1928, *84*: 338–344.

Hinman, A. T., Engel, B. T., & Bickford, A. F. Portable blood pressure recorder accuracy and preliminary use in evaluating intradaily variation in pressure. *Am. Heart J.*, 1962, *63*: 663–668.

Khouri, E. M., & Gregg, D. E. Miniature electromagnetic flowmeter applicable to coronary arteries. *J. appl. Physiol.*, 1963, *18*: 224–227.

Kolin, A. An electromagnetic flowmeter, principle of the method and its application to blood flow measurements. *Proc. Soc. exp. Biol. Med.*, 1936, *35*: 54.

Kolin, A., & Kado, R. T. Miniaturization of the electromagnetic blood flowmeter and its use for the recording of circulatory responses of conscious animals to sensory stimuli. *Proc. natn. Acad. Sci. U.S.A.*, 1959, *45*: 1312–1321.

Lambert, E. H., & Wood, E. H. Use of resistance wire strain gauge manometers to measure intraarterial pressure. *Proc. Soc. exp Biol. Med.*, 1947, *64*: 186–190.

Ledingham, J. M., & Cohen, R. D. The role of the heart in the pathogenesis of renal hypertension. *Lancet*, 1963, *2*: 979.

Lilly, J. C., Legallais, V., & Cherry, R. A variable capacitor for measurements of pressure and mechanical displacements: a theoretical analysis of its experimental evaluation. *J. appl. Phys.*, 1947, *18*: 613–628.

Ludwig, C. *Lehrbuch der Physiologie des Menschen.* Leipzig: Wintersche, 1961. P. 1856.

McLeod, F. D. A doppler ultrasonic physiological flowmeter. *Proc. a. Conf. Engng Med. Biol.*, 1964, 81.

Mellander, S., & Rushmer, R. F. Venous blood flow recorded with an isothermal flowmeter. *Acta physiol. scand.*, 1960, *48*: 13–19.

Olmsted, F. New techniques for continuous recording of cardiovascular functions in unrestrained dogs. *J. appl. Physiol.*, 1962, *17*: 152–156.

Olmsted, F. Phase detection electromagnetic flowmeter—design and use. *I.R.E. Trans. med. Electron.*, 1962, *9*: 88–92.

Olmsted, F., & Aldrich, F. D. Improved electromagnetic flowmeter, a new principle. *J. appl. Physiol.*, 1961, *16*: 197–201.

Olmsted, F., & Page, I. H. Hemodynamic changes in trained dogs during experimental renal hypertension. *Circulation Res.*, 1965, *16*: 134–139.

Poiseuille, M. Recherches sur la force du coeur aortique. *Archs gén. Méd.*, 1828, *18*: 550–554.

Spencer, M. P., Johnston, F. R. & Denison, A. B., Jr. Dynamics of the normal aorta. *Circulation Res.*, 1958, *6*: 491–500.

Sperry, C. J., Jr., Gadsen, C. P., Rodriguez, C., & Bach, L. M. N. Miniature subcutaneous frequency modulated transmitter for brain potentials. *Science, N.Y.*, 1961, *134*: 1423.

Wetterer, E. Eine neue methode zur registrierung der blutromungsgeschwindigkeit am uneroffneten gefass. *Z. Biol.*, 1937, *98*: 26–36.

Whitney, R. J. The measurement of volume changes in human limbs. *J. Physiol., Lond.*, 1953, *121*: 1–27.

8
Measurement of Salivation

RUTH A. KATZ, A.B., GEORGE F. SUTHERLAND, M.D., AND
CLINTON C. BROWN, PH.D.

Historical Development

The knowledge that salivary function was under nervous control and related
to emotional state was implicit in ancient tests of honesty—the hot coal placed
in the mouth did not burn the moist tongue of the fearless innocent. Scientific
interest has been slow to pursue the lead.

Johannes Müller, the great German physiologist of the early 19th century,
was the first to advance the general idea of nervous control of glandular secretions, from his observations on the vagus and the stomach (1839).

In 1832, Mitscherlich studied a case of accidental parotid fistula in man.
Observing changes in secretory rate with diet, mastication, and sleep, he suggested that a nervous pathway was involved. His paper influenced Ludwig in
1851 to test experimentally and prove secretomotor innervation of the chorda
tympani to the submaxillary gland. Ludwig disproved the theory that saliva
was an ultrafiltrate of blood by showing that the gland could secrete against
greater than arterial pressure, and secretion could continue even if circulation
to the gland was interrupted.

Claude Bernard (1856) gave a series of lectures on the chemistry of the
saliva from the different salivary glands. He revived and improved methods of
production of salivary fistulae and investigated the nervous mechanisms of
saliva secretion. Some years later, Heidenhain (1868) studied salivary secretion
from the histological point of view and contributed his theory of trophic and
secretory nerves to gland cells.

Observations of salivary flow in the human subject were limited to those with
fistula due to accidental cuts or burns, until Ordenstein, in 1860, devised the
technique of cannulation. Although frequently painful as well as unreliable due
to saliva leaking out around the cannula, no other way of obtaining samples
of saliva from a single gland was known for many years. Carlson and Crittenden, in 1910, described a device which eliminated the need for cannulating the
parotid gland by covering Stensen's duct with a metal cup from which the

saliva could be collected through a metal tube connected to the cup. Vacuum produced in an attached outer cup held the device in place until dislodged by mastication; this occurred so readily that the authors were discouraged and did not recognize the importance of their discovery.

In 1916 Lashley described a similar parotid cup of silver-plated metal which was less easily dislodged and he has mistakenly been credited with devising the first parotid cup. One of the best known modifications of the Lashley cup was that of Krasnogorski in Russia who in 1926 made a dual chambered cup out of silver, adding a perforated cover to the outer suction ring. Other modifications employing rubber, plastic, and glass as the material for the cup have been reported.

Most of the investigators in this country have been interested in obtaining samples of saliva for chemical analysis. Many were content to obtain samples of whole mouth saliva, stimulated by the chewing of paraffin or even rubber bands, as for instance, dentists primarily concerned with causes of tooth decay. Those who became aware of the differences in composition and rate of flow of the different glands turned to use of the parotid cup as a means of obtaining samples of pure parotid saliva for analysis or for simple measurements of quantity of secretion. Interest was confined to the unconditional aspects of secretion even among those interested in relating salivary flow to psychiatric diagnosis (Busfield & Wechsler, 1961; Busfield, Wechsler, & Barnum, 1961; Davies & Palmai, 1964; Gottlieb & Paulson, 1961; Peck, 1959). Collection of unstimulated saliva has been favored, and recent years have seen a revival of the method of collecting on preweighed cotton rolls in spite of the obvious handicaps to accurate measurements.

There was little interest in developing apparatus to permit accurate, continuous recording of flow rate until the attempt of Finesinger, Sutherland, and McGuire in 1942 to study the salivary conditional reflex in neurotic subjects. Compared to animals, man has a scanty parotid flow; this factor combined with the ease of inhibition of the salivary conditional reflex has caused more than one experimenter to state that the salivary reflex could not be conditioned in man (Bykov, 1958; Kerr, 1961; Richter & Wada, 1924).

With the elimination of sources of error in the apparatus and with its refinement enabling it to register very low rates, Sutherland (1959) has been able to show the salivary conditional reflex in the human subject. By using a single chambered cup which Sutherland had developed in 1957, Sutherland and Katz (1961) reported that collecting under suction reduced the problems due to viscosity of the saliva.

In Russia, Pavlov discovered the conditional reflex while investigating the physiology of the digestive glands, especially the nervous system's effects on digestive secretions. Although he was awarded the Nobel prize in physiology in 1904 for his studies on digestion, Pavlov turned his full attention to the study of conditional reflex and devised a greatly improved method of making a parotid fistula in the dog which made possible chronic experiments, many extending over several years. Although reports of the effects of emotion on saliva had existed in folklore for hundreds of years, Pavlov was the first to discover experimentally and investigate extensively psychic influences on salivary secretion. His discovery of the experimental neurosis in dogs stimulated interest in the application of conditional reflex theory to human psychiatric problems and his theories became the foundation of Russian psychiatry.

The Salivary Glands
General Characteristics

The parotid gland lies in front of and below the ear. Its chief excretory duct, Stenson's, opens on the inner surface of the cheek, opposite the first or second upper molar tooth. The submaxillary gland lies between the inferior maxilla and the digastric muscle and opens at the side of the frenum. The sublingual gland lies farther anterior and empties by separate ducts or by ducts which blend with Wharton's duct.

The salivary glands in man may be classified according to their type of secretion as follows: (1) serous, e.g. parotid (small amount of protein, inorganic salts, CO_2 and ptyalin); (2) mixed, e.g. submaxillary (digestive enzymes, mucus, and CO_2); (3) mucous, e.g. sublingual (mostly mucus and CO_2).

The glands are compound raceomose; a number of acini form a lobule which has a small excretory duct; the small ducts unite to form larger ones, and these again form the chief excretory duct.

Nerve supply of the salivary glands. The innervation of the salivary glands is complex and is illustrated diagrammatically in Fig. 8.1. The sequence of connections for the motor nerves is as follows.

Motor: superior salivary nucleus→N. intermedius→geniculate ganglion→ facial N.→chorda tympani→lingual N.→submaxillary ganglion→submaxillary and sublingual glands; inferior salivary nucleus→glossopharyngeal N.→jugular ganglion→tympanic N.→tympanic plexus→small superficial petrosal N.→otic ganglion→auriculotemporal N.→parotid gland.

Sympathetic supply to the salivary glands traverses the following pathways.

1. Submaxillary and sublingual glands: from intermediolateral cell column of the first and second cord segments→superior cervical sympathetic ganglion→ submaxillary ganglion →submaxillary and sublingual glands.

2. Parotid glands: from the intermediolateral cells of the first and second cord segments→superior cervical sympathetic ganglion→otic ganglion→parotid glands.

Allerent pathways of the salivary glands are as follows.

Sensory, including taste, somatic and visceral afferents, and olfactory.

Taste: (1) from the anterior two-thirds of the tongue→lingual N.→chorda tympani→geniculate ganglion→glossopalatine N.→nucleus solitarius→superior

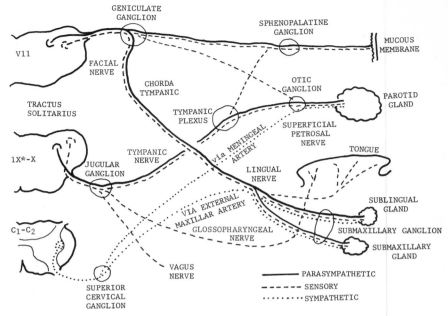

Fig. 8.1. Schematic representation of the nervous pathways for the three major salivary glands. Complete description is given in the text.

salivary nucleus; (2) from the posterior one-third of the tongue→glossopharyngeal N.→petrous and jugular ganglia→nucleus solitarius→the inferior salivary nucleus.

Somatic and visceral afferents: (1) from the submaxillary and sublingual glands→submaxillary ganglion→lingual N.→chorda tympani→facial N.→geniculate ganglion→glossopalatine N.→tractus solitarius; (2) from the parotid gland→otic ganglion→small superficial petrosal N.→tympanic plexus→tympanic N.→jugular ganglion→tractus solitarius; (3) from the mucous membrane of the mouth and nasopharynx: (a) sphenopalatine ganglion→vidian N.→great superficial petrosal N.→geniculate ganglion→glossopalatine N.→tractus solitarius and nucleus and (b) sphenopalatine ganglion→vidian N.→tympanic plexus→tympanic N.→jugular ganglion→tractus solitarius and nucleus; (4) from the viscera→vagus N.→jugular ganglion→nodosal ganglion→tractus solitarius.

Olfactory nerves pass directly to the brain from the upper part of the nose→the olfactory nerve→olfactory bulb→olfactory tract→subcallosal and hippocampal gyri→lateral olfactory stria→amygdala and hippocampus and thence by complex and disputed pathways to the salivary nuclei.

Effect of maturation on flow rate. In a study of the rate of parotid secretion in normal children, Lourie (1943) observed that flow was highest in infants, decreased sharply between the ages of 3 and 6, and then gradually declined until puberty.

Parallel changes at about the same ages in the electroencephalograms of children have been observed with an increase in frequency as the child grows older until he attains the adult range of α rhythm. Such changes with maturation were attributed by Lourie to the development of cortical centers which acted to inhibit the lower salivary centers in the medulla.

Twenty years later, Wang (1964) offered neurophysiological evidence from studies on cats that the basic central mechanism for control of salivary secretion is in the lower brain stem (in salivary nuclei located in the lateral reticular formation medial to the spinal trigeminal tract) and that these centers are regulated by other neural structures in the hypothalamus, amygdala, and cortex whose essential function is to control and integrate the feeding pattern.

The exact pathways involved in the salivary response are complicated and there is still disagreement among authorities on the finer details. Further complications arise from the presence of massive interspecies differences.

Glandular asymmetry. There is agreement on several striking peculiarities of the salivary glands: (1) the relative independence of the rate of secretion of one side from that of the other, and (2) the fact that unilateral stimulation by olfactory, gustatory, or mechanical stimuli produces *ipsilateral* secretion.

By using stereotaxic electrodes, Wang (1964) has reported that the salivary response in cats to minimal stimulation of the salivary nuclei in the lateral reticular formation is largely limited to the side of stimulation. The finding of an essentially ipsilateral response to neural stimulation is evidence for the presence of predominantly uncrossed paths to the gland.

In man, parotid response has been found to be ipsilateral to the site of stimulus application, whether the stimulus be chewing, taste, or smell. Yet with or without stimulation, most subjects show greater secretion on one side or "glandedness," unrelated to handedness, footedness, eyedness, or earedness. Although 90% of the subjects tested by Korchin and Winsor (1940, a and b) were "right-sided," only 44% were right-glanded and although only 10% were left-sided, 41% were left glanded. An interesting but puzzling finding was a marked difference between the sexes. Of the males, 67% were left-glanded but only 14% of the females were.

However, Lourie (1943) found no sex-determined glandedness in children.

General Characteristics of Salivation

Total resting saliva in young male adults has been reported by several investigators as 0.35 to 0.38 cc per min (Schneyer, 1956; Spealman, 1943) (see Table 8.1.).

The salivary reflex is not subject to acts of will. The stimuli required to induce the secretion are specific and can be controlled. They fall into two groups, those concerned with alimentation and those directed to combating irritants.

TABLE 8.1.   *Rates of secretion reported by Schneyer and Levin (1955, a and b).*

	Resting	Stimulated
	%	%
Parotid	26	34
Submaxillary	69	63
Sublingual	5	3

The functions of saliva are to cleanse and lubricate the mouth and teeth, prepare food for swallowing, to assist in the regulation of water balance, and to excrete drugs, alcohol, and metals.

Saliva has a specific gravity between 1.002 and 1.012. The pH of unstimulated whole saliva has been found to range between 5.5 and 7.5 with an average value of 6.7, while parotid saliva is more acid with pH values of 5.5 to 6.0 (Afonsky, 1961).

Saliva contains 98.5 to 99% water, dissolved gases, and 1 to 1.5% salts and organic substances. Parotid secretion is the least viscous because it contains the smallest amount of mucin due to the predominance of serous cells in the structure of the gland. The saliva is activated by orokinase from the buccal glands in the mucous membrane which converts the ptyalin into active ptyalin.

Certain drugs are excreted through the saliva, e.g. quinine, morphine, strychnine, cocaine, etc., which impart a characteristic flavor to the saliva. Pilocarpine increases the salivary flow; atropine decreases it. Some of the tranquilizers cut down the secretion, e.g. chlorpromazine chloride (Dobkin & Palko, 1960; Dobkin & Purkin, 1960).

Adequate Stimuli for Salivation

Mechanical stimulation. A frequently used means of stimulating flow has been the chewing of a flavorless substance such as paraffin or rubber bands. Shannon (1962) found that the amount of parotid saliva, collected bilaterally by the use of parotid cups, increased *directly* with the size of the bolus, whereas extraparotid saliva, obtained simultaneously by spitting, showed almost no increase. Kerr (1961) has observed that parotid output, with chewing rate held constant, was a log function of the stiffness of the bolus.

This led Winsor and Bayne (1929) to study the action of the masseter, temporal, and pterygoid muscles on parotid flow; they found that the greatest flow came from the gland on the side where the muscles were actively engaged. Their subjects performed maneuvers which caused relatively isolated action of these specific muscle groups. Only the muscle action which replicated chewing movements produced significant salivation. They concluded that salivation resulting from chewing movements was a conditional (not unconditional) response.

Flavored gum was used by Weber (1960) who found significant differences between subjects in total quantity secreted, but constancy of secretion for the individual subject over comparable periods of collection from the same gland. Greater secretion was obtained from the side on which chewing occurred with no evidence of glandular exhaustion in 1 hr of chewing.

Gustatory stimuli. Since the time of Pavlov, various kinds of food, acids, and salts have been used to stimulate salivation.

Chauncey, Feller, and Shannon (1963) studied the parotid response to 17 organic acids and concluded that the chief factors responsible for stimulation of chemoreceptors on the tongue, causing the "sour" sensation, were hydrogen ion concentration and structural configuration of the anion. Earlier, Chauncey and Shannon (1960) had measured parotid gland response to all four types of taste stimuli by using various concentrations of acid, salt, sweet, and bitter substances. They found: (1) a logarithmic relationship between parotid flow rate and frequency of stimulus application (swabs/min); (2) a linear relationship between flow rate and the strength of acid and salt stimuli in the lower concentrations; (3) a linear relationship for all concentrations of sweet and bitter substances; (4) no apparent accommodation of the response for 80 to 130 min.

According to Lashley (1916) and Kerr (1961), the sight of food has not produced salivation, even in starved subjects. Their subjects required the taste or smell of food or lemon to stimulate salivation. These findings are in direct contradiction to popular belief.

Olfactory stimuli. Lashley, in 1916, concluded from his experiments with a wide range of odorous substances that there is no unconditional reflex secretion of the parotid to olfactory stimulation. He attributed the increased secretion obtained after smelling amyl alcohol and oil of peppermint to irritation of the mucosa. Apparent support for Lashley's conclusions may be found in the work of Elsberg, Spotnitz, and Strongin (1940) who obtained a marked increase in parotid secretion to odorous substances "which have a distinct trigeminal effect, such as citral, menthol and turpentine. . . but not from odors which have little or no effect on the trigeminal such as coffee." When a stream of air and an effective odor were injected into only one nasal passage, increased parotid secretion was obtained from the ipsilateral gland; a bilateral stream caused increased secretion of both glands.

Somewhat contradictory results were reported by Grisogani (1925) who obtained decreased flow to unpleasant odors and increased flow to pleasant odors. The unpleasant odors such as iodoform and carbon disulfide which he used seem likely to be irritating and therefore act on the trigeminal nerve; perhaps the decrease in flow due to the subject's perception of the stimulus as unpleasant was greater than the increase due to stimulation of the trigeminal.

The location of the salivary nuclei in the lateral reticular formation medial to the spinal trigeminal tract (Wang, 1964) suggests that trigeminal stimulation could readily influence the salivary centers either by direct neural connections or by internuncials in the reticular formation which receives a massive input from the trigeminal.

Relation of Flow Rate to pH and Chemical Composition of Saliva

A positive correlation between pH and parotid flow rate in the human subject has been reported by several investigators (Winsor & Korchin, 1938; Shannon & Prigmore, 1960b; Wenger, 1948). High flow rates tend to raise the pH of parotid secretion from slightly acid to neutral or even to alkaline levels. This could explain why Winsor and Korchin found an inverse relationship between the pH of the stimulus and the pH of the stimulated saliva. Acid, which by definition has a low pH, is an effective salivary stimulus; the resulting increase in the rate of flow produces an increase in the pH of the stimulated saliva. Dawes and Jenkins (1964) obtained pH values for both parotid and submandibular saliva which were markedly higher at high rates of flow than at low, parotid pH rising from 5.55 to 7.90 and submandibular from 5.90 to 7.70. They also noted that

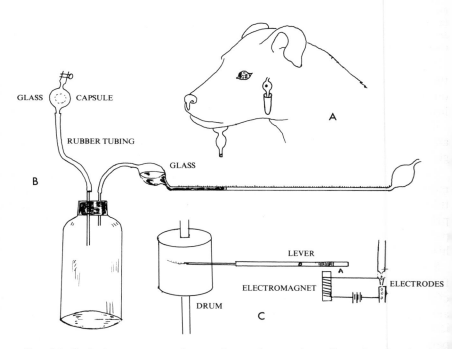

FIG. 8.2. Pavlov's arrangement for securing and measuring salivary flow in the dog. A, the collecting cups are attached over the orifice of the gland which has been brought through the cheek by the creation of a fistula. Later versions used the measuring device shown in B where air displaced from the container moved water along a horizontal measuring tube. C shows an early drop counter with electrical registration.

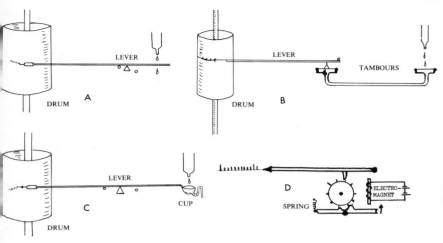

FIG. 8.3. Early drop registration devices. In *A*, the drop deflects a pivoted level producing marks on a smoked drum. In *B*, horizontal tambours served to register the drop and to deflect the writing stylus. The apparatus in *C* permitted the measurement of small standard volumes. *D* is a late version of the apparatus used by Pavlov which permitted a remote electrical registration of drops.

the concentrations of both organic and inorganic constituents were dependent on the rate of flow rather than on the nature of the stimulus applied, except insofar as it influenced salivary flow rate.

Diurnal variation in the pH of mixed saliva has been reported by Henderson and Millet (1927) who concluded that it was related to activity of the digestive glands at different times of the day.

Dutkovic (1965) found differences between parotid and sublingual pH when measured directly at the duct of the gland. Secretion was more acid in the parotid in 49% of the readings and more alkaline in only 10%; in 19% the same pH was obtained from both glands. Values which differed for right and left parotid glands as well as for the sublingual glands were obtained in 22% of his cases.

Saliva is not an ultrafiltrate of blood and its chemical constituents differ from those of blood (Shannon & Prigmore, 1960, a and b). The concentration of potassium in saliva is 5 times as great as in blood, but sodium and chloride are present in one-fifth their concentration in blood and the amount of protein is less than one-tenth that found in blood. The concentration of steroids in parotid fluid varies directly with the serum level. The effect of flow rate varies with the substance in question; concentration of sodium, chloride, bicarbonate, calcium, and total protein is positively correlated with the flow rate; urea and inorganic phosphate are negatively correlated and potassium is independent of flow rate.

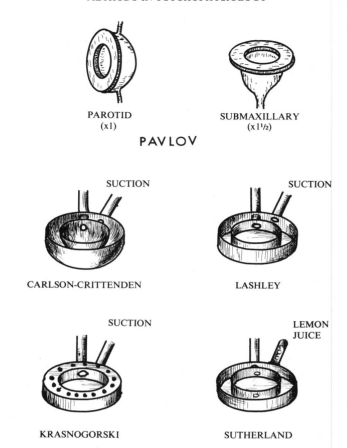

PAROTID
(x1)

SUBMAXILLARY
(x1½)

PAVLOV

SUCTION

SUCTION

CARLSON-CRITTENDEN

LASHLEY

SUCTION

LEMON
JUICE

KRASNOGORSKI

SUTHERLAND

FIG. 8.4. The Pavlovian cups shown were usually made of glass and were cemented to the external surface of the cheek. The remaining collection cups were used with humans and were held in place by suction. With the exception of the Sutherland cup, suction was applied to the external ring only while the saliva was collected in the central chamber.

Devices for Collecting and Recording the Saliva

Pavlov was an excellent surgeon as well as physiologist and perfected an easy method of making a chronic salivary fistula in the dog. He accomplished this by transplanting the duct with a small piece of mucous membrane surrounding it to the outside of the face. He used a hollow glass capsule with a hole on the flat side which cemented over the opening of the fistula with one or two glass tubes for draining into a receptacle. In this way he was able to collect the saliva and measure it in a small test tube (see Figs. 8.2*A* and 8.3).

Next he attached a rubber tube that led to a measuring apparatus consisting of a small bore glass tube (id 2 to 3 mm) with a scale (see Fig. 8.2*B*).

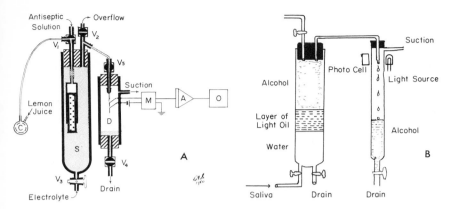

FIG. 8.5. *A*, the Sutherland sialometer; *B*, a modification by Feather. The Feather version dispenses with the collecting syringe and the saliva is collected under light oil. (From Feather, B. *Psychophysiology*, 1965, *1*: 299–303.)

Finally he used a simple type of mechanical or electrical drop recorder which traced the drops on a smoked drum (see Fig. 8.2*C*).

In his book *Conditioned Reflexes* (1927), Pavlov later showed a tracing with an ingenious escapement mechanism operated electrically in which every tenth drop is accentuated (see Fig. 8.3*D*).

The amount of distortion introduced by the flexibility of the rubber tubing and by the entrapped air was considerable, so much so, that the latent period and the rate of flow were usually both inaccurate. It was the custom to select a dog that would give a "good flow" of saliva to minimize these sources of error.

The difficult problem of measuring continuous salivary flow has stimulated various investigators to produce a number of ingenious solutions. These are illustrated in Fig. 8.3.

Contemporary procedures to collect and record the flow of saliva begin with a small capsule held in place by suction with a tube attached leading to the collecting apparatus (sialometer) and the recorder (Carlson & Crittenden, 1910; Lashley, 1916; Krasnogorski, 1931; Sutherland, 1959). These capsules are fashioned out of silver, stainless steel, or plastic (Fig. 8.4).

The sialometers have greatly changed with the invention of polyethylene and Teflon tubing, the modern oscillograph, and the electronic method of recording (Fig. 8.5).

In the device shown in Fig. 8.5*A*, the entire system is held at −11 mm Hg pressure. This suction is transmitted through the apparatus to the collecting cup. The whole area of the cup therefore serves to secure the attachment while the annular ring construction prevents invagination of the mouth of the duct with resulting obstruction of flow.

The saliva excreted is collected in the cup, traverses the PE 190 tubing to the inlet to the sialometer. The sialometer is entirely filled with tap water. The saliva enters the opening of a 20-cc glass hypodermic syringe (selected for smooth operation) held in an inverted position in the sialometer. The saliva displaces the plunger of the syringe, which in turn displaces the water through a connecting tube into a drop counter. The water is formed into drops by a polished 20-gauge stub needle and the drops, in falling, briefly short two platinum wire electrodes. This action pulses a one-shot multivibrator which produces a uniform signal regardless of the length of time the electrodes are shorted. This signal is integrated, amplified, and recorded in one channel of a polygraph. Two such devices are required for bilateral recordings.

The liquid used as an unconditional stimulus (usually lemon juice) is remotely injected via another length of polyethylene tubing which terminates blind at the capsule. Perforations in the terminal length of the tubing allow the substance to spray out on the tongue.

Other methods for collecting saliva which are somewhat less accurate include the following: (1) letting it drop out of the mouth held open to prevent swallowing; (2) using an aspirator; (3) using filter paper or cotton balls to absorb the saliva and weighing at intervals; (4) using filter paper impregnated with various dyes which change color depending on how much is absorbed in a given time; (5) catheterization of the ducts by use of a polyethylene catheter rounded at the ends by warming.

Procedure for Salivary Measurements

The laboratory consists of two adjoining rooms situated in a quiet part of the building in order to eliminate unwanted stimuli. The subject is isolated from the experimenter who applies the signals and reinforcement from the adjoining room. It is convenient to have a one way glass so that the experimenter can view the subject.

The apparatus is illustrated in the schematic drawing in Fig. 8.5*A*. The collecting capsule (*C*), sialometer (*S*), and drop detector (*D*) are in the room with the subject, and the rest of the apparatus including the lemon solution dispenser are in the room with the experimenter. The apparatus has been described in detail above.

Effort should be made to prevent episodic stimuli from reaching the subject. Such stimuli may be walking, talking, shuffling feet, clicking of switches, etc. which may give the subject a cue. Figure 8.6 illustrates a bilateral conditional response to a cue given unwittingly by the experimenter and incidentally shows the size of the conditional response in proportion to the unconditional response. When the subject is ushered into the room the attachments should be made as expeditiously as possible. The same procedure should be used every day; extraneous procedures and talking should be reduced to a minimum.

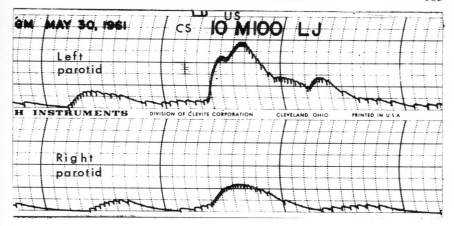

Fig. 8.6. The *upper event mark* depicts a 5-sec auditory conditional stimulus (*CS*) followed by the injection of lemon juice as the unconditioned stimulus (*US*) during the last second of the CS. A salivary conditional response (*CR*) is shown by the increased flow rate of both parotid glands beginning approximately 1 min before the application of the US. The difference in size of the left and right CR and unconditional response *(UR)* illustrate glandular asymmetry.

Before the subject arrives the apparatus must be tested to eliminate sources of error.

Air. All air must be removed from the apparatus. Even a little bubble will vitiate the performance of the apparatus.

Leaks. Most common of all of the troubles are leaks. Frequently the polyethylene or Teflon tubing develops leaks from bending or rough handling. Stopcocks must be clean and properly greased with silicone grease.

Syringes sticking. The syringes must be clean and any grease or foreign material must be removed. To test it lay the clean syringe on an incline and the plunger should move in and out freely.

Normal curve. In the human subject, the parotid is the gland of choice for studying the flow and virtually all of the investigative work has been done using this gland. It is relatively easy to record the secretion (which is watery, unlike that from the submaxillary and lingual) by applying the capsule directly over the opening of Stensen's duct.

Each parotid gland in the resting stage secretes 0.02 to 0.05 ml/min. When stimulated, the parotid may secrete 100 times the rate of the resting gland.

Citric acid solution of 1% sweetened with Sucaryl is an effective stimulus for use in the laboratory because it is an irritant as well as a taste stimulus.

In response to a brief stimulus the secretion rises quickly to a maximum and then begins to fall. After a short while it rises again to a lesser amplitude and this is repeated several times until it once more reaches the resting secretion level; this whole process takes from 8 to 10 min (see Fig. 8.7).

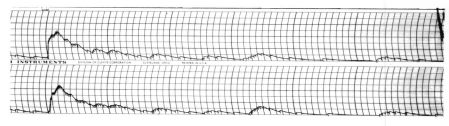

FIG. 8.7. Normal bilateral parotid salivary curves showing their poststimulus course.

It should be mentioned that the salivary mechanism is part of the total digestive process. Satiety inhibits the salivary response to digestive stimuli but not to irritants. When the blood sugar is low, the appetite is augmented and the salivary flow is increased. Illness may result in changes in the flow. The same may be said of certain lesions in the central nervous system as well as drugs.

Salivation in Psychopathic States

Such outstanding physicians as Malpighi, Bichat, and Trousseau believed that both anger and love made the saliva as dangerous as that of a viper.

Let us begin by considering the simple relationship between mental effort and salivation. Early investigators reported both stimulation and inhibition of salivary flow with mental effort. Winsor (1931), measuring the parotid secretion, found a definite inhibition of free (resting) secretion during periods of sustained attention during mental tasks. When he added incentives to greater performance, the flow was further reduced. Applying previously conditioned stimuli to the subject while he was engaged in mental arithmetic produced an inhibition of the conditional responses. He concluded that the inhibition observed during mental effort was attributable to "restraining influence of the cerebral cortex."

Suggestion, both direct and administered during hypnotized states, provides the opportunity to evaluate the effects of psychic activity. Barber, Chauncey, and Winer (1964) administered tests of suggestibility to normal selected 16 male subjects who scored highest, i.e. who were most suggestible, and studied the effects of both hypnotic and nonhypnotic suggestion. They found that (1) hypnosis alone had no effect upon parotid flow, (2) when water, suggested to be "sour," was administered there was significantly increased salivation, (3) when 1.5% citric acid was suggested to be water there was decreased salivation, and (4) both hypnotic and nonhypnotic suggestion seemed equally effective in modifying the salivary flow. Chauncey, Winer, and Barber (1964) continued this line of investigation with a study of 60 normal subjects who rated "least suggestible" on the Barber scale. They used sugar and citric acid in six different concentrations and found that both the suggestions that acid was sweet or that sugar was sour produced *nonsignificant* differences in salivary flow. Their findings supported Barber's in that when either sugar or acid was suggested to be tasteless, there was a significantly lower salivary flow. Apparently the expectation of the subject can modify what seems to be a purely reflex response.

Threat and fear are more purely "psychic" stimuli. Bogdonoff, Bogdonoff, and Wolf (1961) studied the parotid response of 24 dental patients to a stimulus consisting of rotating dental drill brought up to the subject's mouth. No drilling was done. He found that the subjects who were rated "aggressive" by interview ratings showed increased flow rates while those who rated "defensive" showed decreased flow. One subject maintained an unchanged flow and reported that the experience was not unpleasant.

This history of salivary investigations in psychiatric states begins with the work of Strongin and Hinsie in 1938. Hypothesizing that the manic and depressive phases of the manic-depressive psychotic represented two extremely contrasting end points of arousal, mentation, and affect, they studied parotid output in six patients, two in the depressive phase, two in the manic, two during both phases, and a control group of normal subjects. They found essentially what has been confirmed in all of the succeeding work, that the depressive patient secretes much less than normal and less than his own levels in the manic phase. They reported that secretion in the manic phase was only slightly lower than normals. Findings on an additional group, reported in the same paper, showed that deteriorated schizophrenics gave significantly higher than normal parotid secretion.

Their findings lay unnoted for 20 years until Peck (1959) collected whole saliva on dry cotton rolls placed in the mouth and weighed at 2-min intervals. He found that there were "consistent and good correlations between clinical depression and lowered rates of salivary secretion," no differences between the sexes, but surprisingly, a consistently higher flow in both normal and depressed Negroes. Peck also noted a diurnal variation.

Peck then formalized his procedures into the SHP (Strongin, Hinsie, Peck) test and a number of investigators have since used this technique for the measurement of various groups.

Davies and Gurland (1961) found their depressive subjects secreted significantly less than normal subjects under conditions of both resting and stimulated flow.

Busfield, Wechsler, and Barnum (1961) found that reactive (exogenous) depressives salivated more than nonreactive (endogenous) depressives, involutional, or manic-depressives; that females secreted less than males and that there was no correlation between the patients' complaint of a dry mouth and actual measured hyposalivation. Altschule (1964), in a brief review, noted the findings for depressives and added the finding that the parotid salivary flow was high in chronic schizophrenics. He also noted that loud talking, shouting, and crying produced a rise in pH.

Gottlieb and Paulson (1961) made a longitudinal study of 18 depressives with repeated salivary and Minnesota Multiphasic Personality Inventory (MMPI) measures. They found that while the MMPI measures of anxiety and depression declined upon clinical recovery, the salivary secretion rates remained at low levels. They suggested that a low salivary flow rate is characteristic of persons prone to depression, a suggestion that has not been confirmed by subsequent studies.

In a short term study of 22 female depressives, Davies and Palmai (1964) used both the Mecholyl (Funkenstein) test and SHP tests. They found that while mecholyl produced a 10-fold increase in flow rates in both depressive and normal controls, the depressives nevertheless secreted less than the normals. They also found that there was a significant relation between the quantity of secretion and the degree of depression. With recovery, the salivary secretion rates increased to normal levels.

Salivary flow in schizophrenics and depressives was studied by Busfield and Wechsler (1961) in a total of 196 subjects. They confirm the above observations on depressive secretion but add that schizo-affective depressed patients salivated more than depressed patients and less than normals.

Davies and Gurland (1961) studied whole salivary flow in 11 female schizophrenic patients and concluded that schizophrenics secrete less than normals under resting conditions, and secrete less than either depressives or normals under conditions of stimulation.

Busfield and Wechsler (1962) studied the outcomes of antidepressive drug treatment on salivary flow in 68 depressed patients. They found that a significantly high pretreatment salivary flow was prognostic for successful treatment. These data correlate best with successful outcome after treatment with (1) Marplan, (2) nardil, and (3) Tofranil, in that order. They confirmed earlier findings that the patients' subjective complaint of a dry mouth had no prognostic value.

The most recent report is that by Palmai (1965) on 20 female depressives in whom salivary flow was measured every 2 hrs for a 24-hr period; immediately after admission, during treatment, and just before discharge. Parallel tests were performed on control subjects. In the controls, maximum secretion occurred in the morning and reached its lowest level in the evening. A complete reversal of this picture was found in the depressives upon admission; their flow was low in the morning and rose steadily to a maximum value in the evening. In the tests performed just before discharge, the differences between the groups were diminished, just barely reaching significance; i.e. the early morning salivary flow in recovered depressives had reached normal limits.

In summary, the use of the SHP test, which is a comparatively crude measure of the total salivation, has been reported to show consistently that depressives secrete significantly less than normals and patients in other diagnostic categories and that there is an increased salivary flow in the old, chronic, and possibly regressed schizophrenic. While there are many interesting variations in this pattern, i.e. diurnal cycles and long term trends, it would seem that in mental states marked by extreme preoccupation, fixed attention, or concentrated mental effort, the salivary flow provides a most sensitive psychophysiological measure of this alteration (Sutherland, 1959, 1962).

The picture of salivary activity provided in this chapter is less than complete. There is a wealth of information made available by the biochemical analysis of the composition of saliva in different emotional states. The parotid gland seems to offer the unique opportunity to study the synergy or antagonism of the two branches of the autonomic nervous system since parasympathetic activity is mainly reflected in flow changes while sympathetic action results in changes in the salivary chemistry. The measurement of salivary flow and salivary chemistry provides a useful, reproducible, nontraumatic measure of changes in emotional state.

In addition, there is a wealth of additional information in the literature which has not been included in this presentation. Salivary measurements have been used to locate the site and extent of traumatic lesions in humans in the lower brain stem; conditional salivary response procedures have yielded a vast amount of information on the process of learning in the cortex.

More work is needed in a number of areas. There is the need for improvements in the apparatus to be used for continuous recording of flow rates, particularly in the registry of very low flows. There should be additional studies of the differences in salivary flow rates from each of the three types of glands in psychiatric patients and in normal individuals in whom affective arousal has been produced in the laboratory. Simultaneous measures of salivary flow, electrical skin responses, and other commonly used psychophysiological measures may reveal patterns which will be of value in defining reaction types of normal individuals. Further studies are needed in the area of the conditional salivary response in the human subject to resolve the existing controversy as to whether or not salivary conditioning can be demonstrated.

REFERENCES

Afonsky, D. *Saliva and its relation to oral health*. Alabama: Univ. Alabama Press, 1961.

Altschule, M. D. Salivary changes in emotional states. *Med Sci.*, 1964, *15*: 60.

Barber, T. X., Chauncey, H. H., & Winer, R. A. Effect of hypnotic and nonhypnotic suggestions on parotid gland response to gustatory stimuli. *Psychosom. Med.*, 1964, *26*: 374–380.

Bernard, C. *Lecons de physiologie experimentale appliquée á la médecine*, Tome 2. Paris: Ballaere, 1856.

Bogdonoff, M. D., Bogdonoff, M. M., & Wolf, S. G., Jr. Studies on salivary function in man: variations in secretory rate as part of the individual's adaptive pattern. *J. psychosom. Res.*, 1961, *5*: 170–174.

Busfield, B. L., & Wechsler, H. Studies of salivation in depression. I. A comparison of salivation rates in depressed, schizoaffective depressed, nondepressed hospitalized patients, and in normal controls. *Archs gen. Psychiat.*, 1961, *4*: 10–15.

Busfield, B. L., & Wechsler, H. Salivation rate: a physiologic correlate of improvement in hospitalized depressed patients treated with three antidepressant medications. *Psychosom. Med.*, 1962, *24*: 337–342.

Busfield, B. L., Wechsler, H., & Barnum, W. J. Studies of salivation in depression. II. Physiological differentiation of reactive and endogenous depression. *Archs gen. Psychiat.*, 1961, *5*: 472–477.

Bykov, K. M. *Textbook of physiology* (translated by S. Belsky & D. Myshne). Moscow: Foreign Languages Publishing House, 1958.

Carlson, A. J., & Crittenden, A. L. The relation of ptyalin concentration to the diet and to the rate of secretion of the saliva. *Am. J. Physiol.*, 1910, *26*: 169–177.

Chauncey, H. H., Feller, R. P., & Shannon, I. L. Effect of acid solutions on human gustatory chemoreceptors as determined by parotid gland secretion rate. *Proc. Soc. exp. Biol. Med.*, 1963, *112*: 917–923.

Chauncey, H. H., & Shannon, I. L. Parotid gland secretion rate as method for measuring response to gustatory stimuli in humans. *Proc. Soc. exp. Biol. Med.*, 1960, *103*: 459–463.

Chauncey, H. H., Winer, R. A., & Barber, T. X. Influence of verbal suggestion on the parotid gland response to gustatory stimuli. *Proc. Soc. exp. Biol. Med.*, 1964, *116*: 898–901.

Davies, B. M., & Gurland, J. B. Salivary secretion in depressive illness. *J. psychosom. Res.*, 1961, *5*: 269–271.

Davies, B. M., & Palmai, G. Salivary and blood pressure responses to methacholine in depressive illness, *Br. J. Psychiat.*, 1964, *110*: 594–598.

Dawes, C., & Jenkins, G. N. The effects of different stimuli on the composition of saliva in man. *J. Physiol., Lond.*, 1964, *170*: 86–100.

Dobkin, A. B., & Palko, D. The antisialogogue effect of phenothiazine derivatives. *Anesthesiology*, 1960, *4*: 260–262.

Dobkin, A. B., & Purkin, N. The antisialogogue effect of phenothiazine derivatives. *Br. J. Anaesth.*, 1960, *32*: 57–59.

Dutkovic, T. R. Emotions, oral health and salivary pH patterns. *J. dent. Med.*, 1965, *20*: 16–20.

Elsberg, C. A., Spotnitz, H., & Strongin, E. I. The effect of stimulation by odorous substances upon the amount of secretion of the parotid glands. *J. exp. Psychol.*, 1940, *27*: 58–65.

Feather, B. An improved sialometer. *Psychophysiology*, 1965, *1*: 299–303.

Finesinger, J. E., Sutherland, G. F., & McGuire, F. F. The positive conditional salivary reflex in psychoneurotic patients. *Am. J. Psychiat.*, 1942, *99*: 61.

Gottlieb, G., & Paulson, G. Salivation in depressed patients. *Archs gen. Psychiat.*, 1961, *5*: 468–471.

Grisogani, N. The rhythm of parotid secretion in man under the influence of sensations of taste and smell. *Atti Accad. naz. Lincei.*, 1925, *1*: 602–604.

Heidenhain, R. Beiträge zur Lehre von der Speichelabsonderung. *Stud. Physiol. Inst. Breslau*, 1868, *4*: 1.

Henderson, M., & Millet, J. A. P. On the hydrogen ion determination of normal saliva. *J. biol. Chem.*, 1927, *75*: 559–566.

Kerr, A. C. *The physiological regulation of salivary secretions in man.* New York: Pergamon Press, 1961.

Korchin, B., & Winsor, A. L. Glandular dominance in humans. *J. exp. Psychol.*, 1940, *27*: 184.(a)

Korchin, B., & Winsor, A. L. Relationship of certain organic factors to individual differences in human parotid secretory rate. *J. exp. Psychol.*, 1940, *27*: 192–194. (b)

Krasnogorski, N. I. Die letzten Fortschritte in der Methodik der Erforschung der bedingten Reflexe an Kindern. *Jb. Kinderheilk. phys. Erzieh.*, 1926, *114*: 255–267. (a)

Krasnogorski, N. I. Über die Wirkung mechanischer und chemischer Reizungen verschiedener Teile der Mundhöhle auf die Tätigkeit der Speicheldrüsen bei Kindern. *J. Kinderheilk. phys. Erzieh.*, 1926, *114*: 268–276.(b)

Lashley, K. S. Reflex secretion of the human parotid gland. *J. exp. Psychol.*, 1916, *1*: 461–493.

Lourie, R. S. Rate of secretion of the parotid glands in normal children. *Am J. Dis. Child.*, 1943, *65*: 455–479.

Ludwig, C. Neue Versuche über die Beihilfe der Nerven zur Speichelabsonderung. *Z. rat. Med., N.F.*, 1851, *1*: 255–277.

Mitscherlich, C. G. Ueber der Speichel des Menschen, *Mag ges. Heilkunde*, 1832, *38*: 491–521.

Müller, J. *Elementa of physiology* (translated by W. Baly), Ed. 2. London: Taylor and Walton, 1839.

Ordenstein, L. Ueber der Parotidenspeichel des Menschen. *Beitr. Anat. Physiol.*, 1860, *2*: 103.

Palmai, G. The diurnal pattern of salivary flow in normal and depressed patients. *Br. J. Psychiat.*, 1965, *111*: 334–338.

Pavlov, I. P. *Conditioned reflexes* (translated by G. V. Anrep). New York: Oxford University Press, 1927.

Peck, R. E. The SHP test—an aid in the detection and measurement of depression. *Archs gen. Psychiat.*, 1959, *1*: 35–40.

Richter, C. P., & Wada, T. Method of measuring salivary secretions in human beings. *J. Lab. clin. Med.*, 1924, *9*: 271–273.

Schneyer, L. H. Source of resting total mixed saliva of man. *J. appl. Physiol.*, 1956, *9*: 79.

Schneyer, L. H., & Levin, L. K. Rate of secretion by individual salivary gland pairs of man under conditions of reduced exogenous stimulation. *J. appl. Physiol.*, 1955, *7*: 508–512.(a)

Schneyer, L. H., & Levin, L. K. Rate of secretion by exogenously stimulated salivary gland pairs of man. *J. appl. Physiol.*, 1955, *7*: 609–613. (b)

Shannon, I. L. Parotid fluid flow rate as related to whole saliva volume. *Archs oral Biol.*, 1962, *7*: 391–394.

Shannon, I. L., & Prigmore, J. R. The automatic determination of calcium, inorganic phosphate, urea nitrogen and glucose in parotid fluid. *U.S. Arm. Forces Sch. Aviat. Med.*, 1960, *60*: 1–16. (a)

Shannon, I. L., & Prigmore, J. R. Parotid fluid flow rate. Its relationship to pH and chemical composition. *Oral Surg.*, 1960, *13*: 1488–1500. (b)

Spealman, C. R. The volume flow of resting salivary secretion. *Am. J. Physiol.*, 1943, *139*: 225–229.

Strongin, E. I., & Hinsie, L. E. Parotid gland secretions in manic-depressive patients. *Am. J. Psychiat.*, 1938, *94*: 1459–1466.

Sutherland, G. F. The salivary curve: a psychiatric thermometer. *Am J. Psychiat.*, 1959, *116*: 20–24.

Sutherland, G. F. Salivary conditional reflexes in man. In J. Wortis (Ed.), *Recent advances in biological psychiatry*, Vol. 4. New York: Plenum Press, 1962. Pp. 29–37.

Sutherland, G. F., & Katz, R. A. Apparatus for study of salivary conditional reflex in man. *J. appl. Physiol.*, 1961, *16*: 740–741.

Wang, S. C. Central nervous system representation of salivary secretion. In L. M. Sreebny & J. Meyer (Eds.), *Salivary glands and their secretions*. New York: Macmillan, 1964.

Weber, T. B. Rate of flow of parotid secretion during constant stimulation. *J. appl. Physiol.*, 1960, *15*: 929–932.

Wenger, M. A. Studies of autonomic balance in Army Air Forces personnel. *Comp. Psychol. Monogr.*, *19*: No. 4, 1948.

Winsor, A. L. The effect of mental effort on parotid secretion. *Am. J. Psychol.*, 1931, *43*: 434–446.

Winsor, A. L., & Bayne, T. L. Unconditioned salivary responses in man. *Am. J. Psychol.*, 1929, *41*: 271–276.

Winsor, A. L., & Korchin, B. The effect of different types of stimulation upon the pH of human parotid secretion. *J. exp. Psychol.*, 1938, *23*: 62–79.

9

Quantification of Olfactory Stimuli

JAMES W. JOHNSTON, Jr., B.S., M.F., Ph.D.

The last critical review of techniques in olfactometry was published 18 years ago (Wenzel, 1948) prior to the general knowledge and use of gas-liquid chromatography. Consequently, it is deemed worthwhile to describe and compare a few of the modern olfactometers used to investigate human olfactory processes incorporating the improved instrumentation now available for measuring both the vapor concentrations and the homogeneity of the odorant compounds used as experimental reagents. Inasmuch as the period from 1848 to 1948 has been reviewed and modern materials and methods have had a marked effect upon olfactometry, the developments and achievements prior to 1950 are summarized in a brief account. It will be convenient to regard 1950 as the beginning of the modern phase of this science.

The olfactometer permits the control of stimulus intensity over a range of vapor concentrations from subthreshold to the maximum attainable. Another feature is the isolation of the pure odorant to be tested from the ambient air of the laboratory, an obvious experimental need. In human olfaction, the technique has been used to investigate absolute thresholds, difference of stimulus intensity judgments, identification of pure odorants over a range of strengths, and the blending of pure odorants to test a prediction of the composition of a complex odor quality. All investigations employing odor stimuli need to control the stimulus intensity with precision and have an interest in olfactometry since failure to quantify the stimuli in modern research would neglect the important fact that odors may change quality over a detectable range. Olfactometers have already attracted the attention of investigators who study small mammal and insect olfaction by means of electrophysiology directed to the primary receptive process. Investigators of the other human special senses have found olfactometric data to be the best available evidence of smell phenomena for comparative use. This has been particularly true of comparison with the other chemical sense, taste. Absolute thresholds and difference thresholds have long been available, but cross adaptation research has received attention only recently.

History of Olfactometry

The first apparatus for the control of odorous stimuli was devised by Valentin prior to 1850. The device may not be properly considered an olfactometer since it was simply a static method for diluting the vapors by a series of steps. It was not until Zwaardemaker constructed his first model (1889) and invented the term, olfactometer, that there is clear evidence to show that the problem of controlling the stimulus had been analyzed. His instrument was constructed with aluminum walls lined with glass that were removable for elimination of odorants after experimentation. The subject's nose was inserted through a hole in one wall of the odorant chamber after a measured quantity of the reagent in liquid phase was allowed to evaporate inside. Evaporation was expedited by soaking filter paper with the odorant, but some tests were made after allowing the liquid to volatilize from a shallow dish. Thus, the stimulus was diluted in air and presented by means of a static method for inhalation of the vapor. The subjects probably sniffed the stimulus instead of inhaling it gently while in a sitting posture. Unless the experimenter is careful to stipulate gentle inhalations, it is likely that the significantly different mechanics of sniffing were either tolerated or encouraged. Subjects should be disciplined gently to learn to breathe consistently in order to inhale essentially the same volume of gasborne stimulus otherwise the range of volumes could be large enough in some subjects to affect the result in an uncontrolled way. Inasmuch as novices tend to be a little self-conscious when being tested on the "perception or no perception" of a weak odor, practice is needed before their judgments can be used in the analysis of results. The self-consciousness can cause erratic breathing, but this deficiency is soon eliminated by practice under superivision.

Later, Zwaardemaker employed a different controlled stimulus presentation (1904). The liquid odorant was enclosed in a hollow tube with a sealed end that was perforated on the inner surface only. The tube enclosed and slid over another glass tube, open at both ends, which passed through a screen to the subject's nose. This was a simple method for obtaining an apparent quantification of the stimulus (Zwaardemaker, 1925). The unit of measurement was termed the "normal" perceptible minimum odor, but it was not based upon determination of stimulus concentration in terms of the number of molecules of odorant per cubic unit of gaseous vehicle. In fact, two of these sleeve tubes were employed independently and simultaneously by inserting one in each of the subject's nares.

For explicit accounts of the early investigators, Wenzel (1948) recommended Skramlik (1926) and Henning (1916). She gave a critique of the early olfactometer by stating that: "adhesion to the surface is an urgent problem if the same inhaling tube is used for many odorants. Temperature of the stimulus and volume of subject's sniff were largely uncontrolled. And some of the odor-ant escaped from smelling tubes even when none of the perforated inner sur-face was exposed. Consequently, according to Wenzel, it was an error to assume that zero stimulation occurred at zero exposure of the tube with inner per-forations and that a progressive increase of exposure caused a proportional in-crease in the saturation of the air current created by sniffing."

The idea of presenting the stimulus by means of a constant air stream was first proposed for industrial purposes (Allison & Katz, 1919). These men fore-cast by their efforts a trend in olfactometry that is evident in most of the modern instruments. The odorant was confined in a container that may be termed the odorizer unit. An air stream was piped into and out of this space, the odorous air was then diluted, and finally presented to the subject for per-ception and analysis. Odor threshold determinations were made without pro-vision for rapid changes in the vapor concentrations or the species of odorant. A complex system of odor measurement was used due to the number of Venturi-type flow meters in the apparatus. However, the flow of purified air passed at a uniform rate through or over the liquid phase. The odorous air thus produced was then mixed with a second, measured air stream of uniform flow rate in order to dilute the stimulus intensity. Calculation of the vapor concentration was made from the loss of weight of the odorous liquid at several rates of flow.

During the 1920's further research on the constant air stream principle was largely carried out by persons working on insect olfaction. This gave rise to the instruments used by Hoskins and Craig (1934) and the modification by Dethier (1947) and Dethier and Yost (1952). These instruments represented attempts to correct or avoid errors inherent in the earlier olfactometers for human threshold investigation. The *constant air flow principle* had a great advantage for insect work because many flying insects are partially dependent upon air currents to orient them toward the sources of odors which stimulate inherited reflexes. As a matter of fact, Dethier and Yost, (1952) held that pre-sentation of the measured stimulus to the olfactory organ of insects avoided the complications in man associated with the inhalation of the stimulus. These olfactometers were of the Venturi-type and involved the following. "A source of the purified air was split into three streams each of which was metered. These entered a reaction chamber through two ports. One stream passed direct-ly to the port which was to serve as a control. Streams two and three went to the experimental or test port. Of these two, one was passed through odorizing units containing the odorant compound to be tested; the other was used to dilute the first to the desired concentration." The intensity of the stimulus was regulated by varying the ratio of the rates of flow of streams two and three and also the rate through the odorizing unit.

Dethier, like many authors who have described human olfactometers, referred to the odorizing unit as a "saturator." However, unless it can be proven that the air picks up enough odorant at a given rate of flow and temperature such as to equal the saturated vapor concentration of the compound in use (as determined by accepted methods of physical chemistry), we cannot assume that the odorous air is indeed saturated. This problem was solved later (see "Techniques of the Recent and Contemporary Instruments") for metaxylene by determining its weight loss and comparing it with a value calculated from the vapor pressure (Stuiver, 1958). In fact, the unit employed by Dethier was of the wick type designed to speed the evaporation of the liquid phase. The unit may be regarded as the forerunner of the evaporator of a currently used model as it consisted of a test tube with a side arm 1 in. from the bottom. "The tube was filled with alcohol to a point just below the side arm. A sleeve of filter paper extending from the bottom to a point just below the top was slid into the tube. This served as a wick from the surface of which the alcohol evaporated and was carried by the air entering the side arm to other parts of the apparatus." The point is well taken that inasmuch as a known concentration of vapor rather than a saturated one was required, the apparatus was satisfactory. Temperature was held constant and each evaporating odorizer was calibrated for different rates of flow in the presence of various compounds. The vapor concentration was ascertained by measurement of the weight loss of liquid after a measured amount of air had passed. Inasmuch as the stimulus concentrations were not shown to be based upon saturated air, we cannot be certain that the intensities administered were correct.

Soon after the Hoskins and Craig olfactometer was described, an attempt was made to solve the measurement of human olfactory thresholds by means of the *blast injection* of the stimulus into the nasal airway (Elsberg & Levy, 1935). It was also possible to present the stimulus by means of *stream injection*. This technique differed only in the substitution of a continuous flow for the short intervals of flow into the nares with blast injection. The main features of Elsberg's olfactometer were a bottle fitted with a hypodermic syringe and a pair of glass tubes to transport the stimulus to the nares of the subject. A known amount of liquid phase was placed in the bottle and allowed to volatilize until equilibrium was reached with the contained air. This preparation was made at known temperature and pressure, so that a measured volume of stimulus (or odorivector) was presented as a short blast at a calculated pressure. Variations of this technique were evaluated by other investigators and the results are summarized by Wenzel (1948) as well as in a later concise review of the lesser known models (Mateson, 1955).

It is to be regretted that so many authors have uncritically quoted the alleged threshold determinations of Elsberg and Levy since it has been shown that they failed to achieve the conditions they considered necessary for such measures. The working procedures included: (1) obvious precautions such as clean and deodorized parts and protection of experimental odorants against contamination during all steps; (2) control over the stimulus intensity (or measurable vapor concentration); and (3) control over the inspired volume of odorous air or otherwise delivered stimulus volume.

Wenzel (1948) states in her critique the major shortcomings of Elsberg's technique: "There are four main criticisms that are applicable to this general technique. First, it is impossible to determine the number of molecules present in the stimulus. Second, the new air introduced is not purified in any way. Third, odorous materials are used in the construction of the apparatus." Fourth, the pinch clamp that was the on and off valve of the blast injection line was opened by hand. This control made for little uniformity in the onset of stimulation from one trial to the next, as well as in duration of the individual stimuli. Furthermore, the stimulus interval gave a decremental intensity as a consequence of the line pressure lessening to atmospheric.

An attempt to settle the controversy over the presentation of the odor stimulus by blast injection as contrasted with *natural controlled inhalation* has been reported recently (Jones, 1955). Although his data were obtained by the use of flasks, rather than by olfactometry, there have not been any additional comparative studies of this question by olfactometrists reported to date. They have been preoccupied with investigations of olfaction and have sought to justify their choice of olfactometric techniques by logical argument which derives its defense from various physical and chemical experiments. Jones put the question to test and, within the limitations of his cruder experimental controls, has shown that the median human thresholds for *n*-butyl alcohol and safrol are very similar when determined by either blast injection or natural controlled inhalation. Jones' result with *n*-butyric acid contrasted with these two thresholds determined for the same 24 subjects. That *n*-butyric acid had a different threshold may possibly be explained by a slow rate of adsorption or that, once adsorbed, it is very tightly bound to the olfactory neuroepithelium. These physicochemical processes would limit the effective number of stimulating molecules per instant of time either by not having the adequate stimulus impinging quickly enough or by occupying the receptor sites (physiological contact surfaces) too long and thus preventing subsequent incoming molecules from being adsorbed. If the actual vapor concentration was just adequate for a rapid adsorber, for instance, then it might follow that a slow adsorber would need a much greater vapor concentration in order to stimulate a sufficient number of sites. Failing this, the flow of neural impulses (signals) would be inadequate for the perception of the *n*-butyric acid. Although the inspired volumes of odorant vary between individuals, with more men having larger volumes than women, the intraindividual variation in volume is small under the condition of quiet breathing in a resting, sitting posture (Johnston & Sandoval, 1962).

The final design of an olfactometer in the early period of this science utilized the controlled blast injection of the stimulus (Wenzel, 1949). It was held that because of variability in the inspired volumes under conditions of natural breathing, it was necessary to impose a mechanical control of pressure and duration of the stimulus. It was held also that the control of the number of molecules of odorant vapor for each stimulus would be achieved. A sophisticated design, which stressed the measurement and control of the odorant vapor as well as its chemical purity, was developed. In modern terminology, it was a one channel olfactometer because it presented one stimulus of apparently known vapor concentration to both nares of one subject at a time. The goal was to be able to express each stimulus in terms of the number of odorous molecules contained in it by means of direct units of measurement. Stimulus volume was regulated by blowing the odorous air into the subject's nasopharynx under known positive pressure. In order to control the volume injected, it was necessary to control the duration of stimulation as well. Atmospheric pressure was recorded at each session and the vapor pressure of the odorant had to be determined for the experimental temperature.

The following digest of olfactometric procedure relates to experiments with phenyl ethyl alcohol because it does not stimulate the trigeminal nerve, is pleasant and delicate, and does not fatigue over long periods. Room air is pumped by a diaphragm compressor into a reservoir tank. Small volumes are bled from this tank, cleaned by passage through an activated carbon filter, and led into a glass, wash unit. This unit is a sparger as the input air line has a fritted glass disc at the distal end to make fine bubbles of air that rise up through the stimulus liquid. The rate of air flow is not recorded as the calibration of the apparatus is derived from measurements of the line pressure. The odorous air is transported through glass tubing to a second tank with a side tap into a metal pressure equalizer. The tank rests in a constant temperature water bath at 20° ± 0.1°C. Inside the tank is an evaporating dish holding the stimulus liquid. The blind-ended pressure equalizer is similar to a wet spirometer, being half filled with water in its bottom shell. When the solenoid valve, positioned just before the nosepieces to the nares, is opened, the upper shell falls steadily so that the line pressure is maintained throughout the duration of the stimulus. The pressure is read from an open manometer on the effluent end of the olfactometer before the line passes through the wall to the test chamber where the seated subject awaits the blast injection of the stimulus. The solenoid valve is controlled by a Telechron constant speed electrical motor of 1 rpm. The duration of the stimulus and the interval between stimuli may be varied independently, but in the first experiment the duration was held constant at 0.50 sec and the interval between stimuli was 29.50 sec. Each subject had his own nosepiece, a solid glass, olive-shaped bulb around the glass tubing, which was obliquely tilted upward to facilitate insertion into the nares.

The stimulus intensity is defined as the number of odorous molecules per unit of delivered volume and was varied by changing the stimulus volume. Calibration was performed by using every 13 mm of the descending outer cylinder of the pressure equalizer as equivalent to 200 ml. For each of five different weights of the cylinder, the extent of fall in 5 sec was measured. Ten such determinations were taken for each weight. Each series of values was averaged, the mean converted into milliliters and divided by 10 to yield the volume per 0.50 sec. For conversion of weight to pressure, all that was necessary was to read the manometer and convert to the height of a mercury column. Due to the control of temperature and the use of compounds with known vapor pressures, a calculation of the number of molecules in each stimulus could be made. The quantity varied somewhat as the atmospheric pressure varied, although it was never more than an increase of 1.5 times the smallest value of molecules determined on a given day. The error expected due to the variability of the determinations of the various steps in the calculations was not more than 2%. The maximum variability was found in the stimulus volume and the intensity was well above the average absolute threshold or approximately 10^8 molecules. The two intensities of the phenyl ethyl alcohol for determination of the least noticeable difference of strength was 1.42 and 2.06×10^{17} molecules. Unlike Stuiver (1958), Wenzel did not prove the validity of these calculations by using a known saturated vapor in her closed system as the basis for these stimulus intensities at 20°C.

Techniques of the Recent and Contemporary Instruments

The general guides to competent olfactometry that reflect our current knowledge of suitable materials and psychophysiological facts serve to introduce the illustrative models of olfactometers in contemporary use. Threshold determinations are meaningless unless the homogeneity and purity of the chemical compounds is proved because contaminations exert an unknown effect upon odor perception. Rubber, Tygon, Plexiglas, and most plastics should not contact the odorous air stream. Metal tubes more than 2 feet in length should be avoided because of the greater loss by adsorption within them as compared to glass. The test stimulus should not be injected or blasted into the nose under even a slight pressure because (1) when a subject swallows, he will vary the pressure in his nose and affect his sensitivity and reactions to odors, and (2) an injected air stream can cool the mucous membrane and stimulate the thermal receptors within the nasopharynx. Subjects should not work for long periods per day, particularly when the room air is not completely conditioned and odor neutral. A glass funnel or cone should be the effluent that delivers the odorous air to the nares as it is more accurate than separate insertable nose pieces. Each subject should be examined before the test for an abnormality that would obstruct the inhalation of the stimulus or cause a temporary raised or lowered sensitivity to odors. Determinations of stimulus intensity should be based upon several measurements and expressed as a mean value. Two thresholds should be determined for irritating substances, the odor threshold per se and the pain threshold; otherwise, the latter may be confused with the former. Study of the recognized experimental designs for psychophysics and psychophysiology should precede all actual odor measurements.

After 1950, when Mateson (1954) started his investigations of olfactometers and olfaction, the controversy over blast injection with respect to normal inhalation was settled to the extent that only two laboratories are currently using the blast injection principle (e.g. Schneider, Costiloe, Vega, & Wolf, 1963) while other laboratories are using natural inhalation. Three different effluent units for the presentation of the stimulus are used in natural inhalation techniques: (1) an open mouthed glass vessel reminiscent of the smell bottles used by Mayne for flask experimentation (Cheesman & Mayne, 1953) and by Cheesman*; (2) an odor hood surrounding the subject's head that is flushed by purified air and odorous air alternately (Wenzel, 1955) and (Ough & Stone, 1961); and (3) a moulded, glass nose cone and plasticized mouth exhaust cup which fit snugly and comfortably around the subject's nose and mouth, respectively (Johnston & Sandoval, 1960). A glass funnel was a forerunner of the nose cone (Mateson, 1954).

The earlier preoccupation with absolute human threshold determination has recently been revived by studies of complex odor qualities at optimal suprathreshold intensities, and more work has been done with the least detectable difference of strength of a given odor (difference limen, DL). Therefore, more attention has been paid to the odorizer unit of the instrument and most models have utilized the sparger whether or not the research goals were the determination of absolute threshold. One very interesting contemporary instrument used to study absolute threshold in respect to cross adaptation of odors employs a refined *evaporator* for the odorizer (see footnote on p. 14). Inasmuch as it is now possible to measure the stimulus intensity in molecules of odorant per mm^3 of air by means of *peak area* measurements of chromatograms of pure compounds obtained from packed columns in gas-liquid chromatographs (Pecsok, 1959), the problem of whether an odorizer unit is in fact a saturator is not critical unless the investigator continues to use the old method of calculating the intensity (Stone & Bosley, 1965). For most applications, the direct measurement of the stimulus intensity in terms of molecules per mm^3 of air is the best practice and is feasible with packed column gas-liquid chromatography techniques provided that the appropriate phase of adsorbent chemical has been ascertained by trial whenever it cannot be learned from the specialized literature.

The determination of peak areas in the chromatograms is a calculation of the average of at least three independent analyses. Modern chromatographs have a Librascope Continuous Integrator for automatically measuring the area under the curve produced by the recorder of the instrument. When such measurements have been made for a standard amount of the chemical injected into the chromatograph as well as for the experimental vapor, it is possible to calculate the

---

*G. H. Cheesman, personal communication, 1965.

vapor concentration of the latter by comparison with the former using a method of proportions (see below for examples of results). The experimental vapor must be introduced into the apparatus directly by means of a heated tube, condensed at the injection point, and then heated rapidly so that an adequate "slug" of vapor is carried forward into the packed column for analysis by the carrier gas.

Virtually all of the contemporary models employ the continuous flow dilution principle, but it is worth noting that an olfactometer used for determining behavioral responses of laboratory rats has exploited a stepwise dilution technique (Goff, 1961). While Cheesman and Kirby (1959) have designed an air purifier that greatly reduces the vapor pressures of all odorants by immersing them in a cold, liquid bath and thereby ensuring adequate dilution of the vapor phase in air or nitrogen, the Goff stepwise principle should be borne in mind by future designers of human olfactometers.

Since Goff used a gas-liquid chromatograph to calibrate the stimulus intensity, the possible objection to his static method embracing three successive flasks is not valid. Loss of molecules by adsorption on the inner surfaces of the flasks did not introduce an error in the calibration because the measurement was made after any loss by adsorption. Of course, even chromatography is subject to error when the dilution is so great as to be less than one part in a billion parts of air. There is reason to believe that the human olfactory organ is more sensitive to pure odorants than any artificial odor detector of proved dependability. A conservative statement of the all around sensitivity of the tritium foil detector (a soft β-ray emitter) with argon carrier gas is one part in a half billion parts of air. This detector is the most sensitive device for counting the number of vaporous molecules when it is employed with a packed column (as contrasted with a capillary column). When the tritium is energized by the electric current, it emits radiation that transforms the argon molecules to a metastable state so they are part of an electrical field within the cylindrical body (housing) of the detector. Then, as the molecules of a pure odorant pass through the detector, they interfere with the field and the outflowing signals to the amplifier and recorder are modified (Lovelock, 1958). These changes in the outflow are reflected by the movements of the automatic writing pen of the recorder. When a single pure vapor passes through the system, its presence is indicated by a chromatogram with the familiar "spike" shape.

In respect to sparging the odorant liquid in order to produce odorized air, it is important that the instrument design provides correct functional shape and volume in the closed system and a rate of flow of the purified air or nitrogen of less than 2 L per min. A suitable model is the apparatus for the transpiration method of determining vapor pressure of pure liquids (Glasstone, 1946). It was proved that bubbling (sparging) a carrier gas through a liquid phase from a sintered or fritted glass filter produces errors in the determinations because (1) a spray can be mechanically carried over from the solution to the solvent, and (2) the decrease in pressure in a bubble as it rises through the liquid causes expansion and there is a possibility of the initially saturated bubble becoming unsaturated. Inasmuch as the rate of flow of the vehicle (air or nitrogen) is the primary force involved, it is very likely that this error source is more serious in olfactometers for rats and flies than it is for human subjects. In the latter application, it is possible to hold the air or nitrogen velocity in contact with the nasopharynx to less than 2 L/min. Airkem, Inc., usually employs less than 1 L/min with their Mateson multistimulus olfactometer* and the six channel olfactometer described below employs normal flow rates of 0.5 to 1.5 L/min with a maximum of 1.98 L/min (Johnston, 1965, a and b). Another reason for using a constant gentle flow rate on humans is that of avoiding the subject's perception of a current and, most important, to avoid cooling the nasal mucosa since this might stimulate thermal receptors in the airways and become an objectionable associated sensation to the odorant vapor.

Materials and cleaning. In respect to the materials used in the fabrication of olfactometers, much technical data about substances that were once believed to be essentially odorless show that this is not true and will invalidate a closed system if they are used in it. The ideal system would be of Pyrex all glass construction with spherical and nonlubricated joints. When the designer is forced to compromise, metal parts should be small, deodorizable, and preferably of stainless steel. When flexible tubing must be substituted, it should be Teflon. Tygon and polyvinyl chloride have either inherent odor which will contaminate the closed system or they are likely to absorb odors on their exterior and permit them to volatilize into the lumen when the pure odorant vapor is being transported to the olfactory organ. Plexiglas is another type of plastic that is not as odorless as cleaned glass, especially with respect to the adsorption of compounds upon its surface. In fact, the inherent degree of ease and efficiency of deodorizing inner surfaces of olfactometers is an important factor in maintaining adequate experimental control of the closed system. Many authors have failed to note explicitly their cleaning and deodorizing procedure following an experiment. This practice is to be regretted in view of the stringent requirements for cleanliness. In general, it may be stated that there is no more effective cleansing agent than dry heat, and when Pyrex glass has been placed in a muffle furnace at 400°C after a careful washing with a good detergent and rinsing with hot water followed by distilled water, the experimenter has done the best that he can to have an odorless instrument. Cleansed parts must be stored in an odorless, air-tight container until they are assembled for the next experiment. Needless to say, the assembly and testing of subjects must be done in an odor-neutral room which is being flushed constantly in order to eliminate rapidly any trace of extraneous odors.

Multistimulus model. Since Mateson (1955) was the first person to design an odorant-mixing olfactometer, it is desirable to review his requirements even

---

*C. J. D'Angio, personal communication, 1955.

though a comprehensive critical appraisal of the performance of his multi-stimulus olfactometer has not been made available. The instrument should be easy to operate and maintain; yield competent information about and control of temperature, pressure, and humidity of the odorivector (odorant vapor) at all times; permit adjustment of and measurement of stimulus intensity or vapor concentration; handle any odorant regardless of its phase or state, vapor pressure, and inherent strength; permit continuous operation during an experiment; and be suitable for threshold and suprathreshold work with pure chemicals and odorant mixtures.

A detail photograph of the multistimulus olfactometer may be seen in an available journal (Mateson, 1955). The apparatus is used to study one subject at a time. The construction is largely of Pyrex and compressed air is the vehicle. The odorant is sparged and diluted by means of the addition of another stream of pure air. The resultant odor flows from vertically aligned funnels into which the subject's nose is thrust briefly. Unfortunately, this device permits escape of the odorant from the funnel and the subject's nose and mouth even though the duration of each presentation is limited to a few seconds. An opaque screen separates the subject from the tubes and controls behind which the operator sits. A notable attribute of this model is the capacity to present two unknowns which are complex mixtures. The stimuli are vented into an air conditioned room so that the vapors are removed to the outside within a reasonable time. Threshold intensities are calculated from vapor pressures and the other requisite physical factors explained above. It is unfortunate that a detailed account of this olfactometer has not been published since it is an interesting prototype.

Blast Injection

An experimental appraisal of the blast injection principle was made on the Elsberg-Levy olfactometer itself (Jones, 1953). It appeared that the pressure of a given stimulus rather than its volume seemed to cause different effects on human subjects, so it was suspected that the number of molecules in the blast was not important if the concentration of odorant was kept constant. Concentration was maintained constant in this model and Wenzel's (1949). Thus, a threshold determined by blast injection would have a considerably different significance from a threshold obtained by changing the concentration of odorant in the air flow reaching the olfactory organ. These findings resulted from tests of three vapor concentrations by blast injection to ten subjects for *n*-octane and amyl acetate. Since no significant effect of vapor concentration was found, it was concluded that measures provided by this technique cannot be converted into stimulus intensity as expressed by molecules per unit volume. Consequently, the results of blast injection tests are not comparable to thresholds determined by olfactometers which utilize natural inhalation.

Paired Instruments

A two channel olfactometer for the presentation of a pure odorant stimulus was devised for the determination of *odorant quality*. Two identical instruments were built side by side 6 in. apart (Johnston & Sandoval, 1960). Their design was based upon features from the Mateson multistimulus olfactometer, and used an extra coarse, sintered glass filter to sparge bone dry, purified air (Fig. 9.1) through 25 ml of experimental reagent in a specially designed vessel. The fabrication was Pyrex and spherical joints except as noted below. Joints were gasketed with Teflon film.

The air flow was metered by means of Fischer and Porter triflat Flowrators No. 2F-1/8-12-5, float ss 18 and No. 02F-1/8-25-5, float ss 18. The flow rate at the subjects' nares ranged from 1.48 to 1.98 L/min, but the odorizer and air dilution lines flowed more slowly in order to produce desired intensities for optimal judging of the organoleptic qualities of the hitherto unknown odors. The fluctuations (ripples) in line pressure which are a normal incident of compressed air were eliminated by means of the Fischer and Porter differential pressure reducer No. X82626. As a separate air tank was used for each olfactometer, it had a pressure reducer and a purifier unit in its line. The purifier contained factory fresh coconut husk, activated carbon, and granular silica gel, in that order. An innovation to olfactometry was the moulded glass nose cones referred to above and by Johnston and Sandoval (1962). The subject sat on a comfortable stool and placed his face firmly against the beaded edge of the cone so that his nose was enclosed but his mouth was exposed. As soon as the click of one of the three way solenoids signalled that the stimulus was flowing to the nares, he exhaled from the mouth. The regular, gentle breathing helped the subject to abstain from exhaling through his nose into the slightly positive pressure of the eluting stimulus. The line pressure through the solenoid was approximately 0.3 psi and, due to the expansion of the gases, pressure was less at the nares.

This pair of two channel olfactometers served well for paired comparisons of pure odorants; viz. synthetic musks. However, critical testing of the Amoore (Amoore, Johnston, & Rubin, 1964) version of the stereochemical theory of olfaction created a demand for a six channel olfactometer which would permit the blending of four pure odorants in vapor phase and provide increased flexibility of experimental procedures. Utilizing several integral units of the simpler model, the first blending olfactometer was developed in 1962–1963 (Amoore et al., 1964). Following this, the technique of calibration by means of gas-liquid chromatography was improved.

The *six channel olfactometers* made it possible to compare the qualities and strengths of pure compounds, experimental blends of pure compounds, and natural botanical isolates of greatest scientific interest (Johnston, 1965, a and

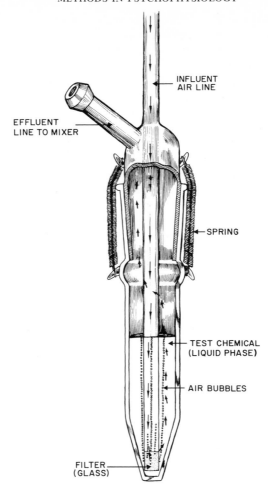

FIG. 9.1. Sparging vessel. A detail of Fig. 9.2. The working volume is 25 ml.

b). A much greater length of glass tubing was enclosed in a constant temperature air bath as compared with the preceding model (Johnston & Sandoval,
1962). The instruments were maintained at 25°C. The ambient air was held
at 24°C and the relative humidity between 50 and 60%. As paired comparisons
of the odorous unknowns were made by the subjects, both of these intricate
olfactometers were fitted into the air bath, which had a gross weight of 550
lbs. The effluent total Flowrators, three way solenoids, and glass nose cones were
placed outside the air bath.

Internal Flowrators in each sparging line and the dilution line permit the
precise control of stimulus intensity when one, two, three, or four stimuli are

being used simultaneously. By these devices, slight modifications of the intensities of the odorants and air can be effected and reproduced. A precise knowledge of flow through each sparger is known at all times and the proportions of the components of an experimental mixture can be varied by minute amounts when it is necessary to adjust for individual subject sensitivity to the chemicals. The Flowrators can measure as little as 5 ml/min of air or nitrogen, but the meter in the dilution line measures a range of 60 ml to 2120 ml/min. There is also a Flowrator of larger capacity to measure total flow downstream of the three way solenoid. The range of this meter is 60 ml to 3660 ml/min.

In respect to sparging of the liquids, the gentle flow rates of less than 1 L/min were an effective check upon aerosol formation; however, each glass line from the spargers conducted the odorous air at least 18 in. to the mixer. Many of these lines served as traps, but the mixers were very effective for this purpose because the odorous air entered at the upstream end. There has not been a single instance of a vapor condensing within the tubes or mixers. An additional preventive was the fact that, in most experiments, the sparging did not produce saturation of the air. As a matter of fact, evaporation weight losses at various flow rates have proven that there is an optimum "pick-up" of the odorant between 0.5 and 0.7 L/min.

In respect to the inner and outer air lines, it was proven that mechanical performance was steady (good) when air flowed through the inner air line to the mixer for all variations of the operation. The outer bypass air line was used only for certain large dilutions of the vapors. The dilution of the flowing stimuli occurred just before the nose cone.

The following dimensions of the crucial parts of the olfactometer will explain the schematic diagram (See Fig. 9.2). The air bath was 1.97 cubic meters capacity, the sparging vessels were 89.8 ml capacity, of which 64.8 ml are headspace above the 25-ml working volume of liquid. The mixers were 106.5 ml capacity, the diameter 3.0 cm, and the length 21.9 cm. The nose cones were 14.6 cm long, with the actual cone 7.5 cm from the center line of the front edge to apex.

The front edge of the cone was roughly triangular in section with a distance of 6.4 cm from the bridge of the subject's nose to the bottom edge that touched between the nose and upper lip. The cones were coated with dimethyldichlorosilane in order to prevent adsorption of odorants on the inner walls.

The determination of the various odorant intensities in terms of molecules per mm^3 of air for the major blending experiment ranged from 1.72 to 121.00 $\times$ 10^8 molecules. As these values are means of three to four individual determinations with a Jarrell-Ash gas-liquid chromatograph, Table 9.1 represents the degrees of precision obtained by using diethylene glycol adipate as the stationary phase in a packed column.

The Tetralin musk was the least precise measurement so it will be repeated with another stationary phase. The synthetic camphor was the most satisfactory determination. The musk was the only reagent among the eight which failed

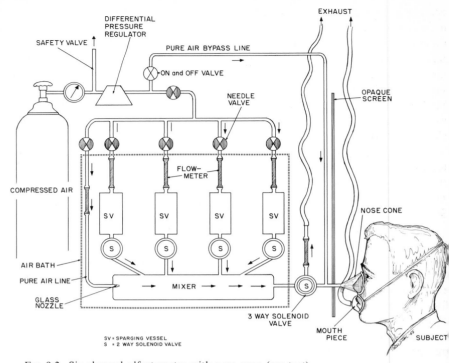

FIG. 9.2. Six channel olfactometer with nose cone (see text).

to exhibit a sharp spike in its chromatogram, but the peak area was measurable with a Librascope.

Two Channel Olfactometer (with Odor Hood)

An instrument appeared in 1959 that was designed to detect differences of subjective odor strength since there are some subjects who cannot perceive a difference which is critical for others (Ough & Stone, 1961). The olfactometer was a mechanical improvement of the last one Wenzel (1955) designed after she abandoned the blast injection method for the continuous flow dilution

TABLE 9.1

	10^8 Molecules per mm³ ($\bar{x}$)	Standard deviation
1, 1, 3, 4, 4, 6-Hexamethyl-7-acetyltetralin.	1.72	0.48
Phenylethylmethylethyl carbinol	1.92	0.24
D. L-Menthone.	18.80	0.20
Synthetic camphor	121.00	0.74

technique. This change was dictated by the finding that many subjects could not perform reliably with blast injection even after long training. They could not control the position of the internal mouth and throat parts which affected the volume of odorous air entering the nasopharynx. However, in the California variation of the new design, the spirometer type of pressure equalizer was replaced by a glass diffusion bulb with 3 L capacity thereby eliminating water from the closed system (Fig. 9.3). Another novel although dubious feature was a plexiglass odor hood into which the subject put his head from below. The opening was then loosely closed with a sheet of Pliofilm. The continuous flow of pure air throughout the hood quickly removed the sensible odors and made it possible to use standard psychophysical procedures. The subject breathed normally with both nostrils. The newest model employed an air current of 9.5 to 10 CFM, the design being a slight alteration of the 1961 model (Stone & Bosley, 1965).

"Room air was pumped in excess of 20 CFM by a high speed blower. The air was passed over a refrigeration coil to remove moisture and to lower air temperature. To prevent the coil from freezing, part of the refrigerated air was allowed to escape. The air was then passed through a heater and filter-bed enclosed in a Lucite housing. The temperature was maintained at 25°C. and the filter was activated carbon. The air current was then passed through a series of valves, a Fischer & Porter flowmeter of 14.6 CFM capacity and, ultimately, into the plexiglass hood." The vehicle of the odorant was high purity, water-pumped nitrogen. It was produced by a Matheson gas purifier, model 450, type A micron filter. This gas was metered by one of a series of three Matheson flowmeters, either model T-600, T-601, or T-602, according to the desired experimental odorant intensity. The nitrogen conduit passed downward through the diffusion bulb and out of a coarse, sintered glass sparger into the experimental liquid phase. The odorous nitrogen was now free to expand within the bulb and leave by a small caliber tube at the top. The sparging vessel was surrounded by a constant temperature water bath. The odorous nitrogen was transported to the main air stream for mixing and dilution enroute to the effluent end of the tube somewhat above the level of the subject's nares.

The apparatus operated in a "before and after" sequence with one of three reference stimuli preceding the unknown stimulus. The test intervals were of 10-sec duration and a rest interval lasted 15 sec. The hood temperature was kept at 25° ± 0.5°C and relative humidity at 50 ± 2.5%. The arrival of a sample (stimulus) was signalled to the subject by a light. All tubing was made of glass or Teflon with Swagelok fittings. In earlier work, *n*-heptyl alcohol, *n*-heptanone, 2-octanone, and ethyl *n*-valerate were tested with the above procedure (Stone, 1964). The authors do not explain how the odorous air was vented to the outside, although their descriptions imply that this was done directly.

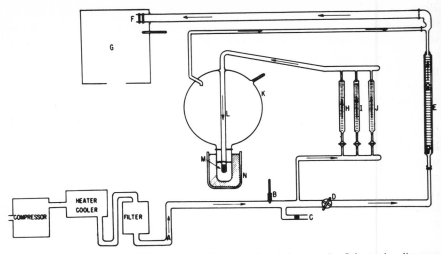

FIG. 9.3. Two channel olfactometer with odor hood (see text). Schematic diagram of the olfactometer. *A*, incoming conditioned air; *B*, thermometer; *C*, air bypass valve; *D*, control valve for large air flow; *E*, large flowmeter; *F*, muffler; *G*, odor hood (plexiglass); *H*, *I*, and *J*, small flowmeters; *K*, diffusion bulb (3 L); *L*, small air flow delivery tube; *M*, sintered glass sparger (coarse); *N*, water bath (control of test liquid temperature). (From Stone, H. *Ann. N. Y. Acad. Sci.*, 1964, *116*: 527–534.)

Calibration values were, for example, acetic acid (190 $\times$ 10^{-4} mg/L of air), *n*-heptanone (31.5 $\times$ 10^{-4} mg/L), and ethyl *n*-valerate (5.4 $\times$ 10^{-4} mg/L). "The flow rates were determined as specified for the particular meters. Determination of test concentrations was by titration of recovered acetic acid with standard NaOH." The data agreed with their earlier findings that air and nitrogen were saturated by the sparging conditions. Knowledge of experimental temperature, vapor pressure of odorants, and gas flow rate was sufficient to calculate stimulus intensities. Gas-liquid chromatography had been used earlier to measure the vapor concentrations, but the specific data are not available.

This interesting olfactometer leaves open the question as to whether so relatively remote a source as the effluent orifice into the hood in reference to the subject's nares yields a realistic measurement of stimulus intensity. The values for the physical factors required by the calculation were not determined at the nares. This problem tends to emphasize the difficulty faced by olfactometrists who study any species of intact vertebrate nasopharynx!

Two Channel Blast Injection Olfactometer

An independently designed instrument was employed in 1957–1958 that combined continuous flow dilution with controlled blast injection (Stuiver, 1958). Some investigations were made with it of absolute sensitivity (threshold), influence of stimulus duration upon threshold, and olfactory adaptation (Stuiver,

1960). In 1963, R. P. Köster, then of the University of Utrecht, gave me an oral report of new work on cross adaptation. He was using two of these olfactometers; however, as Köster did not reply to a letter of inquiry (July, 1965), nothing definite is known of his contemporary use of the apparatus.

The method of treating the room air supplied by a compressor cannot be regarded as purification. The air stream was pumped into a glass washing device (washing substance not stated) and thence into a unit for controlling the temperature (at 17°C) and relative humidity (at 32%) as shown in Fig. 9.4. It was held that such air was "pure" if the outdoor atmosphere was not contaminated. Dependence was placed upon well trained subjects to report immediately any extraneous odors in the glass-walled testing cubicle (cabin). The condensation principle of purifying incurrent air by pumping it over a coiled tube at the temperature of liquid air was not employed because of the expense of processing such large flow volumes.

As in Stone's model (Stone & Bosley, 1965), the air was used for the diluent after the sparging vehicle, nitrogen, was odorized with the experimental chemical. The confluence of these (two) gaseous currents was just before the ultimate unit or *injection apparatus*. This device served as a second stage mixer, on and off valve, and nose piece. The sparging vessel contained an unstated working volume of pure odorant and the incurrent tube was not perforated in any manner. The distal end simply tapered to a small orifice that presumably adequately restricted the size of the nitrogen bubbles. This gas was selected in order to prevent the possible oxidation of the odorants.

After sparging, the odorous nitrogen was diluted by the direct nitrogen stream. Then it flowed through a glass tube to one of three parallel branches. Each of these had been fitted with capillaries of appropriate lengths. This "selector" system determined the volume flow to the main diluting air stream. However, it was possible, when desired, to bypass the injection apparatus by diverting the odorous nitrogen directly across a "selector" branch line to the exhaust tube. The effluent gases were then vented through a ceiling exhaust unit. This was not used to vent the stimulus as it was exhaled from the subject's mouth. Thus, an unknown amount of extraneous odorant was added to the air of the cubicle.

As gas-liquid chromatography was not generally available in 1958, considerable thought was devoted to the problem of calibrating stimulus intensity. A number of capillaries, manometers, and stopcocks were used to control, balance, and measure the line pressures. Inasmuch as the first experiments determined absolute thresholds, the precise calculation of intensity was especially dependent upon a saturated vehicle per se and sensitive, continuous manometric control over the stimulus. A careful scrutiny of the diagram (Fig. 9.4) will show how this condition could be brought about by appropriately closing and opening the stopcocks.

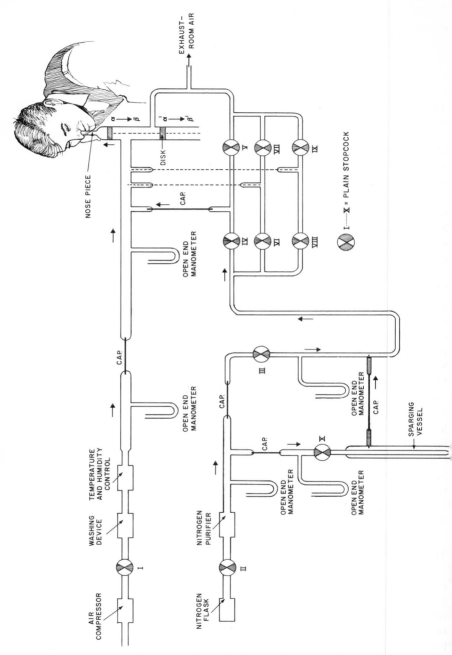

FIG. 9.4. Two channel blast injection olfactometer (see text).

"As the current of injected air experiences a resistance to flow in the nose, it is necessary to give the line between the injection apparatus and the venting tube the same resistance. When these resistances to flow are not equal, pressure in the main air stream, just before the confluence with the odorous nitrogen, changes when the positions of the discs in the injection apparatus are changed from a and b. The odorant vapor concentration in the main line then changes during injection into one side of the nasopharynx because the pressure difference between the air and nitrogen lines changes" (Stuiver, 1958).

That the sparging produced true saturation was proved for this application. The evaporation weight loss of m-xylene was determined as 0.740 gm with an air flow of 2.4 ml/sec during a 7-hour test. Assuming saturation, a loss of 0.724 gm was expected on the basis of 1.75 mm Hg vapor pressure. This was in good agreement with the measured 0.740 gm. However, the assumption that slower rates of sparging flow would also yield saturation like the test flow may be questioned. The pickup of odorants is not directly proportional or linear at all rates of flow at 25°C within the usual range. The threshold of m-xylene was stated as 6.10^{13} molecules/ml for one stimulus volume.

Another blast injection device was designed and used during the period that Stuiver worked on human olfaction. A sophisticated nose piece was used which required the subject to hold his breath during stimulus injection (Schneider et al., 1963). The determinations of the absolute threshold for n-butane were made with nitrogen as the vehicle. The experimenters went to considerable pains to construct a walk-in test room, instead of a glass cubicle or plexiglass hood. The ambient air was recirculated through 20 cannisters of activated carbon by means of a 3-ton air conditioner at constant temperature. The walls of the room were lined with aluminum foil to reduce adsorption of extraneous odors, but the effluent stimulus was vented through the subject's nose and mouth after he removed his external nares from a pair of glass injection tips. Stimulus intensity was given in mole fractions of n-butane in nitrogen as a function of flow rate. The range of flow of the vehicle was between 0.5 and 8.0 L/min. While they reiterated the justification of blast injection on the basis of controlled rate of flow and duration of stimulus, the applicability of the measurements to the natural function of the olfactory organ remains open to grave doubt.

Twenty-four Channel Olfactometer

A significant innovation in design was achieved prior to 1956. This new olfactometer was used for a fundamental study of olfaction by means of cross adaptation. It was the first model to serve a number of subjects in a given session (Cheesman & Kirby, 1959). Furthermore, the latest *air purifier* and odorizer units are outstanding attributes for the determination of absolute human thresholds (see footnote on p. 14). The original version was changed in 1962 to incorporate improvements indicated by experience with the early work. Consequently, the following description and diagram (Figs. 9.5 and 9.6) are presented for the first time since the inventor has generously supplied the author with the unpublished changes.

There are, in fact, two olfactometers, the one with 24 channels presenting the unknown stimuli, and the other with 13 channels presenting the adaptation odorant stimulus. The result is that 12 testing points are before the subjects in a testing room (13 × 7 feet). At each point is a pair of glass capped outlets (*dynamic smelling vessels*) identified by code letters. Every subject smells from each pair, in turn, always sniffing the adapting odorant first and the test stimulus second. Otherwise, the integral units of the two instruments are alike in function, material, and dimensions. Therefore, the following details will refer to both olfactometers, unless otherwise stipulated.

The air distributing glass tubes are 1 in. in diameter with spherical joints. These and the stopcocks are lubricated with a small amount of high grade glycerol. The line pressure is maintained at 5-cm water gauge. Pressure measurements can be made at any time during the operation with differential manometers (gauges in Fig. 9.5) of the leather bellows type. (They are the compound flue draught gauges of industrial boiler applications.) The gauges are side taps in the three main effluent lines just before the ultimate glass capillaries. It is essential to bleed constantly the diluting air, experimental stimulus, and adaptation odorant (in small volumes) into the exhaust duct. Emphasis was placed upon controlling the flows in order to dilute the two odorants to the required vapor concentrations. A calibration curve gave pressure as a function of air flow in liters per min between 0.2 and 1.4.

Capillaries in both branch lines of the olfactometer that present the experimental stimuli are U shaped. They were calibrated at several pressures by measuring the volume of air passing per min from a low pressure gas holder fitted with a constant pressure head. By this means, each smelling point (capped smelling vessel) was given a different vapor concentration by mixing the air and odorant in predetermined proportions. Thus, a series of 12 stimulus intensities were simultaneously available to the judges. The dilution ratios ranged from 1:7.5 to 1:480. Several pure odorants were tested from the array used in an early flask experiment (Cheesman & Mayne, 1953). Quantitative study of the instrumental performance showed that the apparatus apparently achieved the object of providing a series of accurately controlled and steady concentrations of odorous vapor. These were sometimes called the "threshold" series because the subjects were required to report which ones seemed "odorless."

The olfactometer that presents the adaptation odorant has only one pair of U shaped capillaries because one dilution was required at the 12 branches which parallel those of the companion instrument. Neither the dilution ratio nor the substance are known to the author, likewise the measurements of stimulus intensity for the 13 vapor concentrations have not been reported. Cheesman (see footnote on p. 14) is looking forward to using gas-liquid chromatog-

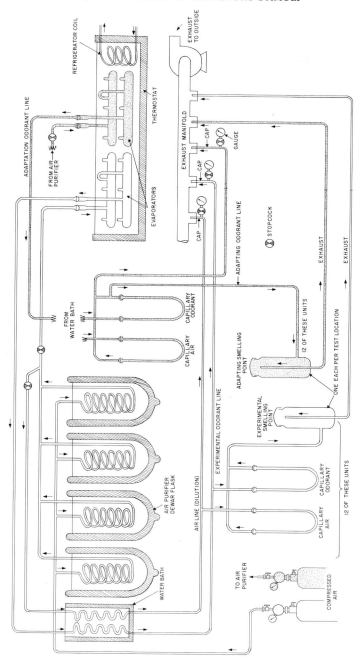

FIG. 9.5. A 24 channel olfactometer (see text).

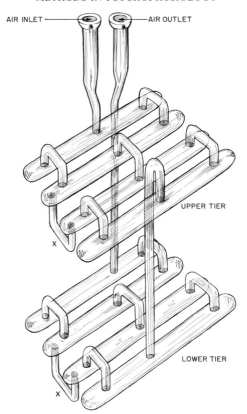

AIR INLET   AIR OUTLET

UPPER TIER

X

LOWER TIER

X

Fig. 9.6. Evaporator. Detail of Fig. 9.5. The odorant partially fills the eight chambers.

raphy for measuring the constancy of the air-odorant mixtures, analyzing for homogeneity of alleged pure compounds, and chemical purification.

Operation of the olfactometers is in accordance with the continuous flow dilution principle. Compressed air flows to an air purifier of four 20 feet, coiled copper tubes, $1/4$ in. in diameter. The coils are connected in parallel and cooled in a large Dewar flask of Dry Ice-alcohol mixture. At the downstream end, a glass-metal seal connects to the all glass system. The air then flows to a fork where stopcocks in each branch control the volume of the air diluting line and the odorous air line. The latter transports some of the air to a unique odorizing unit, the *evaporator* (Fig. 9.6). It has two tiers of four interconnecting chambers each of which is partially filled with the odorant in the horizontal position. (The cross link tubes within each tier facilitate filling and emptying.) The air sweeps over the liquid surface picking up the vapor and goes to a coil in a water bath. At this unit, the air dilution line is also coiled in the bath and both gaseous streams are warmed to the experimental temperature (25°C).

hen the flows pass along the primary branches to the secondary branches oing to the capped smelling points. The water bath warms the adapting odor-nt line as well as the other two lines.

The evaporators of the two independent systems are in a refrigerated thermo-:at containing a glycerol-water bath. Like the cold air purifier, provision for ›w temperatures is very effective to evaporation. Purification by condensation f aerosols avoids the possibility of odorous contamination such as might occur ⁄hen new activated carbon and silica gel are used (Stuiver, 1958). Evaporation ; retarded by lowered vapor pressures of the odorants, a good feature when bsolute threshold concentrations are required. In this connection, perhaps the ripping bottles accessory to the three-necked evaporator flasks, apparently sed at room temperature in an olfactometer designed to stimulate the rabbit's ·lfactory organ, would have been unnecessary (Mozell, 1958). Lowering the apor pressure by cooling the odorants sufficiently might have reduced the olume lost by evaporation to a trivial amount during an experiment.

As the 12 pairs of smelling points protrude through holes in a slanting bench, he group of subjects station themselves separately. When an audiovisual ignal is given, each person removes a glass cap and sniffs the stimulus. The cap ; replaced and the procedure is repeated for the other member of the pair. ¯hen the subject moves to the next smelling point to await the next signal, ⁄hich is given after a predetermined interval (0.5 min). In this way each subject ests all 12 pairs of unknowns and all subjects are required to smell the concen-rations of the series in the same sequence. The subjects' responses are marked ›y them on individual report cards.

There are two possible criticisms of Cheesman's technique: (1) mixers are ιot provided at the confluences of the air dilution and odorous air lines, and 2) the odorants escape into the test room to become extraneous when the glass :aps are removed and the stimuli are exhaled. Without mixers of sufficient size ›r volume it is uncertain that homogenization occurs in the line to the melling vessel. The odorant stream and the purified airstream could laminate ιn the tube. This could present a vapor concentration that is variable from too ;reat to too small. In regard to point two, not only do the experimental vapors ·scape into the test room, its air is continuous with the instrument room hrough a long, horizontal slot in the inner wall. This slot is 6 in. wide and ιbout 12 feet long. Even though the test room is entered by a separate door rom the outside lobby, and is independently ventilated from the outside air ›y a system of fans, the ambient air may not be odor-neutral. This is an im-›ortant requirement for determination of absolute thresholds as background ›dors might affect the subjects' sensitivity.

Five Channel Olfactometer

Before 1962 a well designed instrument was introduced for studying the ›lfaction of vertebrates (tortoise, birds) at the primary level (Tucker, 1963).

Although limited to one preparation at a time, this olfactometer has subjec matter of interest for those investigating man. The olfactory nerve activit was used to monitor the instrumental performance and check the influence o changes. Sometimes the olfactoelectrograms showed the presence of contamina tion in what should have been a purified air response. However, the majorit of "air flow responses" proved that the purifying units of silica gel and activatec carbon or charcoal (Fig 9.7) did not elute biologically detectable odors. Thi evidence corroborates the chromatograms obtained for eight odorants in th six channel olfactometer.

Although recent experience has suggested two changes in the continuou flow dilution system in the diagram, a scrutiny of it will reveal the design an operation. Amyl acetate was the experimental reagent while the gophe tortoise was the subject. The stimulus intensity was so low that a gas-liquic chromatograph was insensitive to the odorized air. Nevertheless, the stimulu was precisely specified at the naris. The air flow ranges were between 0.1 anc 100 ml/sec, which overlaps the working range of some human olfactometers The air streams reached the rotameters at 24° to 25°C, the same temperature a the preparation.

Apparently room air was pumped into an all glass system, but in certain ex periments various gases were introduced into the odorant and diluting flow channels (2, 3, and 4 from *left* to *right*) while the wash channel unit (*on left*) al ways delivered wet air (close to 100% relative humidity). The purifying units were in all channels and two vessels in series contained distilled water or odor ants. The indicated adjustments of the stopcocks with needle valve show the moist wash air going to the *breathing chamber*. The tip of the tortoise head entered a port in the chamber just far enough to place the nares on the edge o the air stream. This position avoided the full force of the air. However, the *wash-odor* switch enables the operator to change to any selection of air, either test or not test. The shunt type pressure regulator was replaced by a conven tional series regulator for delivering air to the pressure reservoir. A valve con striction has been added to the effluent tube to the exhaust in order to maintain a steady pressure head at the manifold rotameters when vapor concentration adjustments are made.

The vacuum pump system was used in some tortoise experiments to evacuate the odor from the choana, i.e. nasopharynx. In recent work with birds, free respiration through the nose was permitted and the suction system was omitted.

The mechanics of the odorizing units were not stated and it was claimed that the odorous air stream was "saturated" with the odorant. A calculation of stimulus intensity was made on this basis, but proof of saturation was not clearly given. The intensity range was stated as 10^{-3} to unity ($10^{-0.05}$) of satu ration, with the accuracy being determined by the rotameters. An appraisal of these data would not be possible until all relevant details are available.

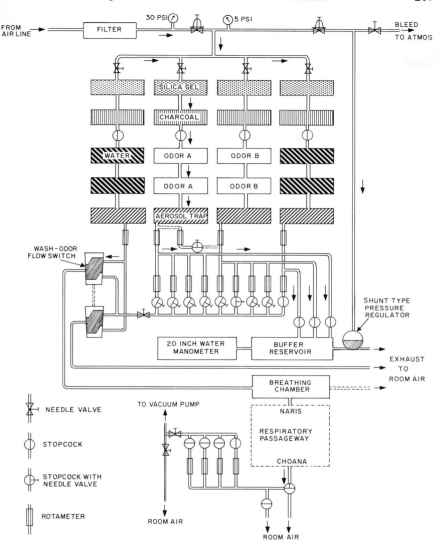

FIG. 9.7. A five channel olfactometer for electrophysiological investigation of small verte-brates (see text).

Discussion

The above case study has not included every contemporary olfactometer being used to quantify the stimulus intensity at representative temperatures. Unmentioned for a variety of reasons are instruments designed by French,

Italian, German, and Japanese investigators. It is believed that the selected descriptions presented show the variety of designs and materials used, and the breadth of conceptual goals subserved by these instruments. Any tendency toward standardization of procedure is not evident because of incomplete performance data. In order to appraise each apparatus and compare them, thorough testing and reporting is needed. Perhaps this conclusion lends credence to the familiar truism that olfactometrists are independent and adopt their own preferences. At least, they are an inventive lot for nobody can buy an olfactometer from a commercial firm.

Nevertheless, one may discern a general quickening of interest in sound operating principle, all glass construction, except for stainless steel valves and Teflon stopcocks, ease of dismantling in order to facilitate deodorization between experiments, and the use of gas-liquid chromatography for stimulus calibration (or specification). Underlying all of these ideals and problems is the perennially overriding one: chemical purity of the odorants used as the unknowns, adaptation agents, and reference standards of odor quality. With preparatory gas-liquid chromatography, it should be possible to have a better international criterion of homogeneity in the reagents. Careful selection of nontoxic compounds with true odors that are amenable to this most dependable method of purification is a must, if the discrepancies in determinations by independent laboratories are to be avoided or understood. The regular use of live animal preparations to ascertain the homogeneity of pure compounds by means of electrophysiological or biological detection would be a check on the gas-liquid chromatography.

Probably the means of a trend toward instrumental conformity and better quality work everywhere would be an international committee of human olfactometrists. They could delineate the specific problems to be resolved, locate the best sources of materials, and recommend the best instrumental designs. If animal olfactometrists were invited to share their ideas with psychophysiologists, a greater impetus could be given to this worthy scientific need. Perhaps the next International Symposium on Olfaction and Taste would be the appropriate forum.

In the meantime, the opinion is ventured that the 24 channel olfactometer will stimulate interest in developing other models to serve other measurement purposes with small groups of subjects. Most current models handle one subject per session. Furthermore, sparging the odorant with the gaseous vehicle was proved reliable at the gentle flow rates demanded by human investigation. Likewise, purifying units of activated carbon and silica gel beds are permissible, at least in certain models, but purification by means of condensation at low temperatures is the method of choice. Nonlubricated joints and valves are required as lubricants have significant vapor pressures at ambient temperatures.

The philosophical debate about the blast injection principle appears to have elicited a negative consensus. Most olfactometrists have avoided this technique during the past 5 years. An acceptable manual of olfactometric procedure has yet to be developed since it would be a major project, both technically and financially, to present all the requisite features and specific procedures. The results of fundamental research on olfaction during 1965 have shown that the primary mechanism of smell is still unknown although there is agreement on what is not sound. Much work will have to be done before the receptive process is clearly delineated. There is no doubt that the indirect method of measuring subjective responses should aid this conceptual research by the following kinds of investigations. Experimental designs for cross adaptation studies at absolute threshold, the determination of functional subjective quality classes to approximate the over-all perception of odors, and the intensive investigation of the judgment of odorant strength as a function of controlled intensity are areas where new contributions need to be made. The psychophysiological necessity for controlling and specifying the stimulus intensity cannot be over-emphasized. The properly designed olfactometer is the only method that will accomplish this.

REFERENCES

Allison, V. C., & Katz, S. H. An investigation of stenches and odors for industrial purposes. *J. ind. engng. Chem.*, 1919, *11*: 336–338.
Amoore, J. E., Johnston, J. W., & Rubin, M. The stereochemical theory of olfaction. *Scient. Am.*, 1964, *210*: 42–49.
Cheesman, G. H., & Kirby, H. M. An air dilution olfactometer suitable for group threshold measurements. *Q. Jl exp. Psychol.*, 1959, *11*: 115–123.
Cheesman, G. H., & Mayne, S. The influence of adaptation on absolute threshold measurements for olfactory stimuli. *Q. Jl exp. Psychol.*, 1953, *5*: 22–30.
Dethier, V. G. *Chemical insect attractants and repellents.* Philadelphia: Blakiston, 1947.
Dethier, V. G., & Yost, M. T. Olfactory stimulation of blowflies by homologous alcohols. *J. gen. Physiol.*, 1952, *35*: 823–839.
Elsberg, C. A., & Levy, I. The sense of smell. I. A new and simple method of quantitative olfactometry. *Bull. neurol. Inst. N.Y.*, 1935, *4*: 5–19.
Glasstone, S. *Textbook of physical chemistry.* (2nd ed.) New York: D. Van Nostrand, 1946. P. 630.
Goff, W. R. Measurement of absolute olfactory sensitivity in rats. *Am. J. Psychol.*, 1961, *74*: 384–393.
Henning, H. *Der Geruch.* Leipzig: Barth, 1916.
Hoskins, W. M., & Craig, R. The olfactory responses of flies in a new type of insect olfactometer. *J. econ. Ent.*, 1934, *27*: 1029.
Johnston, J. W., Jr. Experiments on the specificities of human olfaction. In J. I. Bregman & A. Dravnieks (Eds.), *Surface effects in detection.* Washington, D. C.: Spartan Books, Inc., 1965. (a)
Johnston, J. W., Jr. Experiments on the specificities of human olfaction. *Proc. II int. Symp. Olfaction and Taste, Tokyo, 1965*, in press. (b)
Johnston, J. W., Jr., & Sandoval, A. Organoleptic quality and the stereochemical theory of olfaction. *Proc. scient. Sect. Toilet Goods Ass.*, 1960, *33*: 3–9.

Johnston, J. W., Jr., & Sandoval, A. The validity of muskiness as a primary odor. *Proc. scient. Sect., Toilet Goods Ass.*, 1962 *37*: 34–45.

Jones, F. N. A test of the validity of the Elsberg method of olfactometry. *Am. J. Psychol.*, 1953, *46*: 81–85.

Jones, F. N. A comparison of the methods of olfactory stimulation: blast vs. sniffing. *Am. J. Psychol.*, 1955, *68*: 486–488.

Lovelock, J. E. A sensitive detector for gas chromatography. *J. Chromat.*, 1958, *1*: 35.

Mateson, J. F. The olfactory area and the olfactory process. *Ann. N.Y. Acad. Sci.*, 1954, *58*: 83–95.

Mateson, J. F. Olfactometry: its techniques and apparatus. *J. Air Pollut. Control Ass.*, 1955, *5*: 167–170.

Mozell, M. M. Electrophysiology of olfactory bulb. *J. Neurophysiol.*, 1958, *21*: 183–196.

Ough, C. S., & Stone, H. An olfactometer for rapid and critical odor measurement. *J. Fd Sci.*, 1961, *26*: 452–456.

Pecsok, R. L. *Principles and practice of gas chromatography.* New York: John Wiley & Sons, 1959.

Schneider, R. A., Costiloe, J. P., Vega, A., & Wolf, S. Olfactory threshold technique with nitrogen dilution of n-butane and gas chromatography. *J. appl. Physiol.*, 1963, *18*: 414–417.

Skramlik, E. V. *Handbuch der Physiologie der niederen Sinne. Band I Die Physiologie des Geruchs und Geschnacksinnes.* Leipsig: Thieme, 1926.

Stone, H. Behavioral aspects of absolute and differential olfactory sensitivity. *Ann. N.Y. Acad. Sci.*, 1964, *116*: 527–534.

Stone, H., & Bosley, J. J. Olfactory discrimination and Weber's Law. *Percept. Mot. Skills*, 1965, *20*: 657–665.

Stuiver, M. Biophysics of the sense of smell. State University of Groningen Ph.D. thesis. Groningen: Uitgeverij Excelsior, 1958. P. 99.

Stuiver, M. An olfactometer with a wide range of possibilities. *Acta oto-lar.*, 1960, *51*: 135–142.

Tucker, D. Physical variables in the olfactory stimulation process. *J. gen. Physiol.*, 1963, *46*: 453–489.

Wenzel, B. M. Techniques in olfactometry: a critical review of the last one hundred years. *Psychol. Bull.*, 1948, *45*: 231–247.

Wenzel, B. M. Differential sensitivity in olfaction. *J. exp. Psychol.*, 1949, *39*: 129–143.

Wenzel, B. M. Olfactometric method utilizing natural breathing in an odor-free "environment." *Science, N.Y.*, 1955, *121*: 802–803.

Zwaardemaker, H. Olfaktometrie. *Fortschr. Med.*, 1889, *19*: 721–731.

Zwaardemaker, H. Prazisionsolfactometrie. *Arch. Lary. Rhinol.*, 1904, *15*: 171–177.

Zwaardemaker, H. *L'Odorat.* Paris: Doin, 1925.

10

Research
Electroencephalography

CURTIS MARSHALL, M.D.

Electroencephalography, by definition, is the recording and evaluation of the electrical potentials generated by the brain and sampled at the scalp surface. When one wishes to use brain potentials as a research data source, however, it is more practical to stray somewhat from the strict definition and to derive the samples of the brain potentials in whatever manner most adequately fits the investigation.

The history of the technique shows the influence of a classic series of mis-evaluations, jealousies, and even political struggles, until, in maturation, the technique is approaching a respectable stability just in time to be largely emasculated by computer automation.

While Caton, in 1875, first described the existence of potentials generated by the brain, the first attempted clinical use of these potentials came from Hans Berger who, starting in 1929, published a series of articles "Uber das Elektrenkephalogramm des Menschen" and so, in essence, coined the term electroencephalogram (EEG). Berger's recordings started with a single channel machine and with electrodes consisting of silver wires inserted into the frontal and occipital scalp; although hardly adequate for EEG as we now know it, this was quite sufficient to put EEG on the map as a clinical tool.

Three laboratories which were largely responsible for the practical spread of the technique were those of Gibbs at Harvard, Jasper at McGill, and Walter at the Burden Neurological Institute. All three were prolific both in volume of work and in volume of publications but a vast divergence of approach to the subject occurred from the start. Gibbs, an M.D., rapidly standardized a technique and then concerned himself primarily with the compilation of clinical data and its correlation with electrical patterns. He introduced a nomenclature for these patterns which, in retrospect, was allowed to grow almost haphazardly with no profound approach or control. The technique of his group has re-

221

mained largely unchanged over the years so that, disregarding technical advances, both his early and contemporary tracings can be directly compared. In addition to providing a volume of statistical information, Gibbs has probably trained more clinicians in the field of EEG than all other laboratories in this country have together. Thus, he can be looked upon as the primary agent in the popularization of EEG in the United States. Jasper and Walter were not clinicians in the early days of EEG but were interested, rather, in the neurophysiological aspects of EEG. As a result they worked largely with the perfection of techniques and neuroanatomical correlations as well as with the clinical application of their investigations. They decried the forced standardization of techniques in a field so new, and also opposed the rigid, wave form oriented nomenclature of Gibbs. Their techniques have kept pace with the latest knowledge in the field and for this reason their most recent work cannot be directly compared with their earliest recordings.

In spite of the various prolific investigators in the field, the majority of clinical EEG terminology used today in the United States is based on Gibb's work. Early systems of terminology introduced by various other workers have been discarded in favor of a broader integrated nomenclature under the auspices of the International Electroencephalogram Federation; this system ignores Gibb's popular terminology.

The Electroencephalograph

The equipment consists of (1) a number of balanced, high gain amplifiers with high input impedance showing a flat frequency response curve from about 0.1 Hertz to 120 Hertz, (2) a switching arrangement including calibrating devices, and (3) an output presentation, i.e. ink writer units. In actual application the following descriptions are relatively standard.

Calibration circuit. A square wave is used which may be varied in steps from about 5 μv to 5 mv in amplitude. The duration of the square wave is manually controlled by a simple on-off switch. The calibration signal is inserted in place of the patient; not in series with the patient as is done in electrocardiography. The square wave was chosen as it provides simultaneous information on both the low and high frequency limits of the amplifiers which are immediately available.

Subject connections. Electrodes of silver, tin, tin-lead solder, platinum, or even gold, with ultraflexible insulated lead-off wires are connected electrically with the scalp by a conducting salt paste or solution. These are maintained in position mechanically by the tackiness of the conducting paste, by a fast setting cement such as flexible collodian or melted wax, or by a rubber hair-net or cap. In clinical machines, connections are available for 24 electrodes whereas, for research application, 100 or more connections are often available depending upon the dictates of the experimental plan, the funds available, and the ingenuity of the technician. Most clinical machines use 24 point rotary selector switches which are widely available commercially; for the larger selector systems, however, patch panels are commonly used. A degree of simplification of the electrode selector panel has been achieved by use of a preset switch into which a series of routine montages have been wired, permitting the operator to simultaneously make all of the connections for the inputs of all of the channels in a montage by turning one knob. Two methods of identification of electrodes are in use. First, a numerical method is used with no inherent system of location although most laboratories place odd numbered electrodes on the left side of the scalp and even numbers on the right. The second method, the "International System," is based on percentages of scalp measurements with the actual electrode sites located on a grid of coordinates named after brain areas and distances from the midline. Although the operator is free to apply only those electrodes which fit his system, the distribution of electrodes inherent in the International System fits well with a 21 electrode pattern. Starting with this number of electrodes provides adequate coverage and additional electrodes may be added when special, more precise localizations are desired.

"Known-Unknown" switch. This is often labeled "Cal-Run," or "Calibrate-Patient" and is a multipole switch which selects the input source for the amplifiers of all of the channels, either connecting all of the amplifiers in parallel across the calibration circuit or connecting them individually to the montage selector switches. The Grass model 6 machine has a unique and most versatile push-button switching panel of which the only drawback is its limitation to 23 electrodes. This push-button panel permits use of preset montages, manually set montages, and calibration in various channels at the same time, a most useful facility for both clinical and research applications.

Amplifiers. Whereas most clinical EEG machines have eight channels for simultaneous independent recording, research machines may have 16 channels or more. The characteristics of these amplifiers are important. They must be balanced with a common mode rejection of 3,000 to 1 or better; they should have a high input impedance to prevent "loading" of the subject electrode signal source. Although fairly good operation can be achieved with an amplifier input impedance of 600,000 ohms with the scalp electrode resistances below 7,000 ohms, a 2-megohm input impedance is to be desired and is standard. For many research applications, however, input impedances of 10 megohms will be needed. The double input of the balanced amplifier requires that the voltages from two electrodes be compared within each channel. These two inputs may be designated as the "U" and "D" inputs and defined thus: the "U" input is the one which, when more negative than the "D" input causes an *upward* displacement of the output trace; the converse, of course, is also true and when the same voltage and polarity is presented to both inputs, the output shows no deflection. In writing the electrode connections for a channel, the U connection is always stated first; on a selector panel, the switch controlling the U connection is the *upper* one. In the past, U and D have been variously referred to as "G1 and G2," "1st and 2nd," "Grid and Plate," and "Negative and Positive," the last two are obviously misnomers.

Each channel has its own sensitivity control or controls which are variously labeled as "gain," "amplification," "equalization," etc., and its own selective high and low frequency cutoff controls. These latter controls have been labeled in a confusing variety of terms and numbers, some merely as switch position numbers while others represent time constant, frequency at 50% attenuation, etc. In addition, most EEG machines have "all-channel-gain-controls" as well as ganged controls for all channels for both high frequencies and low frequencies.

Output. Clinical EEG machines in the United States are usually equipped with simple galvanometers driving pens on "Z"-fold paper which is pulled past the writing position at 30 mm/sec (double and half this speed are usually also available). The pens are usually spaced 1 in. on center, requiring a paper width of 8 in. for the standard eight channels. Various more sophisticated write-out methods are sometimes used including rectilinear pen drives, and multichannel cathode ray oscilloscopes with photorecording. The write-out characteristics limit the high frequency response of the entire system so that the simpler and less costly ink writing methods are used when high frequency recording is not required.

Machine Selection

Factors which determine selection of an electroencephalograph for research purposes in the United States are straightforward. Fundamentally, the equipment must not only be capable of doing the job but, of almost equal importance, it must be highly reliable so that machine maintenance will be an insignificant factor in the over-all operation of the project. The two most popular U. S. made EEG machines, Grass and Offner-Beckman, are adequately stable and both companies have designed their equipment to permit simple plug in replacement of defective components. Neither company, however, has any available on-the-spot service organization. Whereas some very high quality equipment is coming in from Europe, the service problem for that equipment has not yet been solved.

If cost of operation is to be considered, standard noncorrosive ink on inexpensive, easily available "Z"-fold paper provides good recording at the lowest cost, this amounting to less than 50 cents per average clinical recording.

The unique features which might determine which of the two above named makes of instrument would best fit a given application are of relatively minor importance here, although it would be well to point out that Offner-Beckman makes a portable machine which can be carried by one man; the Offner-Beckman machine is all solid state and is chopper-stabilized so that all of the models can record with an infinite time constant (direct current). The Grass machines use vacuum tubes in the input stages with solid state output and have very low breakdown rate; the Grass galvanometer and pen assembly is extremely rugged and can withstand an amazing amount of technician maltreatment.

The EEG Technician

While some clinical electroencephalographers are of the opinion that an EEG technician does not need to know about the evaluation of the recording, this opinion is far from universally accepted. If the only function of the technician were to turn switches, load paper, and make entries in the protocol book, a programmed control could be constructed to effectively replace him. Thus, the only justification for the existence of an EEG technician is his ability to "read" the recording and to alter the recording technique so as to obtain a greater amount of more reliable information that otherwise would have been obtained.

Intellectual honesty of the technician is just as necessary in this field as in any other research technique, as is the ability to keep a neat and complete protocol.

Other than the above factors, the technician must be capable, at the minimum, of recognizing equipment malfunction. Ability to repair the equipment is no longer required at our present level of available design.

Electroencephalography Recording Technique

Calibration. The primary object of calibration is to adjust the equipment so that it is recording in compliance with the standards of the laboratory. When this adjustment has been achieved, a single page of known signal should be recorded to become the first page of the EEG record; this will show that the desired performance has been achieved. If during the recording the technician has reason to believe that the characteristics of the machine have inadvertently changed, another page of standard signal should be recorded and preserved. If this confirms that machine characteristics have changed, then corrections must be made. The pages recorded during these adjustments are not to be retained but one final page of standard signal should be recorded and preserved as the recording is resumed. At the termination of the recording, a final page of standard signal should be made under conditions identical with those used for the last page of EEG recording, and in addition, samples of standard signals should be recorded under every *nonstandard* condition which was used in the body of the EEG.

Below is a set of standards typical of those found in first quality EEG laboratories.

1. Paper speed should be set at 30 mm per sec. As standard "Z"-fold paper is 300 mm between folds, at this paper speed each page represents 10 sec which can be easily timed.

2. The calibration battery voltage should be checked with the integral volt-

meter if present, or with an external voltmeter; the calibration voltage should be then selected to approximate the average volatage expected; usually 50 μv.

3. The 50-μv square wave should be recorded with two complete square waves on each 10-sec page which will amount to four deflections (up, down, up, down) spread out evenly across the page. The dimensions of these calibration deflections will then be measured as follows. (a) Amplitude from the base line to the peak of the saw tooth, measured perpendicular to the base line, must be 7 mm.. The actual peak may have to be plotted as the junction of the rising deflection and the return deflection since under certain circumstances it may not be apparent. When the high frequencies of the tracing have been suppressed with the "high frequency filter," the peak may be rounded off; then the rising curve must be extended by drawing and the falling curve must be extended backward until the two intersect; this is the actual peak to be used in calibration measuring. A far more reliable practice is that of calibrating with no attenuation of high frequencies; under these circumstances, the peak of the "overshoot" is not to be measured, but rather, the point where the rising and falling curves intersect. (b) The duration of the time constant should be 0.3 sec. By definition, this is the amount of time, in seconds, needed for the trace to return 63% of the distance from the peak to the base line when it has been deflected by a long duration square wave. (c) The amount of damping present should provide a single peak of overshoot as shown in the Fig. 10.1.

4. All of the pens should write vertically in a line; i.e. when the machine is off, a straight edge should just touch all of the pens and, when so touching, should lie perpendicular to the edge of the paper.

Montages. A series of montages should be planned providing multiple samplings of each electrode. Although there are various techniques of montage composition, each with its own enthusiastic supporters, none can claim to record information unobtainable by the others. The differences are in the degree of clarity and ease of evaluation of the finished recordings. Most research oriented laboratories lean toward the straight line bipolar technique in which the following guides are used: (a) electrodes for one montage are in a straight line; (b) electrodes for one montage have equal interelectrode distances; (c) montages are set by the following plan: a-b, b-c, c-d, d-e; (d) in anterior-posterior montages, it is usual to use half of the channels on each side of the head; linkages running from one side to the other (coronal) are arranged to have symmetrical representation; and (e) anteroposterior and side to side montages recorded simultaneously are often most informative if sufficient channels are available.

Reading a straight line bipolar montage consists of allotting, to each electrode that activity appearing in mirror image in the two adjacent channels sampling that electrode.

Common reference montages are based on the presumption that a specific electrode is available which is devoid of electrical activity; the D input of each

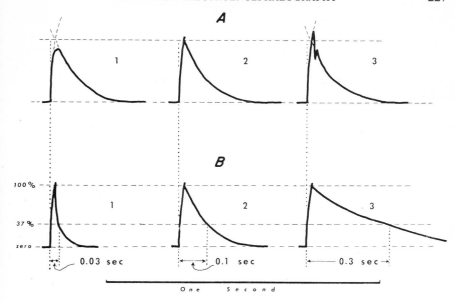

FIG. 10.1. *A* shows the effect on a square wave calibration wave form of altering the high frequency response with the low frequency response remaining unchanged. *1*, poor high frequency response; *2*, correct high frequency response; *3*, accentuated high frequency response. Note the *dashed lines* projecting the rising and falling curves to indicate the point at which amplitude is to be measured. *B*, shows the effect on a square wave calibration wave form of altering the low frequency response with the high frequency response remaining unchanged. *1*, time constant of 0.03 sec; poor low frequency response; *2*, time constant of 0.1 sec; moderate amount of low frequency response as commonly used in clinical EEG; *3*, time constant of 0.3 sec provides more low frequency than above and is technically superior for most purposes.

channel is used as an "inactive" electrode. Any activity appearing in a channel is said (erroneously) to have been picked up by the U electrode. The wide spread technique of joining the electrodes on the two ear lobes and naming this link as "inactive" is grossly in error and is to be studiously avoided.

Reading a common reference montage consists of subtracting from all channels that activity common to all channels, the remainder is allotted to the electrode sampled by the U input of each channel.

The amount of time allotted to recording with each montage depends upon the purpose for which the recording is being made but the total time of recording needed to permit a reasonable statement of "normal record" is 20 min.

Activation. The choice of activation procedures to be used depends upon the individual case but the two simplest techniques, over-breathing and sleep, provide a sufficient augmentation of positive information to warrant their use whenever possible. Photic stimulation is simple in use but the likelihood of obtaining a positive response is so poor that it is often used only in selected cases.

Sleep recording provides a noteworthy increase of EEG data over the simple waking record, but it is only of value if the patient is maintained in dozing or light sleep stages; deep sleep is very likely to suppress the appearance of abnormalities rather than bring them forth.

Terminal calibration. The first page of terminal calibration must be recorded under those exact conditions prevailing during the last page of the recording itself. Then, a sample of calibration signal must be recorded using each of the nonstandard filter and gain settings used during the actual recording.

Actual Application of Electroencephalography

The approaches to the evaluation of EEG data are based on three levels: (1) the spontaneous tracing under conditions of lowered stimulation level; (2) The nonspecific responses to stimulation, and (3) the specific responses to stimuli.

The evaluation of the spontaneous electrical picture requires a definite knowledge of and familiarity with the entire field of EEG. In addition, specific familiarity with the EEG of the species of animal concerned is essential. Although the required background information may be the same, competence in evaluation of human EEG in no way confers competence to read the EEG of the cat, monkey, or dog. The fact that similar patterns are common among the various species constitutes a hazard, not an aid to interpretation as the significances of these patterns often are quite divergent when various animals are compared. An entire volume on the EEG of the dog has been published (Pampiglione, 1963) as an aid to those wishing to use this animal.

One of the most common causes of gross error in the use of EEG in research is the attitude that the investigator only wishes to evaluate one special wave form or specific location or frequency and therefore does not need a broad background or great familiarity with the EEG of the species. The errors which must enter by such a broad pathway destroy any possible value of the study.

The reading of a basic EEG, then, demands a scanning of the tracing of the electrical cortical activity by the "reader" who has a mental image of a normal EEG in its entirety for the species and for the age and situation of the subject. Various montages must be examined which have been planned to provide a series of cross-checks through each electrode and area. The tracing under examination, then passes "inspection" as long as it remains within the limits of normal familiar to the reader. Beyond this, a danger signal is conveyed to the reader who then stops and examines the "deviation" for significance. The *basic* tracing is described in terms of sinusoidal frequencies, nonsinusoidal activity, and wave complexes present as well as their voltages, locations, and symmetries; this material is also noted as being normal or abnormal. Knowledge of the functions of the cortical area being sampled by each electrode is of primary importance and cannot be reasonably omitted from the evaluation. Of vast importance is recognition of the subjects' changing levels of consciousness and their attendant electrical alternations. An attempt is made to correlate the deviations or lack thereof with what is known about the subject and with previous serial EEG tracings, as well as with standard control EEGs.

By far, the most reliable type of EEG reading is that done by the "blind" method in which the reader knows only what situations were presented to the patient in the EEG laboratory. The tracing is described with regard to electrical content with the presumption that serial blind readings of the *same tracing* will yield identical data. If this cannot be achieved, then the reader is insufficiently reliable and the results are of low value. The next step in reading is to attempt to correlate the electrical data, complete with its localizations, with the clinical data; here, a little more freedom is to be exercised, especially when medical diagnosis or treatment is concerned.

The spontaneous EEG is therefore usually considered as being the "second" in the series; the first one in the series, presumably, was normal when the patient was normal although how long ago normality existed is, of course, a moot point. Further serial tracings then provide a changing picture as the disease progresses or regresses. Within any one spontaneous tracing, the situation is assumed to be static as only a "moment of time" is being viewed; the entire tracing covering an hour or two constitutes but a single point on the over-all graph.

Activation procedures. Evaluation of changes in the base-line record with alterations of nonspecific base-line conditions provides a most valuable augmentation of significance. These alterations can be grouped under the heading of *activation* with the understanding that an ideal activation is a change of an environmental or an intrinsic condition which, although itself not causing any direct alteration in the EEG, does cause the brain to present electrical abnormalities which would otherwise have occurred spontaneously but whose transient nature would have caused them to be missed in the "short" sampling.

Activations should be divided into "physiological" and "nonphysiological" types according to the criterion that a physiological activation is one which could have occurred to the subject in his natural environment. For example, a light flash used for a stimulus is within "physiological" limits until its intensity exceeds that of the sun. On the other hand, a nonphysiological activation would be the injection of a drug not normally present in the body. It then follows that any abnormalities occurring in the EEG of a subject exposed to "physiological activations" must be *true abnormalities* of the organism whereas abnormalities occurring as a result of "nonphysiological activations" are of merely conjectural significance to be assessed on the basis of compiled statistics for responses of control normal and abnormal groups of subjects.

One of the most popular nonspecific activation procedures is hyperventilation in which a subject voluntarily blows off CO_2. The resulting biochemical shifts are well documented as an effective method of bringing forth not only electrical seizure patterns but also clinical convulsions in patients who have convulsive disorders of certain types. Due to both the simplicity of the maneuver and the certain significance of a positive result, this procedure should be included in all clinical evaluations as well as in experimental studies on humans as the knowledge that a patient is not electrically normal will modify the significance of the other data obtained.

In addition to activating seizure discharges, other alterations usually occur in the EEG on hyperventilation and must be familiar to the EEG interpreter.

Sleep is another important activation not only for the same reasons cited above but also because it is effective with children who are too young to cooperate for hyperventilation. Even more significant is the fact that a different group of convulsive disorders are triggered into revealing themselves by sleep activation than by hyperventilation. The technician, certainly, must be adept at recognizing levels of sleep as the transition from awake to dozing and from dozing to light sleep are fruitful activations, whereas the deeper levels of sleep usually suppress the appearance of abnormalities.

Specific stimuli used for either activation or for evoked potential studies are, almost exclusively, restricted to the visual, auditory, and tactile modalities. Visual activation is an admirably fruitful technique for many reasons; stimuli can be easily created and controlled over a wide range both within and even in excess of physiological limits, and, more important, the response is fast enough to be easily identified. Flashes have been used singly and in groups as well as with rhythmic repetition rates and even with the timing between successive flashes being controlled by the evoked response of the brain itself. Various colors of light, both positive and negative, can be used to permit more detailed studies.

With a slightly different approach, for example, a specific area of the visual field can be preferentially or differentially stimulated. Such subtleties as rhythmic movements of dimly lit objects can be presented and the frequency of the movements can be readily identified in the EEG derived from the visual cortex.

Automatic Analysis in Electroencephalography

Although the usual method of recording EEG data is a simple time voltage graph with various channels representing the scalp areas, the data is "dead" once it has been written on the paper and can only be evaluated when viewed by the electroencephalographer. The efficiency of utilization of the information must be very low; Walter estimates that it is a fraction of 1%!

On the other hand, if the raw data is recorded on magnetic tape, it then remains "alive" and can be subsequently fed into a data reduction system or it can even be replayed for visual examination on the usual pen and ink write-out. If such a two step write-out is utilized, some marked advantages can be achieved almost as a bonus. While the pens themselves are limited to a maximum high frequency response slightly in excess of 100 cps, it is possible to play the tape back at, for example, one-tenth the recording speed with the paper recorder drive moving at a speed similarly reduced. Under these circumstances the pen frequency limitations remain unchanged and can therefore show an effective increase of high frequency response by that factor of 10; in this example, the high frequency limit would exceed 1000 cps.

A second advantage of using tape recording as an intermediary step is the opportunity for the placing of event markers which precede the event which produces them. Such an arrangement can then be used to "edit" the paper write-out as well as to select portions of the tape for future presentation for automatic analysis, even if that future is only tenths of a second away.

Many efforts have been made to increase information acquisition efficiency through electronic data condensation, each of which approaches, although capable of providing the investigator with valuable and often highly accurate information, can only provide this information after an appreciable time interval of hours or even days. As the dynamic application of data reduction in this field requires that the results of the data reduction and subsequent analysis be available and used to modify the investigation itself, those methods of analysis providing "on line" answers are most likely to prove valuable.

Automatic low frequency analysis. Automatic low frequency analysis is a procedure in which a channel of standard EEG is broken down into its component sine wave frequencies by being passed through a series of sharp-cutting tuned filters. The outputs of these filters are then stored for an "epoch" of 10 sec after which a pen writes out, on the original EEG tracing, a frequency energy graph with the amplitude of deflection indicating the energy stored at each of the filter frequencies during the "epoch." Although this technique is useful for comparing amounts of energy at any frequency occurring in homologous areas or showing changes of energy or frequency distribution under changing conditions, no popular clinical application has been achieved. The apparatus is available from a number of manufacturers in both single and two channel versions.

Toposcopic EEG analysis. Toposcopic EEG analysis as developed by Walter and Shipton (Hill & Pan, 1963) is a beautiful example of a different manner of looking at the same EEG potentials. Toposcopy refers to a presentation in which the EEG information is viewed in a cathode ray tube array which spatially duplicates the electrode pick-up array. As the X and Y axes of the cathode ray tubes are not available for information readout. this must be achieved by Z axis or intensity variation. In the Walter-Shipton toposcope, the area under examination (i.e. the scalp of the patient) is represented by a series of cathode ray tube screens each being fed by a separate channel of EEG, 22 in all. Special circuitry presents an identical sweep pattern to all cathode ray tubes; this pattern resembles the sweep second hand of a clock on some models and a spiral pattern on others. The rate of rotation can be varied from about 1/sec to about 30/sec or can be synchronized with the actual EEG signal of any one channel. When there is a simple ratio between the sweep rate and the EEG frequency rate, segmental patterns appear and can be viewed or photographed for a permanent record which also includes a dial clearly indicating the sweep rate at that moment. In addition to frequency rates, this presentation system provides a very clear analysis of interchannel phase relationships not available by any other method.

Period analysis. Period analysis is a method of viewing the EEG data in terms of time intervals between either base-line crossings or successive wave peaks. The amplitudes of the wave forms are ignored. Burch (1959) has developed an automatic approach to this method of analysis which can, under certain circumstances, reveal clear evidence of very subtle changes and is looked upon by some as the most sensitive method of evaluation of psychotropic drugs available. However, the system can be grossly misleading in the presence of a multiplicity of frequencies or of very complex wave forms.

Averaging. Averaging was first brought to EEG by Dawson who presented the concept that evoked potentials in the EEG were usually not seen merely because they were lost in the "noise" or background. To increase the signal to noise ratio, he developed an instrument which averaged the potentials occurring at a series of predetermined times following a specific stimulation. As the random EEG activity bore no fixed relationship to the time of random stimulation, it averaged out.

Sophisticated commercial averagers have recently become available in which thousands of points, representing specific times as well as changing situations can store data for either visual or computer evaluation. This data is on-line but does require expensive equipment.

Autocorrelation. This is a method of EEG analysis in which a small sample of tape recorded EEG is correlated with itself with a shifting time delay interval. The final reading is a plot of time delay with respect to percentage correlation. A high signal to noise ratio can be obtained for repetitive patterns. A relatively large amount of equipment is needed and the technique is only applicable to certain types of research studies.

Time-space-voltage mapping. Time-space-voltage mapping has been developed by Rémond (1956 & 1960) to a high degree of accuracy by using short samples of EEG tracing from a large number of electrodes oriented in a straight line across the scalp. The final readout consists of space across the scalp as the Y axis, and time progression as the X axis; the voltages, corrected for numerous errors, are then represented on the Z axis which is a series of numbers. Isopotential points are connected to aid in visual assimilation of the data and colors are added to indicate polarity. In actual execution, these maps indicate exquisite dynamic detail of the electrical activity along the line of electrodes but the work is accomplished by a battery of computers and a single IBM card is required for each channel for each interval of the time selected, often 1 msec. This is then not an on-line method.

Conclusion

The most common error found in the application of electroencephalography to research studies is in the realm of insufficient understanding of the most basic definitions and tenets of technique which are bypassed in the investigators enthusiasm for application of what he erroneously assumes to be a rigid, simple, tried, and true method of brain function evaluation.

REFERENCES

Berger, H. Uber das Elektrenkephalogramm des Menchen. *Arch. Psychait. NervKrankh.*, 1929, *87*: 527–570.
Burch, N. R. Automatic analysis of the electroencephalogram: A review and classification of systems. *Electroenceph. clin. Neurophysiol.*, 1959, *4*: 11.
Caton, R. The electric currents of the brain. *Br. med. J.*, 1875, *2*: 278.
Hill, D., & Parr, G. *Electroencephalography: A symposium on its various aspects.* London: Macdonald and Co., 1963.
Pampiglione, G. *Development of cerebral function in the dog.* Washington, D. C.: Butterworths, 1963.
Rémond, A. An integrating topograph. *Electroenceph. clin Neurophysiol*, 1956, *8*: 719.
Rémond, A. Recherche des renseignements significatifs dans les enregistrements electrophysiologiques et mecanisation possible. In A. M. Monnier (Ed.), *Actualites neurophysiologiques.* (2nd ed.) Paris: Masson, 1960. Pp. 167–210.

11

On the Nature of
Classical Conditioning*

ROSCOE A. DYKMAN, Ph.D.

I am a psychophysiologist whose major interest is classical conditioning. The reader can expect to find here, therefore, a psychophysiological approach to the understanding of the processes which take place in conditioning. The reader should appreciate that the emphasis could be reversed; that is, some investigators might be interested in classical conditioning as a technique for learning more about psychophysiology. The reader should also realize that not all psychophysiologists view their field alike. So, at the outset, I shall present my definition of psychophysiology: the study of changes that occur in *multiple* end organs in the presence of some kind of stimulation or uniform background conditions. Note the emphasis on *multiple*. A study of electrical cortical activity or of some isolated motor reaction such as eye closure or flexion is not, to my thinking, a psychophysiological study. Unfortunately, relatively few of the host of conditioning studies that have been done fall within the province of psychophysiology.

Even though investigation of a single response system is not the domain of the psychophysiologist, he can glean from such studies some important clues concerning the processes of conditioning. He can ask whether principles found for a given response system apply to other response systems. The marked extent to which findings from studies of the eye blink response have shaped conditioning theory is undeniable. However, the single system type inquiry has limitations, for comparisons can be made only on a group basis or for other similar groups of subjects and experimental conditions.

*My research has been supported over the last 10 years by Grant MH-1091 from the National Institute of Mental Health. In 1961, I was given Career Research Development Award MH-2504 which along with Grant MH-1091 has allowed me to pursue my theoretical interests in psychophysiology. I wish to acknowledge the help of Dr. Charles R. Galbrecht and Mrs. Peggy Thomasson Ackerman, research associates, who assisted me in the preparation of this chapter.

A major aim of this chapter is to present informaion that will be of importance to psychophysiologists in designing their experiments, not with reference to statistical considerations, but to the basic theoretical issues in conditioning and learning. With some few outstanding exceptions, the literature to be reviewed is American. The theories and studies to be considered are intended to illustrate basic response principles and basic theoretical issues.

Definitions

A classical conditioning procedure is easily identified for the reinforcing agent, whether reward or punishment, is administered without regard to the subject's performance. In instrumental conditioning, the subject can escape punishment or obtain reward by making a response the experimenter defines as correct or appropriate. Operant conditioning is a form of instrumental conditioning wherein the investigator provides cues concerning the correct response by rewarding behaviors which approximate the correct response. Kimble (1961, p. 44) says, "The basic distinction between classical and instrumental conditioning procedures is in terms of the consequences of the conditioned response. In classical conditioning, the sequence of events is independent of the subject's behavior. In instrumental conditioning, by contrast, rewards and punishments are made to occur as a consequence of the learner's response or failure to respond."

Grant (1964, pp. 2 and 3), in commenting on this definition, says, "some precision may be gained by stating that in instrumental conditioning the *availability* of reward or punishment is contingent upon the *S*'s [subject's] behavior whereas in classical conditioning it is not." Thorpe (1956, p. 72) had earlier defined classical conditioning as: "the process of acquisition by an animal of the capacity to respond to a given stimulus with the reflex reaction proper to another stimulus (the reinforcement) when the two stimuli are applied concurrently for a number of times."

Most psychologists consider classical conditioning to be quite different from other forms of learning, a supposition that may or may not be valid. The simplest conditioning involves an extensive part of the central nervous system (CNS), considering the multiple end organ changes evoked. The "connections" or associations elaborated in classical conditioning are probably by no means as simple as human-oriented learning theorists are prone to state. There appear to be multiple connections, both excitatory and inhibitory, at diverse levels of the CNS.

Aside from the dimension of complexity, classical conditioning is a very important form of learning. In the last few years, many psychologists have been returning to the reflex principles of Pavlov and Thorndike, although extending these to cover more complex aspects of psychology. Classical conditioning has and will continue to provide basic data concerning the operation of principles important in all learning. The plasticity functions of the CNS are probably much the same whether one neuron is involved or many, whether learning takes place at one site or many, or whether learning is exclusively emotional in nature, exclusively cognitive, or has elements of both. Further, classical conditioning and closely related procedures appear to be superior to instrumental and other designs in providing clearer insights into central neural processes, regardless of whether the studies monitor end organ changes or neural activity via techniques of implantation. In classical conditioning the experimenter has, as indicated above, strict control of the conditional stimulus (CS) and unconditional stimulus (UCS) and can study timing relationships, inhibition, and emotionality to an extent not possible in other learning paradigms.

In classical conditioning the UCS evokes inborn reflexes called unconditional responses (UCRs). But, the CS also evokes unconditional responses (e.g. looking, listening, and associated general autonomic changes), and such reactions are denoted collectively as the orienting response (OR), or investigatory reflex (Pavlov, 1927). Further, the UCS generally produces certain orienting effects (e.g. looking down at shock electrodes or attending to the food pan). Examples of typical CS are lights, tones, and tactile stimuli; typical UCS are electrical shocks, food, water, air puffs delivered to the cornea, and water loading of the stomach (see Bykov, 1957). It should be clear that the class of stimuli used as CS is usually quite distinctive from the class used as UCS.

Classical conditioning entails simply the pairing of CS and UCS in some prearranged time sequence until the CS acquires some or all of the properties of the UCS. These acquired properties are denoted the conditional response (CR).

Discriminative and Nondiscriminative Conditioning

There are two main forms of classical conditioning: nondiscriminative and discriminative. In the first, a single CS is paired with a single UCS until the CR emerges. Prior to pairing, the CS may be given for a number of trials to show that it alone will not evoke the CR. There are a number of variations possible here, e.g. conditioning to various kinds of CS and UCS, variations in the percentage of trials on which the UCS is given (in partial reinforcement the UCS is not given with the CS on every trial), variations in the time interval between CS onset and UCS onset, and variations in the intertrial interval (time from one paired presentation of CS and UCS to the next paired presentation).

The simplest case of discriminative conditioning involves two different CS, the positive CS reinforced on some or all of the trials by the UCS, and the negative CS never reinforced. In this procedure of contrast conditioning, the CRs evoked by the two CSs are called positive and negative CRs, respectively. Another type of discrimination design is the differential intensity paradigm in which two or more CS are employed but each CS is differentially reinforced by the same UCS. For example, a tone of high frequency may be paired with a large quantity of food while a low tone is paired with a small quantity of food. A variant of this design enables one to compare the effectiveness of different CS (a tone, a light, a cutaneous stimulus) by reinforcing each with the same intensity UCS, an application which has not received proper attention in this country, but is frequently employed by Russian investigators (see Peters, in press). The reader should note that many of the variations in design mentioned for nondiscriminative conditioning apply here, too.

There are a variety of forms of nondiscriminative conditioning: e.g. (1) simultaneous conditioning in which a continuous CS lasting 5 sec or less is paired with a UCS, the latter generally occurring a split second before the termination of the CS; (2) delayed conditioning in which a continuous CS lasts longer than 5 sec before being overlapped by the UCS; (3) trace conditioning in which the CS terminates before the UCS is given; (4) backward conditioning in which the UCS is given before the CS; and (5) higher order conditioning in which a CS that has acquired the meaning, say, of food or shock is paired repetitively with another neutral stimulus in a subsequent procedure. In Form 5 the CS in Step I becomes the UCS in Step II of the procedure (see Pavlov, 1927, pp. 38–41, 88–93).

Two main types of control procedures have evolved in American psychology to show the specificity of the pairing operation. Both will be denoted here as pseudoconditioning controls. In one procedure, the UCS alone is given a variable number of times followed by the CS alone for a variable number of trials (no specific pairing). In the other, CS and UCS are presented in some prearranged random order, generally giving as many of each as are given in the paired conditioning procedure. Responses that occur in pseudoconditioning procedures are thought to depend upon some mechanism of sensitization and not upon true conditioning. No one has sharply distinguished one type of response from the other, but the implicit supposition is that true CRs reflect a plasticity function of the nervous system and that pseudoconditioned responses (PCRs) reflect some transitory change in threshold. We are told that if the CR produced by forward order procedures resembles in latency, form, or frequency the response produced by pseudoconditioning procedures, we should consider the possibility that the CR evoked by pairing is a sensitized response. To many investigators the distinction between PCRs and the CRs or between sensitized responses and CRs is that of nonassociative modifications versus associative modifications (Wickens & Wickens, 1942).

The term sensitization is used in still other ways. Hilgard and Marquis (1940, p. 42) state that sensitization is "The augmentation of an original response to the conditioned stimulus through a conditioning procedure," implying that true conditioning has not occurred since the UCS only augments properties that are already possessed by the CS. The eyelid reflex investigators have denoted certain reactions occurring early in the CS-UCS interval as sensitized reactions, distinguishable on the basis of latency, form, or both, from the so-called anticipatory CR occurring a split second before the UCS (see below).

Major Issues in Conditioning Theory

According to Spence (1951), learning theorists may be divided into major camps on the basis of their stands on the nature of the associative process and the nature of reinforcement. There are two schools of thought concerning the nature of association. The sign-significate (S-S) theorists take the position that learning (association) is a matter of perceptual organization or reorganization (Kohler, 1940; Koffka, 1935; Lewin, 1936; Tolman, 1932). The stimulus-response (S-R) theorists, on the other hand, conceive learning in terms of hypothetical connections or bonds between stimuli (CS) and responses (Guthrie, 1935; Hull, 1943; Miller, 1941; Spence, 1936; Thorndike, 1935). By and large, the S-S theories have derived from experiments other than classical conditioning and indeed are in part, a kind of protest to classical conditioning. The irony here is that Pavlov's theory qualifies, I believe, as an S-S theory, although it is most often called an S-R theory by psychologists.

As for reinforcement, there are those who assume reinforcement—reward, pain-avoidance, or tension reduction—necessary for learning to occur, and those who say the reinforcement is not needed. The latter group tend, in general, to see reinforcement operating to increase the probability of responses but hold that the mere occurrence of the behavior is a sufficient condition for learning.

Although there are exceptions, S-S theorists tend to take the view that motivation operates only indirectly on habit strength; whereas, the S-R theorists generally hold to some principle of effect. Several writers cited by Spence (1951) have not taken an either or position on the reinforcement issue; they see some kinds of learning as dependent upon effect and other kinds as dependent upon contiguity (repetitive occurrence of stimulus and response or of two stimuli). Hilgard (1956) gives a detailed description of various learning theories and the issues which separate them.

Performance versus Learning: An Important Distinction?

Performance is discriminated from learning by most American psychologists as follows. Performance is an empirical construct denoting a measurable behavior or response, whereas learning is a hypothetical construct inferred from changes in response or performance. Learning is defined operationally as a change in performance resulting from practice, training, or conditioning. Changes in a response (say the CR) may emerge from forces other than learning, such as heightened (or decreased) emotionality, maturation, and motivation. To say that a given change in performance derives from learning implies that other factors have been controlled or eliminated in some way (see Hilgard, 1956; Spence, 1951).

The distinction between performance and learning, while logically sound and important, poses many practical problems. To control all nonassociative variables that might alter behavior so that pure learning is reflected is extremely difficult. Motivational factors may, for example, alter performance in the same way as practice or trials. One is then confronted with the problem of estimating the nonassociative and associative (learned) contributions to the response, a problem which can be solved (see Kimble, 1961, pp. 117–128; Spence, 1956, pp. 124–164), but only in terms of certain arbitrary and often debatable definitions.

While performance actually involves learning as a subcomponent, it has been convenient to use the term performance to denote only the nonlearned component of response; i.e. response equals a learned component (habit) plus a nonlearned component (performance). Kimble (1961, p. 117) in this vein says, "It is probably overly optimistic to hope that the factors involved will divide themselves co-operatively into learning and performance variables. Many will, no doubt, turn out to be both." He points out that a performance factor in one situation or system may not be a performance factor in another situation or system. Analysis of variance designs are frequently used to distinguish between performance and learning, but according to Kimble, "they are completely satisfactory only in cases where the evidence points unequivocally to the conclusion that the variable under investigation is a performance variable" (p. 118). The distinction generally made between performance and learning is of importance to psychophysiologists since some regard autonomic responses as representing performance rather than learning (Smith, 1954).

Pavlovian Theory

This section and those to follow present some of the basic theoretical views concerning classical conditioning. No treatment of conditioning, either theoretical or experimental, should begin other than with the contributions of Pavlov. While Pavlov studied mainly conditioned changes in salivation, the basic principles he worked out apply with few exceptions to all response systems. Pavlov's theories have not been accorded the same status in this country as his experimental work. Indeed, the otherwise excellent book on learning theories by Hilgard (1956) does not include a chapter on Pavlovian theory. Four books by Pavlov (1927, 1928, 1941, 1957) are the major references for the material to be presented. Konorski (1948) has written a very good chapter on Pavlovian theory, but the reader is encouraged to consult the source material.

Pavlov's theory of conditioning is an S-S theory. The hypothetical connections that are strengthened by conditioning are internuncials between the sensory center of the CS and the sensory center of the UCS, and not those between the sensory centers of the CS and UCR centers or other motor centers (Pavlov, 1927, pp. 27, 36). Pavlov assumed that the CR depends upon the pairing of CS and UCS but not necessarily in close temporal contiguity. With sufficient reinforcements the CR becomes a replica of the UCR. The UCS is the dominant stimulus and determines the direction of reaction, indeed, actively inhibits all responses antagonistic to the UCR. Reinforcement is the pairing of the CS and the UCS. His theory is a contiguity theory, in that the CS, or its perseverating trace, is connected to UCS processes. This "nonpsychological" view has troubled many investigators who feel there must be something more dynamic in classical conditioning than simple pairing.

Some writers have said that Pavlov overlooked the most important variable in conditioning, namely drive or emotional state (Hull, 1943; Mowrer, 1960). Pavlov (1927, p. 127; 1957, p. 328) did recognize the importance of motivation, as witnessed by experiments in which motivational state was altered. While he did not give motivational variables the same intensive consideration that he gave other variables, this should not detract from the undeniable fact that his experimental output has not been matched either in quantity or quality by subsequent investigators.

Most of Pavlov's work centered on two alimentary CRs, salivation evoked by noxious agents and salivation evoked by food. Typically, he used a long CS-UCS interval, with the time from CS onset to UCS onset most often being 10 to 30 sec. Thus, the CR could occur in the CS-UCS (interstimulus) interval. By contrast, American experimenters have usually employed very short interstimulus intervals (0.5 to 1.0 sec), and autonomic CRs can be observed on nonreinforced trials only. Pavlov showed that the longer the interstimulus interval, the slower the acquisition process and the weaker the CR as measured by the magnitude of secretion; and also that the stronger the CS, the stronger the CR up to some definite limit. He recognized that CS of the same physical intensity but of different modalities were vastly different in their effectiveness as conditioning agents; e.g. auditory stimuli are more effective as CS than visual or tactile stimuli (Pavlov, 1927, p. 94).

The major intervening variables in Pavlov's system are excitation and inhibition, measured by strength of the CR in conditioning and extinction, generalization, and induction (see below). At the empirical level he used the concepts of equilibrium and mobility. The former is measured by the rate at which a subject differentiates positive and negative CRs and the latter by the ability of the subject to respond differently when the meanings of CS are reversed, i.e. when the previously positive CS becomes negative and the previously negative CS becomes positive. In terms of the intervening variables, equilibrium denotes the balance of excitation and inhibition, and mobility the ability of one process to substitute for the other.

Pavlov employed excitation, inhibition, equilibrium, and mobility to "type" animals. He found four main types of dogs, with numerous gradations among them. While Pavlov described his four main types as sanguine, choleric, melancholic, and phlegmatic, these terms do not have the same meaning as was given them by the early Greeks. Pavlov's concern with innate disposition and experience is evident throughout his lectures, whether he was discussing psychopathology or ordinary learning. Since his animals came from outside sources, he recognized as one limitation of his work his lack of knowledge concerning their history (Pavlov, 1957, p. 315). Ultimately Pavlov (1957, pp. 337 and 448) divided his dogs into types on the basis of their behavior in a dynamic stereotype procedure. The stereotype (a system of several CRs evoked in a fixed order) was first established and then the effects on the stereotype of increasing periods of food deprivation, delays of reinforcement, extraneous stimuli, and drugs were studied. The meanings of certain CS were also changed by altering the conditions of reinforcement (mobility phase). The establishment of a stereotype and its subsequent manipulation required a very long period of time, sometimes a year or more. Pavlov's typing procedures have a solid empirical basis and measure very important characteristics of the subject (Peters, in press).

Pavlov recognized two types of inhibition, unconditioned and conditioned. He described two kinds of unconditioned inhibition, external inhibition and disinhibition. External inhibition refers to the interfering effect of a novel stimulus on the CR when it is given during conditioning just before the CS or early in the interstimulus interval. Disinhibition denotes the restorative effect of a novel stimulus on the CR when it is given just before or after the application of the CS during a series of nonreinforced trials (extinction). Disinhibition is manifested in either of two ways, the augmentation of a partially suppressed CR or the return of a CR that has been extinguished. The magnitude of interference (external inhibition or disinhibition) varies with the strength of the CR, the intensity and the nature of the novel stimulus, the drive state of the organism, and the type of dog (Pavlov, 1927, p. 82; 1928, p. 138; 1957, p. 317).

Conditioned inhibition refers to the acquired and cumulative inhibitory effect of a CS under conditions of repeated nonreinforcement. This effect is seen in the extinction phase of nondiscriminative conditioning (extinctive inhibition); in discriminative training when one or more CS are not reinforced (differential inhibition); in compound conditioning when one or more elements of a complex stimulus are not reinforced while the complex is consistently reinforced (differential inhibition); and in delayed conditioning with inhibition increasing as a function of the delay of reinforcement (inhibition of delay). An extraneous stimulus applied during extinction or differentiation has the disinhibitory effect previously described, and this effect is generally greater for extinctive than for differential inhibition, and greater for coarse than for fine differentiation.

Pavlov investigated in considerable detail the generalization of excitatory (positive) and inhibitory (negative) CRs to novel (test) stimuli similar to or radically different from the CS used in the original training. The general procedure is first to establish a positive or negative CR and then apply a test stimulus, differing from the CS, to note the transfer of effects. A negative CS has inhibitory after effects that may last several minutes and act to depress CRs produced by a subsequently occurring negative CS, or confer inhibitory properties on novel test stimuli (Pavlov, 1928, pp. 152–177). In a parallel manner, excitatory after effects of a positive CS also last several minutes and augment responses to subsequently occurring negative and positive CS, as well as confer positive CR properties on previously indifferent test stimuli (Pavlov, 1927, pp. 177–186). Pavlov thought that the generalization of excitation depended on a spread or irradiation of excitation from the CS center (i.e. cortical cells or structures processing the CS) and generalization of inhibition, or an irradiation of inhibition, from the CS center (Pavlov, 1928, p. 162). While irradiation was conceived after the analogy of a volume conductor, the concept is valid provided it is thought of in terms of specific fiber traces (Konorski, 1948).

One method Pavlov used to study inhibitory generalization was to extinguish in a single session (acute extinction) one of a number of previously established positive CRs and then to present the newly established negative CS at various time intervals before the positive CS. In one study the various CS were tactile vibrators placed along the leg of a dog (Pavlov, 1927, p. 153); in another instance, the several CS were different musical tones (1927, p. 165). Inhibitory generalization was found to be greater the more similar the negative CS and the positive CS. Further, inhibition rose to a maximum over a period of seconds to minutes (depending upon the strength of inhibition) and then slowly decayed over a period of several minutes. The inhibitory after effect of a weak negative CS (i.e. a negative CS established by few nonreinforcements) was found to be shorter in duration and less persistent as judged by its capacity to depress positive CRs than that of a strong negative CS (established by a large number of nonreinforcements). Most important, the inhibitory after effect of the negative CS was greater for positive CS of the same analyzer (e.g. all CS auditory) than for positive CS of other analyzers (e.g. the negative CS an auditory stimulus and the positive CS visual stimuli).

Having found that inhibition "irradiates," Pavlov assumed that excitation should exhibit a similar effect, and subsequent experiments were directed toward revealing the principle of excitatory generalization. The general procedure was to produce one positive CR and several negative CRs; e.g. one of several tactile vibrators on the skin was positively conditioned while the remaining vibrators were negatively conditioned. Application of the positive CS was followed by one of the negative CS and a consequent "disinhibiting" effect was noted (Pavlov, 1927, p. 177). Generalization was greater the more similar the positive and negative CS; i.e. the closer together the two vibrators on the skin.

Pavlov also found in differentiation experiments a tendency for inhibitory and excitatory gradients to concentrate as a function of time, i.e. to show less generalization to other stimuli (Pavlov, 1927, p. 155). Differentiation between positive and negative CS as achieved, say, by the contrast method, has the effect of restricting gradients of generalization. The after effects of a negative CS established by differential training do not generalize to test stimuli to the same degree as the after effects of a negative CS produced by an acute extinction procedure. Also, the after effects of positive CS as produced by differential training do not generalize to test stimuli to the same degree as the excitatory after effects of a CS produced by a simple nondiscriminative procedure (Pavlov, 1928, p. 171).

In the course of his studies, Pavlov noted certain important exceptions to the irradiation principles just discussed. He found that giving a *well established* negative CS a few seconds before the positive CS had the effect of increasing rather than decreasing the positive CR. He called this phenomenon positive induction, and he discovered that giving a well established positive CS just a few seconds before the negative CS served further to depress rather than disinhibit the negative CR. This effect, termed negative induction, was found to be far more stable than positive induction. The reader will note that the directional effect is defined in terms of the stimulus that is applied last (Pavlov, 1927, pp. 188–203). Pavlov was able to map out fairly accurately the relation between irradiation (generalization) and induction (reflex augmentation by a process of the opposite nature). His research suggested that excitation (or inhibition) *concentrates* before irradiation begins, and that during the period of concentration there is an augmentation of reflex effects opposite to those of the initial stimulus.

To explain additional complexities of reflex interaction that arose in his experiments, Pavlov (1928, p. 387; 1941, p. 88) hypothesized two properties of the nervous system, excitability and capability. A strong CS has a greater excitatory effect than a weak one, provided the capability of the nervous system is not exceeded. If the capability of the nervous system to respond is exceeded, there ensues a process of generalized inhibition called limiting or protective inhibition. Capability depends upon many things: the type of animal, the health of the animal, drowsiness, psychopathology, etc. Pavlov used the concepts of excitability and capability to explain paradoxical reactions. With a lowering of the capability, a strong and weak stimulus may have equivalent effects (phase of equalization). With a greater reduction of the capability, strong stimuli may be even less effective than weak stimuli in evoking CRs; and with a still greater reduction, positive CRs may vanish and the inhibitory CRs become positive. The explanation is based on the concept of mutual induction, the excitatory focus, now inhibitory, evokes excitation elsewhere in the nervous system including the "point of application" of the negative CS (Pavlov, 1928, p. 356).

Russian versus American Work

Russian experimentation in classical conditioning is inspired largely by physiological considerations and in particular by the work and concepts of Pavlov (see Razran, 1961). On close examination, Pavlovian concepts turn out to be, for the most part, extensions of the reflex principles worked out by Sherrington and Sechenov. By contrast, American experimentation and theory have been largely inspired by nonphysiological considerations, especially the behavioral theories of Hull (1943), Spence (1956), Miller (1941), Mowrer (1950, 1960, 1963), and Osgood (1953). There are, of course, exceptions to the trend in both Russia and the United States.

Russian experimenters generally employ only those kinds of controls that Pavlov developed in his salivary work. They are less concerned with sample size, and the controls tend to be intraindividual rather than interindividual. Thus, in Russian experiments, differentiation or changes from orienting training response patterns constitute adequate evidence of conditioning. In American experimentation, we are more likely to find pseudoconditioning control groups and analyses of variance or factorial designs with matched groups of subjects given different treatments. The Russians are more apt to study animals over relatively long periods of time, whereas Americans do more relatively short term cross-sectional studies using procedures which produce quick and clean results. Certain American work, notably that from Gantt's (1953, 1960) laboratory at Johns Hopkins, has adhered closely to the Pavlovian tradition. Liddell (1944, 1956) in his laboratory at Cornell also used Pavlovian techniques, but he used nonPavlovian explanations in his theoretical discussions.

Without making any judgment as to which approach has been or will be the more fruitful in the long run, I believe that Pavlovian-type work is more likely to favor the discovery of new principles and that American experimentation is better designed to elucidate the quantitative relationships among established variables.

Hull's S-R Theory

Hull (1943) assumed that the basis of learning is reinforcement defined in terms of drive reduction. Drive is an intervening variable denoting the summation of all specific needs of the moment, hunger, thirst, pain-avoidance, etc. A need arises whenever conditions of the biological environment deviate from those optimal for survival, and each need produces interoceptive stimuli, called drive stimuli (Hull, 1943, 1951). The association between a response and a stimulus trace is strengthened if and only if the response is successful in attenuating drive or drive stimuli. According to Spence (1956, p. 57), Hull assumed that "the increment in associative strength or, as he termed it, habit strength depended directly upon the occurrence of the reinforcer."

Secondary drives are very important in the Hullian system. When the trace of a CS is associated with a reduction in drive stimuli, the CS acquires the power to evoke drive stimuli. Thus, a secondary drive is produced; e.g. a tone associated with shock is able to elicit fear in the absence of shock (Hull, 1951, 1952). Hull borrowed this idea from Miller (1948, 1951). Note further that of the responses induced by secondary drive (e.g. fear), those most apt to be established are those most consistently followed by a reduction of the secondary drive. This does not necessarily mean that responses judged to be adaptive will be those that predominate at the end of training.

Learning depends on the number of reinforcements (drive reductions), and the hypothetical associative process strengthened in learning is habit strength. What we actually see in conditioning, from this view, is performance, and the the hypothetical associative process strengthened in learning is habit strength. What we actually see in conditioning, from his view, is performance, and the hypothetical variable upon which performance depends is reaction potential (E). Hull considered reaction potential (tendency to respond) to be a multiplicative function of drive (D) and habit (H): $E = H \times D$. The empirical equivalent of this equation is $CR = N \times D$, where N is the number of reinforcements and D is measured by the period of food deprivation or the intensity of the noxious UCS. Hull (1951, 1952) assumed that habit is independent of the drive level; i.e. it depends only upon the number of reinforcements. Hence, drive alters performance in a nonassociative manner.

There are two other major nonassociative factors which also affect performance: the stimulus-intensity dynamism (V), or intensity of CS, and incentive reinforcement (K), or the amount of reward. The complete specification equation then is $E = D \times V \times K \times H$ (i.e. reaction potential is a multiplicative function of four variables). To explain the negative relation between the strength of response and the time interval between the occurrence of the response and the reinforcing agent, Hull postulates that the reaction potential decreases as a function of delay. In the case of classical conditioning, the optimal CS-UCS interval is about 0.5 sec with a decrease in performance for longer or shorter intervals.

Hull recognized two main kinds of inhibition in conditioning, conditioned, or extinctive, inhibition and reactive inhibition. The latter is akin to tissue injury or fatigue and acts directly to inhibit the CR. Conditioned inhibition is a derivative of reactive inhibition (stimuli associated with the termination of a response and the reduction of reactive inhibition become conditioned to, or evoke, nonactivity). Inhibition, reactive or conditioned, subtracts from reaction potential (Hull, 1951). Reactive and conditioned inhibition are assumed to build up with trials, particularly with short intertrial intervals (massing), and lead to either extinction or CR diminutions during reinforcement.

In extinction there is no primary drive reduction; the occurrence of the CR is not followed by a reinforcing event. At the same time, reactive inhibition (fatigue) cumulates with trials and serves, at least within sessions, to attenuate the CR. A more lasting extinction is achieved via conditioned inhibition where the animal learns that "doing nothing" is reinforcing, reduces the "unpleasantness" of fatigue. This model of extinction, if I understand it, appears to me to be completely erroneous. Surely such an active animal as the dog is not fatigued by the inconsequential amount of effort required to lift his leg to the sound of a tone; and most certainly the model would not apply to general autonomic functions.

In 1952, Hull provided a specific postulate to explain response augmentations in reward situations. The gist of this thesis is that the fractional anticipatory goal response precedes the consumption of food, and the omission of food results in a state of frustration which, in turn, contributes to the over-all drive level. This process accounts for the transitory increase in performance sometimes seen in the early stages of extinction. The eventual extinction, however, depends on conditioned inhibition.

Generalization in the Hullian system depends upon (1) the remoteness of test stimuli (stimuli not involved in the original conditioning) from the CS measured in just noticeable difference units; (2) habit strength alone with D, K, and V constant; (3) the intensity of the CS during conditioning; and (4) the intensity of test stimuli with D and K constant. Hull assumed that conditioned inhibition conforms to the same principles of generalization as habit strength and reaction potential.

Responses do not occur, according to Hull (1952), unless the momentary reaction potential is greater than the reaction threshold (L), and given two or more possible responses, the response that occurs is the one having the highest momentary reaction potential. He assumed further that reaction potential varies inversely with the latency of the response and directly with the amplitude of response, the latter restricted to autonomic conditioning. Hilgard (1956, p. 145) reported that "The effort to quantify sE$_R$ [E] in some absolute manner, independent of the special units used in experiments, occupied a great deal of Hull's attention during his last years."

Contributions of Spence

Spence (1956) has contributed greatly to Hullian theory and has provided many of the constructs with clearer definitions. Unlike Hull, Spence (1956, p. 55) contends that "neurologizing" should be avoided unless the principles outlined "appear in a network of physiological laws." Spence is interested in quantitative laws which show the way intervening variables act together to determine performance. He takes an empirical position concerning reinforcement; while he assumes that reinforcement acts to strengthen habits (S-R connections), he does not specify the precise way in which this strengthening occurs. In general, Spence does not commit himself on issues that have not been or cannot be solved by direct experimentation.

Spence has made an extensive study of frequency curves in nondiscriminative classical conditioning, i.e. changes in the percentage of CRs as a function of reinforcements. He says that failure to find an S-shaped curve based on frequency as a measure indicates that conditioning did not begin at zero level or that the units or blocks of trials over which averages were computed were too large, thus masking the form of the curve in the early trials. In carefully controlled experiments, S-shaped curves are also found for amplitude data, but latency data yield a great variety of curves (Spence, 1956, pp. 61–76).

In discussing Hull's basic multiplicative function ($E = D \times H$), Spence assumes that this law holds only for restricted levels of drive (deprivation up to 24 hr) or the low to middle range of noxious stimulation. In discussing habit strength, Spence carefully avoids neurophysiological speculation. Habit is simply a quantitative factor operating with other factors to determine performance. He does say, however, that the CR will not develop unless the perseverative trace of the CS is acting in the nervous system at the time the CR occurs, and he points out that eyelid conditioning is difficult if not impossible with CS- UCS intervals longer than 2 sec (Spence, 1956, p. 95).

Spence attributes the variation of response from trial to trial to uncontrolled factors in the subject and in the environment, such as the receptor orientation of the subject and his motivational state. Like Hull, Spence calls this factor oscillatory inhibition (O or I_o), but unlike Hull, he assumes O to be normally distributed on each trial.

Spence (1956, p. 99) assumes that classical conditioning is an indispensable part of instrumental conditioning. Consider the rat learning to run a maze. The instrumental responses are the motor movements which bring the animal to the food box; but there are also classical associations between cues arising from the apparatus and food which are tied to and motivate instrumental acts. Spence terms the classical CRs produced in this situation the fractional component (r_g) of the consummatory response (R_g). Hull had employed this concept in describing maze learning, but had not, according to Spence (1956, p. 126), regarded R_g) as primarily a motivator or related it to incentive motivation.

The fractional component response (r_g) gives rise to stimuli (s_g) and s_g are conditioned, in turn, to instrumental acts which bring the animal to food. The mr_g - s_g sequence motivates instrumental acts, and the stronger the r_g, the greater the motivational effect. Incentive motivation depends then, in part, upon learning. Other variables directly affecting incentive motivation are the length of the instrumental response chain and possibly the time of delay of reinforcement.

Spence suggests that learning in instrumental situations may depend upon practice or contiguity while learning in classical conditioning depends upon the operation of the principle of effect. This stand is directly opposite the two factor theories of learning proposed by Schlosberg (1937) and Mowrer (1950). Apparently, however, the principle of effect applies only to aversive conditioning. Spence views classical food conditioning as a case of instrumental conditioning in which reinforcement does not play an important role in determining habit strength.

In discussing how drive reduction occurs in classical aversive conditioning, Spence (1956, p. 180) assumes that D depends upon "an internal, emotional state or response of the organism (r_e) . . . aroused in different degrees with different intensities of such aversive stimuli as shock." Now, as I read Spence, r_e is a kind of unconditioned response persisting for considerable periods of time and showing adaptation as a function of presentations of the noxious UCS. Hence, UCS trials alone, prior to reinforcement, should and do retard conditioning.

There is also considerable individual variability in the vigor of r_e, and Spence cites a number of experiments by himself and his associates in conformity with this assumption. Those best known are experiments showing that subjects with high anxiety as judged from scores on the Manifest Anxiety Scale (Taylor, 1951, 1956b) have a higher level of eyelid performance than subjects with low anxiety. In Spence's theory, the UCS also plays a direct role in strengthening habit.

Spence and associates have also used physiological indicators to place subjects into high and low drive groups. Runquist and Ross (1959) measured heart rate and skin conductance changes as evoked by the UCS (air puffs of median intensity delivered to the right eye). The unconditioned heart rate and skin conductance changes were assigned z scores and the two z scores for each subject added. Then, from 90 subjects, the 20 with the highest and the 20 with the lowest composite z scores were selected as a high and a low drive group, respectively. An additional high drive group was selected by taking the 10% of subjects with the highest z scores for heart rate changes and the 10% with the highest z scores for skin conductance changes. High and low drive groups as selected by the composite z score measure failed to differ reliably in conditioned eyelid performance, although the difference approached statistical significance. But the difference in eyelid performance between low drive subjects and high drive subjects selected by the separate system criterion was statistically significant. The writers interpret these results as in conformity with the concept of autonomic response specificity (Lacey, 1956), and with the supposition by Spence that r_e varies in different subjects.

Runquist and Spence (1959, p. 418) relate the concept of generalized drive to activation theory in the following way. "The concept of level of emotional response as an underlying generalized drive level (D) in behavior theory (Spence, 1958) corresponds quite closely to the concepts of level of activation and arousal level recently discussed by Duffy (1951), Schlosberg, (1954), Lindsley (1951), Hebb (1955), Freeman (1948), and Malmo (1957). These authors refer to arousal level as the intensity dimension of behavior in contrast to its directive aspects. That is, arousal level affects any response being made regardless of what the particular response is. The definition of level of arousal has been in terms of certain physiological measures, such as EEG and autonomic activity (pulse rate, GSR, respiration, etc.). Several recent studies by Malmo and his associates (Bartoshuk, 1955; Malmo, 1957; Malmo & Davis, 1956; Stennett, 1957) have suggested that changes in the level of muscular tension, as measured by muscle action potential (MAP), could also be used to define a level of arousal continuum. In fact, Malmo notes the similarity between arousal level and anxiety as defined by the Manifest Anxiety Scale and suggests the use of physiologically defined arousal level as a possible alternative."

In the study from which the above quote was taken, subjects were placed into high and low drive groups on the basis of responses in pulse rate, muscle action potentials, and skin conductance changes to the UCS. In one analysis, the more reactive group in skin conductance and pulse rate (the 15% of subjects most reactive in each system) gave significantly more CRs than the opposite or low drive group (selected by a composite z score). A second analysis was the same as the first except that another measure of skin conductance was used, "increase in base level conductance over the first 20 trials of conditioning" (Runquist & Spence, 1959, p. 419). Again, high and low drive subjects differed reliably in nondiscriminative conditioning performance.

In Spence's theory, r_e is also the perseverating state of emotionality resulting from past UCS and other stimuli acting on the subjects prior to a given conditioning trial. In many situations, the CS-UCS is too short for the CS to evoke an emotional response capable of facilitating the CR or UCR on the same trial. But with a long CS-UCS interval, conditioned emotional responses to the CS may develop and facilitate the subsequently occurring CR or UCR. The classic studies of Miller (1948, 1951) are cited by Spence as evidence that the CS can acquire conditioned fear properties and that its termination can be used to motivate the learning of new behavior. Spence believes that this conception may also apply to appetitional needs: i.e. r_e may vary with different levels of need as produced by various periods of deprivation.

In postulating how the major variables work together, Spence *tentatively suggests* the following formulas: $R = f(\bar{E}) = H \times (D + K) - I_t$ with $H = f$ (N); $D = f(T_D)$; $K = f(N, T_D, Wg)$; $I_t = f(N, Tg)$. N = number of trials, T_D = time period of food or water deprivation; Wg = the amount of reinforcement; and Tg = time of delay of reinforcer. The reader should note that N (the learning factor) enters into both H and K, but does not enter into D (Spence, 1956, p. 197). Other studies by Spence will be reviewed later in the chapter.

Drive Level or Extraversion?

Eysenck (1957) hypothesized that the correlation between anxiety and conditioning found in Spence's studies arises from the negative relation between anxiety and extraversion. From his point of view, conditioning performance is negatively related to extraversion but not to neuroticism. The implication is that the high drive subjects in Spence's studies were introverts and the low drive subjects extraverts (extraverts tend to have low scores on the Taylor Manifest Anxiety Scale). Eysenck (1957, 1965) assumes that extraverts tend to build up inhibition faster and dissipate it slower than introverts; and that it is inhibition and not drive which is the underlying variable in determining differences in "conditionability" between extraverts and introverts.

Spence and Spence (1964) report data showing level of conditioning to be positively related to anxiety but not to extraversion measures. Spence says that his position differs from that of Eysenck "only when he adds the assumption that neuroticism is not a factor affecting performance" (p. 148). Eysenck's supposition that extraverts are prone to inhibition is not necessarily incompatible with the supposition that conditioning increases with emotionality.

Eysenck (1965, p. 258) reviews studies relating GSR conditioning to extraversion-introversion. He says, "(a) Extraversion (E) is a phenotypic set of behavior patterns which is related to genotypic differences in the relative ease of arousal of cortical excitation and inhibition, extraverts showing greater inhibition, introverts greater excitation . . . ; (b) Cortical inhibition depresses conditioning and facilitates extinction; this assumption follows directly from Pavlov's theoretical concepts and experimental demonstrations."

The studies reviewed by Eysenck show that (1) conditioning performance is poor in extraverts when conditions favoring the development of inhibition, such as partial reinforcement, weak CS, weak UCS, and discrimination learning are used, and (2) conditioning performance in extraverts and introverts is the same when "conditions are such as to preclude the development of inhibition."

According to Eysenck, it is necessary to discriminate autonomic arousal and cortical activation. He says that subjects who are high in anxiety or neuroticism are innately predisposed to react strongly to certain classes of stimuli with general autonomic arousal (i.e. drive is a multiplier of only certain reactions); that subjects who are high in extraversion are innately predisposed to react strongly to certain classes of stimuli with cortical inhibition; and that subjects who are low in extraversion (introverts) are innately predisposed to react strongly to certain classes of stimuli with cortical excitation. Eysenck is not, as I see it, denying the concept of generalized drive, but rather adding other personality variables that may enter to influence the performance of subjects in conditioning.

We should recognize that Spence was also studying psychological defensiveness in his subjects, since scores from the K scale of the Minnesota Multiphasic Personality Inventory correlate substantially, and in a negative direction, with scores on the Manifest Anxiety Scale (Dykman, Reese, Galbrecht, & Thomasson, 1959; Dykman, Ackerman, Galbrecht, & Reese, 1963). Extrapolating from our data, we might say that extraverts (or low anxiety subjects or both) are high in psychological defensiveness relative to introverts. But without additional experimentation to partial out these variables, one would not know the extent to which differences in conditioning performance depend on defensiveness per se. What we seem to have is a constellation of factors related to conditioning performance. Spence and Spence (1964) state that anxiety accounts for only a small portion of the intersubject variance in conditioning performance.

Reciprocal Inhibition Theory of Wolpe

Certainly the most extensive attempt to apply conditioning concepts to human psychopathology and psychotherapy has been made by Wolpe (1958). Wolpe (1958, p. 19) assumes that learning depends "upon the development of functional connections (synapses) between neurons appropriately in anatomical opposition." He views complex learning as basically analogous to simple conditioning. Wolpe (1958, p. 20) says, "Suppose, for instance, I learn that the word 'window' means a window. Hearing the word spoken subsequently conjures up in me the image of a window. This implies that neurones responding to the word 'window' have become so connected to the neurones subserving the visual image of a window that stimulation of the former results in stimulation of the latter."

While Wolpe (1958, p. 23) prefers a drive reduction theory of learning, actually anxiety reduction, he says that his arguments as regards learned psychopathology "will not be affected if it should turn out that the onset of anxiety is all-important to its learning and its reduction of no moment at all." Anxiety reduction is only the special case of drive reduction in the learning of neurotic behavior. Wolpe's most important theoretical contribution is the notion that reciprocal inhibition is the basic process underlying extinction. This concept is a variant of interference theory but is elaborated by a drive reduction hypothesis. Wolpe (1958, p. 30) assumes that "When a response is inhibited by an incompatible response and if a major drive reduction follows, a significant amount of conditioned inhibition of the response will be developed." To back up this conjecture, he cites the experiment in which Pavlov (1927, pp. 29–31) used an electrical stimulus as a CS for food and saw not the slightest symptom of disturbance. The experiment began with a weak shock and the intensity of the shock was gradually increased as the food CR became stronger. Wolpe (1958, p. 30) says, "It would appear that at every stage of the experiment the performance of the feeding response involved a reciprocal inhibition of the mild defense reaction aroused by the electrical stimulus. Because of the drive reduction consequent on the feeding, this inhibition of response became progressively more strongly reinforced to the electrical stimulus." As the conditioned inhibition generated by drive reduction and reflex interference became stronger, the current could be increased without producing its normal defense reaction.

What Wolpe accomplishes by this added drive reduction hypothesis is difficult to understand. One could just as logically assume that the food reflex, being stronger than the defense reaction, inhibits the latter. From my point of view, it is unlikely that the food really reduced the general drive state; indeed it may have increased drive as direct electrical or autonomical recordings might show. It is likely that the drive evoked by food inhibits the drive evoked by shock. Wolpe is correct, I believe, in assuming that repeated reciprocal inhibition may favor one response while eliminating another. He reviews the literature on experimental neuroses, and cites several experiments showing that food responses may be used to inhibit anxiety reactions.

In one experiment, Wolpe produced a "neurosis" via conflict in the feeding situation and trauma such that the animals would not eat in the experimental room. Then, he found a room in which the animal would eat and allowed anxiety to be reduced there by the act of eating. Next he offered the animal food in a room a little more similar to the experimental room, and so on. He was able to get five cats who would not eat in the experimental room to eat there after going through the desensitization procedure. The remarkable thing was that as soon as an animal could be coaxed into eating, his signs of anxiety disappeared (immediate reciprocal inhibition).

Some of the animals were desensitized to visual and olfactory cues associated with the experimental cage and rooms. When the auditory CS (hooter sound) which had been originally paired with shock was reintroduced (trauma procedure), the conditioned anxiety reactions reappeared. The reaction to the hooter sound was then extinguished in one of two ways: (1) increasing the distance between the animal and the CS, and (2) "making use of the stimulus trace and the fact that the effects of a brief sensory stimulus on the nervous system gradually decline in intensity with passage of time" (Wolpe, 1958, p. 58).

Wolpe's two major curative procedures are desensitization and reciprocal inhibition, with the first explained on the basis of the second. The supposition that desensitization is always based on reciprocal inhibition, although interesting, may or may not be true. For example, Wolpe presents data which indicate that relaxation will reciprocally inhibit anxiety reactions. But one might say that anxiety reactions are extinguished, or partly extinguished, as the subject relaxes, and with no supposition of mutual antagonism. Or in the language of conditioning, the secondary drive properties of environmental CS are extinguished by nonreinforcement in a less threatening environment, which generalizes ultimately to the original conditioning room. One could assume that the desensitization process is dependent on reinforcement, namely a reinforcement of mildness, as brought about by the absence of aversive stimuli or a reduction in their intensity (Dykman & Gantt, 1960b).

Two Important Concepts of Gantt and a Point of View

Gantt (1953, 1958 a and b, 1960) noted that general autonomic reactions tend to condition quicker than specific motor and salivary CRs and to outlast the latter in extinction. This difference in rate of conditioning or extinction was called schizokinesis. Gantt has not devoted much attention to how schizokinesis is manifested in differentiation, but in one article (Gantt, 1960), pointed out that the cardiac function follows rather than precedes differentiation of motor CRs. Dykman, Mack, and Ackerman (1965b) have shown that general autonomic differentiation performance reaches an asymptote after motor differentiation performance.

Mowrer (1950) used Gantt's work to support his dual factor theory. Although related, there is a fundamental difference between the views of Gantt and Mowrer. Gantt regards schizokinesis as a naturally occurring physiological cleavage depending on both heredity and environment, and he avoids psychological terms such as drive, motivation, and tension reduction. On many occasions, in discussing psychological terms with me, he has asked, "What can be accomplished by such terms that cannot be accomplished by the empirical data from which they are derived? Why drive instead of food deprivation? Why reaction potential instead of response? Why fear instead of noxious stimulation? What predictions can be made from one that cannot be made from the other? Who can agree as to whether a dog is afraid, happy, or hopeful?" These are the kinds of questions Pavlov raised when psychological explanations were asked or given for his data, and Gantt adheres closely to this tradition.

In commenting on schizokinesis, Gantt (1958b, pp. 77 and 78) says, "I intend to include not only in a narrow sense a difference between the more general emotional components of the acquired responses and the specific ones, but in a broader way, the lack of perfect adaptation that exists in our biological systems. The heart is doing one thing, out of adaptation to present reality, while superficially the individual may be in repose and undisturbed. But beneath, in the autonomic components of the response, there may be violent turbulence. Here may lie the explanation for the persistence of psychogenic hypertension to past experiences long forgotten."

Schizokinesis is conceived by Gantt as an inherent liability in that certain general bodily reactions are quick to condition and slow to extinguish. Given the appropriate environmental circumstances, schizokinesis may lead to a pathological incoordination of systems, thereby operating in opposition to homeostasis.

Another very important concept discussed by Gantt is autokinesis. Gantt (1953) had noted a tendency in some dogs for behavior to become pathological, or more pathological, as a function of time and in the absence of experiences that would explain the observed changes. There is a kind of psychodynamic inertia such that maladaptive reactions, once set in motion, tend to become self-perpetuating. In discussing the mechanisms of autokinesis, Gantt (1958a, p. 19) says, "This autokinesis is something the subject himself contributes, something novel, synthesized out of his experiences, of the traces that remain in the nervous system, and perhaps from functions peculiar to the nervous system of that individual. In the neurotic dogs the autokinesis appears to be detrimental, to be adding new symptoms to the old ones, to continue the pathological course downward. But besides this *negative autokinesis*, there is a *positive autokinesis*, an improvement . . . The positive and negative autokinesis may be compared to anabolism and catabolism."

Autokinesis might be explained by secondary reinforcement, the attachment of cues in the environment to the conditioned emotional reactions produced in the experimental chamber. This presupposes certain bridging stimuli (e.g. persons, other animals, etc.).

A Possible Revision of Schizokinesis and Reservations

Work done in our laboratory indicates that schizokinesis as defined by Gantt is a group or average tendency, i.e. there are individual exceptions to the rule (Dykman et al., 1965b). Further, it is apparent that schizokinesis is dependent upon the CS-UCS interval. The optimal interval for motor conditioning (about 450 to 500 msec) is too short to allow autonomic changes to occur in the interval. Unpublished work by John E. Peters and Clinton Brown in the Pavlovian Laboratory at Johns Hopkins suggests that heart rate increases in vigor as a component of the CR as the CS-UCS interval increases in length from 6 to 30 sec. Dykman and Gantt (1958) reported cardiac CRs in medical students with little evidence of motor conditioning; the CS-UCS interval of 5.5 sec. was *not* conducive to motor conditioning in the human. It would appear then that the longer the interstimulus interval, up to some optimal duration that remains to be determined, the greater the probability an autonomic response will be conditioned prior to a motor response. It should be noted that Gantt employs long CS-UCS intervals (5 sec or more) in all his work.

The study of Dykman et al. (1965b) revealed another complication in regard to schizokinesis. In some dogs certain motor movements other than flexion, such as changes in posture, and eye and ear movements, appeared early in the long interval used (variable interval of 9.5 to 13.5 sec), very early in conditioning, and differentiated before autonomic reactions appeared. On this basis, I redefined schizokinesis to apply to two basic kinds of responses, one which occurred early in the CS-UCS interval (nonspecific) and one which appeared later in the interval (specific). This *revised* definition assumed that both the short and long latency responses were gross organismic reactions consisting of multiple autonomic and skeletal motor components. It was also assumed that general autonomic responses such as changes in heart rate should be called specific when they exhibit an inhibition of delay, i.e. occur with delay proportional to the CS-UCS interval.

Elsewhere (Dykman, 1965), I have hypothesized that the specific motor CR depends both upon the sensitization of automatic reflex pathways in the neocortex and upon the sensitization of lower emotional centers. The latter shape connections in the former and maintain the effectiveness of the CS once the connections are shaped. Conditioned autonomic and related nonspecific motor effects may occur in two ways, through the sensitization of lower arousal and emotional centers and through the sensitization of the same neocortical networks that mediate the longer latency motor CR. Thus, the motor CR measures emotionality in a most uncontaminated fashion after the connections on which it is based have been sensitized. General responses and the UCR, on the other hand, provide the best evidence of emotionality in the early conditioning trials.

In eyelid conditioning, the typical CS-UCS interval is 0.5 sec and there are, in general, several kinds of very short latency motor responses in addition to some responses of slightly longer latency. General autonomic conditioning does occur with such short intervals, but the responses can be seen only on trials in which the UCS is not given. To incorporate this finding, I think schizokinesis might be better defined as a difference in rate of appearance between responses (either skeletal motor, or autonomic, or both) tied closely to UCS onset. The distinction here is between responses that are often denoted in the literature as sensitized responses with respect to those that are called anticipatory responses. Let it be clear, however, that this difference does not warrant the classification false versus true learning; as already noted, both types of reactions may exhibit differentiation.

However it is defined, I have some serious reservations about schizokinesis. It may be that every response system and possibly many different measures within response systems have different acquisition, extinction, and differentiation functions; i.e. a dual classification of CR components such as is proposed by schizokinesis is far too simple. Lacey's work (1956, 1958, 1959) and our own (Dykman, 1959, 1963) on humans suggest individual variation in the hierarchal arrangement of the components of CRs. Individual variation in the ordering of responses is in line with the doctrine of organ specificity, a concept that is supported by a great amount of experimental work.

Contributions of Mowrer

Various writers have postulated two kinds of learning to denote behavior acquired on the basis of some principle of effect and behavior acquired on the basis of contiguity (see "Definitions"). Of these theories, Mowrer's (1950) achieved the greatest prominence, in part because its clinical implications were discussed in considerable detail. While Mowrer (1960) has discarded his original two factor theory, I believe that it will continue to be cited in the conditioning literature. It has a certain elegance and simplicity that will appeal to many workers.

In his original dual factor theory, Mowrer restricted the term conditioning to the acquisition of emotions. Solution learning, by contrast, applied to overt motor acts. He used the term sign learning to denote simple conditioning of involuntary responses depending upon mere contiguity of CS and UCS, or drive induction. According to this theory, sign learning came first in time and motivated solution learning. It was further supposed that sign learning is regulated by the autonomic nervous system and solution learning by the central nervous system, and that autonomic conditioning motivates instrumental acts, learned on the basis of tension reduction. As applied to classical conditioning, Mowrer's theory would say, I believe, that the motor CR is learned on the basis of drive reduction and autonomic CRs on the basis of contiguity, although Mowrer (1960) excluded as solution learning short latency muscular reactions such as the eye blink and the knee jerk.

Mowrer (1960, 1963) now conceives all learning to be sign learning with solution learning a special case thereof. He rejects his earlier two factor theory because it failed to deal adequately with secondary reinforcement and it accepted Thorndike's S-R theory of habit. Thorndikian theory is rejected because trial and error learning does not adequately explain the conditioned fear response; i.e. fear is acquired on the basis of contiguity rather than trial and error learning. The major contribution of Mowrer's new theory is, in my opinion, his treatment of reward situations, wherein he postulates an intervening variable, hope, operationally defined, acting in a manner analogous to fear in aversive situations.

A fear evoking CS elicits active avoidance when the fear state occurs prior to an action of the organism and passive avoidance when the fear state immediately follows some activity of the organism. In the latter case, movement produced stimuli serve as CS and are linked to fear through Pavlovian conditioning (sign learning), and, as a consequence evoke fear, which, in turn, blocks the response. In reward situations, there are two kinds of behavior parallel to the active and passive avoidance of aversive conditioning: active approach and response-facilitation. The former "is exemplified by the family dog coming 'when called'" (Mowrer, 1963, p. 8); the latter is a consolidation of habit as movement produced stimuli are conditioned to hope. The dog, for example, lifts his paw "to shake hands," is petted, and this action produces afferent stimuli which are conditioned to reward and to the intervening variable "hope." As in the case of conditioned fear, hope enters via the simple pairing of the CS and an incentive object. If movement produced stimuli are associated with food, and require the ability to arouse hope, the subject will, "when again hungry, . . . try to 'get more' of *these* ('promising') stimuli" (Mowrer, 1963, p. 9). Practice results in the conditioning of feedback stimuli to central emotional processes such as fear and hope and as this occurs the habit is facilitated. Thus, in the final analysis, all learning occurs via classical or Pavlovian conditioning. This theory is of considerable significance to psychophysiologists in that changes in end organs may enable us to better define "hope" and "fear," and relate these operationally defined variables to input-output variables in a variety of learning situations.

Sensitization and Pseudoconditioning

The controls used by investigators to prove that CRs produced by forward order techniques result from the specific pairing of CS and UCS and not from either one alone are described under "Definitions." The difficulties inherent in separating the associative and nonassociative components of the CR are shown under "Performance versus Learning: An Important Distinction." Here I propose to defend the proposition that sensitization and conditioning are equivalent processes (Dykman, 1965). This is not to say that responses classified by investigators as sensitized responses are of the same form and latency as responses generally classified as CRs. Rather it is to assert that the process of reflex potentiation or facilitation underlying CS augmentations is the same in terms of neuron changes as the process of conditioning—the hooking up of afferent neural processes of CS and UCS. The distinction is not, as already indicated, that of true and false learning (conditioning versus pseudoconditioning), but that of the particular pathways that are sensitized. The theory presented elsewhere (Dykman, 1965) hypothesizes both forward and backward connections, i.e. UCS to CS as well as CS to UCS. Thus, the CS potentiates UCS-structures and the reverse. This does not necessarily mean that all responses elicited by the CS or UCS prior to reinforcement will be potentiated, since the dominant stimulus (UCS) tends to inhibit many of the CS-responses.

Two major classes of responses are elicited in forward order conditioning, one class relatively more dependent upon the onset and the nature of the CS and the other relatively more dependent upon the onset and the nature of the UCS. The first class, as compared to the second, tends to exhibit irregular acquisition functions and more habituation during reinforcement. It is not unusual, however, to find responses of the seond class which habituate in the late stages of a reinforcement procedure, sometimes even sooner (Dykman, Gantt, & Whitehorn, 1956; Dykman et al., 1965). I doubt that these differences in acquisition or habituation permit the inference that the first class of responses do not depend, in part, upon learning, since in most cases the responses produced persist over many conditioning trials. It is hypothesized that *all changes in performance occurring to the CS and prior to the UCS, or during the normal period of the UCS when it is omitted, whether the directional change is augmentation or habituation, result via one primary mechanism, sensitization (an increase in the activity of neural pathways either inhibitory or excitatory).* Thus, learning is a sensitization process, in which pathways repeatedly used are altered; the difference between performance and learning is merely a matter of whether the CS produces CRs that differ from those seen in trials of CS alone prior to reinforcement. The CRs must, however, occur in the interstimulus interval, or if later, during the normal period of the UCR on trials in which the UCS is not given. This leaves open the question of CS modifications. To judge these, we must have a reference point, and this is the response the CS evokes on the first trial (i.e. prior to reinforcement). Any subsequent inhibition of CS responses occurring on Trials 2 through n is then learning (Dykman, et al., 1959). In terms of conditioning, the arbitrary reference point is the last non-reinforced habituation trial, and conditioning effects are generally apparent after one reinforcement.

The above hypotheses, or definitions, differ from the conventional ones most importantly in the supposition of a functional continuity of so-called sensitized responses and CRs. From the above definitions, most of the changes observed in conditioning are learning and not performance. If the drive level is decreased after Trial n, and the CR remains elevated on Trial $n + 1$, this is learning, given, say, an intertrial interval of sufficient length to allow the new conditions of drive to come into equilibrium.

The above suppositions, as indicated, apply to inhibition as well as excitation; inhibitory neurons undergo upon stimulation the same kinds of changes as excitatory neurons. There is direct evidence of axonal endings which, when activated, block synaptic transmission and thus depress reflex activity. Inhibition is parallel to excitation in all respects, latency, duration, occlusion, and spatial and temporal summation. Repetitive stimulation enhances the reflex effects of axonal terminals, either excitatory or inhibitory, presumably causing their enlargement (Eccles, 1953; Lloyd, 1941, 1949). Further, the complete absence of stimulation for a period of 2 to 3 weeks—achieved by severing nerves—results in a permanent loss of synaptic efficiency that cannot be restored by stimulation (Eccles, 1953). The reader should not, of course, infer from this finding that some act learned in the past but not used of late is permanently lost. The critical point is that the intact organism is never without some stimulation.

The most precise experimentation designed to disentangle sensitization effects is in eyelid conditioning. Kimble (1961, p. 56) describes several kinds of responses that are obtained in eyelid conditioning with a CS-UCS interval of only 0.5 sec. There are two short latency reactions: α responses which occur from 50 to 110 msec (same latency as the UCR), and β responses which occur from 120 to 240 msec. There are also two "long latency" responses: the CR with a latency of 250 to 500 msec and voluntary responses with a latency of 200 to 500 msec. In addition, random blinks may occur at any time. The CR can be discriminated by its latency or form from all other responses, with the possible exception of random blinks.

Under conditions of light, the α and β responses tend to habituate, while the longer latency CR shows the "model" or negatively accelerated acquisition function (Grant & Norris, 1947; Spence, 1956). But, why should the habituation of α and β responses be considered any less a true phenomenon of learning than the acquisition of the longer latency CR? Indeed, it is probable that the habituation of the first class of reactions depends in part on the eventual dominance of the second class of reactions; i.e. reciprocal, cross-modality or delayed latency (Harlow & Toltzien, 1940); differentiation (Morrell, 1961); external inhibition and disinhibition (Switzer, 1933); spontaneous recovery intramodality inhibition of one response by another. Dark adaptation favors short latency responses which could interfere with the longer latency CRs (Grant, 1945).

There are several lines of evidence to suggest the similarity of sensitized responses and CRs. Most characteristics exhibited by PCRs are also exhibited by true CRs: gradual acquisition and extinction (see reviews by Grant, 1943 a and b; Harlow, 1939; Harris, 1941, 1943; May, 1949; Wickens & Wickens, 1940); generalization (Grant & Dittmer, 1940; Grant & Meyer, 1941; Harlow & Toltzien, 1940; Shipley, 1933; Wickens & Wickens, 1942); (Harlow & Toltzien, 1940; Wickens & Wickens, 1940); and higher order conditioning (Shipley, 1933). Wickens and Wickens (1942) interpreted pseudoconditioning as a special case of stimulus generalization (CS to UCS).

With regard to pseudoconditioning controls, it is important to note *that a failure to show pseudoconditioning does not mean that the response in question cannot be produced by pseudo or backward order procedures, but only that a given procedure has failed to produce the response* (Harris, 1941, 1943). Most investigators who insist upon pseudoconditioning controls show little appreciation of the principles of reflex interaction (see discussion of conditioning by Hilgard, 1931). First, they fail to recognize the problem of interference when a strong stimulus precedes a weak stimulus. The appropriate UCS-CS interval for pseudoconditioning or backward conditioning may be as important as the corresponding CS-UCS interval in forward order conditioning (Razran, 1956a). Secondly, adaptation or habituation studies suggest that simple stimulation, CS alone or UCS alone, results in faster habituation of effects than occurs in the usual process of paired stimulation (Harris, 1941, 1943; Kimble & Dufort, 1956; MacDonald, 1946; Taylor, 1956a). It may also be that partial reinforcement introduces a novelty effect which tends to prevent CS and UCS habituation (McDonald & Johnson, 1965; Prokasy & Ebel, 1964).

A pseudoconditioning procedure in which the UCS is given alone for several trials and at a *regular* interval may be viewed as time conditioning, for the interval between successive stimuli becomes a CS. If a tone, say, is then introduced, or given at some time other than the previously established interval, the timing sequene is disrupted. A random order pseudoconditioning procedure minimizes all contributions to response: specific CS-UCS pairing, the time interval between stimuli, and the ordering of events. The random procedure does contain certain possibilities for learning, particularly in the case of human subjects with whom it is most often employed. The subject may view this procedure as a discrimination experiment consisting of nonreinforced CS and UCS. The important point is that the *CS should acquire a negative value* provided it is interpreted as nonsignificant. Randomization should allow a low level of positive conditioning, most clearly evident in general autonomic functions such as heart rate.

I would not quarrel with the stand that a random procedure enables one to refer the gains in a pairing procedure back to some "near zero" nonpaired procedure, but I would take issue with the implied suppositions that reliable differences between the two procedures prove that the responses established by the paired procedure are necessarily learned and that there is no learning in the nonpaired procedure. It is illogical to regard modifications occurring in pseudoconditioning as nonlearned responses. Pseudoconditioning and backward conditioning studied intensively will bring into clearer focus a number of factors important in forward order procedures (see Kimble, 1961, pp. 63 and 64), not only the underlying mechanism of learning but the possibility that two way connections are always established in forward conditioning (CS to UCS as well as UCS to CS).

The most informative recent studies of pseudoconditioning are those by Kimble and associates on the eyeblink (Dufort & Kimble, 1958; Kimble, Mann, & Dufort, 1955; Kimble & Dufort, 1956). His general procedure is to pair CS and UCS for a number of trials and then to present a block of trials of UCS only. Kimble found that the trials of UCS alone (following pairing) increased the frequency of CRs in both conditioning and extinction. Apparently very few pairings are required to establish an eyelid CR to the point where it may be maintained or augmented by pseudoconditioning (see also Hilgard & Grant, 1940). Kimble also found eyelid performance in classical pairing superior to that in instrumental conditioning.

Stewart, Stern, Winokur, and Fredman (1961) say that many investigators working on the galvanic CR have failed to provide adequate controls for sensitization. Stewart suggests that the galvanic CR reported in many studies may only be an augmented CS response, the return of the galvanic component of the OR. In support of this view, he says these so-called galvanic CRs do not show a "true" acquisition function, the curve does not increase to some asymptote and remain more or less constant, but reaches a peak magnitude quickly and then habituates. Stewart argues, following the eyelid workers, that the true galvanic CR can be defined by its latency as a component response appearing in the neighborhood of UCS onset.

Lockhart and Grings (1963) accuse Stewart of failing to provide adequate sensitization controls for the pure CR. Noting that the OR in Stewart's study increased in frequency in the early conditioning trials, Lockhart and Grings (1963, p. 563) suggest that Stewart may have been studying only "sensitized error responses," i.e. "GSRs which meet CR criteria on a chance basis." Lockhart points out that latency as a sole criterion of conditioning is less valid than is implied by Stewart, and he argues that if latency is an adequate criterion, there should be little correlation between frequency of ORs which occur early in the CS-UCS interval and frequency of the so-called true CRs which occur later in the CS-UCS interval. Lockhart computed a correlation coefficient of 0.90 between the frequency of "ORs" and CRs in Stewart's study! For this reason, he feels that the differentiation paradigm provides a sounder basis for distinguishing sensitized reactions from CRs.

Kimmel (1964) also argues that the conclusions of Stewart are unsound, because Stewart failed to consider the consequences of the Pavlovian phenomenon of inhibition of delay (an early phase of inhibition and a subsequent phase of excitation) which can create the impression of a double response (one occurring early and one occurring later in the interval). He cites his 1963 study which showed that, as the galvanic CR develops, it moves forward in the CS-UCS interval. He concludes, therefore, that the so-called true CR of Stewart may simply be part of "the dynamically changing CR made to the CS" (Kimmel, 1964, p. 163).

Another study by Kimmel (Kimmel & Pennypacker, 1963) showed galvanic differentiation of two tones, one of which was reinforced. Kimmel (1964) says that if the latency criterion of Stewart had been applied in this instance, he would have been forced to conclude that differentiation is not a legitimate form of learning. He noted further that while differentiation enables one to distinguish between specific sensitization processes and nonspecific sensitization, it does not enable one to distinguish between two forms of nonspecific sensitization, lowering of threshold or an increase in arousal. In the latter case, Kimmel (1964, p. 165) says, random pseudoconditioning *might* be of value in isolating "sensitization of the general arousal type."

Kimmel accepts as CRs the ORs to the CS provided there is a legitimate change as can be shown by control procedures, differentiation, increasing latency, and pseudoconditioning. But he adds that it may be impossible to distinguish between the sensitization and the conditioning of galvanic responses, and "that differentiation of this sort may not be necessary either" (Kimmel, 1964, p. 166). It is obvious that he is struggling with the same problem that I have been concerned with for a number of years (Dykman et al., 1956).

If the criterion of increasing latency is applied to motor responses, we shall have to classify many of them as sensitized responses; for once motor responses appear, they may change very little with training. Furthermore, in differentiation experiments the discriminative effect may be manifested either by decreased (or increased) latency of responses as a function of trials (Dykman et al., 1956; Dykman, 1965).

McDonald and Johnson (1965) reported a study of the GSR in humans which included a control for sensitization. The pseudoconditioning control group received 32 trials with CS and UCS randomly alternated. The experimental group received 30 trials of a 10 sec CS followed by a 0.5 sec shock (60% partial reinforcement schedule). McDonald classified as ORs responses occurring 1.3 to 2.9 sec after CS onset and as CRs responses occurring later in the CS-UCS interval. The OR did not show a significant conditioning effect in either control or experimental subjects, and the CR increased in magnitude only in the forward order group. Unlike *most* other workers in this field, he did obtain an acquisition function for the galvanic CR and assumed that this depended upon the partial reinforcement schedule which prevented the habituation of the UCS. In conformity with the results of Stern, Winokur, Stewart, and Leonard (1963), the frequency of ORs was correlated from 0.56 to 0.61 with frequency of CRs. These correlations are not as high as the one Lockhart computed for the Stewart data.

Returning to the study by Stewart, there is no justification for saying that an augmented OR is not a legitimate conditioning effect if this augmentation persists, as it did, over several trials. Whether a component response habituates is irrelevant to the question of learning, unless one wants to assume that extinction is not a form of learning. Further, we (Dykman et al., 1956, 1965) have shown that the cardiac CR may display maximum differentiation while heart rate levels are decreasing (habituation). One would certainly hesitate to say that this is not learning, whatever the shape of the acquisition curve. Kimmel recognizes, I believe, the major problem in demonstrating conditioning, namely, the dynamically changing form of the CR with trials. There are also effects in the dynamically changing pattern of the CR that go well beyond the interstimulus interval. In conditioning the kidney, for example, and differentially judging by the duration of an antidiuretic effect, the room in which the dog is placed becomes a significant component of both the negative and positive CS (Dykman, Corson, Reese, & Seager, 1962).

The differentiation paradigm proposed by Lockhart is excellent for studying the emergence of different response components. But, in certain cases, differentiation can be achieved at a statistically significant level without the effect being mediated by the CS; i.e. order of stimuli, intertrial interval, or the program of reinforcement may be the agent. We (Dykman et al., 1965) have shown in the dog that those motor responses generally considered sensitized reactions or ORs provide the first signs of discrimination. All that McDonald showed with his pseudoconditioning procedure is that *one* design, out of an infinite variety that might be used, failed to produce the CR, and in this case the subjects learned, I believe, that the CS was not to be followed by shock.

To contrast nondiscriminative conditioning to shock with random reinforcement is most interesting. In the former, the CS is a signal of "danger" and the UCS termination a signal of "relief," to use Mowrer's (1963) terms. In the random method, the CS and the time interval immediately following it constitute a "safety" signal, while the remaining intertrial interval is a "danger" signal. Which procedure is the appropriate sensitization control? Typically, investigators use an extinction procedure (CS never reinforced) as a control for a conditioning procedure, and in the latter the CS has no "instrumental value," the animal gets shocked no matter what he does. In the random procedure, the CS could be said to have "instrumental" value, for the subject learns that he will not be hurt during the CS. Answering the question raised above, then, either procedure might be said to be a sensitization control for the other. The arguments in this area do tend to become circular!

As another example of the interpretive difficulties which occur in conditioning, Smith (1954) hypothesized that all autonomic changes are artifacts of skeletal motor CRs; autonomic functions cannot be conditioned. This assertion ignores the fact that autonomic responses may occur on trials in which all visible motor components are absent and the fact that autonomic changes may occur earlier or later than the motor CR on trials in which both reactions occur (Dykman et al., 1956; Gantt, 1953; Pavlov, 1928, p. 251).

Several studies have shown that cardiac, pupillary, and exophthalmic responses (bulging of eyeball) may be classically conditioned in curarized preparations (Black, Carlson, & Solomon, 1962; Black & Lang, 1964; Solomon & Turner, 1962) and more important, that conditioning in the curarized animal affects later behavior in the noncurarized state. Black et al. (1962, p. 25) said that their work shows "that autonomic conditioning does occur independently of skeletal activity."

Black and Lang (1964) were interested in how the conditioning effects achieved in the curarized preparation, i.e. when skeletal reactions are blocked, may transfer to or affect skeletal reactions in the subsequent nondrug or normal state. He suggests some form of mediation via cognition or discriminated feedback stimuli.

Smith (1964a, p. 77) has questioned the curare experiments and says that "early Es [experimenters] reported muscular activity under deep curarization; and that thinking, quite possibly muscular in nature, is unhampered by curarization." To substantiate this latter conjecture, he cites the work of Smith, Brown, Toman, and Goodman (1947) which showed that curare has no effect on higher thinking processes while paralyzing gross body movements.

Black, apparently incited by Smith to provide better evidence that his autonomic CRs obtained under curare were not just artifacts of skeletal motor conditioning, studied muscle action potentials and found no conditioned motor changes in the presence of a marked cardiac CR. Smith (1964b), in commenting on these results, conceded that if the electromyographic results hold up in other studies, Black's point will be made, and he (Smith) will retract his hypothesis.

Malmo (1965) also attacked Smith's position, by using data obtained from brain stimulation experiments (Malmo, 1963) in which heart rate changes were conditioned in the absence of consistent motor responses. But he says further that the equipment used by Black and Lang (1964) to record muscle action potentials was inadequate to obviate the possibility of muscle potential responses.

Whether or not autonomic changes are always associated with muscle potential changes is of no consequence. It would be just as logical to say that the muscle potential changes are an artifact of the autonomic changes as the reverse. The best guess is that both kinds of changes are regulated by arousal structures in the brain stem. Further, if Smith is to make a valid point, he must, I believe, distinguish between the specific motor CR and nonspecific changes in muscle action potentials.

In summary of this section, we have direct neurophysiological evidence *to suggest* that the basic mechanism of learning is sensitization. Given this, the responses that emerge depend upon the particular pathways excited (or inhibited). The conditioning literature shows relatively clearly that responses which emerge early in the CS-UCS interval do not conform to the same acquisition function as those which emerge later in the interval. Whether one should call these two forms of responses by different names is a moot point. It is the additional assumption that one is not learned and the other learned and that the underlying basis of modification is such as to warrant this distinction that creates difficulty. Sensitization theory places CS augmentations and PCRs in the same category as CRs, not in terms of the specific neural pathways modified, but in terms of the underlying neural changes.

Literature Review

The intent of this section is to review important recent literature not covered or not adequately described in the previous sections of the chapter.

Orienting Response

The orienting response (OR) is a gross organismic reaction consisting of multiple autonomic and skeletal motor components. The OR to stimuli of the CS class has been studied most extensively; indeed, investigators frequently restrict the term to responses of this nature (Grant, 1964). It appears in clearest and most persistent form in subhuman animals; e.g. on the first several presentations of a novel stimulus, the dog will turn toward the source of the stimulus, and this reaction is coupled to general autonomic responses (Dykman et al., 1956; Dykman & Gantt, 1959; Dykman, 1965; Robinson & Gantt, 1947; Pavlov, 1927).

Sokolov (1960, 1963) has studied the OR in detail (autonomic, EEG, and motor components) and developed a neurophysiological theory to explain its habituation. This theory has been cited by a number of American workers (Galbrecht, Dykman, Reese, & Suzuki, 1965; Grings, 1963; McDonald, Johnson, & Hord, 1964; Unger, 1964). Sokolov (1963, p. 11) assumes the OR to be a nonspecific reflex produced by a change in the environment; an OR is the nonspecific "reaction resulting in the tuning of the analyzer [brain structures reached by the stimulus] when exposed to a new stimulus." Uniformity of the environment, say a tone (*T*) and a light (*L*) given in strict alternation, establishes a neuronal model or dynamic stereotype, according to Sokolov.

The neuronal model preserves information concerning the intensity, quality, duration, and order of presentation of stimuli. As long as the pattern of stimulation coincides with the model there is no OR and the cortex maintains its tonic inhibitory effect on the lower brain centers. Any change in the pattern of stimulation releases the downstream inhibitory effects of the neuronal model and causes the OR to appear. Sokolov views his contributions as an extension of Pavlov's work and theories.

Veronin and Sokolov (1960), in a report on the EEG components of the OR, noted appreciable individual variation in the brain areas blocked by a novel stimulus. There is evidence that the autonomic and skeletal motor reactions elicited by different stimuli are not the same (Darrow, 1929; Davis, 1957; Lacey, 1959; Sokolov, 1963; Veronin & Sokolov, 1960). Further, the motor components of the OR are highly specific to the localization of the external stimulus in space. I reserve judgment on the question of whether the OR should be called a nonspecific reflex.

The following findings emerge from studies of the OR. (1) It appears to be an innate response. Wertheimer (1962) reported an OR in a human neonate less than 10 min old; the infant oriented to an auditory stimulus. (2) The OR depends upon the drive properties of the eliciting stimulus and intraorganismic factors (see review by Dykman et al., 1959b). (3) It may be used to measure the effectiveness of a potential CS in conditioning. Winokur, Guze, Stewart, Pfeiffer, Stern, & Hornung (1959) report in a psychiatric patient sample a correlation of 0.65 between the number of ORs and the number of galvanic CRs in extinction. (4) The OR is also affected by instructions given subjects (Berlyne, Craw, Salapater, & Lewis, 1963).

A great number of American workers have studied the OR, but have referred to it by other names (see Darrow, 1929). Much of the relevant literature is reviewed by Galbrecht et al. (1965) and Dykman et al. (1959) Davis, Buchwald, & Frankmann (1955), in the most systematic study ever done on reactions to simple stimuli, reported OR habituation with trials and response magnitude proportional to intensity of the eliciting stimulus.

Unger (1964) studied the habituation of the vasoconstrictive OR. Numbers were presented in order, 1, 2, 3, 4, etc., with an interval of 5 to 25 sec. between stimuli, with the supposition "that forthcoming elements in the sequence would soon be *anticipatorily* primed or triggered" (Unger, 1964, p. 12). Of the 20 subjects studied, 12 habituated (3 successive nonresponses to numbers in series); one number not in sequence was sufficient to restore vasoconstriction. This experiment is particularly interesting in that habituation occurs to stimuli that are not the same on each trial. Unger says that the neuronal model of Sokolov, if it is to explain his habituation results, must be able to reconstitute itself after each trial and in accordance with the predicted nature of the next stimulus.

Of the several American studies of the OR in animals, the best, and the one which has been the source of inspiration for our work and much foreign work, was done by Robinson and Gantt (1947) in the Pavlovian Laboratory at Johns Hopkins. This study reported the motor, cardiac, respiratory, and the salivary components of the OR in dogs. In our most extensive study of the OR (Galbrecht et al., 1965), medical students were given a single tone 12 times/session for 8 days. Mean intrasession (adaptation) curves were similar to mean intersession (extinction) curves, with the galvanic response the measure. This finding, supported by the muscle potentials data (only a few students gave evidence of adaptation in heart rate and respiratory rate), led us to hypothesize that adaptation and extinction are similar neurophysiological processes.

External Inhibition and Disinhibition

As indicated under "Pavlovian Theory," external inhibition denotes the suppression of a CR by presenting a novel stimulus just before, coincidentally with, or just after the regular CS. Disinhibition refers to the restoration of a CR after its submergence by a nonreinforcement procedure (e.g. in extinction or differentiation) by giving a novel stimulus just before, coincidentally with, or immediately after the regular CS. In general, the novel stimulus is given just before the CS, although in the case of very slow responses such as salivation, the interfering effects of a novel stimulus may be observed during the CS-UCS interval. Pavlov (1927) also recognized another form of disinhibition; in trace or delayed conditioning, the CR may be made to occur earlier in the CS-UCS interval by presenting a novel stimulus during the interstimulus interval.

There have been few systematic studies of these forms of mutual interference although they are mentioned in many Russian papers and in some American papers (see Razran, 1956, a and b). Switzer (1933) reported disinhibition of the GSR, and Wenger (1936) reported external inhibition and disinhibition of the GSR. Razran (1939) found that an extraneous stimulus had the customary inhibiting effect on the salivary CR in humans and the disinhibiting effect in extinction. The effect of the extraneous stimulus (in this case a buzzer) in restoring the CR in extinction was greater than its inhibiting effect in conditioning. Merryman (1954), cited by Kimmel and Greene (1964), using a trace procedure found that the magnitude of the GSR as evoked by a novel stimulus occurring at 6 or 9 sec in a CS-UCS interval of 19 sec increased as a function of applications. Further, the GSR was larger when the extrastimulus was given late in the CS-UCS interval than when it was given early. Grings and O'Donnell (1956) found that an interpolated stimulus augments the GSR. Kimmel and Fowler (1961) reported the GSR to a CS plus extrastimulus to increase as a function of the number of conditioning trials. This effect was greater with a visual CS and novel auditory stimulus than with an auditory CS and novel visual stimulus.

Kimmel and Greene (1964) have recently done a very extensive study of extrastimulus effects using 300 undergraduate students at the University of Florida. Subjects were assigned to six groups, receiving 0, 1, 2, 10, 25, or 50 conditioning trials. Then, each group was further divided into five subgroups with the subgroups receiving a single extrastimulus at different times in the interstimulus interval, 0, 25, 50, 75, or 100% of the CS-UCS interval. The conditioning procedure was the long delayed type with the CS lasting 7.5 sec, the UCS (shock) lasting 0.1 sec, and the UCS given 7.4 sec after the onset of the CS. In testing the effects of the extrastimulus at 7.4 sec (100% of the CS-UCS interval), the UCS was omitted. The extraneous stimulus was a 3000-cps tone, 0.1-sec duration, and of low intensity, "it sounded like a 'squeak'" 1964, p. 568). The authors say that the GSR to the CS plus extraneous stimulus increased in negatively accelerated fashion as a function of N [reinforcements], while the GSR to the CS alone went up and, then, went down" (1964, p. 567). In this study, the point of optimal excitation, as measured by the disinhibiting effect of the tone, shifted gradually during conditioning from the "point" of CS onset to the "point" of UCS onset.

This study is probably one of the more significant studies in 1964. Firstly, it shows that the GSR is subject to disinhibition; the CS plus an extraneous stimulus was far more effective than the CS alone. An extrastimulus is more apt to facilitate the GSR than to inhibit it. Secondly, the paper shows that the excitatory effect of the extrastimulus increases in a negatively accelerated manner with conditioning trials. And thirdly, it shows that the excitation gradient in the early trials is negative, sloping away from the point of onset of the CS. Then, as conditioning is established, the gradient becomes positive, increasing excitation from CS onset to some point just before the occurrence of the UCS. Kimmel (Kimmel & Greene, 1964, p. 572) says that while the average magnitude of the galvanic response to the extrastimulus "changed only a little from 25 to 50 conditioning trials, the temporal function changed considerably . . . [thus] the strength of the associative process that underlies these events continues to be influenced by CS-UCS pairings . . . considerably after its near-maximum overall excitatory potential has been achieved." In brief, we have evidence here that the presence of the CR as measured by a type of disinhibition (or gradient of inhibition of delay) continues to develop after the galvanic CR has reached its peak magnitude.

A number of workers in this country have studied the external inhibition of motor CRs. Dufort and Kimble (1958) and McAllister and McAllister 1960) have found that a ready signal prior to the CS retards the development of the eyeblink CR. Pennypacker (1964) found that a novel auditory CS interpolated into the CS-UCS sequence had the occasional effect of eliciting a premature eyeblink response. The usual or typical result was, however, the expected one of external inhibition rather than disinhibition. While the UCR was not affected in any consistent way by the extraneous stimulus, attenuation was observed in certain cases. External inhibition was not related to the number of reinforcements but was related inversely to the total number of CRs given by subjects. He also found that the eyelid CR could be disinhibited by an extraneous stimulus during extinction.

Spence and Weyant (1960) studied the effect of not giving a warning signal on differentiation in low and hig anxiety subjects (Spence and his associates use a warning signal in most of their studies). Differential eyelid performance in this study was found to be similar to differential performance in studies in which a warning signal had been used. There is, of course, a considerable differ?,c? b?tween a standard warning signal given on every trial and a novel extraneous stimulus that occurs infrequently (the typical case of external inhibition). Beyond this, it seems reasonable to suppose that since differentiation generally produces stronger CRs than nondiscriminative training, that external inhibition might be less in differentiation experiments. In this study, the curve for the high anxiety subjects receiving a mild UCS was similar to the curve for the low anxiety subjects receiving a strong UCS.

Reflex Interactions

In any treatment of conditioned reactions, we must consider reciprocal relations between functions. Obviously, the motor responses elicited by an orienting stimulus may interfere with the motor CR, and we know from the work of Pavlov that the orienting response may also interfere with specific salivary CRs.

In the case of general autonomic reactions, however, the rule seems to be one of stimulus summation rather than reflex incompatibility; i.e. those reactions elicited by CS alone may be facilitated by the UCS to produce the so-called autonomic CR. But, there are interactions between systems of importance. For example, the heart rate CR may be dependent to a considerable extent upon respiratory conditioning. If a subject exhales rapidly and then inhales rapidly, the heart will decelerate and then accelerate, i.e. a voluntary respiratory component is superimposed upon the regular sinus arrhythmia. Why voluntary? Because this respiratory-cardiac reflex can be produced "at will" by the subject, even though it may be entirely unconscious in a given conditioning routine. If the subject holds his b eath or increases his rate of breathing (Dykman, 1965; Westcott & Huttenlocher, 1961; Zeaman & Smith, 1965), heart rate accelerates in anticipation of shock. Regular breathing, at least in the human subject, apparently eliminates cardiac acceleration (Wood & Obrist, 1964). Heart rate and respiratory rate are not always as closely coupled as many studies in this area imply (Deane, 1964; Dykman et al., 1959; Malmo, 1963). Such idiosyncrasy is in part a matter of the organization of autonomic functions within different subjects of the same species and the emotionality evoked by the CS (Dykman et al., 1963; Lacey, 1956; Schoenfeld, 1950; Zeaman & Smith, 1965).

Zeaman and Smith (1965), after reviewing the work of the Columbia group (particularly Bersh, Notterman, & Schoenfeld, 1956; Notterman, Schoenfeld, & Bersh, 1952, a and b; Schoenfeld, 1950) and research from his own laboratory, hypothesized that cardiac acceleration in conditioning depends upon anxiety (the conditioned expectation of a noxious agent) whereas cardiac deceleration results from a conditioned attention-response which slows the heart through its effect on respiration. The concept of conditioned attention arose in the experiments of Steward (1962), in Zeaman's laboratory. Steward found that pleasant tones serving as UCS have the same decelerative effect in the vicinity of onset as noxious sounds or shocks.

CS-UCS Interval

The optimal interval for nondiscriminative motor conditioning is about 450 msec (see Kimble, 1961, pp. 156 and 157). Spence (1956), as previously noted, says that little eyelid conditioning occurs with intervals as long as 2 sec. Clearly, so brief an interval is not necessary to elicit the flexion CR in dogs (Dykman et al., 1956; 1965), but it may be needed to produce the flexion CR in humans.

One of the better studies on the eyelid CR is by Hansche and Grant (1960). The effect of four intervals (0.15, 0.35, 0.55, and 0.75 sec) was studied for both CS onset and CS offset. The CS duration was in all cases 1.5 sec, and the UCS duration was from 0.01 to 0.02 sec. Variation of the CS-UCS interval was achieved by presenting the UCS at the four periods of delay during the CS (four groups of subjects), or after the termination of the CS (another four groups of subjects). The optimal interval for both CS onset and CS offset was 0.5 sec.

Experiments by McAllister (1953) and Boneau (1958) show that shifting from short to long intervals during conditioning decreases eyelid performance. Boneau says that a shift from intervals of 0.5 sec to 1 sec (or to 1.5 sec) is to return the CR to a level that would have been obtained had the longer interval alone been used. There have been several recent studies showing that the optimal interval for motor CRs varies in different species of animals (for review of literature and research see Bitterman, 1964; Noble & Adams, 1963; Noble & Harding, 1963).

The literature on nondisciminative autonomic conditioning, ignoring the salivary CR for the moment, is confusing. Studies by several investigators indicate that the optimal interval is comparable to that for the motor response (see Kimble, 1961, for references; Silverman, 1960). These studies suggest, in the main, little conditioning with intervals longer than 0.5 sec. Some really good studies, on the other hand, show that while the optimal interval for autonomic conditioning is about 500 msec, a wide range of intervals are almost equally effective (Jones, 1962; Notterman et al., 1952, a and b; Wickens, 1959; Wickens, Gehman, & Sullivan, 1959; Zeaman & Smith, 1965).

Differentiation experiments to be reviewed below are clear in showing that the optimal interval for autonomic conditioning is longer than 0.5 sec. While the optimal interval for differentiation is longer than the optimal interval for nondiscriminative conditioning, it is unlikely that the magnitude of this difference is so great as to invalidate the supposition that nondiscriminative autonomic conditioning is very efficient over a wide range of CS-UCS intervals, and may be really stronger with long intervals than very short intervals given an adequate period of training. The work of Pavlov is clear in showing that salivary conditioning is best with long intervals. Gerall and Woodward (1958) present evidence to show that the optimal interval for pupillary dilation is 1.5 sec with little conditioning at 0.125 sec and no conditioning at 2.5 sec. It is absolutely clear, then, that considerable autonomic conditioning occurs at intervals which many investigators consider too long for efficient conditioning. Further, the differences noted in the studies just reviewed are sufficient to warrant the conjecture that the optimal interval for different systems is different.

Recently, investigators have begun to study the effect of CS-UCS interval on differentiation. Hartman and Grant (1962b) contrasted eyeblink differentiation at four CS-UCS intervals (400, 600, 800, and 1000 msec), and found discriminative performance to be an increasing function of the length of the interval. This corresponds to results obtained by Grings, Lockhart, and Dameron (1962) for the galvanic CR in mentally defective subjects, although Grings used much longer intervals. Kimmel and Pennypacker (1963) employed four CS-UCS intervals (0.25, 0.50, 1.0, and 2.0 sec) and found differentiation to improve as interstimulus interval increased. Work by Zeaman and Smith (1965) shows clearly that very long intervals, even under trace procedures, are effective in producing cardiac differentiation.

Lockhart and Grings (1964, a and b) studied the galvanic CR under three conditions of reinforcement: (1) CS duration of 5 sec and UCS lasting 0.6 sec given at CS termination; (2) CS duration of 5 sec and UCS lasting 0.6 sec given 0.5 sec after CS onset; and (3) CS duration of 0.5 sec and UCS lasting 0.6 sec given at the termination of the CS. He found two galvanic CRs, a "first response" occurring during the 5-sec period of the CS (observed on trials in which the UCS was omitted for condition 2), and a "second response" occurring in the 5-sec period following the termination of the CS.

Maximum differentiation for both galvanic CRs was obtained after two reinforced CS and two nonreinforced CS. Under condition 1 above, reliable differentiation of both galvanic CRs was obtained. Less reliable, but significant, differentiation of the first CR was also obtained under conditions 2 and 3. But the second CR failed to differentiate under condition 2, and the second CR exhibited better discrimination than the first CR under condition 1. Just looking at the graphs presented, condition 2 provided the most reliable first CR differentiation, and condition 1 the most reliable second CR differentiation.

Lockhart (Lockhart & Grings, 1964, p. 213) hypothesizes that the galvanic CR may not be conditioned to the CS, but reflects a "conditioned cognitive or perceptual discrimination." He says further that differential reinforcement is probably more important that the CS-UCS interval in determining discrimination performance, a fairly obvious fact when we consider the cases of successful differentiation with very long intervals (see Pavlov, 1927). Unlike the abrupt acquisition found in college students, the first CR in mental defectives is slowly acquired (Grings et al., 1962). Autonomic differentiation in mental defectives is similar to that in dogs (Dykman et al., 1956, 1965). Following Razran (1955), Lockhart hypothesizes that mental defectives attain perception via conditioning, whereas college students exhibit conditioning-like behavior via perception.

We (Dykman & Murphree, 1966) have found that a CS-UCS interval of 2.9 sec reversed cardiac differentiation in the dog; that is, the negative CS produced greater acceleration than the positive CS. This finding is in opposition to our earlier studies, but in them the interstimulus interval was at least 5 sec. Subsequent work in our laboratory has shown that the interval of 2.9 sec will eventually produce the usual positive response greater than negative response relation, but 150 to 200 differential reinforcements are required before this effect is seen. The significant "reversed" differentiation occurred with 50 or fewer reinforcements. With an interval of 9.5 to 13.5 sec, the dominance of the positive CS in evoking cardiac acceleration appears as early as the first 10 differential reinforcements (Dykman et al., 1965). And, with a 5-sec interval, differentiation (three CS, each reinforced by a different intensity shock) occurs within 50 differentiation trials (Dykman et al., 1956).

Effects of CS Intensity

There are a great number of studies showing that an increase in CS intensity has the effect of immediately increasing the magnitude of the CR (see Kimble, 1961, pp. 118-122). The American work has attempted to distinguish between performance and learning, and strongly suggests that CS-intensity operates mainly on performance, i.e. nonassociative factors. The Russian work, on the other hand, while not attempting to distinguish between performance and learning, suggests that CS intensity enters directly into learning. Kimble points out that the discrepancy between curves obtained by Russian and American workers, cumulative changes with trials in the former and rather abrupt shifts in the CR in the latter, may be a species difference—the Russian experiments he reviews are on subhuman animals and the American experiments on humans.

Some American investigators have assumed that CS intensity operates on habit. The Perkins-Logan hypothesis (Logan, 1954; Perkins, 1953) assumes an excitatory generalization gradient for a reinforced CS and an inhibitory generalization gradient for intertrial stimuli (background cues) present in the conditioning environment but not reinforced. On an intensity scale, a strong

CS is further removed from background stimuli than a weak CS; thus, a strong CS should, as a consequence, generate less inhibition than a weak CS. A weak CS is like weak intertrial stimuli and through generalization of inhibition evokes a weak CR. Many theorists assume generalization to be a strictly associative affair, provided there is a gradient sloping away from the CS (see Razran (1949) as one notable exception). The generalization under discussion in the Perkins-Logan hypothesis is not, I believe, strictly associative. The CS, regardless of the intensity dimension, is generally quite different from intertrial stimuli. If the CS is similar in dimensions other than intensity alone (e.g. same modality or similar meaning via past training), habit, excitatory or inhibitory, is clearly involved. But should one assume that generalization to stimuli other than to those directly related to the CS is also a case of habit strength when these have not been specifically reinforced? The answer may be yes, and, if so, there is little point to attempting to distinguish between associative and non-associative variables. Certainly conditioning theory would be simpler if, following Pavlov, it assumed only inhibition and extinction and did not try to partial out associative and nonassociative components. The legitimate associative effect in the Perkins-Logan situation, if such exists, is the negative generalization of intertrial stimuli to other similar stimuli and not to a radically different CS.

Hull (1952) hypothesized the CS intensity part of reaction potential (E) as an intervening variable, varying directly with the momentary strength of the stimulus and having no associative properties. Like drive (D), it acts multiplicatively with habit strength to determine response strength. Thus, an increase in the intensity of CS should immediately augment the CR. Hull's postulate, in contradistinction to the Perkins-Logan hypothesis, implies that stimulus offset would not be as effective a conditioning agent as stimulus onset. But several studies have shown the comparable effectiveness of stimulus offset (Champion, 1962; Hansche & Grant, 1960; Logan & Wagner, 1962; Mattson & Moore, 1964).

Barnes (1956), using dogs, paired a brief shock with a tone (800 cps). The continuously acting CS (one at 60 db and one at 80 db) outlasted the UCS. CS durations were 1, 6, 16, and 31 sec, and the UCS, a 0.1-sec shock, was given in each case 0.9 sec after CS onset. Any response beginning after CS onset and prior to shock was considered to be a CR. The strength of the CR (measured by number of responses and latency) varied positively with CS intensity and inversely with the degree of overlapping. The 30 sec overlap group exhibited, however, as high a level of performance as the 15-sec group. With the weak CS (60 db tone), the 30-sec group required more training to reach the level of performance of the 15-sec group, but with the stronger CS (80 db tone) the acquisition functions were similar. Thus, CS intensity would appear to affect habit to some degree, the effect being clearer as the degree of overlap increases. Although contiguity theory would predict little or no conditioning at the longer intervals of overlap, there was considerable responding in the two groups in which the CS outlasted the UCS by 10 and 30 sec. The results seem more in accord with anxiety theory; i.e. conditioned anxiety decreased with the degree of overlap, but reduction was not sufficient to eliminate the CR.

Walker (1960) studied the eyelid CR in relation to both CS and UCS intensity and found that CS intensity affected the short latency responses, but not the longer latency CRs. The longer latency CR was affected more by changes in the intensity of the UCS than by changes in the intensity of the CS. These results would seem to indicate that the UCS intensity affects habit but that the CS intensity affects performance.

Kimmel (1959), in Gring's laboratory, studied galvanic conditioning to three 1000-cps tones of different intensities, each reinforced by the same electrical stimulus. The CS intensities were 35, 75, and 115 db, respectively. Positive results were obtained only for the CS of lowest intensity. Razran (1957) theorized that CR performance will increase with CS intensity, up to some critical point, and that the relationship beyond this critical point is negative. Kimmel interprets his results in support of Razran. In Pavlovian terms, we have a simple example of interference between the galvanic component of the OR (or startle reflex) and the galvanic component of the CR. There are studies to show that CS intensity does not have the same effects on motor CRs as on autonomic CRs (See Kimble, 1961, p. 342).

Champion (1962) studied the galvanic CR as evoked by the termination of on-going pure tones of either 60 or 80 db. Conditioning was superior when the silent period followed the louder tone. This article also reports other experiments which support the Perkins-Logan hypothesis discussed above.

Mattson and Moore (1964) studied the intertrial response and CS intensity in eyelid conditioning. Human subjects were randomly assigned to four major groups: two conditions of CS intensity and two modes of presentation of CS (onset and offset). In conformity with past work, performance to the louder tone was superior to that to the softer tone, but this was independent of the mode. The number of responses occurring in the intertrial period were carefully studied, and contrary to the Perkins-Logan hypothesis, no relation was found between the number of intertrial responses and the CR. Mattson (Mattson & Moore, 1964, p. 400) suggests that the absolute stimulus intensity may act on arousal to increase responding in the intertrial interval. Further, he does not think that the Perkins-Logan hypothesis should replace Hull's concept providing stimulus intensity is conceived in terms of "stimulus change relative to background intensity."

All these stimulus offset studies really show is that turning a stimulus as effective as turning it on, and that the turning off effect, like the turning on effect, conforms to the intensity (stimulus change) principle. The degree of contrast produced by turning off a loud tone is greater than that produced by turning off a soft tone, and the conditioning effect is proportional to the contrast.

Beck (1963) studied CS intensity, UCS intensity, and drive level as measured by the Manifest Anxiety Scale, and found each of these variables to be positively associated with the strength of the eyelid CR. The effect of CS intensity was greater than that found in previous eyelid studies, and Beck (1963, p. 429) attributes this to an "adaptation level phenomenon or contrast effect." Level of adaptation in this study was controlled within individuals by exposing subjects to both loud and soft tones during the course of conditioning. Unlike the study by Walker above, CS intensity affected both short and long latency CRs.

Moore (1964) studied the effects of varying the frequency and intensity of pure tones (CS) in differential eyelid conditioning. Differentiation was found to increase with increasing separation of tones, either in frequency or intensity. Increasing CS intensities tended to increase responding more to the positive than to the negative CS. Differentiation was superior when the positive CS was also the louder of the two stimuli.

Effects of UCS Intensity

Studies in this area report without exception a positive relation between CR performance and the magnitude or intensity of the UCS (Crespi, 1944; Dykman, et al., 1956, 1962, 1965; Dykman & Gantt, 1959, 1960, a and b; Spence, 1956; Zeaman & Smith, 1965). Gantt (1937, 1938) found the unconditioned secretion of saliva to be a linear function of the amount of food given, but the conditioned secretion to be an exponential function of the amount of food given. The most influential and best designed studies in this area are those of Spence and associates.

As indicated under "Contributions of Spence," he conceives drive level to be a positive function of the level of emotionality induced in the subject by the UCS or other aversive stimuli. He assumes that the emotionality generated by noxious stimuli persists for long periods of time, well beyond the duration of the typical intertrial interval. Thus, the CR on any given trial is determined in part by the cumulative emotional effects of earlier trials plus what has been learned (H) on previous trials. But in Spence's theory, habit strength also depends upon the UCS. As pointed out earlier, Spence has suggested the possibility that classical conditioning to noxious agents is governed by some principle of reinforcement, whereas in instrumental reward, conditioning contiguity is the only important principle. In discussing the nature of reinforcement, Spence, Haggard, and Ross (1958) prefer not to be specific and say only that habit strength in classical aversive conditioning depends in part upon the reinforcing (associative) properties of the UCS. Studies by Spence have been much concerned with the teasing out, so to speak, of the nonassociative (perseveratıg drive consequences of preceding UCS) and associative contributions of JCS (see below).

Runquist, Spence, and Stubbs (1958) studied differential eyelid performance ı relation to UCS intensity. Subjects were given 60 conditioning trials with positive CS and 60 trials with a "negative" CS; the positive and negative rials were randomly alternated with the restriction that no more than three ositive (or negative) trials occurred in succession. The positive CS was rein- ɔrced after 500 msec and the "negative" CS after 2500 msec. Subjects were ivided into two groups, one presented with a UCS of relatively high intensity air puff of 2 psi) and one with a UCS of low intensity (air puff of 0.3 psi). The roup receiving the UCS of high intensity was superior (in terms of percentage ·f CRs in each block of 20 trials) to the group receiving the UCS of low in- ensity. Interestingly, the acquisition function for the "negative CR" in the igh intensity group was similar to the function for the positive CR in the low ntensity group. The acquisition functions obtained in this experiment were imilar to those noted by Spence and Farber (1954) in studying anxiety. Low nxiety subjects given a UCS of high intensity exhibited a curve roughly similar o that for high anxiety subjects given a UCS of low intensity. Thus, it would ppear that the emotionality produced by the perseverating consequences of he UCS operates during conditioning in a manner similar to the characteristic motionality of subjects as measured by the Manifest Anxiety Scale. Many ·ther studies could be cited (see Spence, 1956) which show the nonassociative ffects of drive on performance.

Spence et al. (1958) studied eyelid performance in two groups of human ubjects whose drive levels had been equated on the basis of the number of JCS. In one group, a strong UCS was paired with the CS, but a weak UCS vas given at other times unfavorable to the development of the CR. In the ɔther group, the UCS of weak intensity regularly followed the CS, but the UCS ɔf high intensity was given at other times (no close temporal association of this timulus and the CS). Performance was positively correlated with UCS ntensity. Since the levels of drive (D) were equated in this experiment, only he effect of UCS intensity on habit (H) remained, i.e. reinforcement effect per e. There are a number of other studies which indicate that drive may be a de- erminer of habit strength (see article by Beck (1963) for review of literature ınd pertinent research findings).

ompound Conditioning

In compound conditioning the CS consists of at least two elements pre- ented simultaneously or with varying degrees of overlapping. Pavlov (1927, ɔ. 141) noted a tendency for one element of a compound "very commonly o overshadow the effect of others almost completely, and this independently ɔf the number of reinforcements of the compound stimulus"; e.g. a tactile component might overshadow a thermal, an auditory, or a visual component or a tone of high intensity or a tone of low intensity. He also noted, as indicated under "Pavlovian Theory," that the stronger element could become inhibitory through nonreinforcement while the compound retained its strength through reinforcement. If in a compound the weaker element alone is nonreinforced, the compound and stronger element show partial extinction (secondary extinction). When the elements of the compound are given successively rather than simultaneously, the response strength depends upon the order of presentation of elements, the time intervals between the onset of elements, and the intensity of the elements. Pavlov (1927, p. 148) emphasized the dynamic fluctuation of the elements in a compound as conditioning takes place when he said, "the effect of an active cortical cell upon the one next excited varies according to the influence to which it was itself subjected by the cell last stimulated."

Following Pavlov, the S-R theorists take the view that CR magnitude or frequency to a compound CS can be predicted from the responses elicited by the elements of the compound. Summation of responses to elements has been shown in a number of studies. Weiss (1964) has shown that the Pavlovian principle of CS summation extends to operant conditioning. Further attention here will be restricted to some work of Grings and Wickens. For a review of literature in this area, the reader may consult Razran (1961).

Grings and O'Donnell (1956), in a study of 32 undergraduate college students, used colored dots as CS and an electric shock as the UCS. The intensity of the UCS (condensor discharge) was set to produce a consistent galvanic reflex "and a verbal expression of slight discomfort" (p. 355). The interstimulus interval was 0.5 sec and the CS overlapped the onset of the UCS.

In a preconditioning period, the subjects were given four colored light dots in random order (three of which were later to serve as CS). The UCS was then given alone for three trials, presumably to establish shock levels for the subsequent conditioning procedure. Further orienting training followed in which the dots alone were given without shock.

In the early conditioning trials, the subjects were given three of the four dots, two consistently reinforced and one nonreinforced. All four dots were given alone and without reinforcement (test trials) after the fifth and eighth series of reinforcements. After the two positive CS had been reinforced 10 times, and the negative CS given 10 times with no reinforcement, the four dots (none reinforced) were presented in various paired combinations.

The compound stimuli were counterbalanced in different subjects, with the two positive CS labeled $+_1$ and $+_2$, the negative CS, $-$, and the extrastimulus, O. The order of response strength (magnitude of GSR) on test trials was $+_1+_2 >$ $_1O > +_2O$ or $-O > +_1-$ or $+_2-$. Thus, the two positive stimuli had the greatest summative effect when paired, and the negative stimulus and the positive stimuli ne least effect. The extrastimulus decreased the effect of the two positive CS (external inhibition) but increased the effect of the negative CS (disinhibition).

Grings and Kimmel (1959, p. 253) reported galvanic conditioning to various compounds consisting of "colored light dots, a tone, and a tactile stimulus to fingertips." They hypothesized that the magnitude of the galvanic CR "would be greater to compounds consisting of reinforced components, and that these differences in magnitude would be different for different combinations of stimulus modalities involved in the compound" (p. 259). They found that the CS were not equally conditionable, that awareness of experimental conditions facilitated learning, and that the response to compounds of reinforced stimuli was greater than the response to compounds of nonreinforced stimuli.

Wickens (1959), in an excellent paper, raised the question of how the S-R reinforcement principle (the tendency of an S-R link to be strengthened whenever R is reinforced) applies to compound conditioning. As stated, this reinforcement principle does not cover compound conditioning, particularly if one of the elements of the compound is more effective than other elements in evoking the CR. Wickens attempted to bring compound conditioning within the framework of S-R theory. He reported a number of studies done in his laboratory. The first, a study by Lacey, employed a two element CS, CS_1 and CS_2, arranged so that the CS_1-UCS interval was 2 sec, the CS_2-UCS interval 0.5 sec, and the CS_1-CS_2 interval 1.5 sec. The two elements of the compound were a continuous light and a continuous tone; in one group, CS_1 was a tone and CS_2 a light, and in another group, CS_1 was a light and CS_2 a tone. Control groups were given single stimuli (light or tone) with CS-UCS intervals of 0.5 and 2 sec. In conformity with much work in this area, the optimal interval for the galvanic CR was 0.5 sec, with a drop (not too great) at 2.0 sec. But contrary to predictions based on the optimal interval function, the elements of the compound *when given alone* showed an opposite effect: CS_1 given first and 2 sec before the UCS had a greater effect than CS_2 given .5 sec before the UCS. Further, when given singly, the elements of the compound evoked galvanic CRs of greater magnitude than the same stimuli never given as elements of a compound.

In explanation, Wickens assumed that the actual CS is not the sensory event or trace stimulus elicited by the CS, but rather the CS response and its feedback stimuli (in Pavlovian terms, the orienting response (OR)). He further hypothesized sensory conditioning between CS_1 and CS_2 conforming to the CS-UCS interval function (maximal efficiency at about 0.5 sec). The chain of events in compound conditioning is then as follows: external CS_1 evokes OR_1; feedback from OR_1 is the true CS_1; CS_1 becomes conditioned to OR_2 evoked by CS_2; feedback from OR_2 is the true CS_2; and both CS_1 and CS_2 are conditioned to the UCR. Under these circumstances, the point of reference for measuring time is not UCS onset but the onset of CS_2. The longer stimulus produces a greater CR than the shorter stimulus when given alone be cause it taps, so to speak, the optimal interstimulus interval (0.5 sec) separatin CS_2 and the UCS.

In subsequent work, Wickens gave CS_1 at various times before CS_2 whil maintaining the 0.5 sec interval for CS_2 and the UCS. A control group wa also run for each value of CS_1; i.e. subjects were given a single CS precedin the UCS by the same time interval as CS_1 preceded the UCS in compoun conditioning. This experiment led to some very important findings.

One graph shown by Wickens depicts the magnitude of the CR as a functio of the time interval by which CS_1 preceded CS_2. There are three peaks o this graph, at 0, 920 msec, and 2600 msec. With the magnitude of the Cl plotted as a function of the CS-UCS interval, the curve for the groups give single CS also shows two definite peaks, one at about 0.5 sec and the othe at about 2.0 sec. In the latter case, performance level decreased during th period from about 0.5 sec to 1 sec, then increased from about 1.0 to 2.5 sec and decreased thereafter. Wickens says that the peak at 2.5 sec occurs at abou the latency of the galvanic CR and at about the time the CS are terminating

Wickens also found that CS_1 influenced the response to CS_2. Plotting CS_2 a a function of the time by which CS_1 preceded the onset of the UCS, ther were two peaks, one at 0 (no overlap) and the other at about 1.5 sec. Th curves for CS_1 and CS_2, plotted in terms of the CS_1-UCS interval an superimposed on each other, were mirror images. Wickens (1959, p. 188) say: "While one stimulus is moving towards greater similarity to the pattern pro duced by the complex, the other is moving toward a greater difference." I summarizing his results, Wickens states that the findings are consistent wit S-S theory, although he has attempted to make them consistent with S-I theory "by employing the notion of internalized stimuli generated by response to the conditioned stimulus."

Intertrial Interval, Time Conditioning, and Pattern of Reinforcement

A number of studies have shown that massing of reinforcements lowers per formance (see Hull, 1943, pp. 277–280; Kimble, 1961, pp. 125–127; Osgood 1953, p. 348; Woodworth & Schlosberg, 1954, pp. 562 and 563). In general, thi decrement has been considered to be nonassociative.

Prokasy, Grant, and Myers (1958) and Spence and Norris (1950) foun that the classically conditioned eyelid response is impaired by massing. Prokas; and Ebel (1964) also demonstrated that massing attenuates the GSR. They ha four experimental conditions: conditioning with massed trials, sensitizatio with massed trials, conditioning with spaced trials, and sensitization wit spaced trials. The sensitization procedure differed from conditioning in tha CS and UCS were given in a prearranged irregular order (no specific pairings) Conditioning produced galvanic CRs of greater magnitude and greater recruit ment (longer time to peak response) than sensitization. Spacing of trial (mean intertrial interval of 40 sec), in contrast to massing of trials (mean intertrial interval of 20 sec), led to galvanic CRs of greater magnitude and recruitment. The galvanic CRs produced by sensitization procedures decreased in magnitude as a function of trials, whereas those produced by conditioning remained constant. There was no gradual acquisition function for the conditioning group, and conditioning could be discriminated from sensitization only in terms of the decrease in performance in the sensitization group. In extinction, the so-called sensitized CRs had a longer latency than the so-called legitimate CRs. This finding is of interest because sensitized responses are assumed by some investigators to have a shorter latency than CRs.

Working in apparent opposition to the principle of massing is the time interval between trials, which may become an element of the CS. A dog fed regularly at 30-min intervals may learn the time interval so well that he begins to salivate just before the appearance of food or during the first few seconds of the period in which anticipated food is withheld (Pavlov, 1927, p. 41). Gantt (1946; Gantt & Woolsey, 1948) reported cardiac conditioning to time, and noted that cortical ablations disrupt the time CR. Russian work cited by Dmitriev and Kochigina (1959) showed that (1) time interval plus CS summate to determine the strength of the CR; (2) time CRs undergo spontaneous extinction if training is discontinued; (3) the specificity of the time CR increases with training and moves even closer to the period of CS onset; (4) time conditioning is more successful with long interstimulus intervals (1 to 3 min) than with short interstimulus intervals (say, 15 to 30 sec); (5) time conditioning is improved rather than impaired by somnolent states (a fact that does not coincide with S-R mediation theory); (6) time CRs are especially subject to external inhibition and disinhibition, these effects are more apparent the closer the extraneous stimulation to CS onset; (7) time CRs are impaired by high drive conditions; and (8) time reflexes extinguish rapidly and are re-established rapidly by reconditioning. Other work reviewed in the same article showed that leukocyte counts increase just before eating, and that fluctuations in metabolism, pulse rate, and temperature can be conditioned to external events which occur at some fixed time.

In addition to time, the order in which stimuli are given is very important; a dynamic stereotype reaches maximum effectiveness when both the intertrial interval and the order of stimuli are fixed. Order would appear to be a critical factor in simple contrast conditioning (Dykman et al., 1965), and in the terminal stages of conditioning, ordering may become more important than the CS itself. Gantt (1940) gave CS in strict alternation (strong weak strong weak) until a dynamic stereotype to order was established (intertrial interval varied from 3 to 7 min). The strong weak dichotomy here denotes the amount of food used to reinforce the two CSs. After the stereotype was established, CSs were given in other orders (e.g. strong, strong, strong, strong). The CRs to new orders were affected by the previously established order. Gantt (1940, p. 15) says that "The adaptation to the pattern disappears more or less rapidly in different dogs when the old order is changed." He (1940, p. 16) goes on to say that, "Whether the individual stimulus or the 'configuration' to the whole pattern is the dominant factor in the reaction is determined by certain conditions of the experiment, as well as by the constitution of the animal." The ability to form an integrated CR pattern requires a well balanced nervous system.

Grant, Riopelle, and Hake (1950) studied the resistance to extinction of the eyelid CR under four patterns of reinforcement: single alternation (one reinforcement, one nonreinforcement, etc.), double alternation (two reinforcements, two nonreinforcements, etc.), random alternation under the restriction that no more than three nonreinforced (or reinforced) trials could occur in order, and spaced 100% reinforcement. In this last procedure, reinforcements were spaced to correspond to the timing of reinforced trials in the random procedure. Time interval between trials was 30 to 50 sec for all of the procedures except spaced reinforcement. It was found that the random alternation and spaced reinforcement procedures evoked larger CRs than the other procedures in both acquisition and extinction. This result might mean only that subjects in the random and spaced groups had a higher drive level which more than compensated for the ordering of events. Hartman and Grant (1962a) have also presented results which suggest that the ordering of stimuli may not be too important. One possible explanation of the conflicting findings in this area, aside from difference in subjects, is that most of the studies yielding positive results for time conditioning (or a dynamic stereotype) have used far more conditioning trials than have Grant and Hartman.

Effect of Instructions

Instructions, or knowledge of procedures, may either augment or interfere with conditioning (for reviews see Gormezano & Moore, 1962; Hartman & Grant, 1962 a and b; McAllister & McAllister, 1958; Razran, 1955; Woodworth & Schlosberg, 1954, pp. 572–576).

Silverman (1960), studying galvanic CRs in three groups of subjects, employed interstimulus intervals of 0.5 sec and 6 sec, and a random interval on which CS and UCS were not specifically paired. Prior to an extinction procedure, half the subjects in each group were told that the UCS would not be given. The instructions influenced the performance of the 0.5-sec group and the random interval group but had no effect on the 6-sec group. Silverman (1960, p. 125) said that the 6-sec interval may have allowed the subjects to "develop a heightened state of GSR response which is no longer dependent upon the initial instructions."

Nicholls and Kimble (1964) attributed the inhibitory effects of instructions to the habituation of the UCR. A group of subjects given inhibitory instructions showed more UCS habituation than a group given facilitating or neutral instructions. Kimble and Pennypacker (1963) found UCR habituation to be associated with poor CR performance.

Wickens (1938, 1939, 1948) conditioned subjects to move their fingers away from a shock electrode with their hands in the palm down position. The transfer of the conditioned extensor response was subsequently tested in the palm up position. Under these new conditions most subjects responded with flexion rather than the original conditioned extensor CR. Wickens' findings create a problem for any reinforcement theorist who assumes that the only learned response in conditioning is the specific movement pattern that is reinforced. Lindley (1959), in a follow up of these experiments, presented evidence which suggests that the exact form of the transfer reaction depends upon the instructions read to subjects. Wickens' instructions encouraged a reaction opposite to the CR. If subjects are told in the initial instructions to move their hands up from the grid in responding to shock, they will extend their fingers when the palms are down and flex them when the palms are up. But if subjects are instructed to make a movement toward the shock electrode, they will move their fingers in the direction of the shock electrodes in both conditioning and in the subsequent transfer test. Lindley (1959, p. 8) says his results do not contradict "the response of generalization of Wickens," but rather suggest the mechanism underlying such generalization.

Operant Autonomic Conditioning and Conditioning Out-of-Awareness

While operant conditioning of autonomic responses does not fall properly into this review, the work is of such importance as to warrant its inclusion, if for no other reason than the fact that it suggests a mechanism for classical autonomic conditioning.

The first studies of this nature were done by Russian investigators (see Razran, 1961, pp. 91–97, pp. 120–123). Shearn (1962) made delay of shock contingent upon heart rate acceleration and found that the number of accelerations increased with training. Kimmel and Baxter (1964) demonstrated that subjects may learn to avoid shock by giving a galvanic response. In an experimental group, the reinforcing shock was omitted if the subject gave a GSR prior to shock onset "equal to or larger than the smallest GSR made by him in the preliminary CS-only series" (p. 482). Each experimental subject had a matched control who (regardless of his galvanic activity) was not shocked on those trials in which the experimental subject had escaped shock but was shocked on all other trials. Conditioning was noted in both experimental subjects and controls, but the experimental subjects gave galvanic CRs of greater magnitude. Kimmel recognizes (but does not believe) that the conditioned GSR in these experiments might be an artifact of muscular movements.

A considerable body of data suggests that conditioning can occur out-of-awareness. The earliest experiments in this country on "unconscious" conditioning were done by Diven (1937). He conditioned the galvanic CR to the word barn and studied the generalization of the response to other words preceding and following the CS, to words similar to barn in rural connotation, and to neutral words. Lacey and Smith (1954) questioned that a true CR was formed in these experiments, since Diven did not show that the reactivity to all words was greater in his experimental group than in the control group. Diven concluded that subjects could be conditioned unconsciously to the word barn and that the response generalized to other rural words.

Lacey (Lacey & Smith, 1954; Lacey, Smith, & Green, 1955) repeated Diven's experiment but incorporated certain important controls. His word list included eight rural words (e.g. cow, barn, plow) and eight words having no rural meaning (e.g. paper, clock, book, soft). He presented 40 words in all, four of which were repeated six times each. In one group of subjects the word cow was reinforced and in another group the word paper was reinforced. The subject was instructed that he was to chain associate to each word until he heard the command "stop" (i.e. for 15 sec). The word "stop" following paper (or cow) was reinforced with a strong electric shock (13 ma). During each chain association, the subject was also required to tap a telegraph key at an even rate. To quote Lacey et al. (1955, p. 209), the subject "wonders if he gets shocked when his tapping performance has been erratic, or when he produces too few associations. But the pressure of events is too much for him and he has no time to think clearly about these and other possibilities; he must tap and associate, associate and tap."

The subjects conditioned to the word cow showed greater autonomic changes to "cow" than to "paper," and the reverse for the subjects conditioned to the word paper. The degree of cardiac differentiation increased as a function of reinforcements. The subjects reinforced to "cow" generalized their responses to other rural words. Interrogation revealed that conditioning apparently occurred out-of-awareness in many subjects. They could not say which word had been regularly followed by shock. Thus, the unaware subjects seemingly never knew when the shocks were to be given. Lacey and Smith (1954) noted that the CR was weaker than its associated generalized CR, a finding not obtained in other studies.

In the 1955 study, Lacey reports data for a group of 20 subjects who were told in advance of conditioning the word to be followed by shock. The aware subjects immediately developed strong responses which tended to adapt with training. By contrast, the unaware subjects exhibited the typical acquisition curve, but at a much lower level of heart rate activity and discrimination. There was far more generalization for unaware than for aware subjects.

Chatterjee and Eriksen (1960), in an experiment similar to the one by Lacey, found a close relation between the galvanic response and the awareness of subjects. They stated that conditioning is no better than the subject's awareness. In a further report, Chatterjee and Eriksen (1962) found a close relation between verbalized expectancies and cardiac CRs.

Lazarus and McCleary (1951) found that a tachistoscopic exposure of a conditioned nonsense syllable produced a GSR of greater amplitude than a control nonsense syllable. The duration of exposure of the syllables was too short for correct identification. Lazarus termed this process of unconscious discrimination subception.

Several investigators have criticized the interpretations of Lazarus (see Eriksen, 1956), but none has questioned the existence of the phenomenon. The subception effect has been confirmed in at least two additional studies according to Lazarus (1956).

Lazarus (1956, p. 344) points out that it is not necessary "to assume that the physiological response system . . . is a more precise mirror of the physical stimuli than the verbal response system." He argues that a response system may react on a simple categorical basis, say the presence or absence of danger, even though other processes fail to identify the specific components of the stimulus. The subception effect implies that autonomic discrimination can occur in the absence of verbal perception, and not that autonomic discrimination is superior to verbal perception.

Acknowledgments

I wish to acknowledge the help of Dr. Charles R. Galbrecht and Mrs. Peggy Ackerman, research associates, who assisted me in the preparation of this chapter.

REFERENCES

Barnes, G. W. Conditioned stimulus intensity and temporal factors in spaced-trial classical conditioning. *J. exp. Psychol.*, 1956, *51*: 192–198.
Bartoshuk, A. K. Electromyographic gradients as indicants of emotion. *Can. J. Psychol.*, 1955, *9*: 215–230.
Beck, S. B. Eyelid conditioning as a function of CS intensity, UCS intensity, and manifest anxiety scale score. *J. exp. Psychol.*, 1963, *66*: 429–438.
Berlyne, D. E., Craw, M. A., Salapater, P. H., & Lewis, J. L. Novelty, complexity, incongruity, extrinsic motivation, and the GSR. *J. exp. Psychol.*, 1963, *66*: 560–567.
Bersh, P. J., Notterman, J. M., & Schoenfeld, W. N. Extinction of human cardiac response during avoidance conditioning. *Am. J. Psychol.*, 1956, *69*: 244–251.
Bitterman, M. E. Classical conditioning in the goldfish as a function of CS-UCS interval. *J. comp. physiol. Psychol.*, 1964, *58*: 359–366.
Black, A. H., Carlson, M. J., & Solomon, R. L. Exploratory studies of the conditioning of autonomic responses in curarized dogs. *Psychol. Monogr.*, 1962, *76*: 29.
Black, A. H., & Lang, W. M. Cardiac conditioning and skeletal responding in dogs. *Psychol. Rev.*, 1964, *71*: 80–85.

Boneau, C. A. The interstimulus interval and the latency of the conditioned eyelid response. *J. exp. Psychol.*, 1958, *56*: 464–471.

Bykov, K. M. *The cerebral cortex and the internal organs* (translated by W. H. Gantt, (Ed.)). New York: Chemical Publishing Co., 1957.

Champion, R. A. Stimulus intensity effects of response evocation. *Psychol. Rev.*, 1962, *69*: 428–449.

Chatterjee, B. B., & Eriksen, C. W. Conditioning and generalization of GSR as a function of awakeness. *J. abnorm. soc. Psychol.*, 1960, *60*: 396–403.

Chatterjee, B. B., & Eriksen, C. W. Cognitive factors in heart rate conditioning. *J. exp. Psychol.*, 1962, *64*: 272–279.

Crespi, L. P. Amount of reinforcement and level of performance. *Psychol. Rev.*, 1944, *51*: 341–357.

Darrow, C. W. Differences in physiological reactions to sensory and ideational stimuli. *Psychol. Bull.*, 1929, *26*: 185–201.

Davis, R. C. Response patterns. *Trans. N.Y. Acad. Sci.*, 1957, *19*: 731–739.

Davis, R. C., Buchwald, A. M., & Frankmann, R. W. Autonomic and muscular responses, and their relation to simple stimuli. *Psychol. Monogr.*, 1955, *69*: 1–71.

Deane, G. E. Human heart rate responses during experimentally induced anxiety: a follow-up with controlled respiration. *J. exp. Psychol.*, 1964, *67*: 193–195.

Diven, K. Certain determinants in the conditioning of anxiety reactions. *J. Psychol.*, 1937, *3*: 291–308.

Dmitriev, A. S., & Kochigina, A. M. The importance of time as stimulus of conditioned reflex activity. *Psychol. Bull.*, 1959, *56*: 106–132.

Duffy, E. The concept of energy mobilization. *Psychol. Rev.*, 1951, *58*: 30–40.

Dufort, R. H. & Kimble, G.A. Ready signals and the effect of interpolated UCS presentations in eyelid conditioning. *J. exp. Psychol.*, 1958, *56*: 1–7.

Dykman, R. A. Toward a theory of classical conditioning: cognitive, emotional and motor components of the conditioned response. In B. Maher (Ed.), *Experimental approaches to personality*, Vol. II. New York: Academic Press, 1965.

Dykman, R. A., Ackerman, P. T., Galbrecht, C. R., & Reese, W. G. Physiological reactivity to different stressors and methods of evaluation. *Psychosom. Med.*, 1963, *25*: 37–59.

Dykman, R. A., Corson, S.A., Reese, W. G., & Seager, L. D. Inhibition of urine flow as a component of the conditional defense reactions. *Psychosom. Med.*, 1962, *24*: 177–186.

Dykman, R. A., & Gantt, W. H. Cardiovascular conditioning in dogs and humans. In W. H. Gantt (Ed.), *Physiological bases of psychiatry*. Springfield, Ill.: Charles C Thomas, 1958. Pp. 171–195.

Dykman, R. A., & Gantt, W. H. The parasympathetic component of unlearned and acquired cardiac responses. *J. comp. physiol. Psychol.*, 1959, *52*: 163–167.

Dykman, R. A., & Gantt, W. H. Experimental psychogenic hypertension: Blood pressure changes conditioned to painful stimuli (schizokinesis). *Bull. Johns Hopkins Hosp.*, 1960, *107*: 72–89. (a)

Dykman, R. A., & Gantt, W. H. A case of experimental neurosis and recovery in relation to the orienting response. *J. Psychol.*, 1960, *50*: 105–110. (b)

Dykman, R. A., Gantt, W. H., & Whitehorn, J. C. Conditioning as emotional sensitization and differentiation. *Psychol. Monogr.*, 1956, *70*: 15.

Dykman, R. A., Mack, R. L., & Ackerman, P. T. The evaluation of autonomic and motor components of the nonavoidance conditioned response in the dog. *Psychophysiology*, 1965, *1*: 209–230.

Dykman, R. A., & Murphree, O. D. Litter patterns in the offspring of nervous and stable dogs. II. Autonomic and motor conditioning. *J. nerv. ment. Dis.*, 1966, *141*: 419–431.

Dykman, R. A., Reese, W. G., Galbrecht, C. R., & Thomasson, P. T. Psychophysiological reactions to novel stimuli: Measurement, adaptation, and relationship of psychological and physiological variables in the normal human. *Ann. N.Y. Acad. Sci.*, 1959, *79*: 43–107.

Eccles, J. C. *The neurophysiological bases of mind.* Oxford: Clarendon Press, 1953.

Eriksen, C. W. Subception: Fact or artifact? *Psychol. Rev.*, 1956, *63*: 74–80.

Eysenck, H. J. *The dynamics of anxiety and hysteria.* New York: Praeger, 1957.

Eysenck, H. J. Extraversion and the acquisition of eyeblink and GSR conditioned responses. *Psychol. Bull.*, 1965, *63*: 258–270.

Freeman, G. L. *The energetics of human behavior.* New York: Cornell Univ. Press, 1948.

Galbrecht, C. R., Dykman, R. A., Reese, W. G., & Suzuki, T. Intrasession adaptation and intersession extinction of the components of the orienting response. *J. exp. Psychol.*, 1965, *70*: 585–597.

Gantt, W. H. The nervous secretion of saliva: quantitative studies in the natural unconditioned reflex secretion of parotid saliva. *Am. J. Physiol.*, 1937, *119*: 493–507.

Gantt, W. H. The nervous secretion of saliva: the relation of the conditioned reflex to the intensity of the unconditioned stimulus. *Am. J. Physiol.*, 1938, *123*: 74

Gantt, W. H. The role of the isolated conditioned stimulus in the integrated response pattern and the relation of pattern changes to psychopathology. *J. gen. Psychol.*, 1940, *23*: 3-16.

Gantt, W. H. Cardiac conditional reflexes to time. *Trans. Am. neurol. Soc.*, 1946, 166.

Gantt, W. H. Principles of nervous breakdown: schizokinesis and autokinesis. *Ann. N. Y. Acad. Sci.*, 1953, *56*: 143-163.

Gantt, W. H. (Ed.). *Physiological bases of psychiatry.* Springfield, Ill.: Charles C Thomas, 1958. Pp. 12-21. (a)

Gantt, W. H. Recent contributions to objective psychiatry. In *Proceedings of the sixth annual psychiatric institute.* New Jersey: NeuroPsychiatric Institute, Princeton, 1958. Pp. 72-83. (b)

Gantt, W. H. Cardiovascular component of the conditional reflex to pain, food and other stimuli. *Physiol. Rev.*, 1960, *40*: 266-291.

Gantt, W. H., & Woolsey, C. N. Cardiac reactions in partially decorticated dogs. *Trans. Am. neurol. Soc.*, 1948, 131-133.

Gerall, A. A., & Woodward, L. K. Conditioning of the human pupillary dilation response as a function of the CS-UCS interval. *J. exp. Psychol.*, 1958, *55*: 501-507.

Gormezano, I., & Moore, J. W. Effects of instructional set and UCS intensity on the latency, percentage, and form of the eyelid response. *J. exp. Psychol.*, 1962, *63*: 487-494.

Grant, D. A. The pseudo-conditioned eyelid response. *J. exp. Psychol.*, 1943, *32*: 139-149. (a)

Grant, D. A. Sensitization and association in eyelid conditioning. *J. exp. Psychol.*, 1943, *32*: 201-212. (b)

Grant, D. A. A sensitized eyelid reaction related to the conditioned eyelid response. *J. exp. Psychol.*, 1945, *35*: 393-402.

Grant, D. A. Classical and operant conditioning. In A. W. Melton (Ed.), *Categories of human learning.* New York: Academic Press, 1964. Pp. 1-31.

Grant, D. A., & Dittmer, D. G. A tactile generalization gradient for a pseudo-conditioned response. *J. exp. Psychol.*, 1940, *26*: 404-412.

Grant, D. A., & Meyer, H. I. The formation of generalized response sets during repeated electric shock stimulation. *J. gen. Psychol.*, 1941, *24*: 21-38.

Grant, D. A., & Norris, E. B. Eyelid conditioning as influenced by the presence of sensitized beta responses. *J. exp. Psychol.*, 1947, *37*: 423-438.

Grant, D. A., Riopelle, A. J., & Hake, H. W. Resistance to extinction and the pattern of reinforcement. I. Alternation of reinforcement and the conditioned eyelid response. *J. exp. Psychol.*, 1950, *40*: 53-60.

Grings, W. W. Classical conditioning. In M. H. Marx (Ed.), *Theories in contemporary psychology.* New York: Macmillan, 1963. Pp. 495-525.

Grings, W. W., & Kimmel, H. D. Compound stimulus transfer for different sense modalities. *Psychol. Rep.*, 1959, *5*: 253-260.

Grings, W. W., Lockhart, R. A., & Dameron, L. E. Conditioning autonomic responses of mentally subnormal individuals. *Psychol. Monogr.*, 1962, *76*: 39.

Grings, W. W., & O'Donnell, D. E. Magnitude of response to compounds of discriminated stimuli. *J. exp. Psychol.*, 1956, *52*: 354-359.

Guthrie, E. R. *The psychology of learning.* New York: Harper, 1935.

Hansche, W. J., & Grant, D. A. Onset versus termination of a stimulus in eyelid conditioning. *J. exp. Psychol.*, 1960, *59*: 19-26.

Harlow, H. F. Forward conditioning, backward conditioning and pseudo-conditioning in the goldfish. *J. genet. Psychol.*, 1939, *55*: 49-58.

Harlow, H. F., & Toltzien, F. Formation of pseudo-conditioned responses in the cat. *J. gen. Psychol.*, 1940, *23*: 367-375.

Harris, J. D. Forward conditioning, backward conditioning, pseudo-conditioning and adaptation to the conditioned stimulus. *J. exp. Psychol.*, 1941, *28*: 491-502.

Harris, J. D. Studies on nonassociative factors inherent in conditioning. *Comp. Psychol. Monogr.*, 1943, *18*: 1-74.

Hartman, T. F., & Grant, D. A. Effects of pattern of reinforcement and verbal information on acquisition, extinction, and spontaneous recovery of the eyelid CR. *J. exp. Psychol.*, 1962, *63*: 217-226. (a)

Hartman, T. F., & Grant, D. A. Differential eyelid conditioning as a function of the CS-UCS interval. *J exp. Psychol.*, 1962, *64*: 131-136. (b)

Hebb, D. O. Drives and the C.N.S. (conceptual nervous system). *Psychol. Rev.*, 1955, *62*: 243-254.

Hilgard, E. R. Conditioned eyelid reactions to a light stimulus based on the reflex wink to sound. *Psychol. Monogr.*, 1931, *41*: 1-50.

Hilgard, E. R. *Theories of learning.* New York: Appleton-Century-Crofts, 1956.

Hilgard, E. R., & Grant, D. A. Sensitization as a supplement to association in eyelid conditioning. *Psychol. Bull.*, 1940, *37*: 478-479.

Hilgard, E. R., & Marquis, D. G. *Conditioning and learning.* New York: Appleton-Century-Crofts, 1940.

Hull, C. L. *Principles of behavior.* New York: Appleton-Century-Crofts, 1943.

Hull, C. L. *Essentials of behavior.* New Haven: Yale Univ. Press, 1951.

Hull, C. L. *A behavior system.* New Haven: Yale Univ. Press, 1952.

Jones, J. E. Contiguity and reinforcement in relation to CS-UCS intervals in classical aversive conditioning. *Psychol. Rev.*, 1962, *69*: 176-186.

Kimble, G. A. *Conditioning and learning.* New York: Appleton-Century-Crofts, 1961.

Kimble, G. A., & Dufort, R. H. The associative factor in eyelid conditioning. *J. exp. Psychol.*, 1956, *52*: 386-391.

Kimble, G. A., Mann, L. I., & Dufort, R. H. Classical and instrumental eyelid conditioning. *J. exp. Psychol.*, 1955, *49*: 407-417.

Kimble, G. A., & Pennypacker, H. S. Eyelid conditioning in young and aged subjects. *J. genet. Psychol.*, 1963, *103*: 283-289.

Kimmel, H. D. Amount of conditioning and intensity of the conditioned stimulus. *J. exp. Psychol.*, 1959, *58*: 283-288.

Kimmel, H. D. Management of conditioned fear. *Psychol. Rep.*, 1963, *12*: 313-314.

Kimmel, H. D. Further analysis of GSR conditioning: A reply to Stewart, Stenn, Winokur, and Fredman. *Psychol. Rev.*, 1964, *71*: 160-166.

Kimmel, H. D., & Baxter, R. Avoidance conditioning of the GSR. *J. exp. Psychol.*, 1964, *68*: 482-485.

Kimmel, H. D., & Fowler, R. L. Distribution in compound conditioning as a function of the number of reinforcements of a single conditioned stimulus. *Tech. Rep. Dept. Psychol. Univ. Florida*, 1961, *3*.

Kimmel, H. D., & Greene, W. A. Disinhibition in GSR conditioning as a function of the number of CS-UCS trials and temporal location of the novel stimulus. *J. exp. Psychol.*, 1964, *68*: 567-572.

Kimmel, H. D., & Pennypacker, H. S. Differential GSR conditioning as a function of the CS-UCS interval. *J. exp. Psychol.*, 1963, *65*: 559-563.

Koffka, K. *The principles of Gestalt psychology.* New York: Harcourt, Brace, 1935.

Kohler, W. *Dynamics in psychology.* New York: Liveright, 1940.

Konorski, J. *Conditioned reflexes and neuron organization.* Cambridge: Cambridge Univ. Press, 1948.

Lacey, J. I. The evaluation of autonomic responses: Toward a general solution. *Ann. N. Y. Acad. Sci.*, 1956, *67*: 123-164.

Lacey, J. I. Psychophysiological approaches to the evaluation of psychotherapeutic process and outcome. In E. A. Rubenstein & M. B. Parloff (Eds.), *Research in psychotherapy.* Washington, D. C.: Am. Psychol. Ass., 1959. Pp. 160-208.

Lacey, J. I., & Lacey, B. C. Verification and extension of the principle of autonomic response stereotypy. *Am. J. Psychol.*, 1958, *71*: 50-73.

Lacey, J. I., & Smith, R. L. Conditioning and generalization of unconscious anxiety. *Science, N.Y.*, 1954, *120*: 1045-1052.

Lacey, J. I., Smith, R. L., & Green, A. Use of conditional autonomic responses in the study of anxiety. *Psychosom. Med.*, 1955, *17*: 208-217.

Lazarus, R. S. Subception: factor artifact? A reply to Eriksen. *Psychol. Rev.*, 1956, *63*: 343-347.

Lazarus, R. S., & McCleary, R. A. Autonomic discrimination without awareness: a study of subception. *Psychol. Rev.*, 1951, *58*: 113-122.

Lewin, K. *Principles of topological psychology*. New York: McGraw-Hill, 1936.

Liddell, H. S. Conditioned reflex method and experimental neurosis. In J. McV. Hunt (Ed.), *Personality and the behavior disorders*, Vol. 1. New York: Ronald Press, 1944. Pp. 389-412.

Liddell, H. S. *Emotional hazards in animals and men*. Springfield, Ill.: Charles C. Thomas, 1956.

Lindley, R. H. Effects of instruction on the transfer of a conditioned response. *J. exp. Psychol.*, 1959, *57*: 6-8.

Lindsley, D. B. Emotion. In S. S. Stevens (Ed.), *Handbook of experimental psychology*. New York: Wiley, 1951. Pp. 473-516.

Lloyd, D. P. C. A direct central inhibitory action of dromically conducted impulses. *J. Neurophysiol.*, 1941, *4*: 184-190.

Lloyd, D. P. C. Post-tetanic potentiation of response in monosynaptic reflex pathways of the spinal cord. *J. gen. Physiol.*, 1949, *33*: 147-170.

Lockhart, R. A., & Grings, W. W. Comments on "an anlysis of GSR conditioning." *Psychol. Rev.*, 1963, *70*: 562-564.

Lockhart, R. A., & Grings, W. W. Interstimulus interval effects in GSR conditioning. *J. exp. Psychol.*, 1964, *67*: 209-214.

Logan, F. A. A note on stimulus intensity dynamism (V). *Psychol. Rev.*, 1954, *61*: 77-80.

Logan, F. A., & Wagner, A. R. Supplementary report: direction of changes in CS in eyelid conditioning. *J. exp. Psychol.*, 1962, *64*: 325-326.

McAllister, W. R. Eyelid conditioning as a function of CS-UCS interval. *J. exp. Psychol.*, 1953, *45*: 417-422.

McAllister, W. R., & McAllister, D. E. Effect of knowledge of conditioning upon eyelid conditioning. *J. exp. Psychol.*, 1958, *55*: 579-583.

McAllister, W. R., & McAllister, D. E. The influence of the ready signal and unpaired UCS presentations on eyelid conditioning. *J. exp. Psychol.*, 1960, *60*: 30-35.

MacDonald, A. The effect of adaptation to the unconditioned stimulus upon the formation of conditioned avoidance responses. *J. exp. Psychol.*, 1946, *36*: 1-12.

McDonald, D. G., & Johnson, L. C. A re-analysis of GSR conditioning. *Psychophysiology*, 1965, *1*: 291-295.

McDonald, D. G., Johnson, L. C., & Hord, D. J. Habituation of orienting response in alert and drowsy subjects. *Psychophysiology*, 1964, *1*: 163-173.

Malmo, R. B. Anxiety and behavioral arousal. *Psychol. Rev.*, 1957, *64*: 276-287.

Malmo, R. B. On central and autonomic nervous system mechanisms in conditioning, learning, and performance. *Can. J. Psychol.*, 1963, *17*: 1-36.

Malmo, R. B. Comment on the exchange of theoretical notes between Smith and Black and Lang. *Psychol. Rev.*, 1965, *72*: 240-241.

Malmo, R. B., & Davis, J. F. Physiological gradients as indicants of arousal in mirror tracing. *Can. J. Psychol.*, 1956, *10*: 231-238.

Mattson, M., & Moore, J. W. Intertrial responding and CS intensity in classical eyelid conditioning. *J. exp. Psychol.*, 1964, *68*: 396-401.

May, M. A. An interpretation of pseudo-conditioning. *Psych. Rev.*, 1949, *56*: 177-183.

Merryman, J. J. The magnitude of the unconditioned GSR as a function of fear conditioned at long CS-UCS interval. Unpublished doctoral dissertation, Univ. of Iowa, 1954. Cited by H. D. Kimmel & W. A. Greene, *J. exp. Psychol.*, 1964, *68*: 567-572.

Miller, N. E. Studies of fear as an acquired drive. I. Fear as motivation and fear-reduction as reinforcement in the learning of new responses. *J. exp. Psychol.*, 1948, *38*: 89-101.

Miller, N. E. Learnable drives and rewards. In S. S. Stevens (Ed.), *Handbook of experimental psychology*. New York: Wiley, 1951. Pp. 435–472.

Miller, N. E., & Dollard, J. *Social learning and imitation*. New Haven: Yale Univ. Press, 1941.

Moore, J. W. Differential eyelid conditioning as a function of the frequency and intensity of auditory CSs. *J. exp. Psychol.*, 1964, *68*: 250–259.

Morrell, F. Effects of anodal polarization on the firing pattern of single cortical cells. In N. S. Kline (Ed.), *Pavlovian conference on higher nervous activity. Ann. N. Y. Acad. Sci.*, 1961, *92*: 860–876.

Mowrer, O. H. *Learning theory and personality dynamics*. New York: Ronald Press, 1950.

Mowrer, O. H. *Learning theory and behavior*. New York: Wiley, 1960.

Mowrer, O. H. *Learning theory and the symbolic process*. New York: Wiley, 1963.

Nicholls, M. F., & Kimble, G. A. Effect of instructions upon eyelid conditioning. *J. exp. Psychol.*, 1964, *67*: 400–402.

Noble, M. & Adams, C. K. Conditioning in pigs as a function of the interval between CS and UCS. *J. comp. physiol. Psychol.*, 1963, *56*: 215–219.

Noble, M., & Harding, G. E. Conditioning in rhesus monkeys as a function of the interval between CS and US. *J. comp. physiol. Psychol.*, 1963, *56*: 220–224.

Notterman, J. M., Schoenfeld, W. N., & Bersh, P. J. A comparison of three extinction procedures following heart rate conditioning. *J. abnorm. soc. Psychol.*, 1952, *47*: 674–677.(a)

Notterman, J. M., Schoenfeld, W. N., & Bersh, P. J. Conditioned heart rate response in human beings during experimental anxiety. *J. comp. physiol. Psychol.*, 1952, *45*: 1–8. (b)

Osgood, C. E. *Method and theory in experimental psychology*. New York: Oxford Univ. Press, 1953.

Pavlov, I. P. *Conditioned reflexes: an investigative activity of the cerebral cortex* (translated by G. V. Anrep) London: Oxford Univ. Press, 1927.

Pavlov, I. P. *Lectures on conditioned reflexes* (translated by W. H. Gantt). New York: International Publishers, 1928.

Pavlov, I. P. *Conditioned reflexes and psychiatry*. New York: International Publishers, 1941.

Pavlov, I. P. *Experimental psychology and other essays*. New York: Philosophical Library, 1957.

Pennypacker, H. S. External inhibition of the conditioned eyelid reflex. *J. exp. Psychol.*, 1964, *67*: 33–40.

Perkins, C. C., Jr. The relation between conditioned stimulus intensity and response strength. *J. exp. Psychol.*, 1953, *46*: 225–231.

Peters, J. E. Typology of dogs by the conditional reflex method. *Conditional reflex*, in press.

Prokasy, W. F., & Ebel, H. C. GSR conditioning and sensitization as a function of intertrial interval. *J. exp. Psychol.*, 1964, *67*: 113–119.

Prokasy, W. F., Grant, D. A., & Myers, N. A. Eyelid conditioning as a function of unconditioned stimulus intensity and intertrial interval. *J. exp. Psychol.*, 1958, *55*: 242–246.

Razran, G. H. S. Decremental and incremental effects of distracting stimuli upon the salivary CRs of 24 adult human subjects (Inhibition and disinhibition?). *J. exp. Psychol.*, 1939, *24*: 647–652.

Razran, G. H. S. Stimulus generalization of conditioned responses. *Psychol. Bull.*, 1949, *46*: 337–365.

Razran, G. H. S. Conditioning and perception. *Psychol. Rev.*, 1955, *62*: 88–95.

Razran, G. H. S. Backward conditioning. *Psychol. Bull.*, 1956, *53*: 55–68. (a)

Razran, G. H. S. Extinction re-examined and re-analyzed: A new theory. *Psychol. Rev.*, 1956, *63*: 39–52. (b)

Razran, G. H. S. The dominance-contiguity theory of the acquisition of classical conditioning. *Psychol. Bull.*, 1957, *54*: 1–46.

Razran, G. H. S. The observable unconscious and inferable conscious in current Soviet psychophysiology: Interoceptive conditioning, semantic conditioning, and the orienting reflex. *Psychol. Rev.*, 1961, *68*: 81–147.

Robinson, J., & Gantt, W. H. The orienting reflex (questioning reaction): cardiac, respiratory, salivary, and motor components. *Bull. Johns Hopkins Hosp.*, 1947, *80*: 231–253.

Runquist, W. N., & Ross, L. E. The relation between physiological measures of emotionality and performance in eyelid conditioning. *J. exp. Psychol.*, 1959, *57*: 329–332.

Runquist, W. N., & Spence, K. W. Performance in eyelid conditioning related to changes in muscular tension and physiological measures of emotionality. *J. exp. Psychol.*, 1959, *58*: 417–422.

Runquist, W. N., Spence, K. W., & Stubbs, D. W. Differential conditioning and intensity of UCS. *J. exp. Psychol.*, 1958, *55*: 51–55.

Schlosberg, H. The relationship between success and the laws of conditioning. *Psychol. Rev.*, 1937, *44*: 397–399.

Schoenfeld, W. N. An experimental approach to anxiety, escape and avoidance behavior. In P. H. Hoch & J. Zubin (Eds.), *Anxiety*. New York: Grune and Stratton, 1950. Pp. 70–99.

Shearn, D. W. Operant conditioning of heart rate. *Science, N.Y.*, 1962, *137*: 530–531.

Shipley, W. C. An apparent transfer of conditioning. *J. gen. Psychol.*, 1933, *8*: 382–391.

Silverman, R. E. Eliminating a conditioned GSR by the reduction of experimental anxiety. *J. exp. Psychol.*, 1960, *59*: 122–125.

Smith, K. Conditioning as an artifact. *Psychol. Rev.*, 1954, *61*: 217–225.

Smith, K. Curare drugs and total paralysis. *Psychol. Rev.*, 1964, *71*: 77-79. (a)

Smith, K. Comment on the paper by Black and Lang. *Psychol. Rev.*, 1964, *71*: 86. (b)

Smith, S. M., Brown, H. O., Toman, J. E. P., & Goodman, L. S. The lack of cerebral effects of d-tubocurarine, *Anesthesiology* , 1947; *8*: 1–14. Cited by K. Smith, Curare drugs and total paralysis. *Psychol. Rev.*, 1964, *71*: 77–79.

Sokolov, E. N. Neuronal models and the orienting reflex. In M. A. B. Brazier (Ed.), *Central nervous system and behavior*. New York: Josiah Macey, Jr. Foundation, 1960.

Sokolov, E. N. *Perception and the conditioned reflex* (translated by S. W. Waydenfeld). New York: Macmillan, 1963.

Solomon, R. L., & Turner, L. H. Discriminative classical conditioning in dogs paralyzed by curare can later control discriminative avoidance responses in the normal state. *Psychol. Rev.*, 1962, *69*: 202–219.

Spence, K. W. The nature of discrimination learning in animals. *Psychol. Rev.*, 1936, *43*: 427–449.

Spence, K. W. Theoretical interpretations of learning. In S. S. Stevens (Ed.), *A handbook of experimental psychology*. New York: Wiley, 1951. Pp. 690–729.

Spence, K. W. *Behavior theory and conditioning*. New Haven: Yale Univ. Press, 1956.

Spence, K. W. An emotionally based theory of drive (D) and its relation to performance in simple learning situations. *Am. Psychol.*, 1958, *13*: 131–141.

Spence, K. W., & Farber, I. E. The relation of anxiety to differential eyelid conditioning. *J. exp. Psychol.*, 1954, *47*: 127–134.

Spence, K. W., Haggard, D. F., & Ross, L. E. UCS intensity and the associative (habit) strength of the eyelid CR. *J. exp. Psychol.*, 1958, *55*: 404–411.

Spence, K. W., & Norris, E. B. Eyelid conditioning as a function of intertrial interval. *J. exp. Psychol.*, 1950, *40*: 305–313.

Spence, K. W., & Spence, J. T. Relation of eyelid conditioning to manifest anxiety, extraversion, and rigidity. *J. abnorm. soc. Psychol.*, 1964, *68*: 144–149.

Spence, K. W., & Weyant, R. G. Conditioning performance of high-and-low-anxious Ss in the absence of a warning signal. *J. exp. Psychol.*, 1960, *60*: 146–149.

Stennett, R. C. Relationship of performance level to level of arousal. *J. exp. Psychol.*, 1957, *54*: 54–61.

Stern, J. A., Winokur, G., Stewart, M. A., & Leonard, C. Electrodermal conditioning: some further correlates. *J. nerv. ment. Dis.*, 1963, *137*: 479–486.

Steward, J. R. The effect on heart rate of warnings and receipt of pleasant and aversive auditory stimuli. Unpublished doctoral dissertation, Univ. of Conn., 1962.

Stewart, M. A., Stern, J. A., Winokur, G., & Fredman, S. An analysis of GSR conditioning. *Psychol. Rev.*, 1961, *68*: 60–67.

Switzer, S. A. Disinhibition of the conditioned galvanic skin response. *J. gen Psychol.*, 1933, *9*: 77–100.

Taylor, J. A. The relationship of anxiety to the conditioned eyelid response. *J. exp. Psychol.*, 1951, *41*: 81–92.

Taylor, J. A. Drive theory and manifest anxiety. *Psychol. Bull.*, 1956, *53*: 303–320. (b)

Taylor, J. A. Level of conditioning and intensity of adapting stimulus. *J. exp. Psychol.*, 1956, *51*: 127-130. (a)

Thorndike, E. L. *The psychology of wants, interests, and attitudes.* New York: Appleton-Century-Crofts, 1935.

Thorpe, W. H. *Learning and instinct in animals.* Cambridge: Harvard Univ. Press, 1956.

Tolman, E. C. *Purposive behavior in animals.* New York: Appleton-Century-Crofts, 1932.

Unger, S. M. Habituation of the vasoconstrictive orienting reaction. *J. exp. Psychol.*, 1964, *67*: 11-18.

Veronin, L. G., & Sokolov, E. N. The orienting reflex and conditioning. In H. H. Jasper and G. D. Smirnov (Eds.), *The Moscow colloquium on electroencephalography of higher nervous activity. Electroenceph. clin. Neurophysiol.*, 1960, *Suppl. 13*: 335-346.

Walker, E. G. Eyelid conditioning as a function of the intensity of conditioned and unconditioned stimuli. *J. exp. Psychol.*, 1960, *59*: 303-311.

Weiss, S. J. Summation of response strengths instrumentally conditioned to stimuli in different sensory modalities. *J. exp. Psychol.*, 1964, *68*: 151-155.

Wenger, M. A. External inhibition and disinhibition produced by duplicate stimuli. *Am. J. Psychol., 1936, 48:* -456.

Wertheimer, M. Psychomotor coordination of auditory and visual space at birth. *Science, N. Y.*, 1962, *134*: 1692.

Westcott, M. R., & Huttenlocher, J. Cardiac conditioning: the effects and implications of controlled and uncontrolled respiration. *J. exp. Psychol.*, 1961, *61*: 353-359.

Wickens, D. D. The transference of conditioned excitation and conditioned inhibition from one muscle group to the antagonistic muscle group. *J. exp. Psychol.*, 1938, *22*: 101-123.

Wickens, D. D. The simultaneous transfer of conditioned excitation and conditioned inhibition. *J. exp. Psychol.*, 1939, *24*: 332-338.

Wickens, D. D. Stimulus identity as related to response specificity and response generalization. *J. exp. Psychol.*, 1948, *38*: 389-394.

Wickens, D. D. Conditioning to complex stimuli. *Am. Psychol.*, 1959, *14*: 180-188.

Wickens, D. D., Gehman, R. S., & Sullivan, S. N. The effect of differential onset time on the conditioned response strength to the elements of a stimulus complex. *J. exp. Psychol.*, 1959, *58*: 85-93.

Wickens, D. D., & Wickens, C. D. A study of conditioning in the neonate. *J. exp. Psychol.*, 1940, *25*: 94-102.

Wickens, D. D., & Wickens, C. D. Factors related to pseudo-conditioning. *J. exp. Psychol.*, 1942, *31*: 518-526.

Winokur, G., Guze, S., Stewart, M., Pfeiffer, E., Stern, J., & Hornung, F. Association of conditionability with degree of reactivity in psychiatric patients. *Science, N. Y.*, 1959, *129*: 1423-1424.

Wolpe, J. *Psychotherapy by reciprocal inhibition.* Stanford, Calif.: Stanford Univ. Press, 1958.

Wood, D. M., & Obrist, P. A. Effects of controlled and uncontrolled respiration on conditioned heart rate response in humans. *J. exp. Psychol.*, 1964, *68*: 221-229.

Woodworth, R. S., & Schlosberg, H. *Experimental psychology.* (2nd ed.) New York: Henry Holt, 1954.

Zeaman, D., & Smith, R. W. Review and analysis of some recent findings in human cardiac conditioning. In W. F. Prokasy (Ed.), *Classical conditioning.* New York: Appleton-Century-Crofts, 1965.

12
Operant Conditioning

KEITH MURRAY, Ph.D.

History and Introduction to Operant Conditioning

In this section the basic procedures, concepts, and terminology of operant conditioning will be briefly described.

A Comparison of Classical and Operant Conditioning

Almost all of the phenomena found associated with the classically conditioned response may also be shown with operant conditioning procedures. Acquisition, extinction, spontaneous recovery, discrimination, higher order conditioning, and generalization, all find their parallels in the two procedures. Kimble (1961) describes a total of 15 such basic phenomena of conditioning which classical and operant conditioning both display. These many similarities have made experimenters and theoreticians loathe to believe that independent mechanisms exist in classical and operant. However, it remains to date a moot question as to whether one is dealing with one or two clearly differentiated types of learning (with the weight of the evidence tending toward the latter conclusion (Kimble, 1961)). This section will be concerned with the apparent differences between the two procedures. It is likely that psychophysiology will have the most to contribute toward the resolution of these questions of similarity and difference.

Selected Procedures

Psychologists have long recognized the importance of autonomic and central accompaniments of instrumental behavior. The theorists' use of such concepts as "conditioned drive," "frustration," "emotion," and "incentive motivation" reflect the awareness that "inner" events play an important, perhaps the determining role in the regulation and control of "outer" behavior. The operant procedures provide the means for establishing reliable control over behaviors of experimental interest, and of operationally denoting when such behavior is taking place. The introduction of psychophysiological measures into such situations allows the possibility of delineating the underlying neurophysiological events that bear a necessary relationship to the observed behavior. Such data should ultimately reduce the number of hypothetical constructs used in explanation, and leave the remaining somewhat less hypothetical. This section introduces several procedures, selected from a plethora currently available, that would appear to be of most interest to the psychophysiologist. These procedures, by providing operational definitions of "attention," "emotion," "active avoidance," "preference," and "timing," hold the promise of opening these phenomena to experimental attack by using infrahuman species.

Representative Studies: Operant Studies Employing Psychophysiological Measures

This section will review relevant studies in the literature in which concurrent measures of operant behavior and physiological or neurophysiological activity or both were obtained. In general, the studies selected are those which employ "free operant" procedures, although several exceptions to this criterion may be noted. These experiments suggest the range of techniques which have been developed and which are available to the interested experimenter.

It will be quickly apparent that there is a dearth of investigations using psychophysiological measures in conjunction with operant techniques. Such studies which are found in the literature are for the most part of recent vintage. The technological advances in recent years with the advent of electrically "silent" solid state programming circuitry, telemetric devices, appropriate transducers, and automated data reduction systems have made possible studies using relatively unrestrained organisms which were previously impossible.

History and Introduction to Operant Conditioning

History

In 1898 Edward Lee Thorndike published a monograph reporting experimental data on several species of animals tested in simple problem-solving situations. The work employing cats as subjects will be used as an illustration of his technique.

Thorndike used a "puzzle-box" situation which is considered a forerunner to the operant experimental procedure. In this method, the hungry cat was confined in the box until it performed some response defined by the experimenter (e.g. pulling a wire loop, moving a lever), which tripped a release mechanism allowing the subject egress from the box and access to a morsel of food.

The dependent variable used was the time in seconds required for successive escapes. From these data, "learning curves" were plotted. Plotting over trials such a "learning curve" reflects an over-all reduction in the time spent from entry to egress and with grouped data an appearance of orderliness emerges. Unfortunately, the large intertrial and intersubject variability that characterize such curves will usually preclude their use as an experimental device with which to test the influence of other variables.

Thorndike later proposed that problem solution, exemplified behaviorally by a stereotyped response, came about by the strengthening of the specific stimulus-response "associations" which were "satisfying," and the "weakening" of those stimulus-response associations which were "annoying." This was formally presented in 1911 as the "Law of Effect" and in modified form may be regarded as an early statement of the principle of reinforcement; the central concept in the operant analysis of behavior.

In 1930 Skinner first described an experimental method which was the prototype of the procedure that was to become a standard tool in behavioral research. It consisted of (1) a device which delivered a small piece of food each time the rat pushed open the swinging door to a food tray, and (2) a mechanism which caused a pen to make a small vertical step on a moving kymograph record each time the panel was pressed, resulting in a *cumulative curve* reflecting the accumulation over time of the subject's panel pressing responses.

The procedures of Skinner and Thorndike are similar in that they both enclose an unfettered organism in an experimental space and require it to manipulate some aspect of the environment before "reinforcement" is delivered. In Skinner's procedure, however, the morsel of food is delivered automatically upon performance of some selected response, with the subject remaining in the experimental space throughout the session. This precludes the use of a trial by trial analysis, and emphasizes the accumulation of the organism's "free responses" as the recorded data. This modified problem box situation readily allows the automation of response and stimulus events, thus greatly increasing experimental flexibility and control. The increased control, by minimizing variability, will often obviate the necessity for large groups of Ss.

This experimental procedure, with modifications, contains the prerequisite factors for an operant analysis of behavior. For laboratory investigation these are: (1) a suitable enclosure which eliminates the intrusion of extraneous environmental variables; (2) one or more manipulanda* appropriate for the species; and (3) the automation of stimulus and response events.

In 1932 Skinner modified his experimental technique, making a bar press the recorded response, and in 1938 presented the results of a number of investigations employing this procedure and outlining a rationale appropriate for an experimental description of those classes of behavior termed "operant."

Introduction to Operant Analysis

Operant behavior is defined as behavior in which the organism manipulates the experimental environment. The rate, form, and pattern of such behavior

---

* A manipulandum is a device such as a lever or pedal the displacement or movement of which by the S constitutes the recorded "response."

are governed by environmental events which are *contingent* upon the response.

Reinforcement is the central concept in an operant analysis and designates any environmental event that strengthens a given response class (operant). To determine whether an event has an effect upon the strength of a response, preliminary observations must be made of the "spontaneous rate" of responding (the "operant level"). After this, a stimulus change is introduced following the response and subsequent changes in the response rate are observed. Two main classes of reinforcers have been defined. (1) Stimuli which when presented result in an increased frequency of responding and are termed *positive reinforcers* (e.g. food, water, etc.), and (2) stimuli, the removal of which results in an increase of response frequency and are called *negative reinforcers* (e.g. removal of shock, elimination of loud noise). These two operations (i.e. (1) presenting a positive reinforcer, and (2) removing a negative reinforcer) comprise those events often referred to as "rewarding" or to Thorndike "satisfying."

"Punishment" refers to the reversal of these operations, namely the removal of a positive reinforcer or the presentation of a negative reinforcer.

A distinction which may well be more arbitrary than real is usually made between those stimuli which appear to be innately reinforcing (e.g. food, water, sexual contact, etc.) and stimuli which acquire reinforcing characteristics through a specifiable history of conditioning. The former are called *primary reinforcers* and the latter are *secondary* or *conditioned* reinforcers.

In operant research experimental conditions are so programmed that only specific classes of responses are reinforced. These programmed requirements specify the situations in which reinforcement is to be delivered and therefore constitute a *differential reinforcement* of some selected and objective aspect of behavior.

Differential reinforcement may be programmed in accordance with external stimulus events or response events or both. If reinforcement is made contingent upon the presence or absence of an external stimulus, the subject soon responds in accord with the stimulus requirement, only infrequently responding at other times, thus exhibiting a *stimulus discrimination*. As an example, if an organism after initial bar press training is subsequently reinforced only in the presence of a "signal" light, the distribution of responses will shift such that nearly all responses will be emitted during the "light-on" periods. The presence of the light is now termed a positive *discriminative stimulus* (S_D) for bar press behavior. The absence of the light in the experimental situation is a negative discriminative stimulus (S_Δ). The Pavlovian analogues of S_D and S_Δ are the "excitatory" and "inhibitory" or "reinforced" and "unreinforced" conditional stimuli respectively.

Similarly, the requirement for reinforcement may be made contingent upon some aspect of the subjects response (e.g. its topography, duration, amplitude, rate, etc.). Such a situation is appropriate for the development of a *response differentiation*. If, for example, after initial bar press training only those presses of longer duration are reinforced, the distribution of obtained durations will gradually shift upward toward longer times. By gradually increasing the requirement for reinforcement to longer and longer intervals, the subject may finally exhibit responses of a duration significantly greater than those originally obtained.

Operationally, stimulus discriminations are foi nd to result when the programming is such that reinforcement is made to be contingent upon the response occurring *in conjunction* with an exteroceptive stimulus. Response differentiation results when reinforcement is made to occur contingent upon some aspect of the behavior of the subject.

Where differential reinforcement is no longer p ovided to the subject, *extinction* takes place and when the response frequency is reduced to the preexperimental operant level, the response is said to be *extinguished.*

The rule that specifies *when* a response is to be reinforced defines the *schedule of reinforcement.* Schedules are usually restrictions imposed upon the subject with respect to the number of responses required or the time lapsed since the last response or reinforcement or both. Such is the case with the principal schedules described below. The principal schedules of reinforcement are: (1) *continuous reinforcement (CRF) schedule*: every response of a class is followed by reinforcement; (2) *fixed interval (FI) schedule*: reinforcement is made contingent upon the passage of a constant time lapse since the last response or *reinforcement; (3) fixed ratio (FR) schedule*: a predetermined number of responses must be emitted before reinforcement is given; (4) *variable ratio schedule (VR)*: reinforcements occur in no systematic fashion but are presented after an average number of responses has been made; and (5) *variable interval (VI) schedule*: reinforcement is given for a response made after a predetermined average period of time.

Each of these schedules generates its own highly predictable and characteristic cumulative response curve, and thus provides baselines upon which the effect of other variables may be studied.

Schedules of greater complexity are possible. A few have considerable usefulness as experimental tools. Brief descriptions will be given of the following complex schedules: multiple, chained, tandem, and concurrent.

A *multiple schedule* introduces different exteroceptive stimuli which in turn are correlated with different reinforcement contingencies. Accordingly each of the stimuli in the schedule becomes an S_D for some specified operant, and, as such, each denotes an identifiable component of the multiple schedule. The stimuli are presented one at a time, either regularly or randomly. They may be correlated with differing types of stimulus conditions (e.g. types, amounts, or schedules of reinforcement) or with differing response requirements (e.g. topography, rate, amplitude, force). Effectively, the situation presents the organism successive discriminations or differentiation contingencies or both. The presentation of the stimuli associated with each component may be programmed so as to be independent of the subject's behavior, i.e. the subsequent stimuli appear regardless of whether the S responds or not in the presence of the preceding stimulus. Several examples may help to illustrate. (1) Stimuli associated with different schedules. In the presence of a first exteroceptive stimulus (S_1) 25 responses are required before food is forthcoming (FR 25). In the presence of a second different stimulus, (S_2), reinforcement is delivered on a variable interval schedule of 1 min (VI-1). This would be a mult FR 25 VI 1. (2) Stimuli associated with different responses. In the presence of S_1 a chain pull is reinforced; following successful performance and reinforcement, S_2 (a perceptibly different stimulus) is presented and a bar press is required for reinforcement. (3) Stimuli associated with different "qualities" of reinforcers. In the presence of S_1, responses are followed by a "preferred" food (as determined by an independent measure); in the presence of S_2, responding is reinforced by a less preferred food.

It should be apparent that various combinations of schedule, reinforcement, and response requirements may be correlated with their respective stimuli and successively presented in a multiple schedule arrangement. This effectively provides a situation which permits parametric observations or samples of a variety of behavior to be obtained on a single subject used as his own control. The ensuing reduction in "error variance" deriving from such a procedure commends it for certain experimental investigations.

A *chained schedule* of reinforcement also has different exteroceptive stimuli associated with each component. It differs from a multiple schedule in that only the *last* component of the chain is associated with primary reinforcement and the change from one component to the next is contingent upon responding.

Modification of the reinforcing efficacy of any member of the chain may make its effects readily discernible in the preceding components. This technique seems to provide a relatively sensitive and versatile measure of reinforcing strength, unconfounded by the unconditional responses elicited by the primary reinforcer. An example of such a use is provided by Hawkins and Pliskoff (1964) who use this procedure to evaluate the reinforcing effects of differing intensities of electrocortical stimulation. They employed a two lever situation in which the retractible "stimulating" lever is inserted into the cage only after the animal successfully meets a variable interval response requirement on the other lever. The first five responses on the stimulating lever were each reinforced with cortical shock. After the fifth response, the lever was again retracted and the response requirement on the other lever again came into effect. This situation describes a two component chain with the first component maintained on a variable interval schedule of 30 sec and a second component of five responses maintained on a CRF schedule of primary reinforcement. A curvilinear relationship was found between rate of response on the stimulating lever, and the intensity of the reinforcing shock. This would suggest that the higher intensities of shock become less effective reinforcers for behavior. Response rate in the first component, however, was found to be linearly related with the intensity of the shocks in the second component. Apparently the higher intensities of the primary reinforcing events, i.e. cortical stimulation, elicits unconditional reactions which are antagonistic to high response rate hence masking an increasing reinforcement efficacy. The rate of response in the first component, unconfounded with the extraneous unconditional effects of primary stimulation, is free to reflect the increased reinforcing potency of the higher intensities. Hawkins and Pliskoff conclude that brain stimulation reinforcement is not adequately reflected by rate of response on the "stimulating" bar. They further conclude that the chaining technique by providing an index of reinforcing strength unconfounded by unconditional reactions to the primary reinforcer may prove to be a useful analytical tool.

Tandem (tand) schedules of reinforcement are the same as chained schedules with the sole exception that the same exteroceptive stimulus appears in each component. Thus a tandem schedule introduced before or subsequent to training on a chained schedule will provide control observations on the innate or acquired effects of the exteroceptive stimuli employed in the chained schedules.

Concurrent schedules may be used by providing the subject with two or more manipulanda, and reinforcing the responses given to each on independent schedules. A number of studies investigating such schedules have been reported (Ferster & Skinner, 1957; Catania, 1962, 1963, a and b; Herrnstein, 1958, 1961). Interactions between performances occur (Ferster & Skinner; 1957), however, interposition of a change over delay (COD) such that some interval of time occurs between the last response of one lever and the first reinforced response of the other lever will make the performances comparable to a single key performance on the schedule (Catania, 1962). The two key situation appears sensitive to response duration (Catania, 1963, a and b) and relative frequency of reinforcement (Herrnstein, 1961).

Hearst (1960) has used such a concurrent schedule to compare the generalization gradients of appetitive and aversive behavior. Monkeys were first trained on a lever press response to avoid shock with the use of the Sidman avoidance technique which will be described later. After successful avoidance was established, a chain was introduced and a chain pulling response was first rewarded with a food pellet on a CRF schedule, then gradually shifted to a 2-min VI schedule (VI-2). The avoidance schedule was maintained throughout establishment of appetitive behavior. All training took place with the house light at its highest intensity. Then tests to varied lower intensities of the house light were made, following a test procedure similar to that of Guttman and Kalish (1956). Hearst (1965) finds that "the approach gradient is, in contrast, almost completely flat. This may be a consequence of internal cues comprising a larger part of the controlling stimulus complex for avoidance behavior."

Such procedures for obtaining behavior under successive or simultaneous (Hearst & Sidman, 1961) appetitive and aversive control offer the exciting possibility of using such free operant measures while recording by means of indwelling electrodes from those areas of the brain found to have rewarding, punishing, or ambivalent characteristics (Olds & Olds, 1963). Such studies which could provide recordings of neurophysiological change correlated with a performance measure seem to be a necessary and highly desirable adjunct to the brain stimulation studies. Taking measures by means of chronic indwelling electrodes at a number of different loci while the subject first learns then performs discriminant operant or conditional discrimination behavior (Blough, 1957) could lead to a fuller understanding of the structures and dynamic relationships underlying learning. The studies of Hernandez-Peon, Sherrer and Jowet (1956) and Galambos, Sheaty, and Vernier (1956) would seem to point the way.

Comparison of Operant Conditioning and Respondent Conditioning

In a previous chapter the methods, techniques, and concepts of classical conditioning are reviewed. Skinner proposed as had others (Miller & Konorski, 1928) that two types of conditioning could be recognized which he termed type S (respondent) and type R (operant).

Skinner type S is the classical Pavlovian conditioning in which a neutral stimulus is presented contiguous in time with an active stimulus (US) which uniformly elicits some given response (UR). After repeated pairings of the two stimuli, the formerly neutral stimulus (now termed a CS) comes to elicit a response (CR) similar in nature to the UR. The CS may be thought to become a *substitute* for the US.

Type R conditioning, in contrast, provides no comparable control over the initial appearance of the response. In operant conditioning the response must first appear "spontaneously" before reinforcement is presented by the experimenter.

One difference that may be noted between the two situations is in terms of the specifiability of the determining antecedent stimuli. In respondent conditioning there is a relatively simple and manipulable stimulus situation (US) that will initially and reliably evoke the response (UR). In operant conditioning on the other hand those stimulus conditions theoretically responsible for the initial appearance of the response are unspecified, unmeasured, and would presumably reflect a complex multiplicative interaction of interoceptive and exteroceptive determinants. A related distinction between type R and type S has to do with experimenter control over the situation. In classical conditioning the experimenter determines when a reinforced trial is to take place; in operant conditioning the subject's response determines the occasion for reinforcement.

The two procedures differ also in terms of the types of responses obtained as data. In classical conditioning studies, the response recorded is usually a minimal lightweight response (e.g. eye blink) or a covert autonomic response (e.g. salivation, gastric secretion). Consequently, the subject in the classical conditioning study is usually restrained so as to minimize motor behavior and the artifacts of recording which would result from such movement. In operant conditioning the experimenter is interested in the relatively gross motor acts that constitute the operant class under investigation. With no need for concern about movement-produced artifacts, the subject may remain relatively unrestrained. The types of measures employed in the two situations reflect the different emphases, in respondent conditioning the chief indices of strength of response are latency, magnitude, and percentage of responses; in operant conditioning the frequency, rate of response, or distribution of interresponse times serve as the major dependent variables.

A further distinction between the two methods may be made in terms of the similarities of the CR to the UR. In classical conditioning, although the two stimuli may be dissimilar with regard to their nature or the modality affected (e.g. light as CS, food as US), the responses are similar in nature (salivation). In operant conditioning both the stimuli and the responses may be and usually are very different; in this instance any response in the animal's available repertoire may be selected for reinforcement. A related distinction stems from the implications of the two paradigms for learning. In respondent conditioning, which is thought of as substitution learning, no distinction need be made as to the nature of the agent originally producing the response, i.e. acid may be substituted for food as the stimulus for eliciting salivation. In operant conditioning where the Law of Effect is said to apply, the nature of the reinforcing stimulus plays an important role as to the structure of the correlated response (e.g. introduction of food strengthens an approach response, acid—an avoidance response).

To conclude this summary of the more apparent distinctions between the two situations, it should be noted that classical conditioning principles apply most readily where autonomic responses are involved, but, in addition, to certain somatic responses where relatively simple reflex mechanisms underly the response (e.g. eye blink, limb flexion to shock). Operant principles appear to apply only to motor acts and not to autonomic functions. Apparent instance of effect learning of autonomic responses seem to be instances wherein skeletal responses mediate the autonomic response (Hudgins, 1933; Menzies, 1937), or where this is confounding with some other response (e.g. Shearn, 1962).

In general it is the diffuse preparatory responses, the "emotional," "attentional," or "anticipatory" responses, that are readily conditionable by classical principles, whereas effect learning applies particularly to precise adaptive responses (Schlosberg, 1937). Table 12.1 summarizes the chief distinction.

The psychophysiologists can broaden the picture of the total CR to include the autonomic and neurophysiological concomitants to behavior prior to, during, and through the course of performance and subsequent extinction. The

Table 12.1. *Comparison between type S and type R conditioning* [a]

Type S	Type R
Paradigm: $S_1 \rightarrow R_2$ $s_2 \nearrow r_2$	Paradigm: s. . . . .R$\longrightarrow$ S (reinforcement)
Response is elicited	Response is emitted
Stimulus substitution	No substitution of stimuli
Formation of new reflex	Strengthening of reflex already in repertory
"Preparation" by conditioned stimulus for the unconditioned reinforcement that follows; the response does not manipulate the environment	Response "procures" the reinforcement; the response "operates" on the environment
Commonly, if not always, is mediated by the autonomic nervous system, involving smooth muscles and glands	Mediated by somatic nervous system, involving skeletal muscles
Usually measured in terms of reflex latency or magnitude	Usually measured in terms of reflex rate; sometimes, latency

[a] From Keller, F., & Schoenfeld, N. *Principles of psychology,* 1950

spelling out of the invariant relationships between the internal milieu and the behavioral counterpart will provide new insights to those structures and relationships necessary for behavior modifications.

Selected Procedures

Sidman Avoidance Procedure

The traditional avoidance procedure employs a signal which precedes an aversive event (usually shock). Some experimenter-designated response, if performed promptly after the warning signal, prevents the occurrence of the aversive stimulation. The usual dependent variables employed are percentage of correct responses or trials to a criterion.

Sidman (1953, a and b) has devised a free operant avoidance procedure which does not employ an exteroceptive stimulus.

In the initial studies rats were employed as Ss with shock as the aversive stimulus. Brief shocks were programmed to occur at regular intervals (S-S interval) unless the lever depression (Rav) occurs. Each emission of the Rav resets a timer controlling the shock for some specified period of time (R-S interval).

R-S and S-S intervals may be, but are not necessarily, of the same duration. Under these conditions, stable rates of avoidance responding occur, which may be used as a base line upon which other variables may be studied. Within rather wide limits, rate of response may be manipulated by changing the R-S interval (Sidman, 1953, a and b; Verhave, 1959) or by imposing a multiple response requirement for avoidance (Verhave, 1959).

Williams and Teitlebaum (1956) have utilized this procedure to develop and maintain control of a consummatory response. After shaping and establishing a licking response on a 5-sec R-S interval, the schedule was shifted to one that differentially reinforced multiple licks. Successive licks postponed shocks for 1 sec; however, if three or more occurred within 7 sec, shock was postponed for a 15-sec period. Each lick within this period postponed shock for an additional 15 sec.

Under these conditions consumption of a liquid nutrient was effectively doubled. This resulted in an increase from 240 to 406 gm of body weight over a 20-day period during which drinking was reinforced on alternate hours.

This technique has obvious application to investigations of dietary substances, alcoholism, and obesity. One of the disadvantages of the use of avoidance conditioning as a model with which to study aversive control has been the need to appeal to unmeasured covert events (Dinsmoor & Hughes, 1956). The addition of psychophysiological measures to those of rate and qualitative observations would do much to mitigate this objection. In those instances where surgical or drug intervention is used in attempts to directly manipulate inner events, on line monitoring of selected physiological or neurophysiological changes could greatly amplify our knowledge of the mechanisms of control.

'Observing Response' Experiments

Wykoff (1952) reports an ingenious procedure which holds great promise for the experimental investigation of "attention" providing a behavioral measure of when the animal is attending, and an operational index of frequency or "strength" of attention.

In Wykoff's experiment, pigeons served as subjects with key pecking as the response reinforced by food (Rf). Reinforcement was scheduled on an FI 0.5 schedule, alternated irregularly with extinction periods. The translucent response key could be illuminated by projected colored lights which served as discriminative stimuli. The key remained white however, until an observing response (Ro) occurred, turning on the appropriate light behind the key. The Ro consisted of depressing a pedal on the floor of the compartment. With the pedal depressed the key was either red or green; red serving as the positive discriminative stimulus (SD) and green as the negative (SΔ). The key remained lighted as long as the pedal was depressed. Note that the Ro does not increase the probability of ultimate reinforcement since food availability was independently scheduled. Depressing the pedal did, however, allow the S to discriminate between the two conditions. Response duration was found to increase as discrimination developed, and to decrease when the stimuli were reversed or made nondifferential.

Kelleher (1958) reports on a modification of Wykoff's procedure, which provides at least three advantages: (1) control against the adventitious development of a chained response occurring as a consequence of the time restriction being met just after the occurrence of an Ro. This would lead to a contaminating enhancement of Ro's through the occasional close temporal correlation with food; (2) the use of a rate rather than a duration measure; (3) intermittent reinforcement of the Ro.

Kelleher's procedure used discriminative stimuli of short temporal duration so that multiple responses were necessary to keep the stimuli visible. Chimpanzees served as S in a two key situation; the left key correlated with presentation of food, and the right key with presentation of the discriminative stimulus then in operation. Rf was reinforced on a VR schedule, the Ro on a FR schedule. Substantial Ro rates were sustained at FR schedules ranging up to 60, reaching an asymptote at about FR30. The FR reinforcement of Ros displayed the same characteristics as FR schedules of food reinforcement.

Holland (1958) has applied the Ro technique to the study of human "vigilance behavior" by extending the study of schedule effects on Ros demonstrating further "that detections of signals can serve as reinforcements for observing responses, and, further, that the detection data of vigilance studies may reflect the observing response rates generated by the particular schedules employed."

Feed-back Procedures

An extremely provocative set of procedures are those which involve setting up a feed-back loop between the subject and the apparatus, such that the behavior of each influences the other. Békésy (1947) developed this procedure as an audiometric technique. Blough (1957) adapted it to the psychophysical investigation of vision. Two similar methods which hold particular promise when augmented by psychophysiological measures should serve to illustrate the rubrics of these techniques.

Lindsley (1957) coupled the subject to the apparatus by means of a rate analyzer-capacitor-sound generator circuit such that the subject's rate of response controlled the intensity of the tone throughout a range from complete avoidance, i.e. no sound, to a maximal intensity of 30 db. With this procedure he investigated the effects of deprivation and sedation upon the sleep patterns of human subjects.

Weiss and Laties (1958, 1963), with the use of what they refer to as a "titration schedule," coupled their subjects (rats) to a timer driven, two way stepping relay which provided incremental steps of shock intensity. Either single or multiple responses, as programmed, reduced the stimulator output. With this procedure, escape responding, maintained by fractional reduction of the aversive stimulation, may be sustained for prolonged periods of time.

In conjunction with appropriate training, such procedures as these could permit the use of standard psychophysical methods in the determination of absolute difference and terminal thresholds of both intensive and qualitative changes in exteroceptive stimulation. Progressive narrowing of successive steps, as programmed by the apparatus, could provide precise measures of the subjects' capacity for differentiation. It is possible that the utility of these techniques will be limited for difference threshold determination since the procedure would be essentially comparable to that reported by Pavlov (1927) which resulted in "experimental neurosis." However, this potential "limitation" could itself provide a valuable experimental tool.

A Preference Procedure

A procedure used by Autor (1960) illustrates how one or more techniques may be combined to produce yet another useful procedure.

In Autor's study, each of two response keys were programmed for a two component chained schedule. The first components were programmed on identical but independent concurrent VI-I schedules. Different exteroceptive stimuli were associated with the first and second components of both levers. As soon as a first component on either lever is completed and reinforced by the stimulus denoting its second component, only the responses on that lever are effective. After a period of time sufficient for reinforcement to occur on the second component VI schedule, the concurrent first component schedules go back into effect. By varying frequency of reinforcement in the second component on one key, while holding it constant on the other, Autor found that the reinforcing effectiveness of the second component stimulus is directly related to the frequency of food reinforcement with which it is associated. This procedure has been used by others (Reynolds, 1963, a and b; Herrnstein, 1964) and has proved to be a convenient and useful technique for the study of preferences.

The Conditioned Suppression Technique

In 1941 Estes and Skinner introduced a procedure which has found wide application in studies investigating the effects of electrocortical shock (ECS), drugs, intracranial stimulation, and schedules of reinforcement.

The procedure first establishes a lever pressing response for positive reinforcement, usually on a VI or a periodic schedule. While the lever pressing behavior is continuing a "neutral" stimulus is established as a conditioned aversive stimulus by classical conditioning procedures, i.e. a CS such as a click or a buzzer is occasionally presented and terminates with the delivery of an aversive stimulus, usually electrical shock. With the selection of appropriate on and off durations of the CS responding during on periods is attenuated or disappears completely ("conditioned suppression") while being maintained during off periods.

This situation provides what Schoenfeld (1950) has described as the "experimental paradigm for anxiety." The suppression accompanies a "conditioned anxiety response" (CAR) observable in the rat as crouching, immobility, and usually defecation.

The merits of this procedure for an experimental analysis of emotional behavior include: (1) a direct focussing upon the anxiety response as such; (2) wide interspecies generality; (3) stability over time; and (4) ease of quantification (Brady 1957). It has the additional advantage of providing in the same experimental setting operant behavior maintained by positive reinforcement and respondent behavior elicited by the aversive stimulus. Since much is already known of parameters affecting the CAR (e.g. see Brady & Hunt, 1955; Brady, 1957; Sidman, 1959), a considerable empirical base awaits extension from the addition of psychophysiological measures.

Representative Studies

Perez-Cruet, Tolliver, Dunn, Marvin, and Brady (1963) took longitudinal concurrent measures of bar pressing and lever pressing responses in monkeys trained with an SAV avoidance procedure. A continuous red light paired with the programming of the shock avoidance procedure was also present during the 2½ hr experimental session. Lever pressing rate and heart rate in extinction exhibited parallel elevations and declinations except during the terminal phases of the session at which time, while lever responding dropped to its lowest level, heart rate showed a marked increase.

Hefferline (1963), in an ingenious experiment with human subjects instructed to press a lever whenever they heard a tone, successfully established an imperceptible thumb twitch in conjunction with the tone as part of a compound discriminative stimulus for a pressing response. Once the response was established under discriminative control, the tone was gradually faded out until this exteroceptive component was completely removed leaving only proprioceptive feedback to serve the discriminative role. The cumulative record under "muscle twitch" control was scarcely distinguishable from that of the original compound stimulus of "muscle twitch + tone." When queried later the report was given by the subject that he still heard the tone, apparently an instance of "conditioned sensation." In this experiment the concurrent measurement was the electromyographic recording from the left thumb which determined when the experimenter would sound the tone.

Brutkowski (1959) also used a discriminative operant to obtain parallel observations of salivation and a foot lift operant. In Brutkowski's situation, dogs are trained to place their right forelegs on a food tray to obtain food reinforcement when one signal (SD) is given and to refrain from this response when a second signal is given. Effectively this is a three component multiple

CRF extinction situation: an intertrial interval of 3 to 7 min during which responses went unreinforced, then the S$_\Delta$ period which preceded the S$_D$ period of the same duration as S$_\Delta$. He reports a 'distinhibition' of both classical and operant "conditioned inhibitory reflexes" with prefrontal lesions. In general, a parallelism between the two measures was found. Both motor and salivary responses now occurred during S$_\Delta$ and during the intertrial interval and each motor reaction was accompanied by strong salivation; in time the discrimination was again re-established with the motor and salivary responses to S disappearing at the time. Brutkowski does note certain instances where either salivary or motor disinhibition occurred singly.

Malmo (1961) obtained continuous heart rate measures of rats during lever pressing for intracranial septal stimulation. A marked slowing of heart rate followed either self-stimulation or experimenter-presented stimulation. There was no observed habituation of the heart rate slowing response. Malmo suggests that the rewarding effect of septal stimulation may possibly be produced by a parasympathetic (quieting) reaction of the autonomic nervous system.

Hearst, Beer, Sheaty, and Galambos (1960), using multiple chronically implanted recording electrodes, obtained electroencephalogram (EEG) measures in several brain areas during both positively and negatively reinforced discriminant operant performances.

In the operant discrimination for positive reinforcement, a series of clicks served as the S$_D$, clicks were only presented after the subject had waited at least a minute without responding in S$_\Delta$. When this contingency was met, the clicks came on (the S$_D$ Period) and the response occurring 1 min after their onset was reinforced, terminated the S$_D$ and a new S$_\Delta$ period began. This is a chain (Fl-1, extinction) schedule. In this situation there was found to be a distinct decline in the size of the EEG responses in all brain areas measured; in a lever out period (when no responses are possible), the evoked responses from the caudate and hippocampal placements increased markedly over those obtained during the immediately prior discrimination session; decreasing again with reintroduction of the lever with additional discrimination training. So it appears that the performance of the instrumental response suppresses click-evoked EEG responses in some areas and that activity returns when the response is prevented.

In the discriminant operant situation employing aversive stimulation, a multiple schedule was used wherein equal 5-min S$_D$ (clicks) and S$_\Delta$ periods alternated throughout a daily session of approximately 3-hr duration. During click periods, a shock was delivered if the monkey waited longer than 5 sec between responses (S-S interval); during the absence of clicks (S$_\Delta$), no shocks were delivered regardless of whether the animal pressed the lever. During the discrimination phase there was no appreciable click-evoked responses in any of the brain areas monitored. With the lever removed, and after the "phantom pressing" which developed had extinguished, evoked EEG responses appeared in the caudate nucleus, hippocampus, and medial geniculate, with reintroduction of the lever these evoked responses promptly declined in magnitude.

These two experiments were compared with comparable observations obtained in the classical conditioning analogues of the two situations with quite different results. Whether with food or shock as unconditioned stimuli, low levels of hippocampal-evoked responses were never obtained and the other areas showed either an increase or no change.

This experiment provides some of the first evidence of its kind suggesting a fundamental neurophysiological difference existing between classical and operant conditioning.

Bersch, Notterman, and Schoenfeld (1956) took simultaneous records of heart rate and a motor avoidance response in humans. Heart rate conditioning was established prior to avoidance training. Using their scoring procedure, a heart rate drop signified the CR. After avoidance behavior was established there was a significant diminution in the size of the CR.

Collier (1962), using an F1-1 schedule with liquid sucrose reinforcement, took concurrent measures of licking and bar press behavior in rats under two different levels of food deprivation. He found the consummatory response measures (latency, duration, average rate, and momentary rate) insensitive to the deprivation manipulation. With the comparable indices of bar press, the latency and duration indices were functions of both deprivation and satiation (latency shorter and duration longer for high drive group); the average rate was related to deprivation only and the two measures of momentary rate unchanged between the two conditions. In extinction the rate of occurrence of licking showed a much more rapid decline than did the rate of bar pressing.

Miller and De Bold (1965) in a recent experiment obtained simultaneous measures of tongue licking and bar press behavior in thirsty rats reinforced by water in a discriminated operant situation. The peak number of licking responses occurred immediately after the bar press during the interval when reinforcement would be delivered, and fell off with negative acceleration for several seconds before and after this time. Bar pressing and licking both tended to occur in irregular bursts. Licking almost invariably accompanied the bar press activity, however, it occurred fairly often in the absence of such activity. The results reported "are congruent with hypotheses that both licking and bar pressing serve as cues for each other or that both are elicited by common events which could be either postural or central."

Guttman (1964) reports a study by Eisman who measured heart rate while Ss consumed various sucrose solutions. He found the heart rate to be roughly proportional to rates of drinking and instrumental activity and also a logarithmic function of concentration.

Erlich (1964) explored food deprivation effects in rats, obtaining concommitant measures of EEG and heart rate during prelearning, bar press on a CRF schedule, and extinction. He reports deceleration of heart rate during relearning and extinction; monotonically increasing acceleration during bar pressing. EEG data is not reported.

Doehring and Ferster (1962), using human Ss, took measures of heart rate, galvanic skin response (GSR), and rate of eye blink (BR) during performance of a lever press maintained on a mixed schedule of reinforcement (no exteroceptive stimuli present specific to a given component) (FR 20, VI 4, DRL). They found consistent increases in BR; consistent decreases in GSR correlated with the reinforcing stimuli, both changes suggest increased central nervous system activation. The pattern of heart rate changes varied between Ss.

Soltysik and Kowalski (1960) have provided heart rate measures obtained during the course of conditioning an operant avoidance response in dogs. They report a respondently defensive CR (heart rate acceleration) preceding the overt operant avoidance response, which in turn inhibits the ongoing respondent CR. They conclude that "the avoidance reflex represents a peculiar self-stabilizing or self-protecting from extinction, system of positive and inhibitory CRs."

Several investigators have reported studies in which salivary measures have been taken in conjunction with operant responses (Konorski & Wyrwicka, 1950; Wolf, 1963; Shapiro, 1960; Williams, 1965; Kintsch & Witte, 1962; Ellison & Konorski, 1965). These studies agree in the finding that there is no necessary priority of response. The salivary may precede, follow, or not coincide at all with the motor behavior.

When dogs have been shifted recently to Fl or FR schedules, bar pressing can occur considerably before salivation (Kintsch & Witte, 1962). However, if well trained on a DRL schedule (a schedule wherein long pauses between bar presses is differentially reinforced), the salivation regularly precedes the bar pressing (Shapiro, 1962).

Weiss and Laties (1963) report a series of studies relating body temperature to bar pressing reinforced by bursts of heat. A technique was devised which allowed continuous recording of subcutaneous temperature in a free moving rat. Just as it is possible to make a 2-sec burst of heat reinforcing by previous shaving and maintaining an exposure to a cold environment, it is possible to make a burst of cold reinforcing by maintaining the organism in an overheated condition (Paul, 1962). These procedures should prove valuable in studies dealing with metabolic variables, surgical, electrical, or chemical manipulation of thermoregulatory centers, or studies where the presence of a consummatory response confounds interpretation.

REFERENCES

Autor, S. M. The strength of conditioned reinforcers as a function of frequency and prob bility of reinforcement. Unpublished doctoral dissertation, Harvard, 1960.

Békésy, G. V. A new audiometer. *Acta otolar.* 1947, *35*: 411-422.

Bersch, P. J., Notterman, J. M., & Schoenfeld, W. N. Relations between acquired autonom and motor behavior during avoidance conditioning. *USAF, Sch. Aviat. Med.*, 195 No. 56-80.

Blough, D. S. Some effects of drugs on visual discrimination in the pigeon, *Ann. N.Y. Aca Sci.*, 1957, *66*: 733-739.

Brady, J. V. A comparative approach to the experimental analysis of emotional behavior. P. H. Hoch & J. Zubin (Eds.), *Experimental psychopathology*, New York: Grune Stratton, 1957.

Brady, J. V., & Hunt, H. F. An experimental approach to the analysis of emotional behavio *J. Psychol.*, 1955, *40*: 313-324.

Brutkowski, S. Comparison of classical and instrumental alimentary conditioned reflex following bilateral pre-frontal lobectomies in dogs. *Acta Biol. exp., Vars.*, 1959, *XI* 291-300.

Catania, Co. A. Independence of concurrent responding maintained by interval schedul of reinforcement. *J. exp. Analysis Behav*, 1962, *5:* 175 184.

Catania, C. A. Concurrent performances: a baseline for the study of reinforcement magn tude. *J. exp. Analysis Behav.*, 1963, *6:* 299 300(a).

Catania, C. A. Concurrent performances: reinforcement interaction and response inde pendence. *J. exp. Analysis Behav.*, 1963, *6:* 253-264(b).

Collier, G. Consummatory and instrumental responding as functions of deprivation. *exp. Psychol.*, 1962, *64*: 410-414.

Dinsmoor, J. A., & Hughes, L. H. Training rats to press a bar to turn off shock. *J. com physiol. Psychol.*, 1956, *59*: 235-238.

Doehring, D. G., & Ferster, C. B. Psychophysiological responses in a human operant situa tion. *Psychol. Rec.*, 1962, *12*: 251-261.

Ellison, G. D., & Konorski, J. Separation of the salivary and motor responses in instrument conditioning. *Science, N.Y.*, 1965, *146*: 1071-1072.

Erlich, D. Motivational and operant conditioning effects on rat heart rate. Paper read a W.P.A. meeting, 1964.

Estes, W., & Skinner, B. F. Some quantitative properties of anxiety. *J. exp. Psychol.*, 194 *29*: 390-400.

Ferster, C. B., & Skinner, B. F. *Schedules of reinforcement*. New York: Appleton-Century Crofts, 1957.

Galambos, R., Sheatz, G., & Vernier, V. G. Electrophysiological correlates of a conditione response in cats. *Science, N.Y.*, 1956, *123*: 376-377.

Guttman, N. Laws of behavior and facts of perception. In S. Koch (Ed.), *Psychology: study of a science*, Vol. 5. New York: McGraw-Hill, 1964.

Guttman, N., & Kalish. Discriminability and stimulus generalization. *J. exp. Psychol.*, 195 *51*: 79-88.

Hawkins, T. D., & Pliskoff, S. S. Brain stimulation intensity, rate of self stimulation and re inforcement strength: an analysis through chaining. *J. exp. Analysis Behav.*, 1964, *I* 285-288.

Hearst, E. Simultaneous generalization gradients for appetitive and aversive behavior *Science, N.Y.*, 1960, *132*: 1769-1770.

Hearst, E. Stress induced breakdown of an appetitive discrimination. *J. exp. Analysi Behav.*, 1965, *8*: 135-146.

Hearst, E., Beer, B., Sheatz, G., & Galambos, R. Some electrophysiological correlates of con ditioning in the monkey. *Electroenceph. clin. Neurophysiol.*, 1960, *12*: 137-152.

Hearst, E., & Sidman, M. Some behavioral effects of a concurrently positive and negativ stimulus, *J. exp. Analysis Behav.*, 1961, *4*: 3.

Hefferline, R. F. Proprioceptive discrimination of a covert operant without its observatio by the subject. *Science, N.Y.*, 1963, *139*: 834-835.

Hernandez-Peon, R., Sherrer, H., & Jowet, M. Modification of electrical activity in cocklear nucleus during "attention" in unanesthetized cats. *Science, N.Y.,* 1956, *123:* 331-332.

Herrnstein, R. J. A conjunctive schedule of reinforcement. *J. exp. Analysis Behav.,* 1958, *1:* 15-24.

Herrnstein, R. J. Relative and absolute strength of response as a function of frequency of reinforcement. *J. exp. Analysis Behav.,* 1961, *4:* 267-272.

Herrnstein, R. J. Secondary reinforcement and rate of primary reinforcement, *J. exp. Analysis Behav.,* 1964, *7:* 27-36. (a)

Herrnstein, R. J. Aperiodicity as a factor in choice. *J. exp. Analysis Behav.,* 1964, *7:* 179-182. (b)

Holland, J. G. Human vigilance. *Science, N.Y.,* 1958, *128:* 61-63.

Hudgins, C. V. Conditioning and the voluntary control of the pupillary light reflex. *J. gen. Psychol.,* 1933, *8:* 3-51.

Kelleher, R. T. Stimulus producing responses in chimpanzees. *J. exp. Analysis Behav.,* 1958, *1:* 87-102.

Kimble, G. A. *Hilgard and Marquis' conditioning and learning.* (2nd ed.) New York: Appleton-Century-Crofts, 1961.

Kintsch, W., & Witte, R. Concurrent conditioning of bar press and salivation responses. *J. comp. physiol. Psychol.,* 1962, *55:* 963-968.

Konorski, J., & Wyrwicka, W. I. Transformation of conditioned reflexes of the first type into conditioned reflexes of the second type. *Acta Biol. exp., Vars.,* 1950, *15:* 193-214.

Lindsley, O. R. Operant behavior during sleep: A measure of depth of sleep. *Science, N.Y.,* 1957, *126:* 1290-1291.

Malmo, R. B. Slowing of heart rate after septal self stimulation in rats. *Science, N.Y.,* 1961, *133:* 1128-1130.

Menzies, R. Conditioned vasomotor responses in human subjects. *J. Psychol.,* 1937, *4:* 75-120.

Miller, N. E., & DeBold, R. C. Classically conditioned tongue-licking and operant bar pressing recorded simultaneously in the rat. *J. comp. physiol. Psychol.,* 1965, *59:* 109-111.

Miller, S., & Konorski, J. Sur une forme particuliere des reflexes conditionnels. *Séanc. Soc. Biol.,* 1928, *99:* 1155-1157.

Olds, M. E., & Olds, J. Approach-avoidance analysis of rat diencephalon. *J. comp. Neurol.,* 1963, *2:* 120.

Paul, L. Use of temperature stress with cool air reinforcement for human operant conditioning. *J. exp. Psychol.,* 1962, *64:* 329-335.

Pavlov, I. P. *Conditioned reflexes* (translated by G. V. Anrep). London: Oxford University Press, 1927.

Perez-Cruet, J., Tolliver, G., Dunn, G., Marvin, S., & Brady, J. Concurrent measurement of heart-rate and instrumental avoidance behavior in the rhesus monkey. *J. exp. Analysis Behav.,* 1963, *6:* 61-64.

Reynolds, G. S. On some determinants of choice in pigeons. *J. exp. Analysis Behav.,* 1963, *6:* 53-59. (a)

Reynolds, G. S. Potency of reinforcers based on food and punishment. *Science, N.Y.,* 1963, *139:* 838-839. (b)

Schlosberg, H. The relationship between success and the laws of conditioning. *Psychol. Rev.,* 1937, *44:* 379-394.

Schoenfeld, W. N. An experimental approach to anxiety, escape, and avoidance behavior. In P. H. Hoch & J. Zubin, (Eds.), *Anxiety.* New York: Grune & Stratton, 1950.

Shapiro, M. M. Respondent salivary conditioning during operant lever pressing in dogs. *Science, N.Y.,* 1960, *132:* 619-620.

Shapiro, M. M. Temporal relationship between salivation and lever pressing with differential reinforcement of low rates. *J. comp. physiol. Psychol.,* 1962, *55:* 567-571.

Shearn, D. W. Operant conditioning of heart rate. *Science, N.Y.,* 1962, *137:* 530-531.

Sidman, M. Two temporal parameters of the maintenance of avoidance behavior by the white rat. *J. comp. physiol. Psychol.,* 1953, *46:* 253. (a)

Sidman, M. Avoidance conditioning with brief shock and no exteroceptive warning signal *Science, N.Y.,* 1953, *118:*157.

Sidman, M. Behavioral pharmacology. *Psychopharmacologica*, 1959, *1*: 1–19.

Skinner, B. F. On the conditions of elicitation of certain eating reflexes. *Proc. natn. Acad Sci. U.S.A.*, 1930, *16*: 433–438.

Skinner, B. F. On the rate of formation of a conditioned reflex. *J. gen. Psychol.*, 1932, *7*: 274–285.

Skinner, B. F. Two types of conditioned reflex and a pseudo type. *J. gen. Psychol.*, 1935, *12*: 66–77.

Skinner, B. F. Two types off conditioned reflex: a reply to Konorski and Miller. *J. gen. Psychol.*, 1937, *16*: 272–279.

Skinner, B. F. *The behavior of organisms*. New York: Appleton-Century-Crofts, 1938.

Soltysik, S., & Kowalski, J. Studies on the avoidance conditioning II. Differentiation and extinction of avoidance reflexes. *Acta Biol. exp.*, *Vars.*, 1960, *20*: 157–170.

Thorndike, E. L. Animal intelligence. An experimental study of the associative processes in animals. *Psychol. Monogr.*, 1898, *2*: No. 8.

Verhave, T. Recent developments in the experimental analysis of behavior. *Proc. Res. Conf. Am. Meat Inst. Fdn*, 1959.

Weiss, B., & Laties, V. G. Fractional Escape and avoidance on a titration schedule. *Science, N.Y.*, 1958, *128*: 1575–1576.

Weiss, B., & Laties, V. G. Characteristics of aversive thresholds measured by a titration schedule. *J. exp. Analysis Behav.*, 1963, *6*: 563–572.

Williams, D. *Classical conditioning: a symposium*. New York: Appleton-Century-Crofts, 1965.

Williams, D., & Teitelbaum, P. Control of drinking behavior by means of an operant-conditioning technique. *Science, N.Y.*, 1956, *124*: 1294.

Wolf, K. Properties of multiple conditioned reflex Type II activity. *Acta Biol. exp.*, *Vars.*, 1963, *23*.

Wykoff, L. B., Jr. The role of observing responses in discrimination learning. Part I. *Psychol. Rev.*, 1952, *59*: 431–442.

SUGGESTED REFERENCES ON OPERANT CONDITIONING

Honig, W. K. (Ed.). *Operant behavior and psychology*. New York: Appleton-Century-Crofts, in press.

Keller, F., & Schoenfeld, N. *Principles of psychology*. New York: Appleton-Century-Crofts, 1950.

Sidman, M. *Tactics of scientific research. Evaluating experimental data in psychology*. New York: Basic Books, 1960.

13
Methods of Data Storage

GEORGE N. WEBB, EE, M.S.

Present day work in the behavioral sciences not only requires the simultaneous recording of a number of variables but has available to it the sophisticated instrumentation to meet many of its needs. For the investigator who is interested in the correlation of the temporal aspects of a single variable or the correlations, simultaneously or temporally, of many variables, some form of data storage is required.

In this section both "data" and "storage" are generally used with a very broad meaning. Data is assumed to include any information which can be expressed in some quantitative form, stored for review, and analyzed. Thus data may be a series of numbers representing discrete samples or a line on a polygraph showing the continuous value of a variable. The meaning of the term "storage" is more evident although the methods and uses of storage available to us may not be immediately obvious.

As the methods of data analysis change in complexity from those situations using the human visual-mental system to those relying completely or in part on automatic instrumentation, data storage, the means by which physiological information can be preserved and recalled in exact fidelity on repeated occasions, becomes a central process in this science.

Uses of Data Storage Procedures

Before discussing the means by which data storage is accomplished, it is important to point out the conditions which occasion it: the experimental requirements, the nature of the information obtained, and the analysis to be accomplished. Data storage is required for review of the data, for data processing and analysis, and for control purposes.

Figure 13.1 is a block diagram of an experiment in which a subject is being tested for recognition and correlation of sights and sounds. This is a problem combining several presently available techniques which illustrate many modes and uses of storage. In addition, this diagram may serve as an outline in planning experimental procedures which may be useful in checking to see that all of

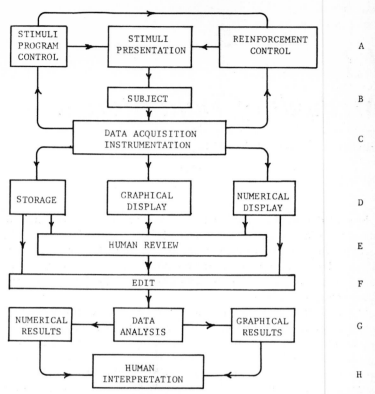

FIG. 13.1. Block diagram of psychological experiment, including aspects from stimuli presentation to interpretation of results, illustrating different kinds of data storage. All levels except *B, C, E,* and *H* contain instrumentation for data storage. The objective of this experiment might be evaluation of the storage function of the human brain.

the necesssary steps have been well considered in advance of starting a study. With the exception of Level C every box contains some storage element, the nature of which should be carefully considered or specified.

Level A represents primarily the operation of presenting the problems to the subject. The objects to be viewed are stored as images on slides (2 × 2) and rear projected on a translucent screen. The sounds are stored on magnetic tape and are presented through earphones in coordination with the pictures. The subject, after hearing the words, or sounds, and viewing the picture, gives some response through an arrangement of levers or buttons. The stimuli control timing program is primarily contained on a second magnetic tape or punched paper tape. The equipment in Level C has two major functions: (1) to acquire response data for both reinforcement control and modification of the stimuli presentation program, and (2) to acquire data for analysis following the experiment. This illustrated experiment may be concerned with testing the operation of the subject's own storage system.

Codes representing the stimuli presented are stored in binary logic elements so that the reinforcement control may make the decision whether or not a correct response was made and the subject should be reinforced. This fact of reinforcement action must also be transmitted to the data acquisition instrumentation for inclusion in the analysis.

Level D represents a major storage operation and provides three physical arrangements. The storage on the left is in some form from which electrical signals can be generated representing the acquired data. Depending upon the particular nature of the methods to be used in analysis, this storage mode may be magnetic tape, punched paper tape, or punched cards. The center graphical display is a visual recorder such as a multichannel ink pen writer. The unit on the right presents numerical data (sequence number, response time, etc.) through mechanical counters, electronically illuminated numbers, or printed figures. These usually require intermediate storage and may be used for information to the operator monitoring the experiment, and in the case of the printed numbers, for future analysis as well.

The human review step in Level E is most important and should be kept in mind in determining the method of viewing the data so that the appropriate storage medium can be used. It is useful, although not always possible, to have the same storage medium used for holding for review and holding for additional analysis. The edit feature is practically always necessary. Often there is artifact which must be found and discarded in the analysis step. Even if there is no deletion editing necessary because there is no artifact, selective editing is required.

The analysis step of Level G may be performed manually or automatically, perhaps by a computer. The results from this analysis can emerge in either numerical or graphical form. The last level, but by no means the least important, is the human interpretation of the analyzed data, Level H. The method of storing the data from the analysis step may be very important in terms of presenting it.

Data Review

At the present time, the most popular method for reviewing data is essentially a manual one and involves visual examination of information depicted in graphic or numerical form. This type of analysis is not possible directly, however, if the data are being generated with such rapidity that they cannot be reviewed adequately in "real time," i.e. at the actual rate at which it is generated. Data storage can be used for holding the data for a more leisurely review.

If the data are to be analyzed in several different dimensions, e.g. amplitude and frequency components of a wave form, distribution of sequence of events, etc., the data may be stored and reviewed by manual or automatic means in order to determine what parts are artifact-free for each analysis. Data may be secured continuously and be artifact free, but only portions of the recording may contain information relevant to the experimental problem. In this case, since the occurrence of such periods of interest cannot be predicted, it is entirely feasible to make a continuous recording and to search the record for the relevant portions. Frequently during the course of an experiment, transient and unexpected phenomena may occur and the point of interest may be prior to the transient. Data storage permits the review of changes occurring prior in time to such events and provides the means for "post-dicting" possible causes.

Many types of storage allow the review procedure to proceed at rates much slower or faster than the rate at which the data was obtained. In this regard, it is important to organize presentation of the data for review in a way which lends itself to review. Man's visual perception system is marvelously adept at quickly reviewing patterns. For instance, Fig. 13.2 represents one way of parallel storage of electrocardiographic data. This photographic presentation of data which had been originally stored on magnetic tape is organized for quick human review.

Data Processing

Data processing may be defined as any manipulation of the original data in order to obtain more useful meaning from it than was available in its original form. Visual inspection of a polygraph record for significant changes in the recorded data is at one extreme of the data processing continuum, while automatic processing by means of electronic computers represents the other extreme in reproducibility, precision, efficiency, and speed. In general, the most precise information may be obtained from data which is stored in its most detailed form. The cost and efficiency of data storage procedures must be carefully balanced against the necessary precision of information which is required in the final analysis. It is not necessary, for example, to detect, store, and display all the ECG complex if only the R to R interval is required. The limitations in frequency response of most biological transducers and amplifiers impose another limitation upon the degree of precision with which biological information may be detected and stored. Consideration should always be given to reducing the data to its simplest, most useable form before storage, since some sacrifice in the quality of the data almost always occurs during the process of storage. In general, some storage of data is required for the most accurate analysis.

Storage for Purposes of Control

Data for the control of experimental procedures may be placed advantageously in storage so that repetition of the experimental conditions may be consistent. Consider the experiment of Fig. 13.1 in which association of words and objects are to be made. Pictures of the objects are stored as projection slides

Fig. 13.2. Contourogram. Contourography is a method of storage display in which semi-periodic signals are organized to illustrate cycle by cycle variations. In this contourogram, electrocardiograms are presented in a compressed manner, organized by triggering the sweep of an oscilloscope on every other R wave. Intensity modulation is made proportional to the signal amplitude and thus allows a very close packing of adjacent sweeps.

(2 × 2). Words and control signals are recorded on magnetic tape. As the tape is played back the control signals operate the projector so that words to be tested for association with the pictures are presented simultaneously. If the tape is played at a uniform rate, thus presenting the picture-word combinations at a uniform rate regardless of the subject's reaction, the control would be called open control since nothing happening within the experiment alters the progress of the presentations. However, if the tape stopped after the word was reproduced and waited for some response from the subject before proceeding, this would be called closed loop control. Some action within the experiment modifies the rate of progress of the experiment. The closed loop features might be much more complex than just waiting for the subject to respond, e.g. the rate of picture presentation might be based upon whether or not the responses were correct or incorrect.

General Comments

It is worthwhile to consider carefully all of the storage methods to be used in a new experiment and not to accept the previously used methods merely on the basis of familiarity. Accepting existing methods of data storage may impose serious limitations upon the precision or fidelity of the final data required or may produce costly inefficiencies due to the preservation of unnecessary information.

It is also prudent to review the uses to which the stored data will ultimately be put to ascertain that the required format and degree of precision will be used and that unnecessary sophistication is not demanded. Such a review should also consider the flexibility of the planned system to meet the growth requirements during its lifetime of use.

Parallel storage of information should also be considered. The signals from the biological preparation may be simultaneously stored in paralleled channels, perhaps in two modalities, in one with full fidelity and in another in a reduced form. During subsequent processing the reduced data may be scanned rapidly to determine if significant information exists and to locate the sections of particular interest. Since this may be performed quite rapidly, a subsequent analysis may be made of the uncondensed data to determine more precise and extensive information.

Methods of Data Storage

The following discussion of data storage methods will be organized under three major heads: (1) methods in which the data, whether continuous or discrete, can be made visible to direct observation and in which all parts are recoverable; (2) methods in which the continuous or discrete data are *not* visible but in which all the parts are recoverable; and (3) methods in which continuous or discrete data are *summed* in the process of storage and only the resultant total can be retrieved.

Storage in Visible Form

This type of storage is characterized by the fact that the data is visible in storage although in some cases it is visible only in coded form.

Manual. Manual storage is the oldest formal storage procedure. In its simplest form it consists of notes written in a book or on a form. Where large amounts of data are to be recorded this may be an inaccurate process. In order to expedite recovery for the purpose of analysis or processing, some consideration should be given to semiautomatic procedures for handling manually recorded data.

Manually recorded data may be entered into punched cards (Bourne, 1963; Gull, 1958; Schule, 1961; Williams, 1964) or punched tape (Gannon, 1965, a and b) immediately upon acquisition. This is an extremely inexpensive means for recording data which are produced at a relatively slow rate in a form suitable for automatic processing. A device for manually punching cards at the experimental site is shown in Fig. 13.3. Although the number being punched is not printed it can be read fairly easily from the card.

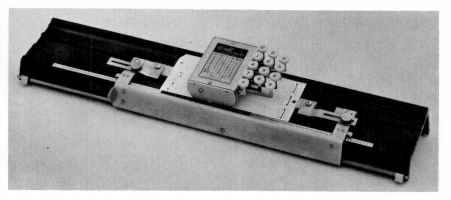

FIG. 13.3. Hand operated card punch for use at data acquisition site. (Photo courtesy Wright Line Data Processing Accessories.)

Edge notched (Bourne, 1963; Gull, 1958; Schule, 1961; Williams, 1964) cards (Fig. 13.4*A*) for manual sorting and special pencil marking cards and forms for automatic processing are available and should be considered. It is possible that a process will be developed in the future which will permit data to be manually entered in a form which is both visually legible and capable of being transcribed by machines similar to those presently used to read coded information on bank checks.

If computer data processing is in order, the use of computer programming coding forms for recording the data may eliminate one copy process by having the written data in the correct form for punching cards.

Graphic instrumentation storage. Graphic instrumentation storage includes those types in which the data is written directly by an instrument and may be viewed immediately or perhaps after some photographic processing. The total category has been divided into four groups differentiated by their writing method. The first two (A and B) are the ones most familiar to the life scientist (see Chapter XV).

Instruments of the first two categories produce a continuous tracing which represents the original signal on paper, film, or photographic paper. Type A instruments produce a tracing by means of an electromechanical system which moves a recording pen at right angles to the direction of travel of folded or rolled recording paper. The actual tracing is produced by diverse means; most commonly by liquid ink carried in a capillary tube to the pen point, by a heated stylus on the pen tip which creates a color change on the paper area contacted, by passing an electrical current through special paper from the pen tip and thus producing a color change, by special inks carried in pressurized reservoirs to hollow tube pens, and by melted wax caused to flow through a capillary pen onto the recording medium.

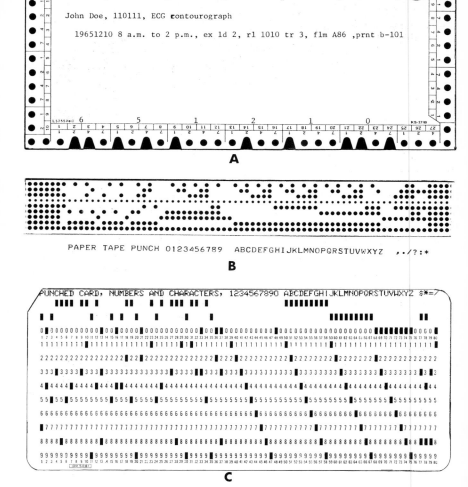

FIG. 13.4. Punched cards and tape. *A*, edge notched card for hand sorting of stored data; *B*, punched paper tape used for computer input; *C*, punched card for computer input.

Type B instruments produce records photographically and the pen or stylus is replaced by a beam of light which is caused to strike a photosensitive surface and is moved in accordance with fluctuations in the signal. Some type of chemical development is usually required and the signal tracing does not become visible until processed. The processing of some light exposed papers is done by ultraviolet light and the results may become visible in the order of a minute.

Both type A and B instruments produce a continuous line written on chart paper and the variations in the signal are depicted by positions and deviations in the line.

Type C instruments also produce a continuous tracing of a signal but are operated by a servo-balancing motor. The writing units in such servo-recorders usually produce a linear excursion and the displacement of the writing unit is produced by variations in the signal. Servo-recorders generally produce "rectilinear" traces in which the writing span is usually much greater than that produced by type A and B recorders, but due to the amount of time required to move the writing element across the recording span they are not suitable for recording high frequency signals (more than a few cycles per sec).

Type D instruments convert samples of the original signal amplitude into a discrete number or code and this is automatically punched or printed onto paper, card, or tape.

There are inherent advantages and disadvantages to each of these four methods with respect to the requirements for further processing the data. Type A and B recorders produce graphic records of higher frequencies than type C and D recorders but the information contained in the tracing may be transcribed only by direct viewing and measurement. Although automatic optical scanners have been developed which translate such records into numeric or electrical form, this is an expensive and complicated process. The essential limitation of such a device is that it is difficult for the machine to distinguish between the signal tracing and the preprinted coordinate lines, a task which is easy for human vision and perception. Therefore, if you desire type A, B, or C recordings but wish to transcribe the data automatically from them by machine, *make all such recordings on blank, unlined paper or paper with coordinate lines of a color or dimension which are invisible to the machine scanner system.*

Instruments of type C and D produce visual records which may be transcribed by machine more easily. The servorecorder may be modified to drive a shaft encoder (Product reference file, 1963), a device which converts the recorder pen motion into discrete step codes which in turn may be readily registered on a card punch, paper punch, or a magnetic tape recorder, usually provided with an incremental drive (Curtis, 1964).

The storage oscilloscope might be included in this section and should be classified in the same general category as the handwritten record. It produces records of transients, but the problems of automatically retrieving data from it are great. There are means available for scanning this storage tube (Acton, 1963) with a television camera but this is a technique to be left to the moon explorers' budget.

There are other types of storage media which produce viewable records but have limited application. The general class is typified by the facsimile record in which the x and y axis scans are at fixed times and rates. Hence the data must be synchronized to these scans and is presented or written as a change in the writing density. The wirephoto used in newspapers is one example. Here the original photo is scanned with many lines, only the intensity of a single dot being transmitted at a time. This storage may have applications for television monitored psychophysiological experiments.

A storage system (Webb, 1965) which places data in a compact pattern form may allow the human visual perception system to perform a useful analysis, and this fact should not be overlooked in this day when it often seems that automatic machine data processing must be used no matter how complicated and expensive it may be.

Visible coded recording. This type of storage is useful both for data which originates as discrete values and for continuous data which must be sampled and a discrete value determined for the sample. Many codes have been developed for representing amplitude and time intervals, in characters, numbers, and bit patterns.

Codes for cards, punched tape (Fig. 13.4B), and magnetic tape are built on arrangement or combination of binary bit information. For instance, a punched card (Fig. 13.4A) shows alphabetical, numerical, or symbol character stored in each column. A punched hole is a "one bit" and no punch is a "no bit." There are 12 rows in each column. It can be seen that the numerals are represented by only one bit. Alphabetical characters and symbols are represented by two or more one bits in each column. Whereas this card uses 12 bit positions for each column, magnetic tape and punched paper tape may use only 6 bit positions and by a more complex code represent a total of 64 characters, alphabetical, numerical, and symbols.

The two most widely used storage forms in this category are punched cards and punched tape (Fig. 13.4, A and C) and are primarily associated with digital computers. The edge notched card is used primarily for hand sorting. For all of these a physical hole is punched into a paper or composition base for recording and the hole sensed by physical, electrical, or optical means on transcription. The primary distinction between punched cards and punched tape is the fact that cards have a specific number of possible characters per card while the tape is essentially continuous. In either case there are a number of positions across the width of tape or card and the numbers or characters to be coded are represented by combinations of one or more punches.

Each of the two methods has its advantages and disadvantages. They both have the disadvantage of requiring a physical operation, punching one or more holes per character, which limits the speed with which the record can be made. In addition, acoustical noise of this operation may be a problem. Either operation can be performed manually or through electrical means, keyboards, or automatic equipment. Either can be provided with printing devices so that the character represented by the code can be read as text. The code bits are also readily visible for checking purposes.

The principal advantages and disadvantages are found in the relative convenience of continuous or segmented data. With the use of punched cards, corrections, deletions, or additions, anywhere in a whole deck of cards can be easily accomplished. Punched tape may be read with much less expensive equipment for a given character reading rate. Card or tape "reading" here means the translation of the hole bit pattern into electrical signals.

Codes for punched cards and punched tape are not standard and care must be exercised to ensure that there is compatibility between existing instruments or installations and contemplated equipment.

Character storage. Character storage, usually decimal numbers, is accomplished by various forms of counters (Fig. 13.5). Short term storage is provided by the immediate view of the number displayed while long term storage is obtained by printing the number on paper or permitting the number to become a part of a sum. The actual storage and additions may take place in mechanical units with the visual display derived from the storage elements or the storage may be in electrical units (Acton, 1963) with a lighted display indicating the number stored.

This type of storage can be useful where a transient value must be held until it can be read or printed. It is also used in the process of counting the number of events. In deciding upon the use of mechanical counters for counting numbers of events it is important to consider the need for information about the temporal distribution of the occurrence of the events as well as the total number. Unless a permanent printing storage is used, along with the printed time, mechanical counting stage units will provide only the total. It is possible to photograph a bank of counters, along with a clock to provide a permanent storage of counts at specific times.

Data Storage not Immediately Visible

This type of storage, typified by magnetic tape recording, holds the data in a form which cannot be viewed directly but can be retrieved for further processing or for display on an appropriate instrument. Here too, the data may be stored as a continuous variable, analogue, or as samples represented by some code. Code is here used as a very general term to designate all kinds of modulation techniques as well as the binary digital systems which are usually included in coded data discussions.

The term analogue, or direct recording, has come to mean that the recording medium is continuously varied relative to some function of the input signal. This is in contrast to the coded recording where samples of the signal to be stored are taken and only a *representation* of this sample is recorded.

Direct magnetic recording. For direct magnetic recording (Stewart, 1958; Weber, 1959) the storage medium is modified in direct proportion to the amplitude of the signal to be recorded. The only readily available modality for this at

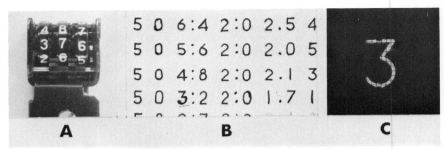

FIG. 13.5 Character storage and display, *A*, mechanical wheel counter with display numbers; *B*, paper strip from printing wheel counter; *C*, electronic display tube for showing a number stored in electronic counter.

present is magnetic tape recording. Research is being done in using paper or plastic tape as storage medium for electric charge with occasional rumors appearing of commercial recorders but none have become operationally useful as yet. There are also a limited number of recorders using film. This discussion will concentrate on the magnetic recording.

The facts of magnetic tape recording are readily apparent to everyone, at least in terms of home tape recorders, which use the direct recording mode. Iron oxide particles are bonded to a thin plastic tape, disk, or drum, so that these particles can be moved past a recording position and then past a playback or retrieval station. The necessity for movement is 2-fold. First, a single magnetic particle can only assume one state of magnetization at one time so many particles are required to represent many values, either simultaneous or sequentially in time. Second, the normal retrieval method uses a magnetic induction coil which is responsive only to rate of change of magnetic fields; hence, the tape or drum must be moved in order to produce the required change. These facts suggest also that this mode of recording cannot indicate a steady state value of magnetization.

Where it is desirable to retrieve a fairly accurate wave form representation of what was stored in direct recording, some means must be provided to achieve this fidelity of reproduction even though the basic relationships between magnetizing force and resultant detectable residual magnetic flux is a nonlinear function. This linearity is achieved by the use of high frequency signal, termed bias, which is added to the lower frequency signal to be recorded.

It must be emphasized here that a bias current *must* be added to the recording signal. The frequency and amplitude of this bias is dependent upon the type of signal, recorder, and make of tape. For the most critical application, each batch of tape may require adjustment of the bias. The second factor to be emphasized is that the basic electrical signal retrieved from the tape is in general the first derivative of the recorded signal. This can be illustrated in two ways. Figure 13.6 shows the response obtained on playback when a sine

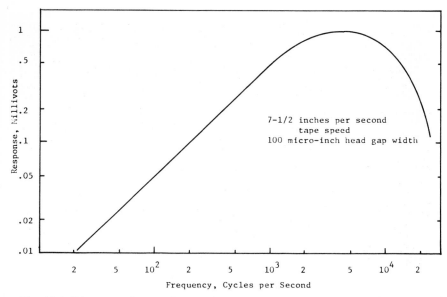

FIG. 13.6. Direct record magnetic tape playback response voltage developed by the play-back head is shown with respect to frequency for a constant current recording signal. The peak amplitude of magnetic flux recorded on the tape was constant for all frequencies. The playback head is responsive to the rate of change of magnetic flux on the tape; hence, the decrease of response at low frequencies. The decrease of response for the high frequencies is the result of the recorded wave length approaching the playback head gap width, i. e. limit of playback head resolving power.

wave was recorded with the peak signal current in the recording head held constant independent of frequency. The slope rising from the left results from the fact that the playback head detects d/dt, that is the *rate of change of magnetic flux*. The droop of the curve to the right is the result of the recorded wave length on the tape approaching the length of the gap in the playback head. There is another extra falloff in response at the left end of the tape caused by the fact that the recorded wave length is longer than the total length of the playback head. Both of these cases can be viewed as inability of the playback head to resolve or "see" the magnetization on the tape. At the high frequency end, the wave length of the recorded signal becomes too small for the playback head gap to detect, while at the low frequency end the recorded wave length becomes so long with respect to the length of the head structure in contact with the head that the wave cannot be resolved. This nonlinear playback can be illustrated with a few recorded wave forms as shown in Fig. 13.7.

Because there is an upper limit for the degree of magnetization dictated by the saturation of the magnetic medium, it can be seen from Fig. 13.6 that as the tape is played more slowly, the absolute amplitude of signal which can be

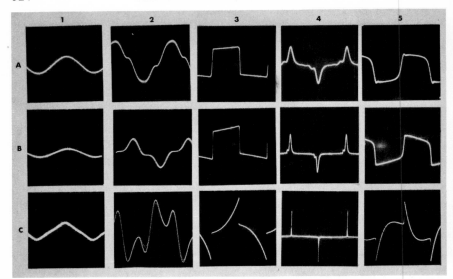

FIG. 13.7. Direct recording magnetic tape wave forms. The wave forms in this illustration were made using a high fidelity radio broadcasting station type of magnetic tape recorder operating at a tape speed of 7 1/2 in. per sec. *Row A*, 1000 cps, *B*, 400 cps; *C*, 40 cps. *Column 1*, response of the playback head for a standard level of record amplitude. (Oscilloscope gain increased by, X 10, for *Row C, Column 1*). *Column 2*, response from the playback amplifier for a sine wave input when no linearizing bias signal was used during recording. *Column 3*, square wave response of the recording amplifier for constant level of input square wave. *Column 4*, response from the playback head for record input signals of *Column 3*, *Column 5*, response from the playback amplifier with normal National Association of Broadcasters (N.A.B.) equalization for record input signals of *Column 3*.

obtained is decreased for a given playback head. At some point in the decrease of the tape speed, the noise due to amplifier, stray pickup, and characteristics of the tape will become greater than the signal, and hence limit the lowest usable speed.

It may be necessary to tailor the record and playback process to particular needs. This may require the use of special record or reproduce heads on the tape recorder or the use of special speeds. The latter is usually the easiest to adjust. In general, if the tape can be moved at a uniform rate, not always a trivial matter, any tape speed within very broad limits can be used for recording as long as the cycles per in. correspond to those of Fig. 13.6.

Figure 13.6 represents the characteristics of a modern high frequency playback head. If the useful high frequency limit of response is taken as 15.0 kc, a packing density, "P," of 2,000 cycles per in. is obtained. If the same high frequency packing density is used at any speed the tape speed becomes $= f/P$ in. per sec where f is the highest frequency to be recorded. If the top frequencies to be recorded are very low, of the order of tens of cycles per sec, it may be necessary to use a tape speed for playback which is faster than that used during recording if normally available playback heads and electronics are to be used. For instance, if an ECG is to be recorded with a frequency response of 0.1 to 40 cycles, the record speed could be 40/2,000 = 0.02 in. per sec or 1.2 in. per min. If the playback speed is 7.5 in. per sec, the speed up will be 375. Thus the 40 cycles will become 15,000 cps and the 0.1 will be 37.5 cps on playback.

The 37.5 to 15,000 cps band width required at 7½ in. per sec tape speed reaches the limits of the best broadcast quality tape recorders operating at this speed. It can be seen from this that it is not a trivial problem to fit a physiological signal into the available direct recording magnetic tape system. A good high fidelity sound system may have a range of from 40 cps to 16,000 cps or a high to low frequency ratio of 400 to 1. This ratio applied to an electrocardiogram yields a frequency range of 0.1 to 40 cycles which could not be classed as high fidelity ECG recording. This manipulation of record and playback speed can often be used to advantage in compressing time for review or analysis.

At high tape speeds problems arise from air flow making the tape flutter and from friction heating the tape and heads. At low speeds, problems of making drive shafts turn uniformly increase, but the greatest problem seems to be sticky friction between the record head and magnetic tape. It is unwise to give absolute upper or lower limits of tape speed or frequency response for special application. Home type recorders operate with tape speeds from 1⅞ in. per sec to 15 in. per sec, television tape recorders may go up to several hundred inches per sec, and low frequency siesmic recorders go down to inches per min.

Present day playback heads for home type recorders provide a signal of the order of a few millivolts at the peak of the curve of Fig. 13.6 at a speed of 3¾ in. per sec. The noise levels of amplifiers used for these signals are of the order of a few microvolts. Another reason why it is difficult to give absolute limits is that the signal to noise ratio which can actually be tolerated varies with the application. An analysis which is operating with narrow frequency bands may be able to tolerate a system with a low, broad band signal to noise ratio.

The following summarizes the direct recording magnetic storage system.

1. The level of magnetization produced on the recording medium is made proportional to the signal to be stored. Any variation in the consistency of the magnetic material or spacing between recording or reproducing heads and the magnetic medium will cause undesirable variation in the stored signal.

2. Wide ranges of tape speed can be used in the recording process, e.g. 15/16 to 60 in. per sec. For best results the recording head should have different characteristics, physical and electrical, from the playback head.

3. For many purposes a small variation in tape speed may be tolerated, i.e.

1%, particularly for voice reproduction where there are few if any sustained notes.

4. The basic playback process produces an output signal which is generally proportional to the rate of change of the signal recorded. If a true reproduction of the original signal is required, then some equalization, i.e. modification of amplitude as a function of frequency, is required to achieve this goal. For the most part, this equalization is performed in the playback operation. However, with a knowledge of the frequency distribution of the components in the recorded signal, it may be possible to have better over-all results if some equalization of the signal is made before recording. What is ideally desired is to have the maximum signal level at each frequency produce the maximum level of magnetization consistent with distortion.

In recording heart sounds, it is found that there are very high amplitude, low frequency signals, below 20 cps, produced by the transducer. The amplitude of the heart sounds then decreases above 20 cps by about a factor of 100 per decade of frequency. Thus in order that the high frequency components may be recorded above the tape noise level, the low frequency signals must be attenuated before recording. Whether or not equalization is used on playback depends upon whether the heart sounds are to be listened to, electronically analyzed, or recorded on paper.

5. The tape speed during playback may be slower or faster than the speed used during recording. The slowest recording speed which can be used is usually dictated by the highest frequency components to be recorded. The slowest playback speed which can be used is generally limited by noise while the highest useful playback speed is limited by the response of the playback head. Since playback is proportional to the rate of change of the magnetized tape, steady state or direct current levels cannot be recovered without special magnetic flux sensitive heads (Hoagland, 1963).

Coded magnetic recording. Coded magnetic tape recording differs from direct recording in that a code representing the signal is carried as discontinuities in the magnetization and not as continuously varying degrees of magnetization. The discontinuities are generally, but not necessarily, changes from magnetic saturation of one polarity to saturation in the opposite polarity. The codes can be subdivided into two groups: those which use some discontinuity rate function and those which use a pattern of discontinuities.

Time function codes. Frequency modulation (FM) (Davies, 1961) is a time function code which is commonly used for analogue recording requiring good wave form reproduction and low frequency response. For this type of recording, a carrier frequency establishes a series of discontinuities along the magnetic tape for a zero voltage input. Increase or decrease in the input voltage will increase or decrease the rate of the discontinuities. Thus the amplitude of the recorded signal becomes a frequency deviation from the center frequency established for zero voltage input. The most common practice is to make a frequency deviation of ±40% of the center frequency value equal to the maximum peak to peak variation of the input amplitude. Upon playback, standard pulses are created for each discontinuity and the "area" of the pulse averaged to reconstruct the original input at the output (Fig. 13.8). The input is sampled at the carrier frequency rate, hence the carrier frequency must be much higher than the signal to be recorded. Also, the carrier frequency must be such that the magnetic tape playback head can resolve the carrier. Thus it can be seen that the signal frequency band width will be lower for a given tape speed than that available using direct recording. In present practice this ratio is of the order of 1:6. The characteristic of the filter circuit which generates the average value of the pulses and attenuates the carrier frequency components must be taken into account in determining FM system band width which must be used for a given signal band width.

Other discontinuity rate function coding systems use the spacing between discontinuities in one way or another. These are called pulse width modulation (PWM), pulse duration modulation (PDM), etc.

Binary bit position codes. The other type of coded magnetic recording uses the discontinuities placed in some known pattern with a wide tolerance allowed in the relative position. This pattern can be arranged along either the length or the width of a magnetic tape. For instance, magnetic tape ½ in. wide may have seven parallel tracks with each track representing one digit in a seven binary digit code. This seven binary digit code would be used to represent all alphabetical and numerical characters, and some symbols. A discontinuity in a given channel indicates the presence of a binary digit represented by that channel. Here the information is contained in the fact of a discontinuity without regard to the rate of detection or its relative position with the discontinuity before or after it. The data stored per inch of tape is lower in this case than with the FM but the accuracy of representation is limited only to the number of digits recorded. This technique is generally included under the heading of digital recording (Hoagland, 1963) and is primarily used in conjunction with digital computers. The amount of increase in tape required for digital recording over that used in FM analogue depends upon many factors, such as the number of channels and the accuracy of the digital representation of the original signal. The following compares tape usage for the given specifications between ½-in. seven track digital recording and ½-in. seven track FM analogue tape.

$$\frac{2500\,(\text{FM signal cps})}{7.5\,(\text{FM tape in./sec})} \times 7 \times \frac{8\,(\text{digital bits/signal cycle})}{550 \times 6\,(\text{digital bits/digital tape in.})} = \frac{5.7\,\text{digital tape in.}}{\text{FM tape in.}}$$

Thus digital recording requires about 6 times the tape that would be used for the same information recorded as FM signals. Digital recordings can be made from edited FM recordings or made directly from the original data. This last

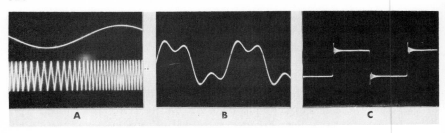

FIG. 13.8. Frequency modulation recording wave forms. *A*, *Upper*, sine wave modulation signal; *lower*, frequency modulated carrier. *B*, reproduction of 1000 cps square wave signal on a channel with 2500 cps band width (7½ in. per sec tape speed, double band width). *C*, reproduction of 40 cps square wave signal with same amplitude and on same equipment as *B*. The ringing of the signal in *B* and *C* is the result of the output filter characteristics which separate the signal from the carrier.

deserves consideration when the data must eventually get into the digital computer and in particular when the data rate does not exceed about 300 characters per sec. When the data rate is this low, a special type of recorder, an incremental recorder, may be used which writes one character, advances the tape to the next position, and waits for the next character. This is in contrast to most other magnetic tape recorders which move the tape at a continuous rate.

Summary of magnetic tape recording characteristics and "standards." There are no universal standards for tape recording systems although there are "standards" accepted as useful practice in each category. In the audio field, the National Association of Broadcasters (N.A.B.) has established recommended standard practice for music and voice. In the area of recording coded information, F.M., P.W.M., etc. the Inter-Range Instrumentation Group (IRIG) (Telemetry Working Group of the Inter-Range Instrumentation Group, 1960) have established governmental standards which are quite commonly, although not universally, followed in instrumentation practice. There is no "best" magnetic recording system; each one has its special advantages and limitations. However, with instrumented data processing there is increased need to make a magnetic tape which can be played on machines in various facilities. The list in Table 13.1 indicates the factors which require careful scrutiny when considering the question of compatibility.

Tape speeds. The most common tape speeds are set in powers of 2, varying up and down from 15 in. per sec. Presently audio, home type recorders generally use speeds between 1 7/8 and 15 in. per sec. A few recorders have used non-standard speeds for special purposes. The state of the art is changing so that modification of tape speeds, for a given specification of band width, by a factor of 2 to 4 from previously excepted limits, is becoming common. Special instrumentation tape speeds extend from 6 in. per min for long term recording to over 120 in. per sec for some video recording.

TABLE 13.1 *Magnetic tape recording features to be checked for interchanging tape between recorders.*

Tape	Modulation method
Width	Direct
Minimum thickness	FM
	Other
Tape reel	
Diameter	Modulation characteristics
Mounting	Signal band width versus tape speed
	Signal equalization
Track geometry	FM carrier frequencies versus tape
Width	speed
Spacing	FM carrier deviation versus signal
Numbering	amplitude
Record playback heads	
Placement	
Stack placement	
Numbering	

Tape width. The three most common widths are 1/4, 1/2, and 1 in. Some small portable recorders are using 1/8 in. tape and television video recorders may use 1 1/2 or 2 in. tape. Special purposes call for varying size and shapes such as disk or sheets.

Tape thickness. The most common tape thickness for many years has been 1.5 mils (0.0015 in.). Modern techniques are allowing 1 mil tapes and for some special application 0.5 mil thickness. The length of playing time for a given size reel of tape varies with the tape thickness and the thickness of magnetic coating. The 1 mil tapes are the standard thickness at present.

Arrangements of recording tracks. Within each tape width group there is a variety of recording track widths, spacings, and head arrangements. The trend is to use the minimum track width consistent with the particular class of service. Table 13.2 gives some indication of the variations now in use with IRIG standards noted.

In general the spacing of adjacent magnetic tracks on the recording tape can be closer than the physical spacing of adjacent recording or reproduce head units. For instance, it has long been standard to have seven tracks on a 1/2 in. magnetic tape. This requires the use of two stacks of staggered recording heads for direct and FM recording but not for digital recording. One stack will carry tracks 1, 3, 5, 7 while the second head will have the intermediate three tracks 2, 4, and 6. These two stacks of heads will usually be placed 1½ in. apart. A problem of interchangeability arises on the placement and numbering of the heads within the stack. They may be numbered 1, 3, 5, 7 from right to left or vice versa. The three-head stack may be placed first or second, with respect to

TABLE 13.2. *Common magnetic tape track configurations*

		Tape Width		
Head track spacing center				
to center		1/4 *in*	1/2 *in.*	1
Full width.	A*	1		7†
0.140 in	A	2	3†4†	
0.140 in..	B	3	7†	
0.136 in..	A	2		14†
(audio stereo)	B	4		
0.070 in..	A	3	7	14
0.070 in..	B	6	14	28
0.036 in..	A	7	14	28
0.036 in..	B	14	28	56

*A, tracks per head stack; B, tracks per tape width using two head stacks with track positions interlaced on the tape.

†IRIG standard spacings.

the direction of tape travel. If the tape stretches between the two stacks of heads differently during recording and playback, a time displacement will develop between the signals recorded on track 1 and track 2.

Many of these problems can be circumvented in the field, but it is wise to remember that there are many combinations of magnetic tape recording devices which must be carefully considered if any interunit recording and playback is anticipated.

Tape travel. Because the primary carrier of the signal information is in terms of the rate at which discontinuities pass the playback head, uniform tape speed during both recording and playback is of utmost importance except for pulse code modulation or digital recording.

There are two basic methods of improving the conditions over those which exist in the home tape recorder where the tape is merely pulled past the record heads. The first is a mechanical arrangement, Fig. 13.9*B*, in which a short section of the tape is held very tightly as it passes the head and is isolated from movement reflected from tape supply and take up reels. The other method, which can be used with FM recording, is electrical and places a stable reference frequency on one track of the tape. Variations of the reference frequency during playback will reflect both record and playback speed variations and a signal derived from these variations can be used for first order corrections of tape speed errors. The specifications for this compensation channel are not standard and can be another source of incompatibility.

As the tape speed is lowered it becomes more difficult to control uniform tape motion, both because it is difficult to make a tape drive capstan turn uniformly at a slow speed and because sticky friction between the moving tape and stationary head makes the tape catch and jump forward.

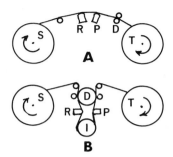

FIG. 13.9. Magnetic tape drives. Two basic types of magnetic tape drives are shown: A open loop; B, closed loop. Type A is the simplest and is used for home and for some instrument type recorders. The drive capstan (D), along with a pressure roller, pulls the tape across the record head (R) and playback head (P). The supply reel (S) provides the hold back tension for maintaining tape to head contact. The drive for the take up reel (T) supplies sufficient tape tension to wind the tape tightly on the reel but not to overpower the capstan drive. The principle of B, is used in the more expensive instrumentation recorders where very uniform tape speed is required. This modification provides a short closed loop length of tape between the two pressure rollers holding the tape against the drive capstan. Since there is a minimum of unsupported tape in this loop a minimum of vibration develops. Further, the closed loop feature isolates the tape motion during record and reproduce, to a greater extent than in A, from variations produced by the S and T systems.

Direct recording equalization. Usually the equalization of amplitude with respect to frequency applied before and after recording represents an attempt to produce a uniform playback response over the band width to be covered. Home type or special recorders sometimes use equalization methods which take into account the nature of the original signal, to produce the best signal to noise ratio for those signals. Other classes of information, such as physiological data, recorded on these units may be distorted or have less than optimum signal to noise ratio.

Frequency modulation. Frequency modulation is the most common method of recording analogue data where retention of wave form is important or where steady state (DC) values need to be reproduced. A carrier frequency signal is established having a center frequency which represents zero voltage input and which varies in frequency with varying input voltage. The common, although not universal, procedure is to have an increase in carrier frequency for positive values of input signal and a decrease for negative values of input signals.

Since the magnitude of the signal is represented by a frequency and change in playback tape speed can produce a change in frequency, uniformity of tape speed becomes of more importance in FM than in direct recording, while uniformity of recording material is only of secondary importance. There are many "standards" and methods being used currently in FM recording; hence it is very important to understand these differences and the potential compatability or incompatibility between recorders upon which your tape may be used.

Frequency modulation carriers. Remembering that the playback of a coded recording involves only the search for unitary events, it can be seen that the primary limitation is the increasing difficulty of separating events at the high frequency end of the useful spectrum. There are presently two standards for FM recording. One is called standard response while the other is called extended response or double band width. Standard response has a center frequency carrier of 54 kc at 60 in. per sec tape speed, while extended response uses 108 kc at 60 in. per sec. These center frequencies are maintained at these ratios of center frequency to tape speed for any speed.

FM signal band width. Since the frequency of the carrier is proportional to the amplitude of the information, the data band width will always be narrower in FM recording than in direct recording (in cycles per sec, not necessarily in octaves). Not only must the highest signal frequency not overlap the lowest carrier frequency (see Fig. 13.10), but a guard band must be provided for filters to separate the signal from the carrier in playback mode. The manner in which this filtering is performed and specified varies with manufacturers. The less expensive units often economize in the sophistication of this filter. In some cases it may be more economical and produce better recordings to use a higher tape speed for a given signal band width than would be used if the signal band width matched the recorder recovery band width. This is particularly true if the magnetic tape does not have to be kept permanently and the necessary record can be made within the length of a tape reel played at the higher speed.

Other modulation codings. There are any number of other codings which can be built around the placing and recovering of discontinuities on the tape. Basically they all, including FM, fall into two main groups. The first group of codings uses time as one of the variables while the other uses arrangement, as previously discussed. The first requires a uniform tape motion, since the information is contained in some function of the rate at which the discontinuities are detected or the time at which a variable event occurs relative to a fixed event. The second uses events placed in a number of channels across the tape or events recorded in series along the tape in some known pattern. Although time is involved in detecting these discontinuities, the information is not modified by changes in tape speed as long as they are detected. Some of the names given to these codings are pulse code modulation, pulse time modulation, pulse duration modulation, pulse width modulation, pulse position modulation, etc.

Generally, as the accuracy and precision of the data transmission increases, the data rate per in. of tape decreases.

Digital recording. Digital recording (Hoagland, 1963) is merely another type of coding on magnetic tape but is generally considered a separate class, primarily from the use point of view. For this a multitrack tape is used in which each track carries information for one digit of a several binary digit code. One com-

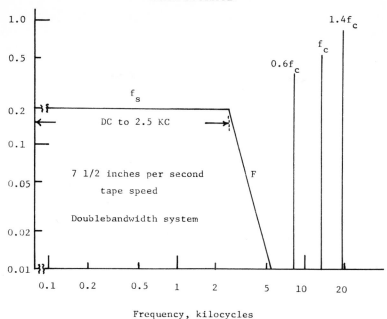

Frequency, kilocycles

Fɪɢ. 13.10. Frequency modulation magnetic tape frequencies. The three lines, 0.6 *fc, fc,* and 1.4 *fc* represent, respectively, the carrier frequency for maximum negative input signal; the carrier center frequency, 13.5 kc, for zero input signal, and the carrier frequency for maximum positive input signals. For demodulation, a train of pulse having constant amplitude and duration is generated at the carrie frequency. By taking the average value of this train of pulses the original signal is regenerated. The relative heights of the three lines represent the amplitude of the fundamental sine wave component of the respective pulse trains. The level of *fs*, the maximum signal output, is shown to the same relative scale to illustrate the requirements of the high cut filter, *F*, for separating the carrier frequency components from the signal. An idealized 24 db/octave filter is shown.

mon type for digital computers uses seven parallel tracks in which six tracks carry digit information for six data digits and one track carries a check or parity digit. There are several ways in which these events are placed on the tape and recovered. (This fact implies that this is another potential source of incompatibility.) For instance, the check digit may be inserted when the number of other digits is even or, in other systems, when the number of digits recorded at a given position is odd. A digit may be represented by a change in magnetization, any change, or only a change in a given polarity. Hence one cannot assume that a 1/2 in. magnetic tape containing digital information may be properly sensed by any computer using 1/2 in. tape.

Discontinuity or "bit" packing density, as well as the code pattern arrangements, are specifications of interest. As the state of the art improves the useful packing density is being increased from the standard 220 bits per in. to 550 bits per in. and sometimes to over 800 bits per in.

Whereas seven parallel bits for ½ in. have long been standard, nine bits are now being introduced for improved efficiency with computers.

Magnetic core storage. Data may be stored in digital form in discrete magnetic elements called cores (Meyerhoff, 1960). Figure 13.11 shows a "core" plane in which data are stored by small donut-shaped ferrite cores strung on wires. Each core represents one binary digit and the wires are used for both mechanical support and magnetic recording and sensing. Since the particle size of one core is much larger than the volume required for one bit of a 200 bits per in. on magnetic tape, the storage capacity of a core memory is much less than for an equal volume of tape. However, since the routing of recording or sensing the core magnetization is completely electrical, the speed with which any given group of bits stored in core can be found is much more rapid than with tape. A typical memory may have from a few hundred to several hundred thousand cores.

Storage for Counting

Analysis of data may require that discrete events, such as heartbeats or responses to stimuli, be counted. The counting may be carried out over short fixed periods of time for rate determination or for long periods as index of activity.

Two types of storage are useful in these summing operations. The first is used to accumulate the count while the second stores the count while it is being visually read, photographed, or printed. Thus if a rate measurement is being made for a 10-sec sampling period, one counter accumulates the number of beats. At the end of the time period, between beats, this number is transferred to a storage display unit which then holds this number in view until the end of the next period.

Mechanical counters. Counting rates of less than about 20 per sec can be accommodated by mechanical wheel counters (Fig. 13.5*A*). The numbers on the wheels can be arranged for viewing or printing. The wheels may also be reset to zero by mechanical or electrical means. Some units are available with electrical contacts so that the count can be transferred to other equipment such as a visual display, card or paper tape punch, or incremental magnetic tape recorder.

Electronic counters. For faster rates, electronic counters, storage registers, and display tube (Fig. 13.5*C*) can be used. Here too, the two types of storage may be necessary, one to accumulate the count and the other to hold the count for transfer or reading.

Accumulative recorders. The accumulative recorder is a direct writing instrument in which the pen moves across the recording paper a fixed amount for each input impulse. Thus a staircase pattern is written with steps of equal

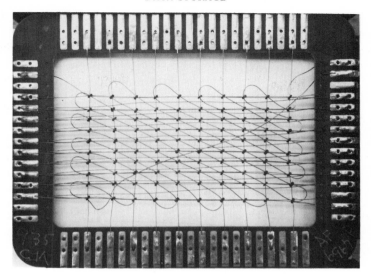

FIG. 13.11. Magnetic core memory plane. Ferrite rings at each intersection of wires act as single storage elements. Coincidence of currents in vertical and horizontal wires through a core changes its magnetization. The diagonal wire senses when a change has occurred. Whereas this experimental plane has 100 cores, a medium size computer memory may have 48,000 cores, mounted in several planes, to make an 8,000 word memory.

height. Information about the rate at which the impulses occurred can be obtained from the steepness of the pattern, since the paper advances at a fixed rate. The height of the staircase represents the accumulated count. When the pen reaches the edge of the paper it resets rapidly so that the total accumulated count is the sum of the number of excursions across the paper times the impulses required for one excursion plus the number of steps in the last staircase. Thus this kind of event storage indicates the total count as well as the temporal pattern of development.

Examples of counting with storage can be taken from Fig. 13.1 which represents a composite of several existing instrumentation systems. A mechanical counter advances each time a new set of stimuli is presented to provide identity of the sequence in the series. When the stimuli are presented, a counter starts summing 10 msec clock pulses to collect the response time. The numbers representing the identity of the stimuli and responses are stored in electronic storage elements and then transferred to a counter for printing. When all the numbers have been counted into the printing counter the series is printed (Fig. 13.5B).

REFERENCES

Acton, J. R., & Swift, J. D. *Cold cathode discharge tubes.* New York: Academic Press, 1963.

Bourne, C. P. *Methods of information handling.* New York: Wiley & Sons, 1963.

Curtis, R. A. Incremental magnetic tape recorders. *Control Engng,* 1964, *11*: 51–57.

Davies, G. L. *Magnetic tape instrumentation.* New York: McGraw Hill, 1961.

Gannon, W. A. Perforated tape readers. *Comput. Des.,* 1965, *4*: 14–46. (a)

Gannon, W. A. Paper tape punches. *Comput. Des.,* 1965, *4*: 18–34. (b)

Gull, C. D. Holes, punches, notches, slots and logic. In R. S. Casey (Ed.), *Punched cards.* Chap. 19. (2nd ed.) New York: Reinhold, 1958.

Hoagland, A. S. *Digital magnetic recording.* New York: Wiley & Sons, 1963.

Meyerhoff, A. J. *Digital applications of magnetic devices.* New York: Wiley & Sons, 1960.

Product reference file: Shaft-angle encoders. *Comput. Des.,* 1963, *2*: 16–41.

Schule, M. *Punch-card methods in research documentation with special reference to biology.* New York: Interscience, 1961.

Stewart, E. W. *Magnetic recording techniques.* New York: McGraw Hill, 1958.

Telemetry Working Group of the Inter-Range Instrumentation Group. *IRIG Document No. 106-60.* Arlington, Va.: Armed Services Technical Information Agency, 1960.

Webb, T. N. Contourogram. *Bull. Johns Hopkins Hosp.,* 1965, *116*: 211–288.

Weber, P. J. *The tape recorder.* (2nd ed) Redwood City, Calif.: Ampex Corporation, 1959.

Williams, A. A. *Tape recording and reproduction.* New York: Pitman, 1964.

14
Telemetry and Telestimulation*

R. STUART MACKAY, Ph.D.

Radio receivers and transmitters can be placed within the body of animals or man in order, respectively, to remotely stimulate excitable tissues or to monitor physiological patterns that are either normal, pathological, or the result of stimulation. These methods allow the subject to remain in what is very nearly a normal physiological and psychological state and, by the use of radio methods, one is able to dispense with lead wires which might tangle, pull loose, or become infected at any penetration of the surface of the body. In studying such things as social interactions, the absence of both equipment and the experimenter can be as important as the freedom of activity. In some cases the advantages of radio methods can instead be realized by using methods which are magnetic, optical, or ultrasonic.

We shall begin with a specific example so that some of the potentialities of these methods can be made as explicit as possible. In Fig. 14.1 is seen a section of a tracing from an eight channel recorder. The subject in this case was a rabbit into which six small radio transmitters had been surgically implanted, each operating simultaneously on a different frequency. The first six recordings depict the decoded signals received from these transmitters. A recording of the breathing pattern as transmitted by an implanted pressure transmitting unit is seen at *a*. Not only breathing rate, but also an estimation of depth and pattern of breathing can be obtained from this record. At *b* is seen the electrocardiogram as transmitted by an implanted transmitter of voltage fluctuations. Tightly wound helices of silicone rubber-coated stainless steel have their ends sutured to the sternum to pick up the electrical activity of the heart, and they are able to carry this signal into the transmitter without danger of breaking due to flexing. At *c* is seen the instantaneous blood pressure as sensed through the intact wall of the abdominal aorta. More will be said

*These projects have been aided by NASA Grant NSG-600.

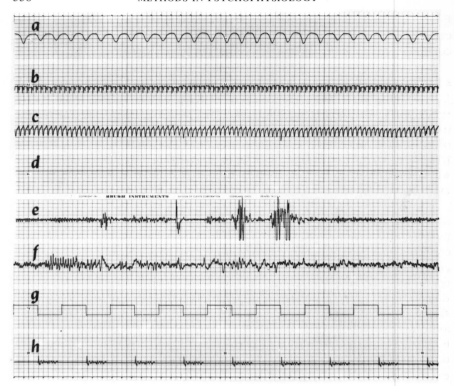

FIG. 14.1. Physiological signals from several simultaneously active transmitters in a rabbit as displayed on a multichannel recorder. Included are breathing, ECG, blood pressure, temperature, acceleration or activity, and EEG. The *bottom two lines* depict the flashing of a lamp in the room, and the response thereto derived from the EEG by a simultaneously active computer of evoked responses. Time markers of 1 sec are at *top* and *bottom*.

later about a method for measuring absolute blood pressure through the intact wall of a blood vessel, with readings being independent of elasticity changes in the intervening vessel wall. A recording of temperature as transmitted by a unit incorporating a thermistor is shown at *d*. In this recording, no change in temperature is observed, even though there is some voluntary activity by the animal. At *e* is seen a measure of activity as recorded from an implanted accelerometer. In this case, a weighted piezoelectric element communicates its signal to a voltage sensing transmitter similar to the one that produced the recording in *b*. At *f* is seen a recording having to do with the electrical activity of the brain. One electrode was pushed into the skull over a sinus, where there is little activity. The other electrode was placed far back on the skull, in order to make it responsive to activity in the optic cortex. This transmitter type was similar to the one used for the recording at *b*, only somewhat more sensitive.

Each of these six transmitters was approximately the size of a large vitamin capsule and was capable of filling a rather large cage with receivable signal continuously for over a year without a change of battery.

At g in Fig. 14.1 is seen the signal from an event marker. With each downstroke of the square wave, there was a bright flash of light in the room. At f, there is no particularly noticeable alteration in the pattern which is in synchronism with these events; however, in a computer of evoked responses (see Chapter 16), it is possible to add up the reaction in successive increments of time following a number of stimulus repetitions, and the "noise" of other activity will average out leaving only that part of the signal which is correlated with the stimulating event. This computation goes on continuously during the experiment and the result is shown recorded at h.

The same transmitter types have proven useful in connection with other species as well. In Fig. 14.2 is seen an x-ray image of the body of a Rhesus monkey into which has been implanted transmitters of temperature, electrocardiogram, acceleration, and blood pressure. In this photograph, the white circle within each transmitter is the battery, and the opaque outline of the transmitter case appears because of the coil wound there to serve as a transmitting antenna. All of these transmitters are placed beneath the surface of the skin. External transmitters could be used but, especially with uncooperative animal subjects, the danger of pulling loose or rubbing off is greatly minimized by implanting. It might be mentioned that under conditions of vigorous motion or in high acceleration situations, one of the implanted transmitters of electrocardiogram is often able to function where even the best surface electrodes communicating their signal directly by wire to a central recorder becomes completely inoperative.

Another method of placing a radio transmitter in a region of interest is to swallow it. This method has been used routinely on human subjects for many years, and indeed, was the first one employed for the radio transmission of signals from within the body. An example of this type of placement is to be seen in the radiogram of Fig. 14.3. A human subject has swallowed a transmitter of the pressure fluctuations associated with peristalsis. Since this transmitter was to be used for an extended experiment, it was restrained from motion onward by a thread (in this case radio-opaque), which is seen extending upward through the small intestine and stomach from whence it travels through the esophagus and is tied to a tooth. In other observations, the unrestrained capsule is allowed to progress onward freely, and will normally emerge in the usual way after 2 or 3 days, still transmitting. A recording from the distal ileum of a human subject is seen in Fig. 14.4. In a, b, and c there are seen periods of activity and of inactivity, and the patterns observed to be associated with a hunger pang. Such recordings as these seem quite sensitive to psychological stimuli, and it would appear to constitute a potentially important method for monitoring stress reactions (Mackay, 1963). The recording in Fig.

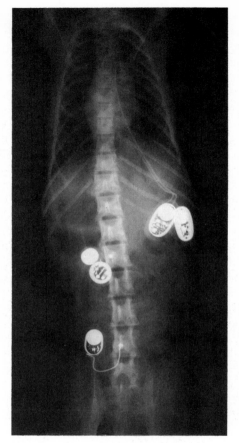

FIG. 14.2. Radiograph of four transmitters implanted in a Rhesus monkey. At the *right* is a blood pressure transmitter whose transducer is affixed to the abdominal aorta. Above that is the transmitter of activity, an EEG transmitter (from which leads can be seen sutured to ribs), and a temperature transmitter. The placement of the electronic components within the antenna coil can be seen although it is probably generally better if this coil does not encircle the metallic battery case.

14.4 was actually made in connection with a clinical study of flatulence. The subject in this case had ingested the transmitter the night before the tests in order to give it adequate time to pass from the stomach. The actual recordings were made the next morning and throughout the day. It has been found that the pattern of activity is not noticeably different whether the subject eats a meal of rice or a meal of beans. In the first generally available article on the subject of radio transmission of information from within the body (Mackay

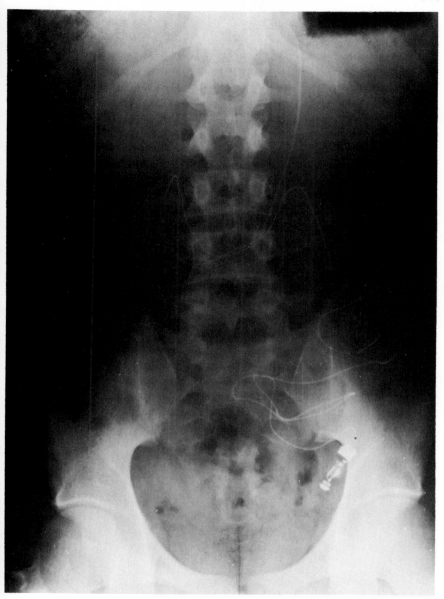

FIG. 14.3. Radiograph of adult human male with endoradiosonde for the transmission of peristaltic pressure fluctuations in the small intestine. In this case, onward motion was prevented by a radio opaque thread seen extending upward through the gastrointestinal tract and tied to a tooth.

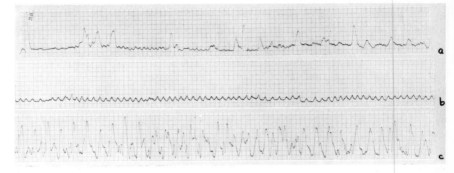

F<small>IG</small>. 14.4. Types of recordings observed with the arrangement of Fig. 14.3. At *a* is the pattern ¹/₂ hr after breakfast with the effect of a deep breath seen at the start. At *b* breathing fluctuations are seen during a period of low activity. At *c* the activity associated with hunger pangs is seen 4 hrs later. A sip of coffee causes a change in such a pattern as the last which can come and go even while the subject is asleep. Emotional factors apparently affect such tracings.

& Jacobson, 1957), we named these tiny transmitters endoradiosondes, but they have often been informally referred to as "radio pills" and, facetiously, as "gutniks." The implanting applications were perfected later, and in part depended upon the development of better power sources.

Most of the present chapter will be devoted to this aspect of the transmission of signals because the processes involved are more subtle than those involved in the remotely controlled stimulation of excitable tissue. There are several reasons for this, the most obvious being that in telestimulation, the most complex part of the apparatus and the most powerful energy sources can be placed away from the animal rather than having to be miniaturized for placement within the animal. Also, in the telemetry of information, the sensor which detects the signal of interest is perhaps the primary consideration in a good design; indeed, some observations have been limited by lack of any presently known adequate sensor. Furthermore, the design of small stable radio transmitters involves a number of factors that have not generally been considered by either physical or biological scientists until recent times, and it is hoped that some of the following examples will familiarize the reader with these aspects.

Some of the variables which have been transmitted from these tiny transmitters are pressure, temperature, pH, radiation intensity, oxygen tension, bioelectric potentials, and the site of bleeding. Several of these have application to psychological studies as well as to the purely physiological ones. It would appear that the use of ingested capsules will find a wide range of relevance, especially when a prime consideration is to leave the subject in an undisturbed state. On a number of occasions, I have given lectures with an arrangement such as was depicted in Fig. 14.3 in place. Even in that case, there was no interference with the speaking process, and the audience was able to watch internal activity on a projection oscilloscope.

A distinction should be made between passive and active devices. A *passive* device might be said to be one which contains no power source of its own, i.e. does not contain a battery. Power can be inwardly induced into receivers for telestimulation and into transmitters for reradiation for telemetry. *Active* transmitters and receivers contain a battery. These definitions become a little more arbitrary when one considers units which are powered by small storage batteries which are periodically recharged by induction from outside of the animal. It might be mentioned that further definitions are required if one wishes to distinguish between units which contain active elements such as transistors or tunnel diodes, as opposed to those which contain only simpler elements such as coils and condensers; both transmitters and receivers can be made either way.

Modulation Considerations

In the transmission of signals either into or from within the body, it is generally true that any method of modulation other than simple amplitude modulation (AM) can be used. This is because the animal is presumably free to move, and thus change his proximity to the receiving antenna, which process will cause amplitude changes that cannot generally be distinguished from changes in amplitude which might be used to carry information. This condition is heightened in the case of a transmitter freely moving within the gastrointestinal tract of a subject. (Many of the other modulation methods are less susceptible to interference by noise, but that is not the main point here.) Simple frequency modulation of the transmitter radio frequency will carry unambiguous information to a receiver since if a certain number of cycles per sec emerge from the transmitter, then, neglecting noise considerations, the same number must arrive at the receiver. This is a very satisfactory method of transmission in many cases, and examples of its use will be cited later in this chapter.

A transmitter can be periodically turned on and off to give a frequency of pulses which carries information. This is an extremely convenient method of transmission, and it does have a further advantage over simple frequency modulation. With simple frequency modulation, any accidental drift in the transmitter frequency will cause an apparent drop in the indicated reading, while a drift in either the transmitter or receiver in the pulse system will not alter the interpretation of the information although extreme drift could cause a total loss of signal. These transmitters also conserve power since they are turned off much of the time.

A compound form of modulation called FM-FM modulation has the same advantages as the pulse frequency modulation. In this case, the variable in question frequency modulates a low frequency oscillator whose output signal is used to frequency modulate the radio transmitter oscillator. Disturbances may cause the high radio frequency to wander, but this will not influence the lower frequency signal. Such a signal can be received by a standard portable FM entertainment receiver whose output will then be a variable audio frequency which can be decoded and recorded. Other forms of compound modulation such as FM-AM are almost as effective.

Special methods of modulation can also be used. Thus a transmitter can periodically switch itself on and off at a rate which carries information. Changes in power supply voltage or temperature will often change the frequency of switching, but will similarly affect the duration of both the on and off periods. Thus the ratio of these two times may be quite insensitive to extraneous influences, thus making "duty-cycle" "pulse period ratio" modulation rather accurate. (The duty cycle of the transmitter can be very precise, but this accuracy may be usable only for pulse rates where the finite rise time of the receiver's intermediate frequency circuits do not compare with the actual times involved.)

All of these same considerations apply both in the transmission of information from within an animal, and to the transmission of coded signal or commands to within the animal.

There is considerable difference in the demands imposed by transmission of different types of signals. Thus the transmission of environmental sounds can be extremely valuable in connection with studies including behavioral patterns, eating patterns, predation, and the general assessment of the cause for various reactions; this variable can often be transmitted by simple amplitude modulation. The voltages generated by the beating of the heart are relatively rapidly changing. Thus this is a relatively easy variable to transmit without confusion being caused by slow drifts in the equipment. If amplitude changes are to be monitored, then some precision of transmission is needed. If all that is desired is the general shape of the various waves of the EKG complex, then amplitude modulation can suffice, and certainly FM modulation would be excellent. If all that is needed is simply heart rate, then requirements are further relaxed. In certain types of experiments, other considerations may actually demand that heart rate be computed within the animal and only the result be transmitted, rather than all of the data.

In general, it is more difficult to transmit the absolute value of a variable than to indicate the magnitude of changes. For example, it is more difficult to telemeter temperature or instantaneous absolute blood pressure than it is to transmit the amplitude of fluctuation of some variable such as the amplitude of peristaltic pressure fluctuations or the amplitude of the pulse. For transmission of absolute variables, it is essential that both the transducer and the transmitter be free from any slow drifts, and a stable form of modulation is required. The transmission of signals to the interior of the body for stimulation purposes is generally less demanding as long as the coded information cannot be confused among the several alternative transmissions that might be employed.

In a blocking oscillator, or in an FM-FM system, the subcarrier oscillator which actually codes the information can have a very low frequency if relatively slowly changing variables such as temperature are to be transmitted. In general, it is only necessary that a few cycles of the information carrying oscillator occur in the time during which some change of interest might be expected. Keeping the frequency low allows the use of a narrow range of frequencies in final transmission, which means that the receiver can be sharply tuned in order to reject extraneous noise on other frequencies. In the case of temperature or pH transmission, a variable click rate in the range of 1 per sec can be timed with a stop watch while listening to a pocket receiver. One can, in general, count clicks occurring in a fixed interval or time a given number of clicks. The latter gives more accuracy in a short time when using a stop watch. In general, if the smallest recognizable time increments occur more frequently than the information cycles, then it is best to time a fixed number of cycles; otherwise, the number of cycles in a given interval should be counted (whether it is done automatically or not).

With regard to the basic choice of radio frequency for a transmission, the higher the frequency the more efficient are small antennas, and the smaller are the corresponding components in the actual circuit. However, very high frequencies are unable to penetrate much thickness of body tissue due to the shielding effect associated with its finite electrical conductivity. Furthermore, in work with freely ranging animals, it will be found that at frequencies for which wave length becomes comparable with the dimensions of common obstacles, there will be shadows and interruptions in the transmitted signal and reflections from other objects which will make it appear that the animal is in a different position from his actual one. These considerations have been treated in some detail (Mackay, 1965), and some aspects will be covered in the next section. The range of transmission frequency used in these laboratories is from about 50 kc (for aquatic animals) to approximately 100 megacycles for somewhat increased range of operations in air. Other considerations such as the frequency limitations on presently available transistors or interference by local broadcasting stations can further influence the actual choice of frequency.

Signal Transmission and Frequency Choice

Some general comments on the transmission of signals through conducting media such as ocean water or living tissue are warranted. The shielding action of such partial conductors can be described by noting that the so-called "skin depth" is the distance a radio signal can travel until it is attenuated to approximately one-third; for ocean water this distance in meters (which depends on conductivity, and hence salinity and temperature) is roughly 240/(square root of frequency). Different types of tissue display differing conductivities (in descending order: lung, muscle, heart, liver, brain, fat; see Schwan, 1957), but one might say that tissue is roughly one-tenth as conductive as ocean water, thus making the range approximately 3 times as much. The same considerations apply to the attenuation of a radio wave traversing the lossy medium as to the pattern of the signal from a pair of current-carrying electrodes immersed in the medium.

In conducting media such as ocean water, the velocity of electromagnetic waves changes with frequency. Thus at 1 cps, the phase velocity is almost that of sound waves in the water. The wave length is correspondingly affected. The rate of attenuation of radio waves of 1 cps is about that of sound waves of 100 kc. There is considerable refraction and reflection at any interface; treatment of the problem of passage through a thin film of material resembles the corresponding problem for light in physical optics.

In communicating such a signal there is generally an optimum frequency of transmission. The lower the frequency, the less is the above mentioned attenuation, but the smaller is the effectiveness of a given size antenna. Thus a radio wave at a given point traveling a distance, d, in tissue to a receiving coil will induce a voltage for application to the receiver terminals that is proportional to frequency times a negative exponential of distance measured in skin depths. Differentiating this relationship and setting it equal to zero defines the optimum frequency which emerges inversely proportional to the square of path length, "d." In addition, a transmitter may be more effective at setting up the signal at a higher frequency which effect usually manifests itself as an exponent greater than unity (two, in some cases) for frequency in the previously mentioned expression; the resulting optimum is still dependent on $1/d^2$, but the constant of proportionality is correspondingly changed. Detailed calculations usually suggest frequencies in the 50- to 100-megacycle range for carrying signals from within animals.

The original experiments took these factors into account, but were carried out in the range of few hundred kilocycles because of transistor and related limitations.

A useful reference with regard to electromagnetic radiation is Schelkunoff (1943, Chap. 6).

In long range experiments on land, the usual considerations of radio transmission apply. High frequency transmission gives line of sight range from small units, although lower frequency transmission employs longer wave lengths that are less reflected or blocked by small obstacles. Approximate expected range calculations can be made (e.g. Pienkowski, 1965) for many circumstances, although prediction is almost impossible for some conditions such as in tropical rain forests and jungles.

Telestimulation

Remotely controlled stimulation can be of a number of forms. Stimulation by flashing light was depicted in Fig. 14.1. The response to sounds or other sensory modalities could similarly be controlled and monitored remotely. Power in electrical form has been induced into the body for a number of clinical purposes. Thus, remotely energized artificial pacemakers for the human heart are well known, and similar pieces of apparatus have been used to empty the neurogenic bladder and to control blood pressure. Perhaps the first mention of the induction of power into the body of an animal for the purpose of stimulating tissue was in the experiments of Chaffe and Light (1934, 1935) in which a transformer-like arrangement was employed. The secondary winding was implanted in the head of a monkey, and larger primary windings were placed around the animal. To avoid the possibility of the animal orienting himself in such a way that no power was coupled from the primary to secondary winding, three separate coil sets were arranged perpendicular to each other around the animal, and they were energized successively so that at least one of them would inwardly induce a signal.

These experiments involve frequencies of transmission where the wave length is large compared with the size and the separation of the antennas, and thus are said to be in the induction field or the near field. In essence, this means that these transmission systems are generally more appropriately considered as transformers than as radio transmitters in the usual sense. The electromagnetic field distributions are somewhat different in the two cases. As mentioned, when dealing with freely roaming wild animals at greater ranges, or when doing tracking studies, the ordinary transmitter types are employed.

One can stimulate excitable tissue with low frequency currents which are simply inwardly induced to a secondary winding within the body, but as has been mentioned, power is more readily communicated at higher frequencies. Thus one can employ what might be considered as a passive crystal set receiver as shown in Fig. 14.5. Here an arrangement is shown which might be employed when it is desired to periodically apply an impulse to excitable tissue. A coil is placed outside of the animal to which is periodically applied a burst of several cycles of a radio frequency oscillation. This induces a signal into a small coil implanted within the animal, which is resonated at the radio frequency by the condenser, C_1. Neglecting possible switching transients, the voltage across the receiving circuit at A is as shown, i.e. it is a series of short bursts of radio frequency energy. Because of the high frequency nature of the oscillations, they would produce little or no effect if applied directly to tissue. The alternations are thus passed through a rectifier which allows current to pass in one direction through the resistor, but not backward. Thus the wave form at B is merely that of A, but with the bottom half removed. It might be noted that since most small semiconductor rectifiers do leak backward somewhat, the resistor shown at B can actually be omitted in a real circuit (since the two points that it connects are actually connected together, through the coil and the backward resistance of the diode). The condenser, C_2, is included so that there is no net unidirectional flow of charge through the electrodes. The impulses at B could

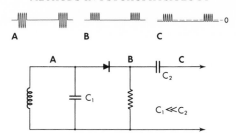

FIG. 14.5. Passive receiver into which signals are induced for the electrical excitation of tissue. In this example, periodic pulses are to be applied to the excitable structure. These pulses are used to momentarily turn on and off an oscillator from whose output coil power is induced into the above circuit. Such an arrangement is suitable for short range transmission only, and no provision is shown for amplitude stabilization.

produce stimulation, but the flow of current in one direction would produce polarization and perhaps decomposition of the electrodes. Stainless steel wires are suitable electrodes for many of these stimulating applications, but if a direct current path develops due to breakdown in the output condenser, the positive electrode can quickly decompose. Thus, the voltage at C centers itself around zero, as shown, with the same area above and below the zero line. The short impulses are still effective in stimulating tissue, and the relatively long recovery between pulses has no effect. This is a highly idealized case, but represents a practical arrangement for remote stimulation of excitable tissue, if changing intensities due to subject movement are controlled or unimportant.

If one wished to allow an animal to move about freely in a more extended environment, then instead of attempting to induce the entire power for the experiment into the animal from a distance, it is more efficient to merely trigger a small receiver on the animal by a remote impulse, and let the receiver then turn on a local stimulator having its own power source. Experiments of this type in some cases are simplified by the ready availability of radio control systems for model airplanes. These are often quite suitable for activating active local stimulators of various sorts being carried by an animal (e.g. see Delgado, 1963). However, for small animals special components of other types should be used, such as those to be shown in Fig. 14.22.

For those interested in back-carried units, a description of a typical piece of presently available model airplane radio control equipment might be useful. Several companies manufacture receivers occupying 1 to 2 cu in. without battery. They are often set to receive signals of a frequency of 27 megacycles. Such a signal in the ordinary way can be amplitude modulated with an audio frequency tone. In the receiver, a coil shakes a row of six small rods of differing lengths at the tone frequency. Different transmitted tones will thus cause the one rod resonant to the selected tone to vibrate a contact and complete the one circuit of choice. The action of such a "resonant reed relay" gives selected action in response to what can be seen to be FM-AM modulation. More contacts allow control of a greater number of independent operations. Thus one contact might turn on a telemetry transmitter, another a different sensor, another administer an electrical stimulus, another a drug or anesthetic, etc.

There are many other forms of stimulation, other than purely electrical, that can be remotely activated. Thus, Delgado (1963) has used remote controls to start the electrolysis of liquid from which the expanding gases forced minute amounts of chemicals into the brains of experimental animals. Baldwin and Ingle (1964) have used a similar pumping arrangement to force small amounts of various chemicals into the nostrils of freely swimming sharks. In the latter case, because of the poor transmission by ocean water of radio waves, coded ultrasonic signals were used to activate this stimulator. The literature in these fields has become so extensive that it is no longer profitable to try to produce a complete bibliography. There are, however, articles having to do with tele-stimulation to which the interested reader may wish to refer (Eisenberg, Mauro, Glenn, & Hageman, 1965; Glenn, Hageman, Mauro, Eisenberg, Flanagan, & Harvard, 1964).

Telemetry

In the early 1950's, my concern with a problem in urology forced me to the conclusion that the only satisfactory method of monitoring pressure changes in the human bladder under certain circumstances was to place within it a small radio transmitter. Two of the original point contact transistors were obtained to attempt such an experiment, but they could not be powered by small enough components. Thus I turned to attempting passive transmission with the help of one of my students, Bob Markevitch (for comments see Markevitch, 1965). We were able to achieve short range transmission of changes in pressure using only a tuned circuit whose inductance was altered through pressure changes on a diaphragm moving a piece of iron-like material toward and away from the coil. Changes in the resonant frequency were remotely monitored by a circuit known as a grid-dip meter. Signals in such a transmission system can fall off with the sixth power of distance, and thus it was felt that the method was rather unreliable for the urological problem, although Mr. Markevitch's 1954 under-graduate research report does describe methods which have now been em-ployed in other short range applications.

A few years later, junction transistors became available, which made small active transmitters more practical. The two first generally available articles on this subject were produced while I was in Sweden (Mackay & Jacobson, 1957; Jacobson & Mackay, 1957). Our first paper described a single transistor cir-cuit which produced a signal containing information about both pressure and temperature, while the second paper described an unusual method for the transmission of pH from an endoradiosonde. This first mentioned circuit is still being extremely widely used today in slightly modified form. With the availability of the junction transistor, a number of other groups in several parts of the world took up some of these activities. Special mention might be made of Marchal, Eklund, Zworykin, Farrar, von Ardenne and Sprung, Wolff, Noller, and Rowlands. Another group of naturalists became interested in longer range operations, principally limited to pure tracking of freely roaming animals. Many developments have been described in the past decade, but only three summaries will be mentioned here since further references can be found within them. Perhaps the most complete recent work is in *Biomedical Telemetry* (edited by Caesar Caceres) of which Chapter 9 (Mackay, 1965) is the most complete description of the type of material being covered in this section. An older book giving the viewpoints of several groups is that edited by L. Slater, *Bio-Telemetry*. The February, 1965 issue of the Journal, *BioScience*, was devoted to biotelemetry, and although restricted to a rather narrow area of the general field, it has useful information and references.

Some Sensor-Circuit Combinations

A few examples will be given to depict some of the possibilities, limitations, and problems with these methods. In Fig. 14.6 is shown an arrangement of an ingestible capsule of the type involved in the production of Figs. 14.3 and 14.4. It is a "Hartley oscillator" modified from that described by Mackay and Jacobson (1957) with an arrangement by which pressure changes produce frequency modulation. The inward motion of a ferrite core toward the coil produces a drop in frequency, while similar motion of an aluminum core increases frequency. Motion of the core is against the compressibility of the trapped air, and thus changes in the elastic properties of the diaphragm due to passage through various body fluids does not alter the calibration of the device. The battery choice in such an arrangement is usually a small mercury cell such as the Mallory 312 which maintains a constant voltage over most of its life. This circuit can instead be powered by inwardly induced power from an external oscillator and coil, and in some of the earliest experiments, it was actually powered by a pair of electrodes in which the gastric juice of the subject produced a battery action. The condenser, C_2, is the tuning condenser, and it is found that in the configuration shown, the condenser, C_1, will periodically charge up due to rectification at the emitter junction of the transistor which turns off the oscillations. These oscillations will resume when the charge on C_1 has leaked off through the backward resistance of the collector junction, which is extremely temperature sensitive in a germanium transistor. Thus temperature information can be transmitted as a variable pulse frequency. Receiving equipment is somewhat complicated in that case, and so if only pressure information is to be received, C_1 is shunted by a 40 K resistor to prevent the collection of charge. If a small silicon transistor is used instead, the resistor should be connected from collector to base, in order to give continuous running.

Other variables can be transmitted by a blocking circuit by making the resistor from collector to base of a silicon transistor large enough so that continuous oscillation does not result. Changes in this resistance then cause a

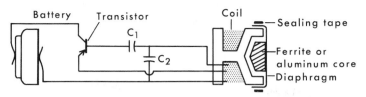

Battery   Transistor   Coil
                  C_1 —Sealing tape
                                  —Ferrite or
                   C_2 aluminum core
                                  —Diaphragm

FIG. 14.6. Layout of commonly used ingestible transmitter of pressure fluctuations for human subjects. A representative size is 0.9 cm in diameter and 1.4 cm in length. This circuit can also transmit temperature (see text). A thin flat core is almost as effective and is somewhat easier to fabricate; at higher frequencies, a modified circuit is used in which an aluminized plastic diaphragm moves near a "pancake" coil of a few turns.

change in the rate of production of pulses. This variable resistance can be a thermistor if temperature is to be monitored, a variable resistance humidity element if moisture is of interest, a small cadmium sulfide cell if light intensity is to be monitored, etc. If uncompensated, these circuits are somewhat temperature sensitive. Tunnel diode oscillators are quite simple and can periodically block or switch themselves off due to a rectifying action, just as in transistor oscillators. But in tunnel diode oscillators, most of the battery power is wasted because of the low voltage required by the diode. (This last can be useful when only low voltages are available, as with remote or thermoelectric energizing.)

The previously mentioned circuit is extremely convenient for anyone to build and thus has been widely used. However, in work with obese human subjects, it became convenient to have a transmitter with a somewhat greater range. In Fig. 14.7 is shown a two stage transmitter in which a variable inductance again modulates the output frequency. The second stage is operated in what is called "Class C," in which the second transistor is turned off most of the time and only allows short pulses of current to pass when its own voltage is extremely low, thus wasting little power within the transistor itself. The output antenna coil is tapped so that the voltage across the entire coil is considerably greater than the battery voltage, thus resulting in a considerably larger output signal. In this circuit, the output antenna arrangement must be rather carefully tuned to the operating frequency of the original oscillator, or else fluctuations in intensity will be observed.

Signals from one of these continuously running oscillators can be received by most standard receiver types. In a so-called "C-W receiver," which is made for receiving continuous wave code signals, there is incorporated a local oscillator whose signal beats with the incoming frequency to give an audible difference tone which varies widely for small changes in the oscillator or transmitter frequency. Thus a C-W receiver can be used directly to accept the signal from one of these transmitters and feed it into an audio frequency meter circuit such as is shown in Fig. 14.8. If this circuit is connected to the loudspeaker connection, then an output voltage is generated which is proportional to the

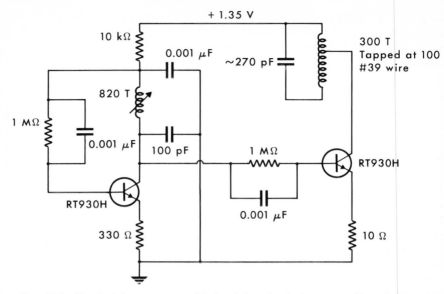

FIG. 14.7. Circuit giving more powerful signal than the single stage oscillator in Fig 14.6. Frequency modulation can depend on inductance changes as indicated or can be produced by changes in the 100 pf condenser in response to changes in some physiological or environmental variable. If the output coil is untapped, the useful signal can increase with a decrease in the number of turns; this coil would normally be wrapped around the outside of the capsule.

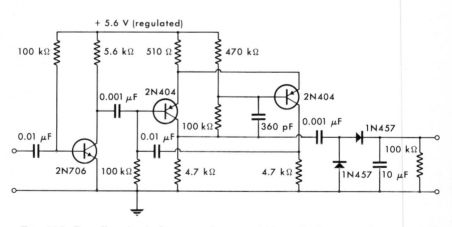

FIG. 14.8. Decoding circuit for converting a variable audio frequency into a variable direct current voltage proportional to frequency and relatively independent of amplitude. The input stage converts the relatively sinusoidal signals from a receiver loudspeaker connection into suitably abrupt voltage excursions which trigger the monostable multivibrator, whose output is rectified and filtered to yield a voltage which can be directly applied to a recorder.

frequency, but rather independent of changes in intensity. It was the direct output of such a circuit that was used to produce the recordings in Figs. 14.1 and 14.4. The variable blocking frequency type of transmission can be directly sensed by any ordinary amplitude modulation receiver, including small pocket transistor receivers. The periodic clicks that come from the loudspeaker can be decoded by the circuit in Fig. 14.8 to give a direct recording. In some cases where slowly changing physiological variables have been involved, a periodically pulsing transmitter has been used with an extremely low click rate which could be timed by ear with the help of a stop watch. This is an extremely simple and accurate method for field or laboratory work, since a watch is simple, rugged, foolproof, temperature insensitive, and resistant to noise (which the operator's ear rejects well), but it is slow and tedious in use. If FM-FM transmission is used, then the signal from an FM receiver can be decoded with the circuit of Fig. 14.8 to give a direct recording. Such circuits are mildly temperature sensitive if uncompensated and thus are preferably protected from large excursions (e.g. by placement in an insulated box or the investigator's armpit in field work).

The monitoring of temperature supplies a number of convenient examples of circuit types. Thus, in Fig. 14.9 is shown one of the previously mentioned blocking oscillators, in this case, controlled by a thermistor. To give greater range with the limited voltage of a single cell, the coil was again tapped down. Most of the radiation in the outgoing signal comes from this coil. In some cases, it is possible to leave out the tuning condenser attached across the coil, especially if the coil is not connected as shown, tapped down from one end. This arrangement will operate for a number of weeks before the battery must be changed. Calibration is slightly affected by surrounding conductors and thus is best done in a vessel of physiological saline. In Fig. 14.10 is shown another transmitter type which performs a similar function. Here, a multivibrator is used to switch on and off an output oscillator periodically. By using extremely high resistance components, the total current drain on this circuit is only a few microamperes, and transmission can be obtained continuously for 1 to 2 years with a single battery. The signal from this circuit tunes more sharply than that from the previous circuit.

A similar transmitter giving a longer range signal is shown in Fig. 14.11. In this case, a thermistor controls a multivibrator to give a periodic impulse to shift the frequency of an oscillator which runs continuously. This transmitter operates near 100 megacycles, and thus can be used with the readily available portable FM receivers. By working in this high frequency, one obtains a range of well over 100 feet for over a month with this slightly larger size battery. The germanium diode shown at the top of the figure helps temperature compensate the oscillator frequency against drifting. Even most cheap FM receivers have an "automatic frequency control" circuit which allows them to track slow changes in transmitter frequency. If the tuning condenser in the

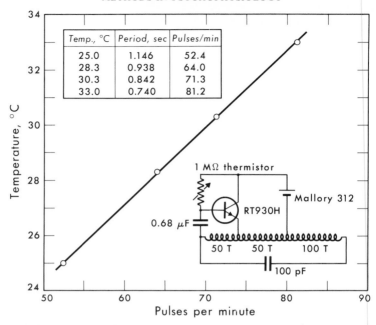

Temp., °C	Period, sec	Pulses/min
25.0	1.146	52.4
28.3	0.938	64.0
30.3	0.842	71.3
33.0	0.740	81.2

FIG. 14.9. Temperature transmitter using a blocking or squegging oscillator to generate periodic pulses which can be timed with a stop watch while listening to any AM receiver. The battery can be connected to the right hand end of the coil without a tap if a weaker signal is acceptable.

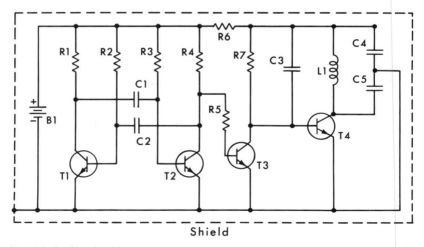

FIG. 14.10. Circuit with total power drain of approximately 5 microwatts in which an astable multivibrator periodically turns on an output transmitter at a rate which transmits temperature. One set of commercial parts which has been employed is: *B1*, Hamilton No.

505 (1.5 v); *C1*, Gulton G-MIN-V-.005-Z (5000 pf); *C2*, Gulton G-MIN-V-.0015-z (1500 pf); *C3* and *C4*, Scionics pellet (430 pf); *C5*, Vitramon (100 pf); *L1*, 500 turns No. 39; *R1* and *R4*, thermistor Fenwall GA62J1; *R2* and *R3*, thermistor Gulton 71DM10; *R5* and *R7*, 5 megohm; *R6*, Ceradot resistor (100 K); *T1*, *T2*, *T3*, and *T4*, transistor MT-101. As smaller newer components become available, they can be used in such circuits. In 1966, several of these units had been running continuously for four years without a battery change.

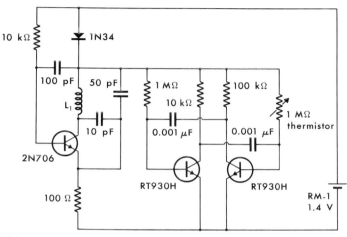

Note:
L_1 4 turns of #18 wire, 1 cm diameter
Frequency of operation approximately 88 Mc

FIG. 14.11. Temperature transmitter giving approximately 100 foot range at frequencies near 100 megacycles. The temperature controlled multivibrator periodically changes the oscillator collector voltage to yield a signal with FM-FM modulation. This can be detected by any simple FM receiver, and there is found a large percentage change in the useful information frequency being carried in the small percentage band width passed by the receiver. Small changes in this circuit accompanied by an increase in battery voltage through the use of several cells in series will correspondingly increase the range. Most of the radiation is from the small coil, although before compacting the circuit into a final unit, some extra signal can be radiated from the circuit as a whole.

transmitter is chosen to have a negative temperature coefficient, as most small ceramic condensers do, then the transmitter will not drift out of the range of the receiver, thus giving continuous unattended reception for days at a time. Small changes in the oscillator voltage produced by the multivibrator cause changes in the collector capacity of the transistor, which produces the frequency modulation that carries the information. Thus changes in the transmitter frequency do not matter, it being the lower audio frequency modulation that carries the information. The voltage changes give FM-FM modulation rather than fully turning off the oscillator for periodic pulses. The signal is picked up on an inexpensive standard portable FM receiver through its whip antenna.

More complete temperature compensation is achieved by using two diodes in series. The range can be increased to hundreds of yards by the use of two to four cells, but then the base resistor should be increased to 51 K, the emitter resistor to 240 ohms, and a 100 pf condenser connected from base to ground (negative side of battery). Some amplitude modulation accompanies the frequency modulation.

There is a way by which temperature can be reliably transmitted in the form of a simple frequency modulated signal. Oscillators are often stabilized at a particular frequency through being controlled by the oscillations in a quartz crystal. Such oscillations occur very accurately at the frequency of a mechanical vibration which is extremely stable. Quartz crystals can be cut in various ways, and depending on the angle of cutting, they will show differing temperature coefficients as shown in Fig. 14.12. Thus to produce an extremely stable oscillator, one would cut the crystal at an angle that would give a zero temperature coefficient. On the other hand, a quartz crystal can be cut to give a definite change in frequency for a change in temperature, and thus a crystal controlled oscillator can also be used to give a thermometer action. In receiving such a signal, one would probably have a constant frequency quartz crystal oscillator to beat against the incoming signal, thus giving a difference frequency which would undergo large percentage changes for small percentage changes in the original frequency. Crystals become very small and fragile for frequencies above about 30 megacycles, but a crystal of this frequency placed in an oscillator feedback path can lead to radiation of stable signals near 90 megacycles if the oscillator is tuned to this harmonic.

In the use of all these circuits, as was mentioned, motion of the animal can produce changes in intensity of the received signal. With a single receiving antenna there will be certain orientations of the transmitter for which the signal will actually drop to zero. This null may be so sharp that loss of the signal would be extremely unlikely, or at most, momentary. But if the range is such that the signal is becoming somewhat weak anyhow, then one would prefer to have an omnidirectional receiving system which would assure that the transmitted signal can never be lost. One can place near the animal (e.g. along the corners of its cage) three perpendicular receiving antennas, one of which will always have some signal induced into it. These three signals can be combined in several ways in order to give a constant output. It can be shown that one way of combining the signals is to pass each of the three through a frequency doubler, and receive the double frequency signal in an ordinary radio. This signal of double frequency still contains the frequency modulation information, and will never vanish for any orientation change of the transmitter. One can instead switch between antennas cyclically and continuously, or one can start electronically switching to one of the other antennas whenever the signal at the one being monitored vanishes. If this cycling process is made slow, then one can obtain records such as shown in Fig. 14.13. Here are shown some temperature observa-

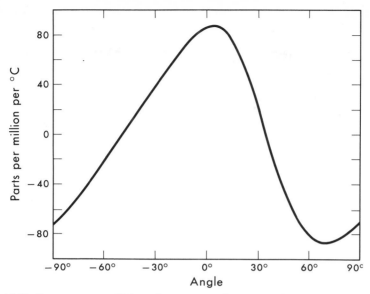

FIG. 14.12. Temperature coefficient of quartz crystals cut at different angles about the X crystallographic axis. For maximum transmitter stability, a cut of very small coefficient is chosen. Choosing a cut with large temperature coefficient allows frequency modulated temperature transmission.

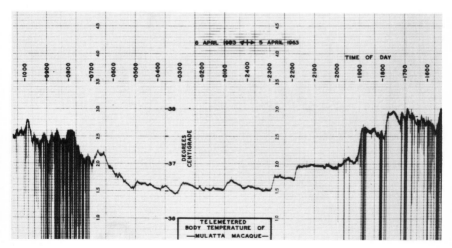

FIG. 14.13. Daily temperature cycle telemetered from within the abdomen of a female monkey free to move about in a cage. Play causes momentary loss of signal in the omnidirectional receiving-recording system, and thus the density of the vertical lines is a measure of activity. Disturbance of such an animal by attempts at ordinary temperature measurement tends to bring about activity and a rise in temperature.

tions from the abdomen of a female monkey in connection with fertility studies with Lusted and Charters at the Oregon Regional Primate Research Center. Temperature is shown for a full day-night period, and it is seen that the temperature is low in the evening and higher in the day. Motion of the animal caused momentary loss of signal, which started a cycling process during which the recorder ran back to zero since it saw no signal. Thus the frequency of vertical lines is a measure of activity, and it is seen that the temperature is higher during periods of activity. This is a convenient type of display for two pieces of information at once. It also emphasizes the fact that disturbing an animal to measure its temperature by ordinary means can rather drastically change the temperature to be measured.

In Fig. 14.14 are shown other types of transmitters for electrical signals. The input to these circuits employs what is called a field effect transistor, which allows one to obtain an extremely high input resistance. Thus such a circuit is suitable for accepting signals from pH electrodes, oxygen tension electrodes, sodium ion electrodes, etc. Similar circuits in the future will probably depend on the use of related "MOS" transistors, but they presently are not very effective at limited supply voltages. In the top circuit, the germanium diode temperature compensates the unit. Here also, changes in the input voltage frequency modulate the multivibrator which directly generates a radio frequency signal which is radiated from the coil. A blocking version for generating periodic pulses of fixed amplitude is shown below. The resistor in the oscillator quency modulate of the multivibrator which directly generates a radio frequency signal which is radiated from the coil. A blocking version for generating periodic pulses of fixed amplitude is shown below. The resistor in the oscillator emitter allows better tuning of the radio frequency. The circuit can be temperature compensated by two germanium diodes placed in series in the position of the one above. These circuits are valuable for physiological studies, and it is hoped that they will be applied to various psychophysiological studies. The use of a multivibrator as a frequency modulated oscillator is extremely convenient at intermediate frequencies; at higher frequencies, the voltage sensitivity of the capacitance of the collector junction was useful, as was depicted in Fig. 14.11. Passive voltage transmitters have been built but tend to respond to motional changes in energizing voltage.

It is expected that the use of ingested transmitters will become increasingly important in human and animal subjects, where they will allow one to place otherwise encumbering equipment out of the way, and permit the exploration of otherwise inaccessible regions. A transmitter has been constructed (Mackay, 1965) from which projects a pair of platinum electrodes that sense small low frequency voltages, and uses them to frequency modulate an oscillator whose radio frequency output is delivered out through the same pair of electrodes. These electrodes then set up radio frequency current within the body of the subject who has ingested the transmitter, thus converting the body into a transmit-

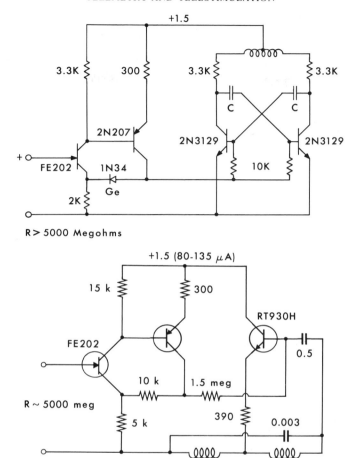

FIG. 14.14. High input resistance circuit employing a field effect transistor (FET) to frequency modulate an output oscillator. At the top the oscillator is an astable multivibrator for which temperature compensation is shown in the form of a germanium diode. At the bottom is a similar circuit without temperature compensation in which a blocking oscillator generates periodic pulses of radio frequency at a rate which depends on the applied electrical signal. Such a signal might come from electrodes used to monitor various chemical changes. The blocking circuit is here shown employing two separate coils rather than having the transformer action of a tapped coil, and the emitter resistor makes the circuit more responsive to tuning action in the resonant circuit.

ting antenna. (This arrangement will be shown in Fig. 14.16.) This method has been used to explore changes in untethered aquatic animals such as the dolphin, since such an antenna can project a signal through many feet of ocean water. Both heart voltages and EMG potentials are seen in recordings from such a

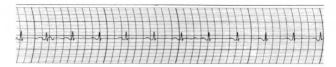

Fig. 14.15. Human electrocardiogram telemetered from sensors consisting of a pair of platinum electrodes held to the chest by suction cups. The range of this transmitter was such that its signal could be sensed everywhere within a pool of ocean water 50 feet in diameter.

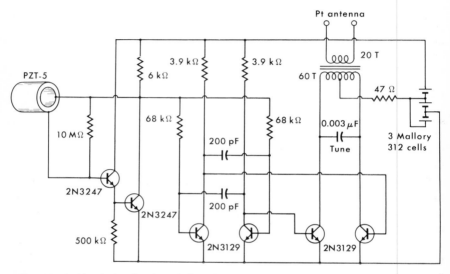

Fig. 14.16. Circuit details of a unit for telemetering sounds sensed by a piezoelectric hollow cylinder. By using low frequencies and a current dipole antenna, transmission can be obtained from aquatic animals as well as terrestrial ones. With standard components, this entire circuit including output transformer, but exclusive of batteries, can be formed into a cylinder 0.25 in. in diameter and 0.75 in. in length.

unit. The possibility of feeding an animal a capsule and then leaving it to remotely monitor heart rate seems like an important potentiality. The same small transmitter can be used to transmit EKG from external electrodes upon the chest of a man as in Fig. 14.15.

In Fig. 14.16 a circuit similar to the one mentioned above is seen, but it is modified to transmit the voltages generated by sounds hitting a hollow cylinder of piezoelectric ceramic. The over-all circuit is quite stable, although pyroelectric voltages are generated in the ceramic by temperature changes. This transducer rejects slow pressure changes (which could be restored by a suitable integrating circuit in the *receiver*; see Mackay, 1965). If the received signal is recorded on magnetic tape, then it can be fed through different filters to emphasize different aspects of interest as in Fig. 14.17. This recording is from the

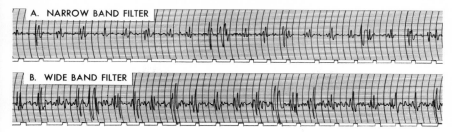

FIG. 14.17. Signals transmitted by the circuit of the previous figure when in the stomach of a dog. Heart rate can be determined from the regular pulsations, and the larger amplitude signals are associated with regular breathing sounds. These signals were recorded on magnetic tape for restudy by various analyzing methods. For example, *A* depicts the result of playing the recording through a Kronheit adjustable filter with both the upper and lower cutoff frequencies set at 10 cps. The event marks are in synchronism with the animal's pulse.

stomach of a dog. Both heart beat and breath sounds are visible. The effects of movement of the subject are still under exploration. The same transmitter hung by a thread behind the heart in the esophagus of a human should supply more information than the usual phonocardiogram.

Several experiments have been performed on dogs which have ingested such a unit built small enough to swallow, but too large to spontaneously pass from the stomach. In one case, after 2 weeks, the animal regurgitated the transmitter, chewed it thoroughly into small pieces, and swallowed the components. The animal remained happy and healthy throughout, with the parts eventually passing normally. Spontaneously fragmenting transmitters (Mackay, 1965) may prove valuable in delaying passage from stomach, although they would suitably encapsulate the individual component packages.

One of the most interesting parameters to many groups is blood pressure. One can insert a catheter into an artery and connect this to a standard transmitter unit, but one must then administer heparin to prevent clotting, which converts the subject into a bleeder. There is a method which appears to provide the possibility of monitoring pressure through the intact wall of blood vessels, while giving indications which are independent of elasticity changes in the intervening vessel wall. The method makes use of the principle of the Mackay-Marg tonometer, which has proven so valuable in clinical work with the eye (Mackay, 1964). The general principle is depicted in Fig. 14.18. If a force transducer is surrounded by an insensitive coplanar annulus, and this combination is pressed against the wall of a body cavity until the cavity is flattened to beyond the sensitive region, then bending forces are taken up by the annulus rather than being sensed by the transducer. Similarly, tissue tension forces are radial, and can neither push nor pull on the transducer. A number of other errors (discussed elsewhere) also do not make themselves felt, and the only force that is effective is the intracavity pressure. Neither the

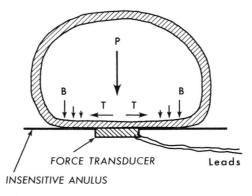

FORCE TRANSDUCER   Leads

INSENSITIVE ANULUS

FIG. 14.18. Principle of measurement of intracavity pressure, such as blood pressure, through the cavity wall. A force transducer is surrounded by a coplanar "guard ring" which takes up bending and tension forces in the intervening wall, leaving the pressure alone to be sensed. On the abdominal aorta of a representative dog, a deflection of 0.0005 in. can be allowed in the transducer before the elastic properties of the vessel wall start to affect the indications.

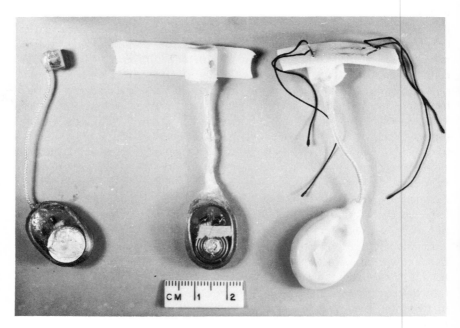

FIG. 14.19. Blood pressure units. On the *left* is seen the transducer at the top with a shielded cable running to the transmitter. At the *center* is seen the added cuff for holding the transducer into contact with an artery; contact for a year has been successful. On the *right* is a unit completely covered with silicone rubber to minimize tissue reaction. The circular object at the bottom of the transmitter is the battery which can also be seen in Fig. 14.2.

elastic forces, nor changes therein due to viscoelastic, pharmacological, or other effects are sensed. One specific arrangement for such a unit is shown in Fig. 14.19 where small transducers are shown connected to separate transmitters which can be placed at any convenient location within the body. The transducer is cast into a silicone rubber cuff which contains a strap molded over Dacron mesh. The artery is slipped into the notch in the cuff which is then strapped into place. Such units (Mackay, 1965) have been in place for over a year on an artery without damage. The tracing at c in Fig. 14.1 was transmitted from such a unit. The force transducer in that case was a variable inductance unit, and in such cases, precise reliability is of extreme importance. The restoring force should be supplied by a metal spring so that there will be no unreliability from that source. In units of this type which are to transmit the absolute value of a variable, one must pay great attention to the fact that plastics are rather permeable to body fluids. This matter has been discussed in some detail elsewhere (Mackay, 1965), but it might be stated here that special precautions must be taken with units which are to be implanted in a body for more than about 2 weeks. In some cases, it is necessary to encapsulate the transmitter in glass or ceramic, or in a metal transistor can. The units shown in Fig. 14.19 are coated with silicone rubber, not that this slows absorption of body fluids into the transmitter, but it does prevent foreign body reactions by the host. In order to be certain of acceptance of such a unit by the body, it must be cleaned to remove foreign material and sterilized in Zephiran chloride diluted 1:1000. Indications from such a unit as this are effectively referred to the atmospheric pressure that existed at the time they were constructed, rather than the present ambient pressure, and thus indications must be corrected for barometric changes. This last problem is of little importance in connection with the endoradiosondes for transmitting peristaltic activity, since usually only the amplitude and frequency of relatively rapid fluctuations are of importance.

Other cardiovascular parameters can be transmitted. Thus changes in stroke volume, e.g. under stress, can be estimated by noting the change in alternating current resistance between two electrodes implanted through the wall of the left ventricle. In this case, radio transmission of the signal eliminates the possibility of pneumothorax.

In many cases, it is convenient to have a small, low-powered internal transmitter communicate its signals to the outside of the body where a more powerful transmitter will rebroadcast these signals to a remote point. Thus booster transmitters can be useful. Even those workers who might normally only be interested in tracking animals to detect their activity patterns should keep in mind that one can track a booster transmitter as well as a transmitter which is carrying no useful information. Under these conditions, even the passive transmitters (Mackay, 1965) can supply valuable information. Thus one of my students, Mr. Carter Collins, has been able to achieve short range transmission from pressure transmitting units only 2 mm in diameter and 1 mm thick. Such units have applicability in conjunction with very small animals or they might be employed in special cases such as monitoring intracranial pressure following brain surgery, in which case a passive transmitter might be left in place for the life of the subject. Booster transmitters for use with these lower powered units must have some arrangement for preventing their own output from activating their input. In pulse modulated transmitters, this can be done by activating the output transmitter momentarily with a switching circuit which will not allow the receiver to be active until the transmitter has been turned off from the previous pulse. In the case of continuously oscillating transmitters, such frequency shifting circuits are also convenient in adapting readily available receivers to unusual frequency ranges not normally covered, but which could be necessary in a particular experiment. Thus underwater experiments are typically done at a very low frequency, and the circuit of Fig. 14.20 is used to shift this frequency into the band received by a normal AM entertainment receiver. An amplifier to increase the level of the input signal is seen in this figure. At the *lower part* of the figure there is a local oscillator whose output is combined at the *right* with the amplified input signal. The difference frequency is then applied to a coil, in this case coupled to the broadcast receiver. The same frequency shifting arrangement can be used in a booster transmitter. It is necessary to impose a frequency shift between input and output. This can be done with the help of a local oscillator whose signal is mixed with the incoming signal to give a somewhat different frequency signal for re-transmission.

Superregenerative receivers are very simple and sensitive, and they have a tendency to reradiate a signal at the incoming frequency. Thus they can also act as a booster transmitter of weak signals originating within a subject. External transmitters on a harness or collar arranged to transmit some variable of interest can usually be set to give ranges measured in miles, unless the animal is very small or low to the ground.

Aquatic animals such as dolphins have taken on increasing interest, and are difficult to study under "normal" conditions by the usual laboratory methods. Radio signals have been transmitted from within *Tursiops truncatus* by ingested transmitters, but for ranges over 100 feet in ocean water it is useful to transmit signals via high frequency sound waves. The circuit of Fig. 14.20 has been used both to receive 100 kc electrical signals and also the signals of 100 kc sound falling on a piezoelectric ceramic cylinder. A blocking oscillator temperature transmitter employing sound signals for these purposes is shown in Fig. 14.21. It is a higher powered version of the other blocking circuits which makes use of a transformer formed on a small ferrite "cup core." The signal is in the form of periodic pulses to be timed with a stop watch. Transmitters in aquatic mammals can perhaps be powered in unusual ways, e.g. by the pressure changes associated with periodic surfacing.

In some cases, there are useful alternatives to telemetry. Thus a subject can carry a small recorder of events for later examination. A chemical recorder of

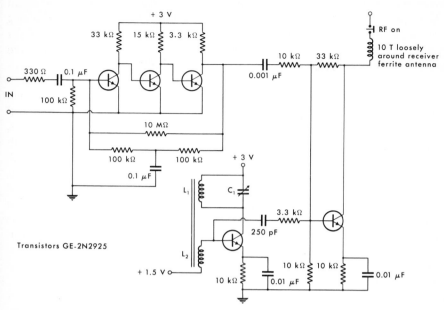

FIG. 14.20. Frequency shifting circuit. The incoming signal is amplified at the *upper left* and added to the signal from the local oscillator at the *bottom*. These two signals combine in the transistor on the *right*, which is biased almost to cutoff for maximum nonlinear action to yield a new frequency which can be sensed by a standard receiver. Similar frequency shifting combinations can be used in booster transmitters.

temperatures has been mentioned (Argue, 1965). Tiny magnetic or mechanical recorders can be valuable when dealing with dolphins, since in some cases, there are objections to both radio and acoustic transmission. If the time course of a single event, whenever it occurs, is the parameter of interest, then it is not always necessary to continuously "unwind" some time base or time reference. On an X-Y plot, one can plot the variable in one direction and its rate of change in the other. When the event takes place, a curve which can later be interpreted will trace itself out from the origin and back; periodic intensity changes give the rate of progression.

Many more transmitter and receiver types could be described, but it is hoped that the previous examples will give an investigator a general idea of what is possible. There are many related procedures which have been mentioned elsewhere. Thus one might employ ultrasonic energy for either transmission or reception in humans and in terrestrial and aquatic animals. Activity in various regions can be sensed by the motion of a small ingested or implanted permanent magnet if a compass or magnetometer is placed outside the subject. Power can be induced into a subject not only for stimulation or for energizing monitor-

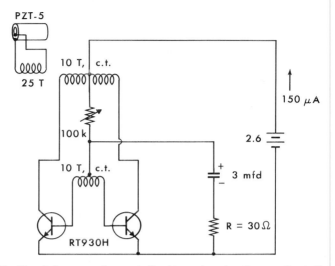

Fɪɢ. 14.21. Circuit for generating periodic ultrasonic pulses for aquatic studies. The three coils are wound on a ferrite cup core, and the output voltage is applied to a hollow cylinder of piezoelectric ceramic. The pulse rate is controlled by the 100 Kc resistor, which can be a thermistor, and the resistor (R) controls the pulse duration. The same circuit can drive an antenna. Paralleling the battery with a small sized high capacity tantalum condenser increases the signal strength in such circuits.

ing devices, but to perform various actions as well. Thus, it is probably possible to build a unit which will take a biopsy by remote control. We are working on a unit which, when activated by an external radio signal, will either open or close a clamp around a blood vessel. It is felt that if the blood supply to a particular region were selectively interrupted, then changes in some pattern could be observed and significant conclusions drawn. Similarly, it is known that ultrasonic energy can temporarily interrupt a nerve pathway, and thus implanted ultrasonic transducers might be remotely activated to observe changes produced. Similarly, pulsed ultrasonic energy can be used to explore internal body structures through the collection of the time sequence of echos, and these methods can actually be used to build up something that corresponds to an x-ray image, but with significant advantages in terms of safety and clarity in soft tissue structures.

More complicated circuit functions can be incorporated in smaller spaces as electronic technology progresses. In Fig. 14.22 an integrated circuit wafer upon which has been formed by various photographic processes 132 identical and distinct complete circuits is shown. Each is a complete multivibrator unit with transistors, resistors, etc. This silicon wafer is approximately 1 in. in diameter, and can be broken into its elements for individual mounting in small, hermetically sealed cans. These multivibrators are quite suitable for use in transmitters

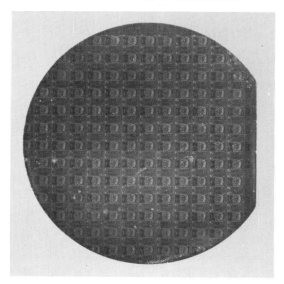

FIG. 14.22. Enlargement of a silicon wafer containing over 100 separate multivibrator circuits. When separated, these can be used as transmitters of signals which produce a change in resistance in an associated sensing transducer or they can also function as electrical stimulators of tissue. When used for telemetry, transmitter size is still limited by the antenna and the battery (if the latter is present).

of the type shown in some of the previous figures. The output from one applied through a diode, when energized by a slightly higher voltage, serves as an excellent electrical stimulator for excitable tissue. Similar sized components can be used to switch on and off the stimulating action.

In conclusion, it might be mentioned that some workers may make use of telestimulation and other workers may make use of telemetry. On some occasions, it will undoubtedly be expeditious to use both at once, noting the response to remotely controlled stimulations, and perhaps modifying the stimulation as one observes changing responses. In this sense, these processes allow what could almost be considered as a dialogue carried on at great range between the experimenter and his subject.

Acknowledgments

In this work, I have been assisted by Barbara Dengler, George Rubissow, Sam Toy, Ernest Woods, Harvey Fishman, Fred Jenkinson, Don Buchla, and Jean Mackay. Rudy Schaffter is presently using the ultrasonic temperature transmitting units to study temperature cycles in fish, and Carter Collins is using the tiny passive pressure transmitters to investigate those factors which affect intraocular pressure.

REFERENCES

Argue, G. Electrochemical devices. *Ind. Res.*, *Chicago*, 1965, 85–90.

Baldwin, H., & Ingle, G. A remote control technique for the study of olfaction in sharks. In W. E. Murry & P. F. Sal.sbury (Eds.), *Biomedical sciences instrumentation*, Vol 2. New York: Plenum Press, 1964. Pp. 217–228.

Chaffee, E. L., & Light, R. U. A method for the remote control of electrical stimulation of the nervous system. *Yale J. Biol. Med.*, 1934, *7*: 83–128.

Chaffee, E. L., & Light, R. U. Supplementary notes on the remote control of electrical stimulation of the nervous system. *Yale J. Biol. Med.*, 1935, *7*: 441–450.

Delgado, J. Telemetry and telestimulation of the brain. In L. Slater (Ed.), *Bio-telemetry*. New York: Pergamon Press, 1963. Pp. 231–250.

Eisenberg, L., Mauro, A., Glenn, W. W. L., & Hageman, J. H. Radio frequency stimulation: a research and clinical tool. *Science, N.Y.*, 1965, *147*: 578–582.

Glenn, W. W. L., Hageman, J. H., Mauro, A., Eisenberg, L., Flanagan, S., & Harvard, M. Electrical stimulation of excitable tissue by radio-frequency transmission. *Ann. Surg.*, 1964, *160*: 338–350.

Greatbatch, W. X-ray technique for evaluation of exhaustion and detection of mechanical defects in implantable mercury batteries. *Med. Elect. Biol. Engng.*, 1965, *3*: 305–306.

Jacobson, B., & Mackay, R. S. A pH endoradiosonde. *Lancet*, 1957: 1224.

Mackay, R. S. Radio telemetry from inside the body. *New Scient.*, 1963, *19*: 650–653.

Mackay, R. S. Application of physical transducers to intracavity pressure measurement, with special reference to tonometry. *Med. Elect. Biol. Engng*, 1964, *2*: 3–19.

Mackay, R. S. Telemetering from within the body of animals and man: endoradiosondes. In C. Caceres (Ed.), *Biomedical telemetry*, Chap. 9. New York: Academic Press, 1965. Pp. 147–235.

Mackay, R. S., & Jacobson, B. Endoradiosonde. *Nature, Lond.*, 1957, *179*: 1239–1240.

Markevitch, V. V. Letter to the editor. *Med. Elect. Biol. Engng*, 1965, *3*: 322.

Pienkowski, E. Predicting transmitter range and life. *Bioscience*, 1965, *15*: 115–117.

Schelkunoff, S. *Electromagnetic waves*, Chap. 6. New York: Van Nostrand, 1943.

Schwan, H. P. Electrical properties of cells and cell suspensions. *Adv. biol. med. Phys.*, 1957, *5*: 148–160.

15

The Measurement of Physiological Phenomena

LESLIE A. GEDDES, Ph.D., M.E.E.

A century ago, William Thomson, Lord Kelvin, pioneer in the application of the physical sciences to the benefit of mankind, made two statements which describe the goals and difficulties in the acquisition of physiological data in psychophysiological investigations. He said, "When you can measure what you are speaking about and express it in numbers, you know something about it" and "A fundamental requisite of a measuring instrument is that its application to make a measurement shall not alter the magnitude of the thing measured." Although it is not always possible to meet these two requirements in psychophysiological studies, their importance should never be neglected. Whenever a physiological event is measured, the method of measurement should be evaluated in terms of these requirements. It will be the purpose of this chapter to discuss the methods for the detection and display of physiological events in the light of these requirements.

Traditionally, in the measurement of physiological events, a continuous time display of amplitude has been the technique most widely employed. Practically every investigator desirous of obtaining this type of presentation has encountered similar difficulties. In assembling the apparatus three steps were taken. (1) A recorder such as a multichannel electroencephalograph, electrocardiograph, or some type of polygraph was purchased. Such devices reproduce on a suitable recording surface the electrical events presented to them. (2) After purchase of the polygraph, it was discovered that few manufacturers provide transducers for easy connection to the equipment to permit recording physiological events. Industry was then scoured for transducers adaptable to physiological studies. The most promising transducers were then purchased and modified to meet the requirements of the physiological events, or adapters were constructed to join the transducers to the recording apparatus. (3) A development program was carried out to generate the sensors necessary for detection of the phenomena of interest.

Despite some difficulties, many ingenious instruments have been constructed and placed in operation. However, primarily as a result of varying transducer conversion efficiencies and special energizing requirements, such as carrier voltages and power supplies, the recording equipment tended to have some undesirable characteristics. Usually the urgent need to place the system in operation did not permit analysis of the compatibility of the transducer with the rest of the apparatus. Frequently, the over-all operating characteristics of parts of the system were excessively good and the expense of such parts often forced the investigator to make compromises in other parts of the instrumentation. Each channel was often different throughout. In many channels there were frequently several controls which performed the same function or were interlocked in some way. The original flexibility of the polygraph channels was lost, thereby making it difficult to align related physiological events. Because of this difficulty it was not possible to keep on hand a spare channel which could be substituted for one in which a component failure occurred. It became almost impossible to add or to change channel configurations as progress of the experiment dictated.

Frequently, special knowledge or training was required to operate the equipment; usually only the investigator and his engineer or technician possessed this talent. When one of these moved on, the apparatus was used less and, as the inevitable failures occurred, the instrumentation finally fell into disuse.

Although many of these problems seem insurmountable, they are not. Fortunately, the situation is slowly changing and transducers for physiological events are becoming available commercially. Moreover, adapters are also being provided by transducer suppliers to permit connection of their units to existing recorders. However, full awareness of this situation is not at hand and sound judgment must be exercised before expending funds to obtain recording apparatus. When contemplating development of a recording facility for physiological events, attention should be directed toward adoption of what is known as the "systems engineering" approach which requires that the equipment consist of interchangeable functional modules having the maximum flexibility for interconnection.

In nearly every electronic system employed to measure a physiological event, it is possible to identify three distinct functional units. Although there is no general agreement for the names of the three, there is no dispute about the existence and role of each. The author chooses to identify the units as the transducer, processor, and reproducer; a combination of the three constitutes a single measuring channel. The most familiar example of this three part system is the hi-fi record player shown in Fig. 15.1A. In this instrument the transducer is a pickup, the stylus of which tracks the variations in the groove of the record; an amplifier accepts and enlarges the signal from the pickup to a level suitable for the loudspeaker, the reproducer of choice for appreciation of the data. Of importance in the system are the conversions which take place. The pickup

A. THE HI-FI RECORD PLAYER

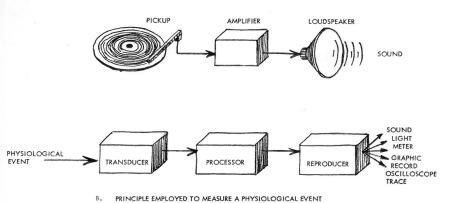

B.   PRINCIPLE EMPLOYED TO MEASURE A PHYSIOLOGICAL EVENT

FIG. 15.1. Principle of a measuring instrument.

converts the variations in the record groove to a proportional electrical signal. The amplifier enlarges the signal to the level required to energize the loudspeaker. The loudspeaker converts the electrical signal to sound, the optimum form of display for appreciation by the human senses. Figure 15.1*B* shows these same three functional units as they are employed in the measurement of physiological events. The physiological event is applied to a transducer which converts it to an electrical signal. This signal is altered by the processor to a form which is adequate for energizing the reproducer which displays the event in the form most suitable for appreciation by the human senses.

The transducer, sometimes called a sensor, detector, or pickup, is sensitive to and discriminates the characteristic property to be studied and selectively converts changes in the property into an equivalent electrical signal. In a very real way the transducer is akin to a sense organ in its sensitivity to changes of one particular kind of energy and in its ability to transform this energy into the electrical code of the processing system. The transducer differs from a sense organ in that it must interpose no alteration of its own in the conversion of changes in the property as described by duration, frequency, and intensity. Unlike the sense organ it must not adapt or accommodate.

The processor, sometimes called a signal conditioner or modifier, handles information submitted by the transducer in an appropriate way for ultimate reproduction. Processing techniques such as addition and subtraction as in a bookkeeping machine, multiplication, or electronic mathematical computation are typical operations of the processing device. Processors may be called upon to introduce time lags or scramble information as in communication systems, or integrate widely disparate data as in artillery fire control systems. In physiology, the appropriate processing is often far simpler, for in many instances the main problem is one of multiplication, or more simply stated, amplification. Care must be taken so that no distortion will be introduced between the input and output in the course of processing, i.e. linear characteristics are to be achieved. Thus, the problem of the processor in physiological studies is largely the provision of amplification with characteristics appropriate for the type of data being handled. It is of course recognized that the processor in physiology may be called upon to perform other functions. It may filter undesirable frequencies as in phonocardiography, it may integrate such signals as air or blood flow velocity with time to give volume. It may differentiate signals to permit study of the rate of change of an event. It may perform a vector analysis of wave forms, such as in the vectorcardiogram.

The reproducer, often called the output transducer, indicator, or display device, portrays the event in the most appropriate form. Traditionally graphic recording pens have been the reproducers most frequently used for indicating the magnitude of the changes experienced by a physiological event. When the change is rapid, the inertia of graphic recorders prevents faithful reproduction, hence, the virtually inertia-less electron beam of the cathode ray oscilloscope is required.

Sometimes instead of recording the amplitude-time course of an event, it is of more value to know its numerical value, as for example systolic and diastolic blood pressures. In such instances, digital display devices are the reproducers of choice. In some applications, the number of events per unit of time or in a given time is the quantity which contains the useful information; typical examples are heart and respiratory rates. In such cases, rate meters or time-controlled totalizing counters are the appropriate reproducers. Occasionally it is of value to signal the occurrence of the event by a flash of light or a burst of sound; the latter type of reproducer is often employed in monitoring an event while the investigator is occupied with other tasks.

Thus, it is apparent that the measurement of a physiological event is dependent on the availability of an appropriate transducer and the provision of an adequate means to process and display the signal produced by the transducer. While the inventory of electronics is replete with all manner of processing and reproducing devices, it is poorly stocked with transducers for the detection of physiological events. As yet, no full scale attempt has been made to develop standardized transducers for physiological phenomena. Many transducers have been described by various investigators but their widespread use has been limited by two serious drawbacks, one is that the conversion efficiency or electrical signal output per unit of physiological event is often small. The other is that those available now, often borrowed from industrial and other specialized fields, are based on a wide variety of principles and are heterogeneous in their energizing requirements and outputs. As a result, these transducers, excellent as they may be in their own right, tend to be expensive and are often extremely difficult to adapt to the needs of experimentation in the biological sciences. Because the key to the successful measurement of physiological events lies in the availability of adequate transducers the principles underlying such devices will be described in some detail.

In discussing transduction, it is necessary to distinguish between a transduceable property and a principle of transduction. A transduceable property may be defined as that singular characteristic of an event which distinguishes it from those around it and to which a principle of transduction can be applied. A principle of transduction is any one of the methods of converting the transduceable property to an electrical signal. For example in the measurement of the amount of oxygen in a mixture of respiratory gases containing nitrogen, carbon dioxide, and water vapor, a transduceable property of oxygen is its paramagnetic property, i.e. it is attracted into a magnetic field while the other gases are diamagnetic and are repelled. Practical use of this transduceable property was made by Rein (1944) to create an oxygen transducer.

In Rein's transducer the gas sample to be analyzed was divided and drawn equally through two parallel tubes and then recombined. Midway along each tube was a connection and between them was connected a differential pressure indicator. Ahead of the take-off for the pressure indicator on one tube and beyond it on the other, Rein caused a strong magnetic field to be passed through the gas in the tube. Thus the oxygen in the gas sample was concentrated in the regions where the magnetic fields were applied. The concentration of oxygen changed the resistance to flow of the sample and resulted in a pressure difference which was indicated by the differential pressure indicator. Thus the concentration of oxygen was read in terms of a pressure difference.

In this example, the transduceable property was the paramagnetic property of oxygen. The principle of transduction employed a magnetic field and a differential pressure indicator. While Rein reported successful use of this device using a U-tube manometer as the differential pressure indicator, the pressure difference was so small that he viewed it with a microscope. With the high sensitivity differential pressure transducers now available, it would seem that a renewed interest might be evidenced in Rein's use of the paramagnetic property of oxygen to create an oxygen transducer.

In many instances there may be more than one transduceable property and principle of transduction. Whenever a choice is to be made, a good criterion to be applied is that of Rein (1940), which might be paraphrased as maximum efficiency in the transducers, a minimum of electronics. Standardization and miniaturization should also be considered as highly desirable features.

In the conversion of a physiological event to an electrical signal many methods are employed. The event can be made to vary directly or indirectly, resistance, capacitance, inductance, or the magnetic linkage between two or more coils. The photoelectric and piezoelectric phenomena are extensively used. The thermoelectric effect and the Hall effect are employed to detect temperature differences and magnetic field strength, respectively. In some cases, changes in the conducting properties of biological material can be employed as a means of transduction. Application of the principles of transduction embraces all of the phenomena of the flow of electrons or ions through solids, liquids, and gases or a vacuum or both. In practice, however, it is convenient to use only a few of these possible modes.

In summary, it can be stated that the successful transduction of a physiological event to an electrical signal requires the identification of a transduceable property and the application of a principle of transduction. The conditions which must be met for faithful reproduction of the event will be discussed subsequently. A high conversion efficiency, i.e. transducer output per unit of physiological event, is a desirable feature which guarantees an absolute minimum of equipment required for processing and display.

I. Transducers
Resistance Transducers

The resistance of a solid or liquid conductor to the flow of direct or low frequency alternating current depends on the resistivity of the material and its length, and it is inversely proportional to the cross-sectional area. In a uniform conductor with axial symmetry, where the current density is uniform, the resistance of such a conductor can be expressed mathematically by

$$R = \frac{\rho L}{A}$$

where R is the resistance (ohms), L is the length (centimeters), A is the cross-sectional area (square centimeters), ρ is the resistivity (ohm centimeters).

An idea of the resistance offered to the passage of direct or low frequency alternating current exhibited by some of the familiar substances can be obtained from the data in the Table 15.1.

A variation in any one of the factors in the mathematical expression will alter the resistance of a conductor and provides a means for transduction. For example mechanical deformation (variation in L, ρ, A) alters the resistance and is responsible for the resistance change exhibited by strain gauges. The resistivity of many materials is strongly temperature dependent. This fact permits the use of such conductors to detect temperature. The resistivity of some materials depends on stress and other factors such as the presence of a magnetic field or radiant energy. These effects will be discussed later.

Thermoresistors

The variation in resistivity of metallic conductors has been extensively used to measure temperature. While any metallic conductor can be used to construct a thermoresistor, choice of the material is usually based on linearity or thermal sensitivity. Near room temperature the resistance of most metallic conductors increases almost linearly with temperature. Over a limited temperature range

Table 15.1 *Resistivity of materials*

Material	Resistivity	Temperature	Reference
	ohm/cm	*°C*	
Silver	1.59×10^{-6}	20	*Handbook of Chemistry and Physics, 1962–1963*
Copper	1.72×10^{-6}	20	*Handbook of Chemistry and Physics, 1962–1963*
Gold	2.44×10^{-6}	20	*Handbook of Chemistry and Physics, 1962–1963*
Platinum	10×10^{-6}	20	*Handbook of Chemistry and Physics, 1962–1963*
Mercury	95.8×10^{-6}	20	*Handbook of Chemistry and Physics, 1962–1963*
Carbon	3500×10^{-6}	0	*Handbook of Chemistry and Physics, 1962–1963*
Saline, 5%	14.94	18	*Handbook of Chemistry and Physics, 1962–1963*
Saline, 0.9% (dc)	72	18	Burger & Milan, 1943
Human plasma (1 kc)	62	37	Rosenthal & Tobias, 1946
Human blood (1 kc)	131.2	37	Rosenthal & Tobias, 1946

the increase in resistance approximates 0.3 to 0.5% per degree Centigrade. Fig. 15.2*A* illustrates the variation of resistance with temperature for copper. Often platinum (0.37% per °C) is employed as the temperature-sensitive material. Such thermoresistors, often called resistance thermometers, are usually low in resistance. The change in resistance is usually measured with a Wheatstone Bridge. Because the temperature-induced resistance change is small, thermal gradients existing along the interconnecting wires often cause errors. To eliminate them compensating leads are employed in the manner shown in Fig. 15.3. In this circuit at the temperature to be measured, the three other resistors in the bridge are made equal to that of the thermoresistor.

While virtually any material can be used as a temperature transducer, it is more advantageous to use one which is extremely sensitive to temperature. Such a resistor is called a thermistor and usually consists of a mixture of metallic oxides, sulfides, and silicates. The temperature-resistance characteristic of thermistors is logarithmic. In many thermistors the decrease in resistance is approximately 5% per degree Centigrade increase in temperature (Fig. 15.2*B*). Thus when they are placed in a suitable circuit, a large electrical signal can be obtained for each degree of change in temperature. Because of their large thermal coefficient compensating leads are not usually required.

Thermistors are very convenient transducers for the measurement of temperature at virtually any site on or within the body. They are also employed to

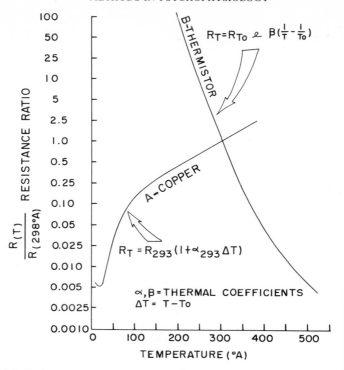

$$R_T = R_{T_0} \, \ell^{\, \beta(\frac{1}{T} - \frac{1}{T_0})}$$

B-THERMISTOR

A-COPPER

$$R_T = R_{293}(1 + \alpha_{293}\Delta T)$$

$\alpha, \beta = $ THERMAL COEFFICIENTS
$\Delta T = T - T_0$

RESISTANCE RATIO $\frac{R(T)}{R(298°A)}$

TEMPERATURE (°A)

FIG. 15.2. Resistance versus temperature of copper and a typical thermistor. *A*, from Swenson and Emslie, 1954. *B*, from the *Thermistor Data Book*.

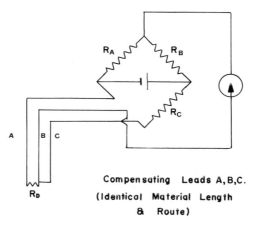

R_A R_B

R_C

A   B   C

R_D

Compensating Leads A, B, C.
(Identical Material Length
& Route)

FIG. 15.3. Compensated bridge.

measure the flow of fluids and gases. When heated slightly and placed in a stream of gas or liquid, they are cooled becoming thereby transducers of velocity. If the cross-sectional area confining the fluid is constant, the resistance change can be calibrated in terms of volume flow.

Strain Gauges

Strain gauges are conductors which when stretched change their resistance. When most metallic conductors are elongated, their length increases and cross-sectional area decreases; hence, the resistance increases. The resistance change is usually larger than that accountable on the basis of the alterations in dimensions. With some materials, there is a decrease in resistance with elongation.

When stretched, the maximum resistance change of a strain gauge element is on the order of 1% and the elongation permissible is extremely small; approximately a few thousandths of an inch per inch of gauge. Thus the strain gauge is essentially an isometric device and can only be applied to detect small extensions. Because of the modest change in resistance, it produces a relatively small electrical signal in typical applications (10 to 100 mv). However, its linearity, ease of application, low cost, and rapidity of response make it a valuable transducing element for small mechanical displacements. By use of appropriate springs or other take-up devices, strain gauges can indeed be employed for detection of movements of greater magnitude.

Perhaps the only defect of strain gauges in the biomedical application is their sensitivity to temperature. With many strain gauge elements, the temperature change in resistance is an appreciable fraction of the strain-induced change. This defect can, however, be eliminated by using another strain gauge element as a compensating resistor. An increase in efficiency along with temperature compensation can be obtained by using four active strain gauges in a bridge circuit. All are affected by temperature change and hence the bridge remains balanced. It is unbalanced by strain appropriately applied to all four elements; strain in the same direction is applied to diagonal arms of the bridge and in the opposite direction to adjacent arms.

Strain gauges see service in blood pressure transducers and myographs of various designs. They are widely used industrially, come in standardized forms, and many manufacturers can supply the electronic processing equipment on an off-the-shelf basis.

Electrolytic Strain Gauges

A type of strain gauge which has seen considerable service in biomedical research is the electrolytic resistor consisting of a rubber or plastic tube filled with mercury or an aqueous electrolyte. The ends are capped with two metallic electrodes.

The mercury gauge was introduced by Whitney (1949) and the aqueous electrolyte gauge was revived by Müller (1942) and Dalla-Torre (1943). Such devices are easy to construct, inexpensive, and can be temperature-compensated and produce a substantial electrical signal per unit of elongation. Almost any degree of elongation up to 100% of the relaxed length can often be employed. Such gauges have been used to detect changes in the size of an organ such as the heart, bladder, or kidney. They have also been used in plethysmographic studies of the digits and limbs. When wrapped around the chest they can be employed to sense the changes in circumference which occur with respiration.

Mercury-in-rubber strain gauges made with small bore elastic tubing (approximately 0.5 mm id) exhibit a resistance in the range of 0.02 to 0.2 ohm per cm of length. The resistance change with extension closely approximates linearity after a slight initial stretch. The response time is rapid and can be as short as 10 msec for a 35-mm gauge (Rushmer, 1955, a and b, 1956; Lawton, 1959). Temperature compensation is required if such gauges are to be employed in situations of varying temperature (Whitney, 1953; Honda, 1962).

There are some difficulties encountered in using mercury-in-rubber strain gauges. Because of the corrosive nature of mercury, the electrodes have a limited life. Their low resistance requires that a substantial current be passed through them to obtain a reasonably large signal. The difficulty was overcome by Elsner (1959) and Honda (1962), who used a transformer to couple the strain gauge to the measuring bridge and alternating current to energize it.

When the conductor is an aqueous electrolyte the resistance is much higher. Copper sulfate with copper or platinum electrodes has been employed extensively to detect a variety of events such as respiration and the pulsatile volume changes in limbs as blood enters and leaves. The resistance depends on the concentration of the electrolyte and geometry of the gauge. In typical applications resistances in the kilohm range are common. To delay decomposition of the electrodes and electrolyte, only alternating current should be employed.

Aqueous electrolyte strain gauges, while convenient, easy to construct, and inexpensive, are not without their defects. Decomposition of the electrodes which often proceeds when the gauge is not in use limits the life of the gauge. The resistance of most electrolytes is temperature dependent and usually decreases by about 2% per degree Centigrade increase in temperature. Hence temperature compensation may be necessary in some applications.

Potentiometer Transducers

Rectilinear or conventional rotary potentiometers can be employed to detect movement when the moving object can develop a moderate force and when the movement is not rapid. Low torque rotary units capable of continuous rotation and rectilinear potentiometers with strokes up to 10 in. are available commercially.

Although there are few applications of this type of transducer at present, its unusually high efficiency makes it attractive for many purposes. Respiration has been detected by connecting a chest band to a rotary potentiometer.* The author (Geddes, Hoff, & Spencer, 1961) has converted the rotation of a spirometer pulley to an electrical signal by using a low torque potentiometer. The bulging of the belly of a muscle was detected by using caliper arms connected to a miniature potentiometer (Geddes, Hoff, Moore, & Hinds, 1966). A truly isotonic myograph for slowly contracting muscles could be constructed by mounting a pulley on a low torque potentiometer and passing a cord over it; one end connected to the muscle, the other to a weight. Contraction of the muscle would move the same weight through a distance measured by the pulley on the potentiometer shaft. Industrially the potentiometer transducer is used in many Bourdon tube pressure transducers. In these devices, the movement of free end of the Bourdon tube is measured by a low torque potentiometer.

In most applications of potentiometer transducers, a relatively large signal is obtained. The size of the signal depends on the voltage applied to the potentiometer which is limited by the maximum wattage dissipation of the potentiometer element. The relationship of output versus motion also depends on the type of potentiometer and the impedance of the associated circuitry. With wire-wound potentiometers, the output is stepped as the sliding contact moves from one wire to the next. If the resistance is high and the wire size is small, the steps are fine. If the resistance element is a carbon film, the output is stepless.

Capacitive Transducers

When considering capacitive transducers it is convenient to designate a capacitor as a device consisting of two conducting surfaces separated by an insulator (dielectric). The dielectric can be a solid, liquid, gas (air), or a vacuum. The capacitance, or charge per volt, of a simple parallel plate capacitor is given by the following approximate expression

$$C = \frac{KA}{d}$$

where C is the capacitance, A is the area of the plates, d is the separation between them, K is the dielectric constant of the material in the space between the plates. For practical calculation, an air condenser consisting of metallic plates 1 sq. in. in area separated by 0.1 in. has a capacitance of 2.17 $\mu\mu$ f.

The expression indicates that the capacitance can be changed by varying the area, separation of the plates, or by altering the material between them. Usually the capacitance is changed by varying the distance between the plates. If the separation is kept very small with respect to the size of the plates, the capacitance varies inversely with separation. Such a method of operation permits detection of a very small movement. If the plates are kept a constant dis-

---

*R. Adams, personal communication, 1962.

tance apart and moved parallel to each other, the effective area is altered and a much larger range of motion can be detected. A good survey of mechanical configurations possible with such transducers was presented by Foldvari and Lion (1964).

To obtain an electrical signal related to the capacitance change, a sine wave of voltage is applied across the capacitor. The magnitude of the current, I is given by the following expression

$$I = E2\pi f C$$

or substituting from above

$$I = E2\pi f K \frac{A}{d}$$

where E is the voltage, f is the frequency in cycles per sec, C is the capacitance in farads. $1/2\pi f C$ is the reactance to the condenser. Thus it is apparent that a current can be obtained which depends on the factors which determine capacitance (A, K, d).

The capacitance change is often detected by placing the condenser in a bridge circuit which is balanced for the zero-event condition. When the event appears, the capacitance change unbalances the bridge giving rise to an electrical signal. It is important to note however that with this arrangement a change in capacitance in either direction will unbalance the bridge. To obtain a direction-sensitive signal, it is customary to initially set the bridge off balance by an amount dictated by the magnitude of the largest change in capacitance to be encountered which drives the bridge toward balance. Thus with no event there is a steady signal and when the event causes the capacitance to change, the output from the bridge increases and decreases tracking the changes in the event.

With the capacitance bridge, direction sensitivity can be automatically obtained by use of a phase-sensitive detector. Such a device compares the output of the bridge with the oscillator voltage applied to it. As the capacitance change drives the bridge through the balance point, there is a phase change which is recognized by the phase-sensitive detector.

Another method of detecting the capacitance change consists of placing the transducing capacitor across the tuned circuit of an oscillator. Variations in capacitance of the transducing capacitor will vary the frequency of the oscillator. The change in frequency can then be processed to a useable electrical signal.

Another system for detection of capacitance change was developed by Lion (1964). With this method, the transducer is a differential capacitor energized by unidirectional pulses. The event is coupled to the transducing element in such a way that one-half of the transducer experiences an increase in capacitance, the other a corresponding decrease in capacitance. The main advantages of the arrangement are high stability, direction sensitivity, and the circuit arrangement permits one terminal of the oscillator, the transducing capacitor, and the detector to be at the same potential which can be ground.

The capacitance change principle is usually employed to detect displacement. It is frequently employed to measure the distension of an elastic diaphragm exposed to blood pressure. There are a few applications in which a living subject has constituted the dielectric. These will be discussed in the section describing the impedance method.

With a small separation between the plates of the capacitance transducer, the efficiency is high. If the separation is large, the signal obtained is quite small and considerable processing equipment is required. In most practical applications the capacitance change is small, and because the output impedance is high, the transducer is coupled to the processing equipment with a shielded cable. In many applications the characteristics of the shielded cable merit special attention because its capacitance is in parallel with that of the transducing capacitor. Therefore a mechanically stable low capacitance coaxial cable is required. Often movement of the cable produces an undesirable capacitance change which results from a slight movement of the outer shield relative to the inner conductor. This capacitance change produces a signal which is indistinguishable from that produced by the transducer. Special coaxial cables in which a layer of conducting powder has been applied to the dielectric directly below the shield are relatively free of such spurious signals.

In many instances, the problem presented by the high output impedance can be eliminated by locating some of the processing circuitry in the capacitive transducer. With this technique it is usually possible to incorporate an impedance transformer which provides a low output impedance, thereby eliminating the problems encountered with long interconnecting cables.

The extreme flexibility of the capacitance method is perhaps its most attractive feature. In most applications it is employed to detect dimension change without direct contact with the moving object. For this reason capacitive transducers are often called proximity gauges and are free from loading, frictional, and hysteresis errors.

In the applications in which living tissue constitutes part of the capacitor, it is not at all times clear whether only capacitance changes are being measured. Frequently the circuit contains a resistive component which varies. What is actually measured is an impedance change. A discussion of the applications of the impedance method will be presented elsewhere in this chapter.

Inductance Transducers

The inductance of a coil depends on its length, radius, number of turns, and the magnetic permeability of the space in which it lies; the most important portion is the region within the coil. The following formula for the low frequency inductance of a single layer air-cored coil was given by Wheeler (1928).

$$L = \frac{n^2 \, r^2}{9\,r + 10\,L}$$

where r and L are the radius and length in inches, n is the number of turns, L is the inductance in microhenries. This formula is accurate for coils in which the length is many times greater than the diameter.

If the magnetic permeability of the region within the coil is increased, as by the insertion of a core of magnetically permeable material, the inductance is increased. Thus the reactance of the coil ($2\pi fL$) will be increased. If the coil was carrying alternating current before insertion of the core, insertion of the core will reduce the current. Coupling the core to an event permits use of the inductance method for transduction of displacement.

Single inductors, in which a change was produced in the magnetic permeability of the region within or at the end of the coil, have been employed in transducers. In many instances pressure has been the event detected. One outstanding application of the inductance transducer to measure dimension change was due to Rushmer (1954, a and b). He successfully implanted a small coil with its moveable core inside the left ventricle of a dog's heart; the coil was sutured to the ventricular wall and the core to the septum. As the heart beat and the diameter changed, the core moved within the coil causing inductance changes, which, when recorded in the unanesthetized dog, indicated changes in stroke volume and the size of the heart during a variety of experimental conditions.

One commercially available* catheter tip pressure transducer employs a single inductor with its core attached to a tiny elastic diaphragm exposed to the pressure to be detected. The inductance forms part of the frequency-determining circuit of an oscillator. As the core is displaced by pressure applied to the diaphragm, the inductance change alters the frequency of the oscillator. The frequency change is processed to derive a signal proportional to pressure.

In many instances it is more convenient to use two or more inductors in transducers. If two coils, L_1 and L_2, are joined in series and their magnetic fields link, the inductance is: $L = L_1 + L_2 \pm 2\,M$ where M is the mutual inductance between them which depends on the interaction of their magnetic fields. Thus varying the relative portion of the coils, as by rotation of their long axes or by changes in separation, will give rise to an inductance change.

If the two coils are not joined and an oscillator is connected across one and a voltmeter is across the second, the voltmeter will indicate a voltage, the magnitude of which is proportional to the coupling between the coils. Relative displacement of the coils, as in the cases above, will alter the voltage indicated.

There are many applications of two inductance transducers. One of the early catheter tip pressure transducers described by Gauer and Gienapp (1950) employed two inductances in series, in which the coupling between the fixed coils was altered by a change in the position of a core coupled to an elastic diaphragm. Scher (1953) described a two inductance flowmeter consisting of a

---

*Dallons Laboratories, El Segundo, California.

magnetically permeable paddle mounted in the axial stream of a tube carrying blood. Outside the tube and on either side of the paddle were two coils which constituted the arms of an inductance bridge which was balanced without blood flow. Flowing blood deflected the paddle and altered the coupling and hence the inductance of the assembly thereby unbalancing the bridge and providing a flow-dependent signal.

Two coils arranged to operate as a transformer are often employed in transducers. For example Pieper (1958) constructed a catheter tip velocity flowmeter in which the coupling between two coils was altered by variation in the position of a magnetically permeable sleeve, the position of which was dependent on flow velocity. This miniature device, which was stabilized in the axial stream of a vessel by an umbrella-type support, exhibited excellent dynamic characteristics responding linearly to flow up to 45 cm per sec. The frequency response was equally good: being uniform up to 20 cps.

Another practical application of the two coil variable transformer was due to Benjamin, Mastrogiovanni, and Helveig (1962). In their transducer, the two coils were mounted in a small chamber which was attached to the skin over a pulsating artery. In the chamber immediately above the artery, a rubber diaphragm carried the moveable coil and the frame of the capsule carried the other coil which was fixed in position. The coil on the rubber membrane was energized by a 100-kc oscillator and its position was modulated by the pulse. Amplification, rectification, and graphic recording of the signal produced a pulse tracing of high fidelity.

The linear variable differential transformer (LVDT), popularized by Schaevitz (1947), is a device which consists of three coils in which there is mutual coupling. The usual configuration of this device takes the form of an energizing coil mounted centrally between two identical secondary coils connected in series opposition. This configuration is illustrated in Fig. 15.4. With the core symmetrically located in the center of the energizing coil, the voltage induced in each secondary coil is equal. With the coils connected in series opposition the sum of their voltages is zero. Displacement of the core in either direction increases the voltage induced in one coil and decreases that induced in the other. Thus the sum of the two voltages is one which is proportional to the displacement.

It is worthy of note that an output is produced if the direction of motion is in either direction from the null position. To obtain a direction-sensitive signal, the core can be offset and the displacement can start from a fixed position on either side of the null point. Thus forward or backward movement of the core will produce an increasing or decreasing signal; however, with the mode of operation the total range of core excursion is restricted.

Another method of obtaining direction sensitivity is to employ a phase-sensitive detector. If the output voltage is compared with the excitation voltage, it will be seen that there is a phase reversal of 180° as the core moves from one

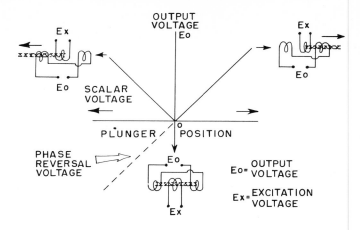

LINEAR VARIABLE DIFFERENTIAL TRANSFORMER

FIG. 15.4. Linear variable differential transformer.

side of the null to the other. Thus by employing a phase-sensitive detector which can identify this transition, direction sensitivity is automatically obtained without curtailment of the range of core motion.

Differential transformers see extensive service in transducers. One of the first inductive catheter tip blood pressure transducers employed a four winding differential transformer. In this device, described by Wetterer (1943), an oscillator was connected to the primary which consisted of two coils and the detecting system was connected to two secondary coils connected in series opposition. An elastic diaphragm was coupled to a moveable core which altered the coupling between the coils when pressure was applied. The small mass of the moving parts and the high stiffness combined to produce a transducer having a rapid response time.

A larger position transducer was described by Tucker (1952) who employed a three winding transformer energized by the power line. By varying the coupling between the energizing coil and one secondary and appropriately adding the voltages from both secondaries, he was able to create a transducer which was accurate to 0.005 cm over a 1-cm range of motion. The device provided enough power to energize a recording pen without the use of an amplifier.

Schafer and Shirer (1949) mounted an LVDT inside the barrel of a 2-ml syringe, which was fitted with an elastic diaphragm, the deflection of which displaced the core of the LVDT. Erdos, Jackman, and Barnes (1962) described the use of an LVDT in an isotonic myograph. In this device the muscle specimen under study was connected to a beam type balance. The motion of the balancing weight, which occurred with contraction of the muscle, was measured by variations in the position of the core of the LVDT.

Because of the small size and low mass of the core of most LVDTs, an insignificant load is imposed on the event being measured. The response time is determined largely by the event to which it is coupled providing a high frequency current is used for excitation. The LVDT is relatively insensitive to temperature variations and produces a signal in the millivolt range in most applications. Units are commercially available with displacement ranges extending from ±0.005 to ±1.00 in. Rotary variable differential transducers are also available which produce an output which is linear with rotation for ±45° in most models.

Piezoelectric Transducers

The piezoelectric phenomenon is a characteristic of many crystals which can be demonstrated by placing electrodes on appropriate crystallographic faces and applying stress to the crystal. When the stress is applied in the appropriate direction, charges are displaced and a voltage appears at the electrodes. The magnitude of the voltage is dependent on the material, its size, the axis along which the electrodes are placed, and the distorting force. Since crystals are relatively hard, the distorting force produces only a slight deformation. Thus the piezoelectric crystal is an isometric force transducer. Parenthetically, it is to be noted that the application of a voltage to the electrodes distorts the crystal. These two features of piezo crystals are responsible for their widespread application in industry and biomedical studies.

In addition to the piezoelectric effect existing in naturally occurring crystals, it can be induced in certain ceramic materials, notably barium titanate. With the application of a voltage to electrodes on such ceramics, there occurs a reorientation of the crystalline structure which persists after removal of the voltage. The orientation so developed renders the crystal piezoelectric. This technique permits construction of piezo crystals with shapes other than those dictated by natural crystalline structure.

Piezo crystals see extensive use industrially. A large number of phonograph cartridges and microphones contain them. Many accelerometers and vibration pickups employ such crystals as transducing elements. In all of these applications they produce an appreciable voltage. Piezoelectric crystals are also used to convert a varying voltage to mechanical motion. They have been employed in earphones, loudspeakers, graphic recorders, and many devices which produce ultrasound.

When employed as transducers, piezo crystals develop a voltage in the millivolt range in many typical applications. However, because piezo crystals are high impedance devices, the voltages can only drive small currents through devices coupled to them. Thus when employing piezo crystal transducers only high input impedance circuits should be employed.

Another important characteristic of piezo crystals relates to their response to a sudden and sustained force. When exposed to such an input, the transducer develops a voltage almost instantly but due to leakage within and without the crystal, the voltage cannot be maintained. Thus the piezo crystal cannot be employed to detect static events; it is only applicable to the detection of changing events. The sine wave frequency response available from most piezo crystals extends from a few cycles per sec to many kilocycles per sec; the upper frequency response is usually limited by the structure to which the crystal is coupled.

In biomedical studies there have been numerous instances in which the piezo crystal has been employed as the transducing element. In microphones or directly applied to living subjects it has been employed to detect acoustic phenomena, such as heart and Korotkoff sounds. A phonographic cartridge in which the needle has been replaced by a wire screen mounted to a bracket makes an inexpensive drop detector (Hoff & Geddes, 1955). Drops striking the screen twist the crystal and produce a sizeable voltage pulse. A crystal element (removed from a phonograph cartridge) when suitably mounted makes an excellent pulse transducer. Miller and White (1941), Rappaport and Luisada (1944), Lax, Feinberg, and Cohen (1956), and Geddes and Hoff (1960) all constructed high fidelity pulse pickups from crystal elements by converting them to pressure transducers.

Because of their ability to deform quickly with the application of a voltage, piezoelectric crystals are used extensively to produce ultrasound and see service in ultrasonic blood flowmeters in which the difference between up and downstream transmission time of an ultrasonic signal is processed to yield a flow signal. The many sonar type devices in which a burst of ultrasound is sent into living tissue and reflected from tissues of differing texture use both properties of piezo crystals.

An ingenious biomedical application of the piezo crystal to produce movement was described by Pascoe (1955). He was faced with the problem of advancing a microelectrode into a nerve cell which was enveloped in a tough membrane. By mounting the microelectrode on a piezo crystal and applying a pulse of voltage, the electrode was instantly advanced 20μ and the tip of the microelectrode penetrated the cell without damage.

In summary, the piezoelectric crystal is characterized by a high conversion efficiency and stiffness. When distorted, an appreciable voltage is produced which cannot be maintained nor can it deliver an appreciable current. It is thus an efficient high impedance nearly isometric transducer for force.

Photoelectric Transducers

In the transduction of physiological events photoelectric transducers are employed in two ways. In one, the intensity of light of a given wave length contains the desired information; in the other, changes in intensity carry the desired information; the color of the light being relatively unimportant. In the first category belong colorimeters and spectrophotometers; in the second are the various devices in which a physiological event is caused to modulate light intensity as by moving a shade.

There are three basic types of photodetectors, the photoemissive (phototube), the photogalvanic (barrier layer cell), and the photoconductive (photoresistor). Each has its own special response to light and each has different electrical characteristics which recommend it for certain tasks. The following brief review of the operating principles and characteristics is presented to enable the reader to select the type of phototransducer best suited to his particular needs.

Photoemissive transducers. The photoemissive photodetector consists of an evacuated or gas-filled bulb with two electrodes. On one, the cathode, is a coating of specially prepared material which releases electrons when light quanta are absorbed. The other electrode, the anode, usually consists of a thin rod or loop of wire. A polarizing voltage (50 to 200 v) applied to the electrodes causes the electrons released by the photoemissive surface to flow to the anode. The electron flow constitutes a current which is linearly related to the intensity of the light striking the photocathode. In the vacuum type, the current is small and is not employed to operate an indicator directly; it is usually led through a high resistance and the voltage developed across it is applied to an amplifier having a high input impedance.

Currents approximately 10 times larger can be obtained from photoemissive detectors by incorporation of selected gas mixtures. When this technique is employed, the primary electrons released by the photocathode collide with gas molecules and produce secondary electrons and ions, thereby increasing the available current. To avoid the creation of a glow discharge, lower polarizing voltages are employed.

Photoemissive detectors respond quickly to changes in light intensity. Many vacuum types exhibit a response time of 10^{-6} msec while the gas types are much slower with response times of 0.1 to 0.5 msec. With each type a small current, called the dark current, flows with no illumination. Typical values for vacuum phototubes are 10^{-8} to 10^{-9} amp while those for gas-filled photo-tubes are 10^{-7} to 10^{-8} amp.

The spectral sensitivity of photoemissive tubes extends from the near ultraviolet through the visible into the near infrared region. If special ultraviolet transmitting envelopes are employed, these devices can operate well into the ultraviolet region. Most photoemissive detectors do not exhibit much sensitivity to radiation beyond 800 m in the infrared region. The spectral sensitivity of the photoemissive detectors and many of the other photodetectors is described by the letter S followed by number. This designation refers to standard spectral sensitivity curves recognized by most manufacturers of photosensitive devices. Table 15.2 lists the approximate wave lengths for the spectral peaks and half sensitivity points.

By incorporating additional anodes, called dynodes, each connected to higher potential, a considerable current amplification can be obtained via secondary emission. Photoelectrons released by the photosensitive surface are drawn to and strike the first dynode releasing electrons which are attracted to the second dynode which is at a higher potential, (75 to 150 v), where the process

TABLE 15.2. *S-curve data**

Spectral Designation	For Maximum Response	50% Points
S1	800	620–950
S3	420	350–640†
S4	400	320–540
S5	340	230–510†
S8	36	320–540
S9	480	350–580
S10	450	350–590
S11	440	350–560
S12	500	Narrow band
S13	440	260–560
S14	1500	760–1730
S15	580	500–660
S17	490	310–580
S19	330	190–460
S20	420	325–595
S21	450	260–560†

*Data derived from RCA photosensitive devices and cathode ray tubes, 1960. Radio Corporation of America, Electron Tube Division, Harrison, New Jersey.
†Interpolated values.

is repeated. With 10 or more stages, a current gain of several million can be obtained.

The spectral sensitivity of such a photomultiplier is that of the photosensitive surface. With no illumination, there is a small dark current amounting to approximately 10^{-7} amp. The response time is short; being on the order of 10^{-8} sec. Because of its extremely high sensitivity and short response time, it is ideally suited to detect the brief flashes of light emitted when radiation strikes the specially prepared crystals employed in scintillation counters.

Photovoltaic transducers. The photovoltaic cell, sometimes called a photogalvanic cell, is in essence a light battery. Unlike the photoemissive detector, which requires a polarizing voltage, the photovoltaic cell produces a voltage which can drive an appreciable current through a low resistance circuit. In many cases when the cell is fully illuminated, enough current is produced to operate a milliammeter or relay.

One of the most popular of the photovoltaic cells consists of a sandwich of a thin coating of selenium on an iron or steel backing. Above the selenium is a thin transparent film of metal. The region between the selenium and metal film is called the barrier layer. When this layer is illuminated, electrons are displaced and a potential is developed, the metal film becomes negative and the selenium positive. Completion of a circuit between the two electrodes causes current to flow.

Other substances, such as cuprous oxide in contact with gold or platinum, are often used in photovoltaic cells. Diffused junction silicon cells are also available commercially. The high efficiency of the silicon cell in converting light flux to electrical energy has earned it the name "solar battery." Such a cell, when illuminated by bright sunlight, will produce a power of approximately 60 milliwatts per sq in. of photosensitive surface.

The spectral sensitivity of most selenium photocells resembles that of the human eye (300 to 700 m). For this reason such devices are employed in illumination and photographic exposure meters. Many colorimeters and a few spectrophotometers also employ photovoltaic cells. A few of the members of this family exhibit a sensitivity to infrared radiation.

The relationship between light intensity and the voltage developed by photovoltaic detectors is not linear if they are operated without a resistive load. At saturation, a typical open circuit voltage is 200 to 600 mv. If a resistive load is placed across these devices, the current flow becomes more linearly related to light flux as the resistance is decreased. Hence it is necessary to employ low resistance galvanometers or measuring circuits to indicate light intensity if a linear scale is desired.

Perhaps the most undesirable characteristics of the high efficiency photogalvanic cells are their sensitivity to temperature and their long response time. Temperature sensitivity can be minimized by connecting the proper value of resistor across the photocell. With many photocells, there is an optimum value of resistance which will minimize the sensitivity change with temperature. This resistance value is not necessarily that which yields the maximum power transfer of linearity of current with light flux.

The response time of most photovoltaic cells is much longer than that of photoemissive detectors. Many photocells exhibit a response time of 5 msec. A few of the newer miniature types claim to have a response time in the region of 0.1 msec. Thus if these devices are to be employed in systems in which light modulation techniques are employed, the modulation frequency must be commensurate with the response time of the photocell.

Photoconductive transducers. The photoconductive or photoresistive cell consists of a thin film of material such as germanium, selenium, silicon, or a metal halide or sulfide which, when exposed to light or some other form of radiant energy, exhibits a decrease in resistance. When light quanta are absorbed by the material, electrons are released into the conduction band and if a voltage is applied to the film, a current will flow. With most photoconductive cells, the decrease in resistance is large, from megohms in the dark to a few hundred ohms when intensely illuminated. This wide resistance change is not linear with light intensity.

Most photoconductive cells exhibit a good sensitivity to visible light, a few are sensitive to ultraviolet and the majority are very sensitive to infrared radiation. The spectral peak of many can be shifted further toward the infrared region with cooling. The spectral peak of lead sulfide is around 2300 mμ while that of cadmium sulfide is in the region of 600 mμ.

Comparison of phototransducers. With such a variety of different photo-detectors it is worthwhile reviewing the prominent characteristics of each type. For linearity with increasing incident radiation, rapidity of response, and immunity from thermal effects, the photoemissive type is superior to the photovoltaic cell and photoconductor. Its spectral characteristics lie predominantly in the visible region with few types showing a sensitivity to infrared radiation. Only a small output current is produced for a high polarizing voltage. However when the small current is passed through a high resistance, a large output voltage is obtained. The fragility of the glass envelope restricts operation of the device to situations in which only low impact forces are encountered.

Photovoltaic cells offer the advantage of a high output current and low voltage which can energize rugged galvanometers, relays, or other low impedance circuits without the use of an external source of voltage. The slow response to a flash of light limits their application when light modulation techniques are employed. They are temperature sensitive and rugged. The spectral sensitivity of some types strongly resembles that of the eye and for this reason, they are extremely practical for illumination meters.

The photoconductive transducer is a sensitive, relatively high resistance photoresistor which requires the use of an external voltage to obtain a current related to the intensity of radiant flux. Although sensitive to visible light, the peak spectral sensitivity of most types lies toward the red and infrared regions. The large resistance change with a change in illumination makes these devices useful as light sensitive switches which can be used to operate a variety of devices. The response time varies from a fraction of a millisecond to several tens of milliseconds. Photoconductive cells are rugged, small, and usually inexpensive and available with a variety of spectral sensitivities.

Applications of photoelectric transducers. Photoelectric detectors are extensively employed to measure biochemical events through processes by which a change in color or optical density is caused to take place. Their use in spectrophotometers and colorimeters are examples of this type of application. There are fewer applications in which photodetectors are connected to the living subject to measure a biochemical event as it occurs. However, two applications are noteworthy; the measurement of cardiac output by the dye dilution method and the measurement of oxygen saturation of the blood. In both applications, flowing blood is examined for changes in optical density.

In the dye dilution method, a sample of nontoxic and of nonstimulating dye is injected into the venous system and the concentration of the diluted segment is recorded as it appears in the arterial system. Measurement of the dye concentration is accomplished by causing arterial blood to flow through a colorimeter which consists of a chamber for the blood mounted between a light bulb and filtered photodetector. The wave length employed for the measurement depends on the dye employed. Dyes which have their spectral absorption peak around 600 to 640 mμ and others maximally absorbing around 800 mμ are employed; the choice of one over the others depends on many factors. Two requisites are that the dye must remain in the circulation for at least one trip and that the detector be calibratible. Calibration is achieved by measurement of blood samples containing known concentrations of dye. Cardiac output is calculated by measuring the area under the concentration-time curve for the first passage of the injected material. To find the duration for a single pass, it is necessary to extrapolate the descending portion of the concentration curve to zero concentration. The area divided by the duration of the curve gives the mean concentration for that time. The concentration for a minute is then determined by simple proportion. Dividing the amount injected by the average minute concentration gives the average cardiac output for 1 min.

The measurement of oxygen saturation indirectly consists of measuring the transmission of light at two wave lengths after passing through a highly vascularized arterial bed. The pinna of the ear is the site most frequently employed. The transducer usually consists of a small light bulb which transilluminates the vascular bed and two photogalvanic cells; one covered with a filter which transmits at 640 mμ and the other covered with a filter which transmits at 805 mμ. The signal detected by the 640 mμ channel contains information on the amount of blood in the optical path and its saturation. The signal detected by the 805 mμ channel is dependent on the amount of blood in the optical path but is independent of saturation. Oxygen saturation is proportional to the ratio of the logarithm of the transmission at 640 mμ to the logarithm of the transmission at 805 mμ. For each transducer a calibration curve is constructed on the basis of chemically analyzed blood samples drawn from subjects with different saturations.

Reflectance type oximeters have also been developed. In these devices, the filtered photodetectors are placed on either side of the light source. The assembly is often placed on the forehead or any area which is flat and has high vascularity.

Photoelectric oximeters can function as plethysmographs to indicate changes in the volume of blood in the optical path. Heart rate can also be obtained from the optical pulse. Many of the transmission ear oximeters are equipped with pressure capsules which permit blanching the tissue in the optical path. This technique, adapted to oximetry by Wood, Knutson, and Taylor (1950), under favorable circumstances permits measurement of ear blood pressure. Thus from an oximetry transducer, a considerable amount of information can be obtained.

There are numerous applications of photodetectors in which the color of the light is unimportant. In some such applications, the event to be transduced is caused to move a shade placed between the light source and the photodetector. Force, displacement, and rotation can all be measured employing this technique. Photoelectric plethysmographs in which the change in reflected light indicate volume changes have been described by Hertzman (1938). With modern photodetectors a large signal can be obtained from such devices.

In many photoelectric plethysmographs, the heat from the bulb dilates the vessels in vascular bed. In some applications this is highly desirable because a large pulsatile signal is obtained. However, when it is desired to monitor changes in the degree of vasoconstriction such heating cannot be tolerated. To overcome this potential source of error, one manufacturer* has developed a reflectance photoelectric pulse pickup in which the vascular bed is illuminated by "cold light" produced by an electroluminescent panel.

The photoelectric principle has been used to construct high efficiency myographs, pneumographs, blood pressure transducers, drop counters, plethysmographs, and to convert the position of a moving mirror to an electrical signal. Choice of the photodetector was determined by the circuit to which the device was to be connected and the amount of change in light intensity.

Photodetectors have much to recommend then for transduction purposes. They are available with small or large photosensitive surfaces and with a variety of spectral sensitivities. In typical applications, a relatively large signal can be obtained for a small change in light intensity. In many biomedical applications, the response time errors are insignificant. In the applications in which a shade is caused to be moved between the photodetector and light source, there are no frictional or hysterisis errors.

Certain precautions must be observed when photodetectors are employed. Shielding from stray light must be provided. If an incandescent bulb is employed as the light source, a very stable power supply must be employed to guarantee a constant level of illumination. The use of two photodetectors in a differential configuration diminishes the need for a highly regulated power supply.

Thermoelectric Transducers

At the junction of two metals there arises a temperature-dependent potential. This phenomenon, first discovered by Seebeck in 1821, has been extensively employed to measure low and high temperatures. Although a single junction can be employed, it is usually more practical to employ two junctions connected in series opposition as shown in Fig. 15.5. The voltage generated by such a couple, due to the difference in temperature between the junctions, is

---

*Statham Medical Instruments, Los Angeles, California.

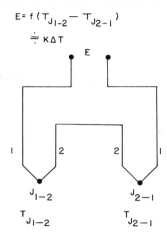

$$E = f(T_{J_{1-2}} - T_{J_{2-1}})$$
$$\doteqdot K\Delta T$$

FIG. 15.5. The thermocouple.

measured with a millivoltmeter or potentiometer. The voltages developed by various thermojunctions are given in Table 15.3.

In many practical applications it is often necessary to separate the measuring and reference junctions and under such circumstances special consideration must be given to the interconnecting wires. It is usually not convenient to make the connecting wires of the materials employed for the thermojunctions. Thus a third material, that of the connecting wires must be introduced. The junctions of the connecting wires with the thermocouple materials are also thermoelectric generators and great care must be exercised to maintain them at a constant temperature. In practice these junctions often constitute the reference junctions and must be kept at constant temperature so that the voltage developed will be dependent on the temperature of the measuring junction.

Thermocouples were employed very early to measure the temperature of the skin and internal organs and to measure the heat radiated by the body. They have also been employed in transducers in which a physiological event was

TABLE 15.3 *Thermoelectric sensitivities.*

Material	$\mu v/^\circ C^*$
Platinum-platinum, 13% Rhodium	6.5
Chromel-P-Alumel	41.0
Iron-Constantan	54.0
Copper-Constantan	42.8

*Values given are the average for a reference junction at 0°C and for the range 0° to 100°C. From the *Handbook of Chemistry and Physics.*

caused to develop a temperature difference. In one of the older flowmeters, the thermostromuhr or heat flowmeter, two thermojunctions were placed axially in a blood vessel. Between them was a heating element which warmed the blood. The upstream thermojunction monitored the temperature of the blood and the downstream one measured the temperature of the blood warmed by passage over the heating element. The voltage from the thermojunctions, reflecting the temperature difference, was calibrated in terms of blood flow.

Although the thermocouple has been recently overshadowed by the thermistor, some of its attractive characteristics are again being recognized. For example, the potential developed by the thermojunctions is dependent on the temperature and the materials and not on their size. Thermojunctions are voltage generators, i.e. thermoelectric converters, and need only be connected to a potential indicator to measure temperature. Newer materials and techniques of manufacture offer promise of themojunctions with a high efficiency and small size. Germanium, silicon, and selenium when paired with platinum exhibit thermoelectric voltages 10 to 30 times greater than those presently in use. New manufacturing techniques have made it possible to construct miniature thermocouples having a small thermal mass and short response time. Reed and Kampwirth (1964) described thermojunctions vapor-deposited on quartz fibers small enough to be inserted into a single living cell for measurement of the temperature of the cytoplasm. They stated that a response time in the range of microseconds was possible. A response time (0 to 95%) of 115 msec was given by Gelb, Marcus, and Dropkin (1964) for slightly larger thermojunctions ($25\,\mu$). One manufacturer* reported a response time of 0.1 sec (0 to 63%) for thermojunction made from No. 40 gauge wire. Standard ultraminiature couples produced by the same supplier exhibit a response time of 0.05 sec.

In the construction of thermocouples certain precautions must be observed. The material from which the junctions are made must be homogeneous. Attention must be given to the method of fusing the elements to form the active junction. Leeds and Northrup Bulletin RP 1.4 covers many of the important details of construction and describes the techniques for gas, electric arc, and resistance welding.

By virtue of its ability to generate a voltage which can drive a current through a load and thus produce power, the thermocouple is a device which can convert heat to electrical energy. Although the efficiency is low, it has no moving parts to wear out. Thus, in some low power biomedical applications it could be employed to convert the heat of metabolism to electrical energy.

When a current is caused to pass through a pair of thermojunctions, one is cooled and the other is warmed. This phenomenon is known as the Peltier effect. By using this technique it becomes possible to create a heat pump. The Peltier effect is used extensively in industry and is beginning to be employed

---

*High Temperature Instruments Corporation, Philadelphia, Pennsylvania.

in biomedicine. Yamazaki (1965) and Hayward, Ott, Stuart, and Cheshire (1965) have reviewed many of the ways in which the Peltier effect has been employed to cool tissues and biological fluids. Because the cold produced by thermojunctions is easily controllable, precise temperatures can be maintained. The smallness of size, quietness of operation, and freedom from moving parts and the ability to switch over from cooling to heating will undoubtedly make Peltier generators attractive devices for biomedical studies.

II. The Measurement of Physiological Events by Impedance

On some occasions it is necessary to detect a physiological event for which there is no transducer. In many instances, detection can be accomplished if the event can be caused to exhibit a change in dimension, conductivity, or dielectric. Thus with electrodes appropriately placed to encompass the event it is often possible to pass a high frequency alternating current through living tissues and measure a current or current changes which are related to the physiological phenomenon. The opposition to the flow of alternating current is called impedance and is defined as the ratio of the applied voltage divided by the current. Because of the reactance of circuits which contain biological material between a pair of electrodes, the current and voltage are seldom in phase.

The impedance technique is elegantly simple and practical for those phenomena which produce a large change in one or more of the three quantities referred to above. Often the body need not be penetrated and if the electrodes are small, they offer little restraint to the event. Galvanic potentials do not contribute to the detected signals and often the same instrument and electrodes can be employed to detect a variety of physiological events. With appropriately placed electrodes and relatively simple equipment, the impedance method has been employed to show changes in skin impedance throughout the year and in subjects with thyroid dysfunction. Respiration, blood flow, the contraction of the three types of muscle, the activity of nerve cells, the GSR, the position of the eye, heart sounds, the activity of salivary glands, the number of cells in a sample of blood, and the clotting time of blood have all been measured using the impedance technique. A review of these studies was presented by Geddes and Hoff (1964).

When the impedance method is employed, sometimes the impedance is dissected into the resistive and reactive components, at other times the undissected impedance value is employed to describe the physiological event. At present a number of studies are underway to determine the relationship of impedance and its components to certain physiological events. These data are required to determine the calibratibility of the method. In many instances exact calibration in true physiological terms is difficult to achieve. Nonetheless it is to be noted that an uncalibratible signal which directly reflects a physiological event has considerable value for monitoring responses under a variety of experimentally controlled conditions.

When current is passed through living tissue, special consideration must be given to the structures between the electrodes. Often skeletal, cardiac, and smooth muscle, nerve fibers, sensory receptors, and glands form part of the current carrying circuit. The parameters of stimulation for these tissues can be found in their strength duration curves. On these curves the chronaxie, or duration of a stimulus of twice the threshold intensity of an infinitely long stimulus, has been chosen as descriptive of the general time course of an effective stimulus; being short in rapidly acting tissues and long in slowly responding tissues. Stimuli with durations less than the chronaxie must be much higher in intensity to stimulate; typical strength-duration curves rise steeply in this region. Brazier (1951) gave chronaxies of 0.2 msec for mammalian nerve and 100 msec for smooth muscle. To minimize or avoid stimulation, pulses having durations many times shorter than the chronaxie must be employed. Sinusoidal current having frequency of 5000 cps could conceivably stimulate the most rapidly responding tissues, calling attention to the need to use higher frequencies.

Quite apart from stimulating structures within the body, if the electrodes are placed on the surface of the skin, it is desirable to prevent stimulation of sensory receptors immediately under the electrodes. To examine the parameters of this problem, Geddes (1962) determined the threshold of sensation by using a variable frequency sine wave oscillator. This relationship was determined for electrodes on the human thorax and is shown in Fig. 15.6. It illustrates that frequencies high in the kilocycle region must be employed if stimulation of sensory receptors is to be avoided.

The use of high frequencies is further emphasized when the effects of stimulating the myocardium are considered. Strength duration curves of mammalian myocardium are found to have chronaxie values of 0.05 to 0.1 msec (Hickman, Geddes, Hoff, Hinds, Moore, Francis, & Engen, 1963). Slowly repetitive stimuli of these durations evoke single contractions but there is a real danger of ventricular fibrillation if the repetition rate is increased, or if single stimuli of high intensity fall in the early phases of the relative refractory period (the "vulnerable" period of the myocardium). To eliminate any possibility of such potentially lethal stimulation, low intensity and extremely short duration pulses, i.e. high frequencies, are mandatory. Although a frequency of current can be chosen which will not stimulate, it is important to employ an intensity which will not cause heating in the tissues. Even a small amount of heat alters blood supply and cellular metabolism.

There is a large body of literature which describes the impedance of cells and fluids of living organisms. The resistive and reactive components provide information on the electrical nature of the structures making up the biological material. The extensive studies made by Schwan and associates (Schwan, 1955, 1963; Schwan & Li, 1953; Schwan & Kay, 1957) should be consulted by those desirous of investigating this interesting aspect of impedance.

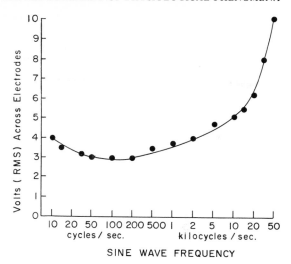

FIG. 15.6. Threshold for sensation using sine wave AC.

When the impedance technique is applied to the measurement of physiological events, two methods are employed. In one, the electrodes are in direct
ohmic contact with the tissue; in the other they are insulated or placed near the
tissue. In the former case, a low impedance circuit results; in the latter a relatively high impedance capacitive circuit is formed.

The extensive studies of impedance plethysmography are examples in which
electrodes are in direct contact with the tissues. Perhaps less familiar are those
in which the electrodes do not contact the biological material. For example
capacitor plates have been placed before and behind the thorax of humans.
Movement of the thoracic cage due to respiration and heart sounds, the beating
of the heart within the chest, and the perfusion of the lungs with the blood
ejected by the heart all modulated the capacitance. In the same category is an
application in which uterine movements in the rat were measured. The mother
rat with the uterus exposed constituted one "plate" of the condenser; the other
was a stationary one placed above the uterus. Uterine movements, which varied
the capacitance, were thereby recorded without direct contact with the uterus.

Two and four electrode systems are currently employed to derive a signal
from a physiological event using the impedance technique. With the two electrode arrangement, two types of circuitry are employed; when four electrodes
are used, one circuit configuration is popular. All circuits require a source of
alternating current and employ a detector which usually consists of an amplifier
connected to a null-type indicator, a vacuum tube voltmeter, or phase-sensitive detector.

In many instances the physiological event changes the impedance by a small amount and it is only the change which contains the useful information. Under these circumstances, the voltage reflecting the change in impedance is amplified and displayed without dissection into resistive and reactive components. If separation of these components is desirable, phase-sensitive detecting systems are necessary.

While the circuits to be described are those most frequently employed to measure impedance, others have been used. When the circuit formed by the electrodes and tissue is mainly capacitive, the change in capacitance produced by the event is often employed to change the frequency of an oscillator. In such instances, a frequency-sensitive detector is employed to recover a signal proportional to the physiological event.

When two electrodes are used, the impedance bridge circuit diagrammed in Fig. 15.7A can be employed. In such an arrangement, the oscillator voltage is applied to one diagonal of the bridge and the detector is connected to the other. When the ratio arms, Z_1 and Z_2, are resistors of equal value, the impedance bridge becomes a comparison bridge. The balancing arm, RC, usually consists of parallel resistance and capacitance decade units which are adjusted to balance the bridge for the nominal impedance between the electrodes. At balance, the value of the balance arm gives the equivalent parallel resistive and capacitive components of the tissue electrode system. If R and C are placed in series and the bridge is balanced, the values of R and C give the equivalent series circuit between the electrodes. These equivalents are valid only for the frequency employed.

In practice, after balancing the bridge, it is customary to unbalance it slightly by the addition of a resistance in series with the subject to guarantee that the voltage from the bridge increases and decreases with an increase and decrease in the impedance of the subject. The amount of resistance added is dictated by the maximum change in impedance which drives the bridge toward the balance point.

A change in impedance which reflects a change in the physiological event unbalances the bridge and produces an output which, after amplification and rectification, is displayed graphically. It must be emphasized that an output is obtained if there is a change in either or both the resistive or reactive components. Identification of the magnitude of each requires the use of a phase-sensitive detector.

The other two electrode system is diagrammed in Fig. 15.7B . Current from the oscillator is fed to the electrodes symmetrically through two resistances (r and r) which are high with respect to the total impedance between the electrode terminals. With this circuit configuration, the current through the subject is determined by these resistances and the oscillator voltage and is relatively independent of the electrode impedance. The detector is connected across the electrodes and the voltage present is a function of the nominal imped-

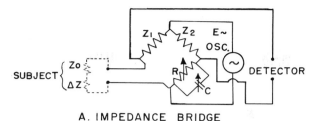

A. IMPEDANCE BRIDGE

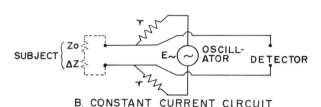

B. CONSTANT CURRENT CIRCUIT

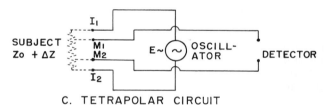

C. TETRAPOLAR CIRCUIT

FIG. 15.7. Impedance measuring circuits.

ance between the electrodes and any change due to the physiological event. Rectification of this voltage, after amplification, yields a large constant signal plus a smaller one proportional to the impedance change due to the physiological event. The larger signal, reflecting the nominal impedance of the tissues between the electrodes is usually blocked by a capacitance or biased off with an opposing voltage.

The third method, that which employs four electrodes, is diagrammed in Fig. 15.7C. In this circuit the oscillator voltage is fed to the insertion electrodes, I_1 and I_2, which are farthest apart on the preparation. Between them are the measuring electrodes, M_1 and M_2, which receive a voltage proportional to the current flowing and the impedance of the tissue. Amplification and rectification of this voltage yields a signal proportional to the tissue impedance between the measuring electrodes and any changes reflecting the physiological event.

Each of the three circuits has unique characteristics which are ideal for some applications and less suitable for others. Of the three, the bridge circuit has been the most commonly employed. The wide range of impedance which can be measured is an attractive feature of this configuration. With appropriate components, it can be employed to detect the changes in capacitive reactance when the electrodes do not touch the subject or the impedance changes when they are in intimate contact with the preparation. Calibration of the balance arm (RC) permits derivation of an equivalent circuit for the preparation between the electrodes at the frequency employed. Comparison between the oscillator and detector voltages and the phase angle between them permits dissection of the output signal into its resistive and reactive components.

One of the difficulties with the bridge circuit relates to isolation of the detector and oscillator circuits above ground potential. If the oscillator and subject are to be grounded, as by grounding their common point, the detector circuit must be lifted above ground by an appropriate isolating device. Practically this requires the use of a special low capacitance transformer.

Another drawback to the bridge circuit lies in its adaptation for physiological recording. If the arm (Z_1) adjacent to the preparation is not high with respect to the impedance of the tissue, there arises the possibility of obtaining a signal from the physiological event dependent on the nominal level of impedance between the electrodes. Such a situation can arise because the amount of current flowing through the preparation will be largely determined by the nominal electrode impedance. Should the electrode impedance change, the size of the voltage produced by the same impedance change due to the physiological event will be dependent on the value of the electrode impedance. This undesirable feature of the bridge circuit can be minimized by a calibration technique in which a resistor of known value is switched into the circuit in series with the subject. To obtain a signal which is not dependent on the electrode impedance, the adjacent arm (Z_1) of the bridge can be made high in resistance with respect to the impedance between the electrodes. This technique converts the bridge to a constant current circuit.

The bridge circuit may be employed to measure the impedance between electrodes which are being used to record a bioelectric event if the oscillator and detector are isolated from each other and ground and if the bridge is made to have the constant current characteristic and the detector has a high input impedance. If the oscillator voltage is low and its frequency is beyond the frequency spectrum of the bioelectric event, only simple filtering is required in the bioelectric recording apparatus.

Many of the inconvenient characteristics of the bridge circuit can be eliminated by use of the constant current circuit shown in Fig. 15.7B. With this circuit, the oscillator voltage is applied to the electrodes through two series resistors, r and r, a hundred or more times the nominal impedance between the electrode terminals. In this circumstance, the magnitude of the electrode impedance will not determine the current flowing through the subject. Thus, the signal due to a change in impedance reflecting the physiological event will not be dependent on the electrode impedance.

In the constant current circuit, the input impedance of the detecting system connected across the electrodes is made high with respect to the impedance between the electrode terminals. While the level of electrode impedance will determine the size of the static signal presented to the detector, the same change in impedance, reflecting the physiological event, will always produce the same size of signal. Another feature of practical value in the physiological application of this circuit is the few controls needed for its operation. If direct-coupled recording is required, only one control is needed to buck out the large voltage due to the nominal impedance between the electrodes. A second control can regulate the amplitude of the display.

A less attractive feature of the constant current circuit is that it can be used to measure events over a smaller range of electrode impedance. As long as the series resistors are high with respect to the impedance between the electrode terminals, the configuration will function as a constant current circuit. However with a wide range of electrode impedance, the amplifier and demodulator are presented with a wide range of carrier voltage on which is superimposed the smaller changes due to the physiological event. For general purpose application of this circuit, there is need to provide a wide dynamic range in the amplifier to guarantee linearity of reproduction. For this reason it sees optimum service when the impedance method is employed to detect physiological events when the impedance between the electrodes is low, i.e. when the electrodes are in intimate electrolytic contact with the subject.

Since the constant current circuit is a balanced system, a requisite which sometimes presents practical difficulties is isolation of both the oscillator and detector from ground and each other. When accomplished, no change in operation will occur if either or neither side of the input is grounded. Provision of this feature and a high input impedance in the amplifier-demodulator circuit permit connecting the constant current circuit to electrodes which are employed for the measurement of other events.

A prime requisite of the constant current system is high stability in oscillator voltage. Small variations in amplitude, such as noise or ripple, will appear with the output signal. When direct-coupled recording is employed, the stability requirements for the oscillator can be lessened by deriving the bucking voltage from the oscillator.

With the constant current circuit it is also possible to employ a detector which will permit dissection of the impedance into its resistive and reactive components. In many applications this is unnecessary. With the circuit shown in Fig. 15.7B, a change in either capacitive reactance or resistance or both will alter the output of the system. If only the change in impedance, without its dissection, reflects the physiological event, the constant current circuit with its few controls and freedom from influence of nominal electrode impedance, is unusually practical for the measurement of a variety of physiological events.

The tetrapolar arrangement, shown in Fig. 15.7C appears to be a favorite of those who measure peripheral pulses by the method known as impedance plethysmography. Nyboer (1944, 1950, 1959) and Bagno (1959) have presented good accounts of the physiological application of this type of circuit. In this configuration, the current is admitted to the subject by electrodes which are distant from the measuring electrodes. With a uniformly conducting medium there exists a uniform distribution of the current through the preparation which lies between the measuring electrodes. With a high impedance detecting system, the voltage picked up across the measuring electrodes is independent of their impedance. If the output impedance of the oscillator is made high with respect to the impedance between the injection electrodes, I_1 and I_2, the constant current feature is achieved. Such a condition permits accurate measurement of impedance changes which occur between the detecting electrodes which reflect changes in the internal current distribution.

With the tetrapolar circuit, a high order of stability is usually attained by bucking the oscillator voltage against the detected signal. When this is done it is possible to employ a phase-sensitive detector to dissect the impedance change into its resistive and reactive components. Less attractive, in some instances, is the fact that the tetrapolar method requires the application of four electrodes to the subject. In some cases this may be inconvenient and unduly restraining.

When the impedance being measured by any of the three circuits just described is not dissected into its reactive and resistive components, it is not at all times clear which component contains the information on the physiological event. In some studies, the equivalent circuit is strongly reactive while in others the configuration is resistive. More studies remain to be carried out to discover, in each case, whether the resistive or reactive component contains the most useful physiological information. To illustrate some of the events which can be detected by the use of impedance, the following examples are cited.

Respiration

Respiration is easily detected by the impedance method. With electrodes placed on the thorax of man and the experimental animal, the impedance between them is modulated by respiration. With inspiration there is an increase in impedance. The size of the impedance change per unit of air moved depends primarily on the size and location of the electrodes, the size of the subject, and the species.

Goldensohn and Zablow (1959), Geddes, Hoff, Hickman, and Moore (1962), McCally, Barnard, Robins, and Marko (1963), Allison, Holmes, and Nyboer (1964), Kubicek, Kinnen, and Edin (1964), Baker and Geddes (1965), and Hamilton, Beard, and Kory (1965) have all carried out studies which indicate that there is a good correlation between impedance change and the volume of air breathed. Baker and Geddes (1965) reported 50 kc impedance changes of 1.5 to 6.5 ohms per L for adults of heavy and light builds. In these studies the electrodes were placed along midaxillary lines at the level of the xiphoid process.

In the dog, with electrodes in the same location, they have obtained a range of impedance change of 50 to 70 ohms per L of air breathed.

Fig. 15.8 is a record of transthoracic impedance and respired volume measured by a spirometer. While this record was being made, the subject was directed to vary his breathing pattern to demonstrate the correlation between impedance change and air volume. The electrocardiogram, shown on the same record, was obtained from the same electrodes employed to detect the respiratory impedance changes (Geddes, 1962).

Figure 15.9 illustrates the respiratory impedance changes in the anesthetized dog. In this study the electrodes were located at the level of the fifth pair of ribs along midaxillary lines. The electrocardiogram was recorded from the same pair of electrodes. Quite apparent in the respiratory record are cardiac impulses which were made more apparent by arresting respiration by stimulation of the afferent fibers of the left vagus nerve.

The Impedance Cardiogram

In the impedance respiration record, the small changes in impedance which are correlated with cardiac activity can be better detected by placing electrodes, consisting of strips of flexible metal braid, around the neck and around the chest at the level of the xiphoid process. With this configuration the impedance changes due to respiration are attenuated. Fig. 15.10 illustrates the impedance cardiogram made with electrodes in this location. The electrocardiogram, derived from the same electrodes, is shown for reference purposes.

The factors which underlie the thoracic impedance cardiogram have not as yet been completely identified. It is obvious that electrodes in this location "see" both extrathoracic and intrathoracic circulations and that there are obvious difficulties in delineating the contribution of each. To evaluate some of the factors underlying the phenomenon, Bonjer, van der Berg, and Dirken (1952), in a series of ingenious experiments in the dog, offered evidence that the impedance pulse reflects the systolic discharge from the right heart which distributes blood into the pulmonary vascular circuit which occupies a prominent position between the electrodes. Because of this fact, considerable attention is being given to further study of the impedance cardiogram with a view to its calibration in terms of stroke volume. Because there is as yet no simple indirect method for determining cardiac output (stroke volume × heart rate), impedance cardiography, if calibratible, would be a most valuable technique. Preliminary studies in this direction carried out by Patterson, Kubicek, Kinnen, Noren, and Witsoe (1964) are most promising.

Rheoencephalography

If electrodes are placed on the head of man and animals and a record is made of the impedance changes between them, there occur pulsatile changes which are synchronous with cardiac activity. Although the electrodes encom-

ECG

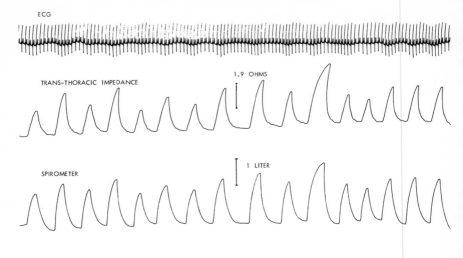

FIG. 15.8. Respiration and the electrocardiogram in the human.

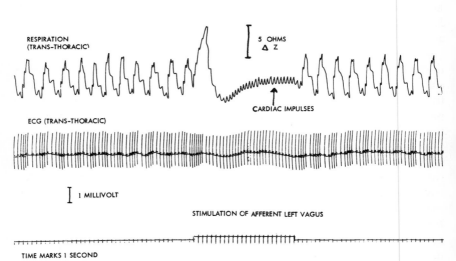

FIG. 15.9. Respiration and the electrocardiogram in the dog.

pass two circulations, the extracranial and intracranial, there is evidence that a substantial part of the impedance pulse reflects cerebral circulation. Another chapter in this book discusses the various clinical applications of rheoencephalography (REG). The history, many of the factors which contribute to the

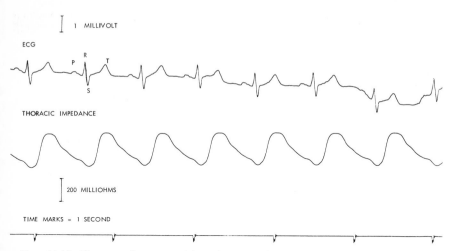

FIG. 15.10. Electrocardiogram and impedance cardiogram in the human.

signal, and some of the changes which are seen in disease were reviewed by Jenkner (1962), Lifshitz (1963, a and b), Geddes, Hoff, Hall, and Millar (1964) and McHenry (1965).

A typical REG of a normal subject is shown in Fig. 15.11. In this record, the electrodes were arrayed as shown; forehead to mastoid, and the impedance changes were measured at 70 kc. The first and fifth channels are the EEG and the second and fourth, the REG. Lead II ECG was included for reference purposes. The EEG and REG recordings were made from the same pair of electrodes.

In this record, it is observed that the REGs from the right and left sides are slightly different in wave form. This is a fairly common finding in normal subjects. The pulse transmission time from the heart to the head is evident from the relationship between the QRS complex of the ECG and the onset of the impedance pulse. This interval is often described as the appearance time. It is customary to measure the amplitude and the rate of rise of the impedance pulse. At present these parameters constitute the quantitative measurements derived from the rheoencephalogram. While dramatic alterations can be produced in the REG by a variety of factors, the clinical significance of this signal awaits further investigation.

Eye Movements

In psychophysiological investigations, the position of the eye and the movement it executes are often factors of interest. A record of this event is called an electro-oculogram (EOG). Traditionally there have been two methods em-

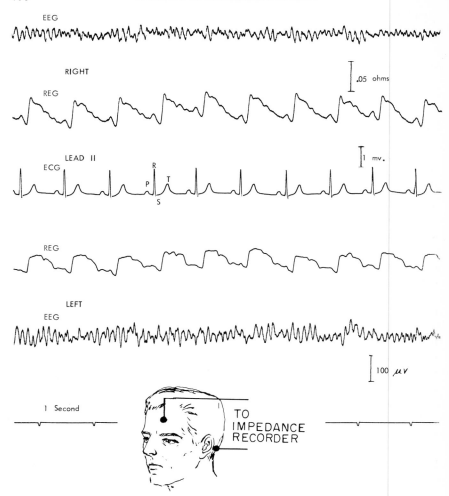

FIG. 15.11. Electroencephalogram, rheoencephalogram, and electrocardiogram in the human.

ployed to measure eye position. In one method, two pairs of electrodes are placed above and below or at the inner and outer canthis of one or both eyes. Kris (1960) has shown that the voltage appearing between such pairs of electrodes is a function of the deviation of the eye from its central position. The other method, one of high precision but more difficult to employ, is due to Robinson (1963) who embedded search coils in a contact lens securely applied to the cornea. When the eye was placed in an alternating magnetic field, the voltages induced in the coils were a function of the position of the eye. Both methods have their advantages and difficulties. The former method provides a small signal which is often accompanied by muscle action potentials and galvanic electrode potentials. The latter requires the use of a specially fabricated contact lens and rather complex equipment.

Sullivan and Weltman (1963) have shown that eye movements can be recorded by using the impedance method. The author has verified their observations on man and the horse. Because a signal free from electrode potentials and muscle artifacts can be obtained with open or closed eyes, the technique has some attractive features. To illustrate the type of signal obtained, a pair of electrodes were placed above and below one eye of a human subject. The electrodes were connected to a direct-coupled impedance recorder and to a high gain preamplifier to permit recording the electro-oculogram along with the impedance oculogram. Figure 15.12 illustrates the record obtained. The upper trace shows the impedance oculogram (ZOG), the lower the EOG. The subject was instructed to gaze from one object to another; both in a vertical plane. In the center of the record the subject was instructed to clench his jaw. The EOG record illustrates the muscle action potentials which are absent from the impedance tracing.

Figure 15.13 is an impedance oculogram made on a horse during the induction of anesthesia (Geddes, McCrady, & Hoff, 1965). In this species there are conspicuous oscillatory eye movements when the animal is lightly anesthetized. The figures on the record indicate the frequency of the eye movements in oscillations per min. Although the phenomenon is somewhat dependent on the type of anesthetic employed, many veterinarians employ the eyeball movements as indicative of the depth of anesthesia.

Sullivan and Weltman described a nearly linear relationship between impedance change and eye position in vertical plane. The author has verified these observations. When the impedance method is employed to record horizontal eye movements, the size of the signal and the linearity appear to be less. No studies have as yet been conducted to determine the optimum location of two pairs of electrodes to obtain purely orthogonal signals.

Muscular Contraction

Frequently it is necessary to detect the contraction of skeletal muscle without attachment of the tendon to a myograph. Traditionally the EMG has been employed as an indicator of muscular contraction but this signal does not directly reflect the amount of contraction and in some circumstances cannot be conveniently employed. Another method, developed by Geddes (1966), consists of measuring the force developed at the belly of a muscle by the use of the caliper myograph. In instances when it is not practical to apply such a myograph and when the EMG cannot be employed, it may be advisable to investigate use of the impedance method to derive a signal related to muscular contraction.

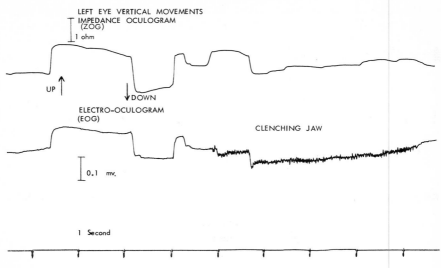

FIG. 15.12. Impedance oculogram and electro-oculogram in the human.

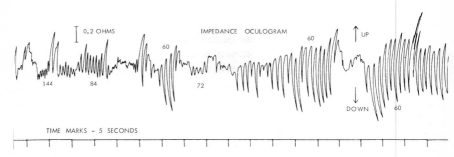

FIG. 15.13. Impedance oculogram in the horse.

Dubuisson (1933) recorded the contraction of frog muscle by recording impedance changes between pin electrodes inserted into the muscle under examination. The author has confirmed Dubuisson's data and applied the technique to humans using surface electrodes. To illustrate the type of signal obtainable, two pairs of electrodes were placed on the skin over the biceps muscle. One pair was placed over the origin and insertion, the other was placed across the belly of the muscle. Impedance changes were recorded at 50 kc while the subject contracted the muscle voluntarily.

The records obtained are shown in Fig. 15.14. With the electrodes placed along the muscle, a standing subject lifted and lowered a 5 lb weight from a position of full extension of the elbow through an angle of approximately

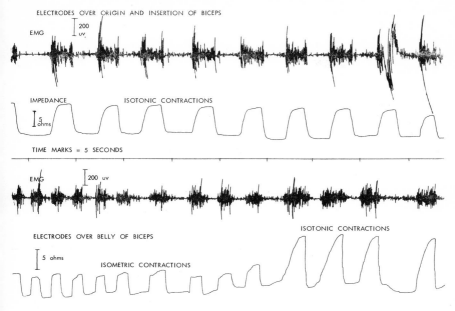

ELECTRODES OVER ORIGIN AND INSERTION OF BICEPS

EMG   200 uv

IMPEDANCE   ISOTONIC CONTRACTIONS

5 ohms

TIME MARKS = 5 SECONDS

EMG   200 uv

ELECTRODES OVER BELLY OF BICEPS

ISOTONIC CONTRACTIONS

5 ohms   ISOMETRIC CONTRACTIONS

FIG. 15.14. Impedance myograms and the electromyogram in the human.

90°. The EMG and impedance changes were recorded from the same electrodes. In the lower part of the record, below the time line, are the recordings obtained from electrodes over the belly of the muscle. In the first portion of the record the weight was clamped, resulting in isometric contraction of the muscle. Just past the middle of the record, the weight was released and the muscle contracted isotonically.

When the impedance method is employed to record muscular contractions, great care must be exercised in interpreting the records. The impedance change is not necessarily proportional to the force and amount of contraction. The electrodes measure only the impedance between them which during muscular contraction may vary with other factors. Furthermore, the greatest impedance change may occur at the beginning, middle, or near the end of contraction. However, despite the lack of direct correlation with muscular contraction, the impedance method can provide an easily obtainable signal indicative of muscular activity.

Conclusion

The practicality of the impedance method to detect a variety of events and to measure a bioelectric event from the same pair of electrodes are perhaps its greatest attributes. The chief drawback relates to calibrating the impedance signal in true physiological terms. In some cases, calibration can be achieved, in others it is virtually impossible. It is perhaps too early to state the true value of the method.

III. General Specifications for Transducers

A transducer is in reality the sense organ for the electronic processing equipment. By its very nature it is a highly specialized device possessing sensitivity to but one type of energy. For this reason it is difficult to discuss the merits of these devices in a general manner. Nonetheless a few characteristics of high quality transducers can be stated which will serve as a basis for their evaluation.

Irrespective of the event being measured, the transducer, insofar as possible, must obey the first rule of instrumentation, i.e. when connected to the event, it must not alter it. In psychophysiological studies, this is not always possible and the possible degree of alteration must always be borne in mind. Frequently, it is necessary to employ indirect methods which partially isolate the transducer from the event. When this occurs it becomes essential that the transducer exhibit a high degree of selectivity for the phenomenon being measured so that adequate rejection of other events occurs.

The transducer should obey the three criteria for the faithful reproduction of an event. Briefly, these are amplitude linearity, frequency response, and freedom from phase distortion. To the first requirement must be added adequate dynamic range in one or both directions so that large and small amplitude signals can be handled without distortion or causing irreversible damage to the transducer. In addition, the input-output characteristic must be free from hysterisis and spurious signals.

The second criterion requires that the frequency response of the transducer must be equal to or better than that dictated by harmonic analysis of the wave form of the event. The third criterion, freedom from phase distortion, requires that frequency components differing in time at the input of the transducer must appear with the same time differential after transduction. These requirements will be described in detail in the section which discusses the criteria which must be satisfied for the faithful reproduction of an event.

Although it is highly desirable to obtain a linear signal from all transducers, there are instances in which this is not always possible. Occasionally a transducer produces a signal which is not directly proportional to the event. For example, the resistance change of thermistors is not linear with temperature. Under such circumstances, linearizing networks are necessary unless presentation of the event is acceptable with a nonlinear calibration. Sometimes a nonlinear signal arises by the nature of the physiological event itself. For example, the redness of the blood reflecting the degree of saturation of the blood with oxygen, is related to a logarithmic ratio of red and infrared transmissions. Under these conditions it becomes difficult to obtain a single transducer which produces a signal linearly related to oxygen saturation.

There may exist many transducers for a given event. In choosing the best one it is useful to reconsider Rein's criterion, maximum efficiency in the transducers, i.e. a large electrical signal per unit of physiological event is a highly desirable quality. Moreover the output should be examined for stability both in terms of sensitivity and base line or zero event signal.

The means for calibration should be carefully investigated. A transducer which does not lend itself to calibration directly in terms of the physiological event has limited value and sees service in producing wave forms which can only be analyzed in the time domain. For example frequency, wave form, and time relation to another event form the basis of analysis of data acquired by uncalibratible transducers.

Finally, transducers tend to be expensive devices. For this reason selection of a particular type should also be based on its ability to be incorporated into an existing processing or display system. Fulfilling such a requirement paves the way for the creation of a modular system which can accept a variety of transducers for many purposes.

Ultimately the transduced event is displayed by an indicating device. It is important to consider this fact because the type and use of the data frequently dictate the degree of precision required. Precision and cost are inextricably linked and often become the basis for bargaining.

IV. Recording Electrodes

In presenting an electrophysiological event to an amplifier, a pair of electrodes fulfills the role of a bioelectric transducer. As such the electrodes must be designed to transfer the bioelectric event efficiently and with minimum distortion to an amplifier input stage with the appropriate matching characteristics. It is usually the event and its anatomical location which dictate the type of electrodes to be used and the characteristics of the electrodes which dictate the type of amplifier input circuit required. When large area electrodes are employed, the restrictions on input impedance are not too severe and most vacuum tube and high input impedance transistor amplifiers suffice. However, when small electrodes and in particular microelectrodes with their high impedance are employed, special low capacitance high resistance input circuits must be used to transfer the bioelectric event to the amplifying system. Thus, distortionless insertion of the bioelectric event into the recording apparatus requires that special consideration must be given to the electrical characteristics of the electrodes and the input stage of the amplifier.

Types of Electrodes

Many types of electrodes have been used to detect bioelectric events. A few of the more familiar types are sketched in Figs. 15.15 and 15.16. A practical

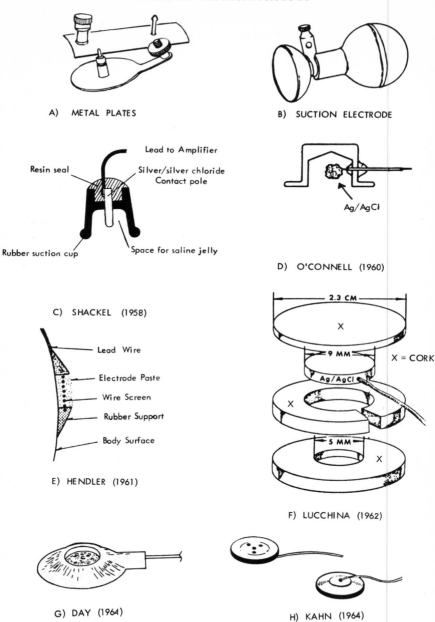

A)   METAL PLATES

B)   SUCTION ELECTRODE

Lead to Amplifier

Resin seal   Silver/silver chloride
                    Contact pole

Ag/AgCl

Rubber suction cup   Space for saline jelly

D)   O'CONNELL (1960)

C)   SHACKEL   (1958)

Lead Wire

Electrode Paste

Wire Screen

Rubber Support

Body Surface

E)   HENDLER   (1961)

2.3 CM

X

9 MM   X = CORK

Ag/AgCl

X

5 MM

X

F)   LUCCHINA   (1962)

G)   DAY   (1964)

H)   KAHN   (1964)

FIG. 15.15. Recording electrodes I. *E*, from Hendler, E., & Santa Maria, L.J. *Aerospace Med.*, 1961, *32*: 128; *F*, Lucchina, G. G., & Phipps, C. G. *Aerospace Med.*, 1962, *33*: 230.

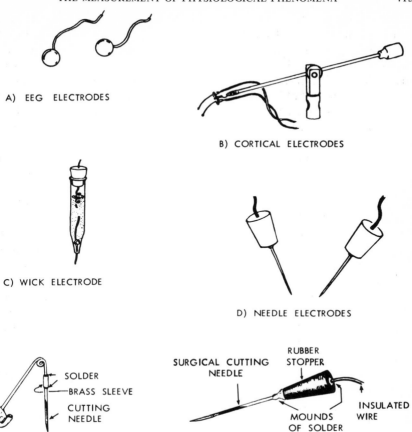

A) EEG ELECTRODES

B) CORTICAL ELECTRODES

C) WICK ELECTRODE

D) NEEDLE ELECTRODES

SOLDER
BRASS SLEEVE
CUTTING
NEEDLE

SAFETY PIN
ELECTRODE

SURGICAL CUTTING
NEEDLE

RUBBER
STOPPER

INSULATED
WIRE

MOUNDS
OF SOLDER

E) CUTTING ELECTRODES

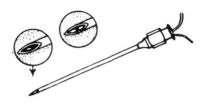

F) HYPODERMIC ELECTRODE

FIG. 15.16. Recording electrodes II.

means for their comparison is on the basis of electrode area* and an important characteristic is the impedance measured between the electrode terminals. When large area electrodes are used, it is customary to measure the direct current resistance between the electrode terminals. However, direct current resistance does not by itself describe the electrical circuit constituted by the electrodes and the biological material. To adequately describe the circuit, it becomes necessary to know the resistive and reactive components at all frequencies. It is also important to note that the term electrode impedance, as frequently employed when surface electrodes are being described, is the impedance measured between the electrode terminals which includes the tissue-electrode interface impedance at each electrode as well as that of the biological material between the electrodes. In general, the smaller the electrode, the higher the impedance. The frequency-impedance characteristics of electrodes of various sizes will be discussed in some detail in this chapter.

Among the largest recording electrodes are those used for electrocardiography (Fig. 15.15A), consisting of two rectangular or circular plates of German silver (nickel silver)† or nickel-plated steel. When applied to a subject with electrode jelly, typical direct current resistance values are in the range of 2 to 10 kilohms; the high frequency impedance amounts to a few hundred ohms. In 1910, James and Williams reported that such plate electrodes replaced the more cumbersome electrolytic electrodes traditionally used for recording the ECG. As used then, the metal plate electrodes were separated from the subject by cotton or felt pads soaked in concentrated saline.

A variant of the electrocardiograph electrode which permits quick application is one contained in a strip of adhesive tape. The electrode (Telemedics, 1961) consists of a light weight metallic screen backed by a pad for electrolytic paste. Measuring approximately 1½ in. square, the electrode adheres well to the skin and exhibits a relatively low resistance. The adhesive backing holds the electrode in place and retards evaporation of the electrolyte. These electrodes and standard plate electrodes are commercially available.

A very useful type of electrode is the suction cup electrode (Fig. 15.15B), the forerunners of which were described by Roth (1933) and Ungerleider (1939). The suction electrode is extremely practical as an ECG chest electrode and is well suited for attachment to flat surfaces of the body and to regions where the underlying tissue is soft. Although this electrode is physically large, it has a small area since only the rim is in contact with the skin.

An electrode, popular in aerospace studies and frequently used on exercising subjects, is the floating electrode, occasionally referred to as the liquid electrode.

---

*The area referred to here is calculated from the physical dimensions of the electrodes and not the effective area which, in the case of many specially prepared electrodes, is often much greater.
†Nickel silver is an alloy of nickel, copper, and zinc and contains no silver.

In this type of electrode, the metal does not contact the subject directly; contact is made via an electrolytic bridge. The possible reasons for the superior performance of this type of electrode will be discussed toward the end of this chapter.

The principle embodied in the floating electrode was used by the electro-physiologists of the last century. At that time it was customary to employ a metallic electrode in contact with an aqueous solution of one of its salts contained in a porous plug. Surrounding the plug was a saline solution which contacted the subject. As time passed, the awkwardness of this type of electrode led investigators to contain the salt of the electrode metal in a kaolin plug or paste which adhered to the electrode. Between the kaolin and the subject was a film of saline. Occasionally the saline was omitted and contact with the subject was via the salt of the electrode metal.

The modern version of the floating electrode takes many forms. Among the first to separate the electrode from the skin and provide contact via a thick film of electrolyte were Clark and Lacey (1950). Their use of the electrode was in recording the GSR. Shackel (1958) embodied the principle in an interesting suction cup floating electrode consisting of a silver-silver chloride rod mounted centrally in the cup which was filled with electrode jelly. This electrode, shown in Fig. 15.15C, was found to have remarkably high electrical stability despite movement of the electrode on the skin. The direct current resistance between a pair applied to the forearm was 2000 to 7000 ohms.

A similar high stability floating electrode, consisting of a silver-silver chloride sponge in a small enclosure resembling a top hat, was described by O'Connell, Tursky, and Orne (1960). This electrode, illustrated in Fig. 15.15D, was designed for GSR measurements. A type of floating electrode popular in aero-space medicine, and now extensively employed for recording bioelectric events on moving subjects, is shown in Fig. 15.15E. In these electrodes, the metallic conductor is mounted in a flat rubber or plastic washer which is cemented to the skin by special adhesives.* The washer holds the electrode away from the skin and contact is established via a thick film of electrolytic paste. Choice of the electrode materials and electrolytes depends on the event and circumstances of measurement. Monel wire screens (Hendler & Santa Maria, 1961), crossed tinned copper wires in a segment of rubber tubing (Rowley, Glagov, & Stoner, 1961), stainless steel screens (Roman & Lamb, 1962), chlorided silver screens and plates (Day & Lippitt, 1964; Skov & Simons, 1965), and discs of a compressed mixture of silver and silver chloride (Lucchina & Phipps, 1962 and 1963; Kahn, 1964) have been employed with considerable success. The direct current resistances measured between a pair of these electrodes applied

---

*Eastman 910, Eastman Kodak Company, Rochester, New York. Stomaseal, 3M Manufacturing Company, St. Paul 6, Minnesota.

to the skin varies considerably with the method of preparing of the skin, the type of conducting electrolyte, and the area of the electrodes. In practice direct current resistances varying from about 2,000 to 50,000 ohms are typical.

Hendler's and Day's electrodes are illustrated in Fig. 15.15. In Day's, holes were drilled in the silver electrode before chloriding. There were no holes in Skov's electrode. Lucchina's (Lucchina & Phipps, 1962) electrode, shown in Fig. 15.15F consisted of a disc of equal parts of silver and silver chloride made by first grinding then compressing the mixture under a pressure of 20,000 psi. The disc was then mounted in a cork ring which held the electrode away from the skin. With a pair of these electrodes applied to the abraded human thorax, the authors reported a direct current resistance of 500 to 2,000 ohms.

Lucchina and Phipps made a series of electrodes having different amounts of silver and silver chloride. They measured the voltage difference and resistance between similar pairs. They found that decreasing the amount of silver chloride decreased the resistance but increased the voltage difference. The converse was found to be true. Although they noted that the presence of a very tiny amount of silver chloride reduced the potential difference between a pair of electrodes, they recommended a 30% silver and 70% silver chloride mixture as the best compromise between voltage difference and resistance.

The electrodes described by Kahn (1964) are illustrated in Fig. 15.15H. In these electrodes, which are commercially available,* the disc of silver-silver chloride is mounted behind a baffle in which holes have been drilled. Contact between the electrode and skin is via the electrode jelly which fills the holes.

In electroencephalography, solder pellets, a few millimeters in diameter, are sometimes applied to the cleaned scalp and contact is established with an electrode paste. Occasionally small needles are inserted subcutaneously. In most studies, however, small silver discs approximately 7 mm in diameter such as those shown in Fig. 15.16A are employed. Sometimes the discs are chlorided and occasionally they are separated from the scalp by a washer of soft felt. Contact with the cleaned scalp in both cases is via an electrolytic paste. In practice the direct current resistance measured between a pair of these electrodes on the scalp varies between 3,000 and 15,000 ohms.

When the electrical activity of the exposed cortex is recorded, it is customary to employ silver ball electrodes approximately 1 mm in diameter, bare or chlorided and sometimes covered with a small cotton pad. Geddes (1949) described the preparation and use of these electrodes which are illustrated in Fig. 15.16B. The direct current resistance between a pair of these electrodes spaced a few centimeters apart on the human brain is in the kilohm range.

In some studies, it is often necessary to employ a pair of what have come to be known as nonpolarizable electrodes. One type frequently employed is illustrated in Fig. 15.16C and is usually made from a medicine dropper filled

---

*Beckman Instruments, Spinco Division, Palo Alto, California.

with physiological saline and terminated by a cotton wick at the tapered end. A cork in the large end holds a chlorided silver wire in contact with the electrolyte in the dropper. These electrodes were described and thoroughly investigated by Burr (1944 and 1950). They are frequently used for direct current recording because a pair can be made having a voltage difference as small as 10 μv or less. The direct current resistance of two cotton wick electrodes in saline is in the kilohm range. Kahn (1965) described electrodes of this type in which the metal consisted of a compressed mixture of silver and silver chloride. The electrolyte employed was saline and in some instances plasma. The voltage difference between a saline filled pair varied between 10 and 50 μv. When 0.1 μamp was passed through the electrodes for 15 sec, the polarization voltage was of the order of 5 μv.

Electromyographers often find it convenient to use a variety of electrodes; some are placed on the skin while others are inserted directly into the muscle under examination. For precise localization, steel needle electrodes are inserted directly into the muscle. Usually the electrodes are coated with an insulating varnish and bare only at the tip. Frequently one needle electrode is paired with a metallic plate on the surface of the skin. Figure 15.16D illustrates this type of electrode which was described by Jasper, Johnson, and Geddes (1945). When the shaft of the needle electrode is coated with insulating varnish, the area of the electrodes in contact with active tissue is quite small. In the case of Jasper's needle electrode, the area was approximately 0.2 sq mm.

Occasionally it is necessary to record from animals with thick dry hides and the use of plate electrodes is impractical. To overcome this problem, Geddes, McCrady, Hoff, and Moore (1964) developed two types of cutting electrodes shown in Fig. 15.16E. These electrodes are made like surgical cutting needles and have bevelled sharpened shanks which permit easy insertion through the hide.

When cutting electrodes are used, movement artifacts can be minimized by inserting the needles in a manner such that the area of the bare metal electrode in contact with the tissues is constant. The safety pin electrode should be inserted through a pinch of skin and fastened. When the pinch is released, the skin will press against the head and spring of the safety pin. The head, back, and spring of the pin should be insulated. The connecting wire is soldered to the brass sleeve and the sleeve and solder connection are all covered with insulation to prevent their contact with body fluids. To provide strain relief for the solder joint, the connecting wire is passed through the coils of the spring and tied. Similarly with the needle electrode shown on the *right*, it is advisable to insulate the soldered portions of the electrode and part of the shank above the cutting edge and insert the electrode into the animal far enough so that no bare needle protrudes.

When recordings are to be made on subjects experiencing large vibration or acceleration forces, it is important to make the electrodes as small and light as possible. Thompson and Patterson (1958), Sullivan and Weltman (1961), Roman and Lamb (1962), Lucchina and Phipps (1962), and Simons, Prather, and Coombs (1965) have described such electrodes and demonstrated their value. Sullivan and Weltman's electrode weighed 2 mg and consisted of a Mylar film 1 mil in thickness on which was deposited a metal film. The center of the electrode was filled with electrode jelly and Eastman 910 adhesive* was employed to cement the electrode to the subject. Remarkably clean electro-myograms were obtained on exercising subjects. Thompson's electrodes consisted of small pieces of silvered nylon applied to an area of skin which had been lightly sanded. The electrodes were applied with a special conducting adhesive. While the electrodes were small and performed remarkably well during vigorous movement, the resistance between pairs was in the vicinity of 100,000 ohms, a characteristic which demanded the use of an amplifier with a very high input impedance.

Edelberg† described a most interesting low mass electrode which was made by electrodeposition of silver into the layers of the skin. The resistance between a pair of silver depositions was remarkably low and no electrolytic paste was required; the silver spots were virtually terminals on the subject. The only drawbacks to these remarkable electrodes are the black spot made by the silver and their limited life. As time passes the silver undergoes chemical changes and the spot eventually disappears. Nonetheless, the obvious advantages of these electrodes indicate that investigation of their use will continue.

Precise localization of bioelectric events requires the use of very small electrodes. Two types of such electrodes are the monopolar and bipolar hypodermic electrodes (Fig. 15.16F) which were first described by Adrian and Bronk (1929). The monopolar electrode was made with No. 36 gauge wire (96 μ in diameter) and the bipolar electrode contained two No. 44 gauge wires (80 μ in diameter). These electrodes exhibit direct current resistances in the range of tens of kilohms.

Electrodes described as micro in dimensions are of two general types; metallic and nonmetallic. The former type usually consists of a slender needle of a suitable metal sharpened to a fine point or formed by electrolytic etching. Grundfest and Campbell (1942) described the method of grinding fine wires to produce 5 to 10 μ points. Grundfest, Sengstaken, and Oettinger (1950) gave complete details of making 1 μ stainless steel electrodes by the technique of "electropointing." Hubel (1957) described a similar method for electropointing tungsten wire to obtain electrodes with a tip diameter of 0.4 μ. Such metal microelectrodes are coated almost to the micro tip with an insulating material, frequently baked hard in an oven. Guld (1964) described a technique for insulating platinum microelectrodes with a glass covering.

---

*Eastman Kodak Company, Rochester, New York.
†R. Edelberg, personal communication, 1963.

Sometimes microelectrodes are made by heat-pulling a metallic powder in a glass tube to capillary dimensions. The metal and glass employed must have the same thermal coefficient of expansion or breakage will occur during cooling. The electrode surface is formed by breaking the fine capillary to expose the bare metal. In this way the glass forms the electrical insulation. This technique was described by Svaetichin (1951) and Dowben and Rose (1953). Metal microelectrodes have also been constructed by electrolytic deposition of a metal in a microcapillary glass tube. Details of this method were given by Weale (1951).

The nonmetallic microelectrode consists of a glass micropipette filled with an electrolyte compatible with the fluid inside or bathing the cell being studied. Connection to the electrolyte is made by means of a larger wire dipping into the electrolyte filling the shank of the micropipette. It thus resembles the larger wick electrode made from a medicine dropper (Fig. 15.16C). There are numerous descriptions of this technique in the literature and many microelectrode fabricating machines are commercially available. Excellent reviews of the fabrication techniques have been presented by Kennard (1958) and Frank and Becker (1964).

In the search for precise knowledge of the mechanisms underlying bioelectric phenomena, the microelectrode has made it possible to measure the magnitude of the resting membrane potential and the action potential of an intact single cell and even parts of it. Previously, attempts to measure the membrane and monophasic action potential relied on killing or damaging the cells under one electrode and placing the other electrode on uninjured cells. There arose much ambiguity concerning the conditions at the site of injury. However, with the advent of electrodes small enough to be inserted into single cells without excessive damage, it became possible to measure membrane and action potentials with precision.

Electrode Electrolytes

When metallic electrodes are placed on the surface of the body, conducting pastes or electrolytic solutions are employed. If the electrodes are to be left in place for extended periods, evaporation of the electrolytic solution usually occurs. In some instances it is possible to locate the electrodes in body cavities and use the fluids in these regions as the electrolytic conductor; in others the cavity can be employed as a container for the electrolyte. Although not all of the body cavities can be employed in unanesthetized subjects, consideration should be given to use of the nose, ear, mouth, axilla, navel, rectum, vagina, and urethra. Sometimes electrodes in these and other areas can be combined with other transducers such as electrical thermometers or heart sound pickups. Often the metallic cases of these devices can serve as active, indifferent, or ground electrodes. In some fluid-coupled pressure transducers, the fluid within them makes direct contact with the metallic case of the transducer which is usually grounded. If this occurs, a ground connection is automatically placed on the subject. While this may be desirable in many instances, it may constitute a hazard in others. For example if the subject comes in contact with the "hot" side of a voltage which is ground-referred, the low resistance ground path through the transducer might result in the passage of a sizeable current through the subject if the voltage is high.

In many instances careful attention must be paid to the choice of the electrolyte employed with a surface electrode for it may produce its own effects. The constituents of some electrode pastes can produce allergic reactions, erythema, or discoloration of the skin. Some species of ions stimulate cells, others are toxic. For example a high concentration of calcium chloride, as was used in the older electrode jellies and pastes, causes sloughing of the skin. The ionic composition of electrolytes merits special consideration when recording the GSR. For example Edelberg and Burch (1962), conducted a series of ingenious experiments in which the responses at test and control sites were compared and found that solutions of molar (M) calcium chloride, ammonium chloride, and potassium sulfate potentiated the GSR by 100 to 300%. Aluminum chloride potentiated the GSR by 1000% and zinc chloride (0.5 M) approximately doubled the response. Very dilute acids, alkalis, and detergents decreased the response. A solution of 0.05 M sodium chloride had negligible effect on the GSR and he recommended its use for this purpose.

The characteristics of several of the earliest electrode jellies were investigated by Bell, Knox, and Small (1939). Using lead electrodes (14 × 5 cm) on human subjects they measured the direct current resistance and 300 cycle impedance with the following under the electrodes: 1% saline; a paste of saline, glycerine, water, and pumice; soft green soap, and a commercially available electrode jelly which contained crushed quartz. They found that when the electrodes were wrapped in gauze and soaked in saline and applied to the subjects, the direct current resistance was highest (3080 ohms). With the other electrolytes in direct contact with the electrodes and skin, the resistances were 2010, 2040, and 1100 ohms, respectively. By analyzing their results they quickly found that the presence of an abrasive reduced the resistance considerably. They were able to show that the resistance with green soap was divided by three when crushed quartz was added and the mixture rubbed into the skin. They also found that lightly rubbing the dry skin with glass paper (fine sand paper) "so that it lost its sheen and white color" and then applying the electrolyte, the direct contact resistance and impedance values were very low and extremely stable.

A similar method for obtaining a low resistance was described by Shackel (1959). The method, which he called the skin drilling technique, is painless when properly employed. To use it, the area of skin where the electrode is to be placed is first cleaned with an antiseptic solution. The region is then abraded with a dental burr in a hand tool. Only the epidermis is eroded and no blood is drawn. The amount of abrasion required depends on the type of skin. Kado* reported that deeply pigmented skin requires more abrasion. In a few seconds, tissue fluid can be seen seeping into the drilled depression. The area is then cleaned with alcohol or acetone. If the skin has been drilled to the proper depth the subject should feel a slight tingling sensation when cleaned with either of these solutions. The electrode jelly is then applied and the electrode secured to the region. To test the value of the technique, Shackel compared the resistance values obtained with and without drilling. The drilled sites constantly exhibited resistances one-fifth to one-tenth of those of undrilled areas. When the electrodes are removed the drilled site is again cleaned with an antiseptic solution. Lanolin cream is then rubbed in and the site soon becomes invisible.

Another method of obtaining a low resistance contact with the skin was described by Asa, Crews, Rothfield, Lewis, Zucker, and Bernstein (1964). Faced with the difficult problem of telemetering the human fetal electrocardiogram, they developed an electrode paste which produced a reduction in contact resistance. By mixing equal parts of a commercial electrode paste with silver oxide, resistance values of 1,500 ohms were observed. Without the silver oxide in the paste the resistance was 4,000 to 10,000 ohms. The method was evaluated by the author who confirmed the reduction in resistance but with some subjects the paste produced a reddening of the skin. More studies will be needed to fully appraise the value of this novel idea.

It is thus important to recognize that the electrolytic solution used to achieve contact with the body fluids may not be without effect. What may appear as an artifact in the record of a bioelectric event may be an enhanced GSR. On the other hand, if one is attempting to record the GSR, the electrolyte may enhance or diminish the response. Scarification of the region under the electrode can produce unwanted voltages. Edelberg and Burch (1962) reported that while cuts or skin punctures reduce skin resistance, they also reduce the GSR.

While most of the commercially available electrode pastes are satisfactory for recording bioelectric events, various authors have presented their own recipes. Among these are Jenks and Graybiel (1935), Bell et al. (1939), Thompson and Patterson (1958), Shackel (1958), Lykken (1959), Edelberg and Burch (1962), and Asa et al. (1964).

Electrode Potentials

When contact is made with living tissue via electrodes in contact with electrolytes a galvanic cell is created and chemical reactions take place. There is a tendency for the electrode to discharge ions into solution and for ions in the

---

*R. T. Kado, personal communication, 1965.

TABLE 15.4*   *Half-cell potentials.*†

	v		v		v
Al	+1.66	Ni	+0.25	Ag	−0.7991
Zn	+0.763	Pb	+0.126	Pt	−1.2
Cr	+0.74	H	0.000	Au	−1.50
Fe	+0.44	Cu++	−0.337		
Cd	+0.403	Cu+	−0.521		

*From *Handbook of Chemistry and Physics*, 1962–1963.
†Values for unit activity and 25°C referred to the hydrogen-hydrogen ion couple.

electrolyte to combine with the electrode. The net result is the creation of a charge gradient; the spatial arrangement of which is called the electrical double layer. Although it is known to be exceedingly complex in organization and occupies a region immediately adjacent to the electrode, in its simplest form the double layer has been pictured as two parallel sheets of charge of opposite sign. Parsons (1964) has described electrodes in terms of the reactions at the double layer. Electrodes in which no net transfer of charge occurs across the metal electrolyte interface are designated by him as perfectly polarized. Those in which unhindered exchange of charge is possible are called perfectly non-polarizable. Real electrodes have properties which are between these idealized limits.

In practical electrodes the electrode-electrolyte interface appears to resemble a voltage source and capacitance in parallel with a relatively high resistance. The exact values of these components are not constant and are nonlinearly dependent on many factors which include the kind of metal, the type and concentration of the electrolyte, temperature, frequency, and current density. The voltages encountered vary between 0 and 2 v (see Table 15.4). The equivalent capacitances are remarkably large for most metals; a typical example is mercury in contact with normal saline which exhibits a capacitance of 10 to 70 μf per cm² (Grahame, 1941).

The voltage developed at an electrode-electrolyte interface is designated as the half-cell potential. The total voltage between a pair of electrodes is thus the sum of the two half-cell potentials. Because it is impossible to measure the potential developed at a single electrode, an arbitrary standard electrode has been chosen and electrode potentials are measured with respect to it. The standard electrode is called the hydrogen electrode and consists of a platinum surface in contact with a solution of hydrogen ions (of unit activity) and dissolved molecular hydrogen; the activity of the latter is specified by requiring it to be in equilibrium with hydrogen at 1 atmosphere of pressure in the gas phase (Janz & Kelly, 1964).

Inspection of Table 15.4 indicates that when dissimilar metals are employed an appreciable voltage can be produced. When such electrodes are connected together through the input resistance of the measuring device, a current will flow. The consequences of this situation will be discussed later. The table also indicates that a galvanic cell of zero potential will be created if the metals are identical. In practice, despite use of the same material for both electrodes, some potential difference can be measured between a pair of electrodes. In many instances, the presence of such a potential would not be objectionable if it were stable. Usually it is not and its variations constitute a source of artifact. For example, Forbes (1934) studied the potential difference between amalgamated lead mercury electrodes in contact with a lead chloride solution which was applied to a chamois in contact with the skin. In 10 electrodes, potential differences ranging from 0 to 600 μv were measured. The spontaneous voltages variations ranged between 1.3 and 6.8 μv. A more extensive study was carried out by Greenwald (1936) who measured the potential difference and resistance of pairs of calomel, zinc, and zinc-zinc sulfate electrodes used for recording the electrodermal response. The calomel and zinc electrodes were measured with saline as the electrolyte. The zinc-zinc sulfate electrodes consisted of a zinc plate in contact with a kaolin paste made with zinc sulfate. Between them was a saline solution. The potential difference between the calomel electrodes, prior to passage of direct current to measure resistance, ranged between 1 and 20 μv and became considerably higher after the direct current resistance had been measured. The zinc plates exhibited a potential difference of 450 μv which quadrupled after the passage of direct current. The zinc-zinc sulfate electrodes exhibited a potential difference of 180 μv which tripled after the passage of a direct current.

In a similar study Lykken (1959) investigated the potentials developed by many of the electrodes used for the measurement of electrodermal phenomena. He measured the potential difference between pairs of stainless steel, zinc, zinc mercury, silver, silver mercury, silver-silver chloride, lead, lead mercury, and platinum electrodes. In each case the electrolyte was saline. Pairs of zinc and zinc mercury in contact with zinc sulfate and saline were also measured. During the first hour of measurement the various electrodes exhibited the following voltages: stainless steel, 10 mv; zinc, 100 mv; zinc mercury, 82 mv; silver, 94 mv; silver mercury, 90 mv; silver-silver chloride, 2.5 mv; and platinum, 320 mv. The others listed exhibited a voltage difference of approximately 1 mv. Edelberg and Burch (1962), while conducting GSR studies, reported that stainless steel and aluminum produced high random noise levels. Solder, silver, and copper produced slow wave artifacts. O'Connell et al. (1960) examined the galvanic potentials developed by various electrodes made from silver, lead, and zinc. The highest potential was produced by the zinc-zinc chloride pair (13 mv) and the least (0.2 mv) by the silver-silver chloride electrodes affixed to a sponge.

Often, a pair of electrodes made from the same piece of metal when placed in 0.9% saline and joined through a resistance will frequently produce a fluctuating noise current which can often be eliminated by connecting the electrodes together and allowing them to reach a stable equilibrium with the electrolyte. This technique has often been employed by electrophysiologists to quiet their electrodes. A related observation has been that newly prepared electrodes are often noisy and with the passage of time the noise decreases. Another method of quietening electrodes is to deposit from a large electrode, a uniform film of material covering both recording electrodes. In this way the minute differences in electrode material are eliminated and pairs of electrodes can be made having a very small and stable potential difference.

The principle described above is frequently carried out when silver electrodes are first made. On making a new set of cortical electrodes (Fig. 15.16B) having 1 ½ mm silver balls, the author was surprised to find that when the electrodes were placed in 0.9% saline and connected to the recording system they produced an unstable random noise signal of several hundred microvolts. Figure 15.17A illustrates the type of record obtained. The noise was diminished by maintaining all of the electrodes positive by about 3 volts with respect to a silver plate (1×2 in.) in the saline for 2 min and reconnecting them to the recording equipment without moving them from their position in the saline. This process is known as chloriding. The noise record obtained is shown in Fig. 15.17B.

To further examine the possible mechanism, the electrodes were scraped to remove the coating and they became noisy again (Fig. 15.17C). The electroplating current was applied again but in reverse this time and much of the electrode noise again disappeared (Fig. 15.17D). Finally, the electrodes were made quietest by the simple procedure of chloriding them after the electrolytic cleaning (electrodes negative 3 v for 3 min). The polarity was then reversed (electrodes positive) and with a milliammeter in the circuit the current was turned on and interrupted when the current started to fall. After connecting the electrodes to the amplifier, the noise record obtained is shown in Fig. 15.17E. To illustrate that all of the noise cannot be attributed to the electrodes, Fig. 15.17F shows the inherent noise level of the amplifying channel under open and short circuit conditions.

The preceding discussion of electrode potentials was presented to alert the reader to recognizing the possibility of the presence of voltages of nonphysiologic origin. In order to have confidence in the magnitude of the voltage appearing between the electrode terminals, electrodes should be routinely checked for stability without the bioelectric event interposed.

Often relatively little attention is given to the large unstable potentials developed when the electrode wires come in contact with electrolytes. Special precautions should be taken when a carefully prepared electrode is connected to the wire which joins the event to the recording apparatus. In the early days of electrocardiography, Pardee (1917) recommended that the connecting wire should be riveted to the electrode and the use of solder avoided. Henry in 1938 called attention to the fact that if the solder connection joining the electrode to the interconnecting wire became wet with an electrolytic solution,

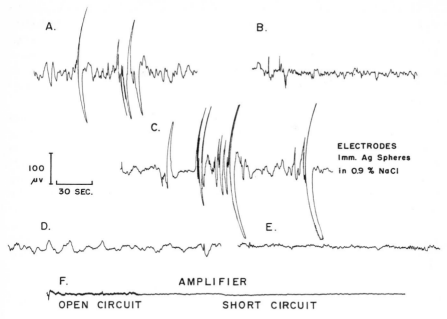

FIG. 15.17. Electrode noise.

there developed a multimetal electrolytic cell which developed unstable voltages and caused eventual corrosion and breakage of the connection. The simple practice of covering the solder connection to the electrode with a waterproof coating will not only produce a more stable electrode but one which will last longer.

There is undeniable evidence throughout all of the literature which indicates that silver-silver chloride electrodes appear to be the most stable electrically. However, there is a paucity of information on the proper preparation of such electrodes. An excellent review of the properties and method of preparation of such electrodes was presented by Janz and Taniguchi (1953). This authoritative paper is recommended reading for those who desire to employ silver-silver chloride electrodes.

Another useful piece of information derives from a consideration of the double layer; namely the effect of its mechanical disturbance. It will be recalled that the electrodes which were found to be relatively free of movement artifacts were of the floating type in which the electrode-electrolyte interface was removed from direct contact with the subject. Because the double layer is a region of charge gradient, i.e. a source of potential, disturbance of it gives rise to a change in voltage which, although small electrochemically, could be large with respect to the size of many bioelectric events. Movement artifacts produced by disturbance of the electrical double layer are in the frequency range of many of the bioelectric events. Hence filtering techniques can seldom be employed with success. Therefore the electrical stability of an electrode is considerably enhanced by stabilization of the electrode-electrolyte interface. This face has been shown practically when attempts have been made to measure bioelectric events on moving subjects. For example Forbes, Cobb, and Cattell (1921) were perhaps the first to record bioelectric events on a moving subject when they employed a type of floating electrode to record electrocardiograms and electromyograms on an elephant. When standing, elephants sway from side to side which makes it difficult to obtain artifact-free records with plate electrodes. The electrodes employed by Forbes consisted of a zinc electrode in the neck of a funnel filled with zinc sulfate. The opening of the funnel was covered with a permeable membrane soaked in saline. Two rubber-gloved assistants held these electrodes against the inner surfaces of the forelimbs of an animal. The electrocardiogram was successfully recorded by a string galvanometer.

In a study of the heart rate of perspiring miners derived from the ECG, Atkins (1961) found that the main source of artifacts was due to contact variations between the electrode metal and skin. When the electrodes were separated from it by a layer of filter paper or gauze soaked with an electrolyte, electrode artifacts practically disappeared.

Roman and Lamb (1962), using their miniature floating electrodes, applied to the skin at either end of the sternum, presented some truly remarkable records of the ECG in which no artifacts were to be observed when the electrodes were tapped or struck or when the subject was jumping or engaged in vigorous activity. These electrodes were employed for monitoring ECG changes in pilots flying in high performance aircraft. Lucchina and Phipps (1962) similarly showed that their electrode (Fig. 15.15F) was free from artifacts when pressure was applied to it or when it was displaced. To prove their point, high quality electrocardiograms were recorded from ambulatory subjects. Such floating electrodes have been employed successfully to record the ECG of astronauts, laborers, swimmers, and a variety of subjects exercising vigorously.

To record the EEG on moving subjects Kado, Adey, and Zweizig (1964) constructed interesting electrodes in which the electrode metal was tin in contact with a tin chloride solution in a small ceramic chamber. Contact between the ceramic chamber and the skin was via a sponge soaked in physiological saline. Other than removing oil from the scalp, no special precautions were required for the installation of the electrodes. When carefully applied, these electrodes produced remarkably stable EEG recordings in subjects who were moving their heads rapidly.

Electrode Impedance

In addition to developing a half-cell potential, each electrode exhibits an impedance which is dependent on the nature of the double layer. This impedance is often called the polarization impedance. Through the impedance of both electrodes and the input impedance of the recording apparatus there flows a small current derived from the bioelectric event. Because the input impedance of most bioelectric recorders is high, the current is small and the voltage drop caused by the electrode impedance is usually negligible. However, as will be pointed out later, this situation does not always obtain and under such circumstances in addition to a loss of amplitude, undesirable wave form distortion of the bioelectric event can occur.

Electrode impedances are complex and difficult to measure with high accuracy on living subjects. The term electrode impedance really refers to the impedance at each electrode interface and does not include the impedance of the biological material between the electrodes. Frequently, however, the term electrode impedance is used to describe the total impedance of the circuit between the electrode terminals. Such an impedance of course includes the impedance at both electrodes and that of the biological material between them. If the total impedance between the electrode terminals is measured at different frequencies, the nature of the circuit created by electrode impedance will manifest itself since the resistivity of many body segments is fairly constant with frequency in the low and audio frequency region. The total impedance between the terminals of pairs of some of the electrodes diagrammed in Figs. 15.15 and 15.16 was measured over a limited frequency range. For all electrodes the current was maintained at the same level at all frequencies. To examine the importance of current density, currents of 0.1 and 1 mamp were employed. Impedance-frequency measurements were made using pairs of ECG plate and floating electrodes, EEG discs, and bare EMG needles. Each pair was installed carefully in the manner typical of each application. Humans were used for all studies except those employing needle electrodes. In this case, anesthetized dogs were used. The impedance values were dissected into resistive and reactive components.

There were often appreciable differences between individual electrodes of the same type. When this occurred, a large number of electrodes were tested and the data were averaged. The effect of current density although detectable, turned out to be smaller than the variability between electrodes of the same kind. The values plotted include the electrode impedance and that of the subject between them. In each case direct current resistance was measured using a low current ohmmeter. Figure 15.18 summarizes the data obtained. The contours of the impedance-frequency curves are similar to those obtained on a variety of similar electrodes by Barnett (1937), Offner (1942), Burns (1950), Gray and Svaetichin (1951), Tasaki (1952), Gesteland, Howland, Lettvin, and Pitts (1959), Plutchnik and Hirsch (1963), and Schwan (1963).

For all electrodes, the direct current resistance was higher than the high frequency impedance, pointing to the fact that if a low current ohmmeter is used to measure the resistance, the value obtained, although indicative of continuity of the circuit, only approximates the low frequency impedance of the circuit.

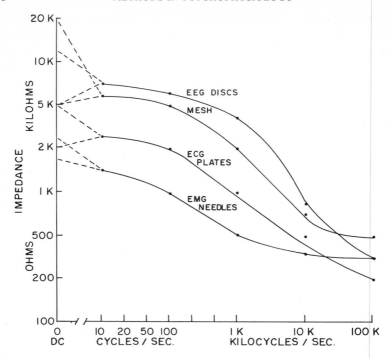

Fig. 15.18. Electrode impedance.

In the 10 to 100 cps region, the impedance approximated the direct current resistance. Above this frequency range the impedance decreased progressively, reaching values many times smaller than the magnitude of the direct current resistance. In the case of the needle electrodes, the impedance at nearly all frequencies was lower than that of the larger surface electrodes. In addition, the impedance-frequency characteristics of needle electrodes did not exhibit as clear a low frequency plateau as seen with surface electrodes. However, it is to be noted that the needle electrodes were in intimate contact with body fluids which is probably the reason for their low impedance.

While the figures given for the impedances of large surface electrodes can be called typical, a large variation may be encountered which is dependent on the quality of application to the subject. To demonstrate this point, Schmitt, Okajima, and Blaug (1961) measured the 60 cycle impedance between standard ECG electrodes on subjects prior to taking routine electrocardiograms. Although a median value of 2,400 ohms was obtained, even under well controlled conditions impedances 4 times this figure were encountered. In the series, which employed technicians familiar with attaching electrodes to humans, individual interelectrode impedances as high as 100,000 ohms were encountered.

While the physical size of the electrode appears to most directly determine the electrode impedance, a factor worthy of note is that the effective area of the electrodes is increased by wetting of the skin by electrolytic solutions (e.g. electrode paste or perspiration). Blank and Finesinger (1964) directed attention to the importance of this factor when measuring the resistive component of the galvanic skin reflex. Effective area can also be increased by special treatment of the electrode metal. Electrodeposition of a spongy layer of metal greatly increases the area and reduces the impedance. Use of this technique was described by Marmont (1949), Svaetichin (1951), and Dowben and Rose (1953).

An approximate equivalent circuit which relates the bioelectric generator and electrode impedance to the electrode terminals is shown in Fig. 15.19. The voltage of a typical bioelectric generator is designated by $E_{(t)}$ which in most cases is a propagated action potential of 70 to 100 mv and represents the voltage excursion of the membrane potential when the cell is excited and recovers. In some cases $E_{(t)}$ consists of variations in membrane potential. R and r are voltage divider impedances which account for the attenuation of the bioelectric event by the volume conductor action of body tissues and fluids. R_p and C_p are the resistive and capacitive components of the electrode polarization impedance. $E_{a,b}$ are the half-cell potentials of the electrodes. The polarity of these voltages depends on the electrode metals and the electrolytes. In some respects the electrode-electrolyte junction resembles a leaky electrolytic condenser.

Looking toward the event from the terminals of the electrodes, the impedance-frequency characteristic of this circuit resembles the data shown in Fig. 15.18. Looking outward, the bioelectric generator sees an impedance which attenuates the amplitude of its signal. The attenuated event is coupled to the bioelectric recorder through the electrode impedance and if the input impedance of the bioelectric recorder is not high enough, frequency dependent distortion can occur.

Input Impedance of the Bioelectric Recorder

When bioelectric events are recorded, it is traditional to make the input impedance of the bioelectric recorder very many times larger than the electrode impedance. When this technique is employed, only a small current flows through the electrode impedance and there is a minimal loss of voltage at the electrode-tissue interface. However, if the bioelectric recorder has an input impedance which is low with respect to the electrode polarization impedance, there can occur a distortion in the wave form of the bioelectric event. Because of the resistive and reactive components of the electrode polarization impedance, the various components of a complex wave will not be presented to the input stage with the same relative amplitudes as they occur in the complex wave. Moreover, phase distortion accompanies such amplitude-frequency distortion and the time relations between the various frequency components of

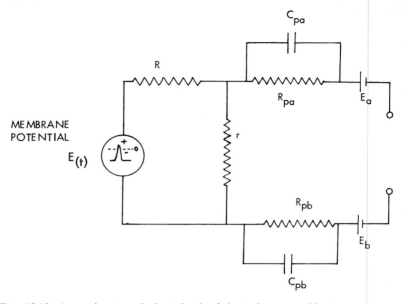

FIG. 15.19. Approximate equivalent circuit of electrodes on a subject.

the complex wave will be altered. In addition, it has been shown by Schwan (1963) and Schwan and Maczuk (1965) that the resistive and reactive components of electrode polarization impedance of platinum iridium electrodes changes when high current densities are encountered. Similar investigations carried out by Weinman and Mahler (1964), who studied electrodes of various metals, verify the nonlinear characteristic of electrode polarization impedance at high current densities. If the input impedance of the bioelectric recorder is so low that high current densities result, it is possible for the electrode impedance to become dependent on the amplitude of the bioelectric event. If this occurs, then small and large amplitude signals will be injected differently into the input of the bioelectric recorder. It is thus apparent that the use of an input stage which does not have an impedance that is very high with respect to the electrode impedance virtually guarantees that the bioelectric event will be distorted in its insertion into the recording apparatus. High electrode current densities can occur when the electrode area is small, as it is with metal microelectrodes, and a conventional amplifier is employed with such electrodes.

It has already been shown that wave form distortion of clinical significance does occur when high resistance electrodes are used with recorders having a low input resistance. In the early days of electrocardiography, when string galvanometers with their relatively low resistance (3000 ohms) were used, Lewis (1915) showed that a normal ECG was distorted when recorded with polarizable platinum electrodes. In such cases, attenuated P and T waves and an enhanced S wave were recorded. Similarly, Pardee (1917), using a string galvanometer and German silver electrodes applied to a bandage soaked in saline, showed that the calibration signal was distorted when the area of each electrode was decreased from 300 sq cm to 8 sq cm. With the smaller electrodes the calibration pulse, instead of rising rapidly and exhibiting a flat top, showed a sharp overshoot and an RC-type decay to the sustained plateau. On turning off the calibrate signal, there was an undershoot and RC decay to the base line.

The practical importance of these facts in recording the electrocardiogram was again demonstrated by Roman and Lamb (1962). These investigators applied miniature floating electrodes to the chest of a human subject and used them first with an amplifier having a high input impedance to obtain control records. They then lowered the input impedance of the amplifier by connecting different resistances across it. The distortions in the ECG were what would be called clinically significant, consisting of an increase in the height of the S-T segment and a slight depression in the latter part of the T wave.

Figure 15.20 illustrates the type of distortion encountered when recording the ECG with high impedance electrodes and an amplifier with a low input impedance. This illustration shows lead II electrocardiogram in the anesthetized dog. Stainless steel needle electrodes such as those shown in Fig. 15.16D were employed. The needles were insulated to within 1 mm of the tip. The geometric area in contact with the body tissues and fluids was approximately 1 sq mm.

Figure 15.20A shows the control electrocardiogram recorded with an amplifier having a 4.4 megohm resistive input impedance. Figure 15.20, A to H, illustrates changes produced by placing resistors of successively lower value across the input of the amplifier. During the various trials, the electrodes were not disturbed. In Fig. 15.20, A to G inclusive, the recording sensitivity was the same. In Fig. 15.20H, the recording sensitivity was quadrupled to more clearly enable comparison with Fig. 15.20A.

The outstanding changes seen in these records are those expected in a system which is deficient in low frequency response. Such a situation could be predicted on the basis of the general nature of the impedance-frequency curves of electrodes. With 200 k across the input terminals, there are noticeable P and T wave changes. With 100 k, and especially with 50 k across the input terminals, the P and T waves are dramatically changed; both becoming diphasic. As loading is increased there is a continued loss of over-all amplitude and in G and H, which were both recorded with 10 k across the input terminals, the resemblance to the control record is all but lost. In Fig. 15.20H, recorded with 4 times the amplification, the ECG is seen to be vastly different than that shown in Fig. 15.20A. The outstanding differences are the loss of

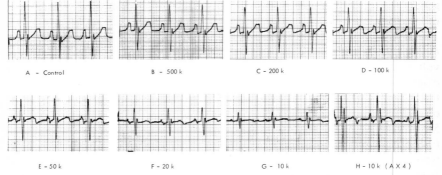

FIG. 15.20. Distortion in the ECG produced by lowering the input impedance of the bioelectric recorder. (From Geddes, L. A., & Baker, L. E. *Med. & Biol. Eng.*, in press.)

P and *T* wave amplitudes and the addition of diphasic components to each. The QRS complex has similarly been changed by exaggeration of the *S* and *R* components.

These results, which are consistently reproducible are in agreement with those described by Roman and Lamb (1962) and point out the need to use an input stage which has an input impedance many times larger than that of the bioelectric generator-electrode system.

The distortion illustrated in Fig. 15.20, *C* to *H*, is primarily due to two factors. First, with loading, i.e. the use of an amplifier input circuit which is not high with respect to the electrode-bioelectric generator system, the electrode polarization impedance becomes a dominant part of the input circuit and the voltage drops and phase shifts for the various components of the complex wave are different. Second, with loading, the electrode current density is increased and the resistive and reactive components of the electrode polarization impedance become nonlinear and the magnitude of the electrode polarization impedance becomes a function of the amplitude of the bioelectric event. Thus small and large amplitude signals will encounter different impedances. The exact contribution of each of the two sources of distortion is as yet unknown for the various electrodes employed for recording bioelectric events.

Not only does an increase in current density alter the electrode impedance, it changes the half-cell potential. Even with such a relatively nonpolarizable electrode as the calomel cell, current alters the half-cell potential, Rothschild (1938) showed that the maximum safe current density for this type of electrode was 15 μamp per cm². The exact limits of current densities permissible for the various types of electrodes have not as yet been adequately investigated.

Ohmic Noise

Another important characteristic of electrodes derives from a consideration of the ohmic component of the electrode impedance. All resistors are noise generators, producing voltages of all frequencies. The noise voltage results from the random motion of the electrons in the material making up the conductor. The actual voltage measured is dependent on the magnitude of the resistance, the absolute temperature and the bandwidth of the recording system. This voltage varies as the square root of these quantities and increasing any or all of these three factors increases the noise voltage displayed by the recording system. For example, Terman (1943) stated that the noise figure for a 500,000 ohm resistor at 27° C operating into a system with a bandwidth of 0 to 5,000 cps is 6.4 mv r.m.s. Although ohmic noise may not be an important factor when bioelectric recordings are made with large low resistance electrodes, when the electrode resistance is high, as it is with microelectrodes, and the bandwidth of the recording equipment wide, resistive noise played a finite limit on the smallness of the signal detectable.

Conclusion

Although many penetrating studies of electrodes have been made, much more remains to be investigated before there is an adequate description of the electrical nature of the circuit between a pair of electrodes from which a bioelectric event is recorded. Only when this is accomplished will it be possible to ascribe a proper magnitude to the type of distortion to be expected with the various electrodes and recording systems. This statement, made by Curtis and Cole (1938) nearly 30 years ago still retains much validity. "Unexplained effects, analogous to polarization impedance are found at metal-electrolyte interfaces, in imperfect dielectrics and internal viscosity of solids, but the equation which describes them all is purely empirical and the use of the term polarization impedance is an admission of our ignorance."

In summary, it is obvious that electrodes can produce their own signals and distortions. To minimize the galvanic potentials, the electrodes should be of the same metal and each should contact the same type of electrolyte. While a steady electrode potential may not be bothersome, it nonetheless causes current to flow through the input resistance of the bioelectric recorder. Often this is not objectionable but if electrodes are moved, the resistance of the circuit will change and result in a change in current flowing through the input circuit. The use of electrodes with equal half-cell potentials and the use of a high input impedance recording apparatus will minimize this type of artifact. Disturbance of the double layer at either electrode will also alter the half-cell potential. Stabilization can be attained by protecting the double layer by moving it away from the source of the movement. This is one of the reasons for the superiority of the floating electrodes. Maintenance of a low current density at the electrode interface will reduce the tendency for the electrode impedance to distort the wave form of a bioelectric event. Large area electrodes and the use of a high input impedance bioelectric recorder minimize the risk of encountering this type of distortion.

V. Criteria for the Faithful Reproduction of an Event

Even without adopting any system of transduction, it is possible to set forth general conditions which, if satisfied, will guarantee the faithful transduction of a physiological event. It is either necessary to impose these same conditions on the three parts of the channel, the transducer, processor, and reproducer, or to incorporate any necessary compensation so that the over-all system will meet the criteria if the individual parts do not.

In any system which converts information of one form to be reproduced in a different form, three criteria must be fulfilled. Because of the extreme importance of these criteria, their meaning must be clearly understood. Despite the fact that many of the underlying factors are of necessity technical and complex, simple examples can be chosen to illustrate their importance. From a discussion of them many valuable conclusions can be drawn which will facilitate application of the criteria.

Any system designed for faithful reproduction of an event must possess: (1) amplitude linearity; (2) adequate bandwidth; and (3) phase linearity.

The first requisite, amplitude linearity, calls for the input-output characteristic to be proportional in the working range. If, for example, the input is doubled, say in the positive direction, then the output indication must be doubled also. Similarly, if the operating range extends into the reverse direction, then negative inputs must be reproduced by a proportional output indication in the opposite direction.

Before the second and third criteria can be discussed it is necessary to establish the relationship between sine waves and waves of nonsinusoidal form. All waves of nonsinusoidal form are designated as complex waves. By the use of the Fourier series it is possible to show that any periodic wave can be dissected into the sum of a series of sine and cosine waves which, when added in the correct proportions, will reproduce the original event. The sine and cosine waves which have the same frequency as the complex wave are the fundamental or first harmonic. Those having twice and thrice the frequency are called the second and third harmonics, etc.

These facts are stated mathematically by saying that a periodic complex wave can be analyzed into an infinite series consisting of a constant, plus harmonically related sine and cosine waves. Expressed in this form the series may be written as follows:

$$f(t) = \frac{a_o}{2} + a_1 \cos wt + a_2 \cos 2\ wt + a_3 \cos 3\ wt + \cdots + a_n \cos nwt$$
$$+ b_1 \sin wt + b_2 \sin 2\ wt + b_3 \sin 3\ wt + \cdots + b_n \sin nwt$$

from which

$$a_n = \frac{1}{\pi} \int_o^{2\pi} f(t) \cos nwt\ dt$$

$$b_n = \frac{1}{\pi} \int_o^{2\pi} f(t) \sin nwt \; dt$$

In order to use the series to analyze a wave form it is necessary to calculate the coefficients, a_o, a_n, and b_n, some of which may be zero. However, for purposes of this study it is not necessary, nor is it profitable, to perform the extensive calculations to show the validity of the theory. Many waves have been analyzed and the coefficients have been published. Selection of two examples, the square wave and blood pressure curve, will suffice to show the value of the notation.

One of the most difficult waves to reproduce is the square wave shown in Fig. 15.21 which instantaneously increases its value from zero to a maximum, maintaining this value for a time before reversing itself below zero by the same amount and for the same time, then returning abruptly to zero again. When this wave is analyzed for its harmonic content, some of the coefficients are zero and the series reduces to the fundamental and an infinite series of odd harmonics in which the amplitude of the higher frequency components decreases, i.e. the very high frequency components contribute less to the resynthesis of the original wave. The Table 15.5 lists a few of the harmonic amplitudes for the square wave.

TABLE 15.5. *Harmonic amplitudes of a square wave*

Harmonic	Amplitude
	%
Fundamental (A)	100
3rd (B)	33
5th (D)	20
7th (F)	14

In Fig. 15.21B the first and third harmonic components $(A + B)$ have been summated to yield the curve labeled C. In this case, even with only two components, the beginnings of the square wave start to emerge. In Fig. 15.21C, the first, third, and fifth components are summated to produce *Curve E* which is a better representation of the original wave, and in Fig. 15.21D, the first, third, fifth, and seventh components when added together produce *Curve G*, an even better likeness of the original wave. Adding more and more harmonics would further improve the reproduction and theoretically the addition of an infinite number of the ever diminishing amplitude high frequency components would reconstitute the original wave.

The arterial pressure pulse is a good example of the utilitarian value of harmonic analysis. Hansen (1959), using a high fidelity system, recorded the arterial pulse wave and applied harmonic analysis to it. His data (redrawn) are

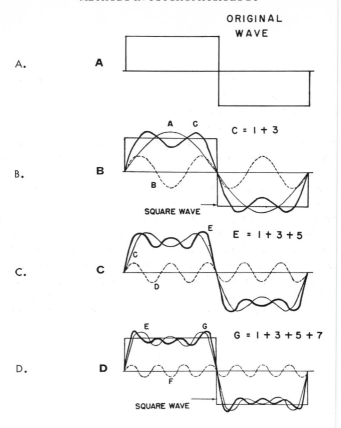

FIG. 15.21. Analysis of a square wave. (From *Radar electronic fundamentals*, War Dept. Tech. Manual TM 11-466, 1946.)

plotted in Fig. 15.22*A* and show the degree of fidelity obtainable by summating the first six harmonics (Fig. 15.22*A, part b*). It is also to be noted that the amplitudes of the higher frequency components are progressively less with increasing harmonic numbers; the sixth being present with an amplitude of slightly more than 10%. Figure 15.22*B* illustrates this point.

To obtain a more faithful reproduction, addition of many more of the smaller and smaller amplitude high frequency components would be required. Thus, the amount of frequency response required is closely related to the degree of fidelity desired.

From these relatively simple examples two very important conclusions can be drawn. The first is that the frequency of the complex wave determines the frequency of the fundamental component. The second is that the sharpness of the reproduced wave is determined by the number of high frequency com-

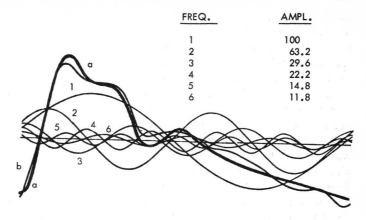

FREQ.	AMPL.
1	100
2	63.2
3	29.6
4	22.2
5	14.8
6	11.8

A.   FOURIER ANALYSIS OF A BLOOD PRESSURE CURVE

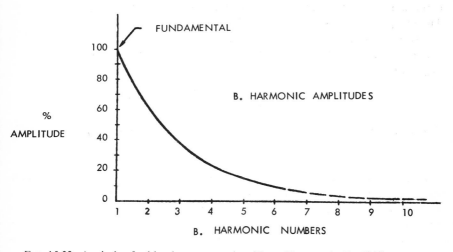

Fig. 15.22. Analysis of a blood pressure pulse. (From Hansen, A. T., 1949).

ponents added. Thus the bandwidth required for reproduction of these waves would extend from the frequency of the complex wave to the highest harmonic deemed important for adequate reproduction of the sharp portions of the complex waves.

Note that in the two examples cited, the waves chosen were symmetrical about the zero base line. If they were not, the analysis would have shown the same components with one notable exception. The exception would be that a_o, the frequency independent coefficient, would have a value other than zero, for it is average amplitude over a complete period. It is obvious that a train of unidirectional pulses must have an average value. In the case of the arterial pressure wave, a_0 would be the mean pressure. Thus, to reproduce a train of unidirectional pulses with accuracy, it is necessary to provide a frequency response extending from 0 cps to a frequency high enough for full reproduction of the highest harmonic deemed important. In practice, the high frequency response is made to include the 10th or sometimes the 20th harmonic.

Perhaps of equal importance to the cases in which the criteria are satisfied are a few in which some of the criteria are not fulfilled. To illustrate the types of distortions possible, the following examples are presented. Because the square wave is one of the most difficult to reproduce, it is useful to examine the effects of alteration of the amplitudes of the harmonics on the reproduction of this wave form. Terman (1943) showed that if only the low frequency components are attenuated, the square wave will have a concave top as sketched in Fig. 15.23A. On the other hand, if the low frequency components are enhanced, the top of the square wave will be convex as in Fig. 15.23B.

If the component harmonics are present in their proper amplitudes but the components are displaced in time, a characteristic type of distortion occurs. Time displacement is not customarily expressed in milliseconds; it is usually measured in degrees of phase shift. For example if the time delay for a given frequency, f, is t, and since the period, T, is equal to 360°, the phase shift $\emptyset$ in degrees is

$$\emptyset = \frac{t}{T} \times 360°.$$

The fact that $\qquad T = \dfrac{1}{f} \qquad$ permits expressing the phase shift

in terms of frequency, i.e. $\emptyset = tf\,360°$. Thus with equal delay for all frequencies ($t = k$), then $\emptyset ° kf$, i.e. the phase shift must be linear with frequency. It is to be noted that the amount of delay is usually relatively unimportant as long as it is the same for all frequency components.

Figure 15.24, A and B, illustrates the effect of phase distortion on the reproduction of the square wave. In this illustration the harmonic components are present in their correct amplitudes but time displacements have been caused to occur. In Fig. 15.24A, the fundamental leads the higher harmonics, and in Fig. 15.24B, the reverse condition exists. In each case the type of reproduction is shown by the *dotted lines*.

Phase distortion is usually present when only minimal loss of amplitude response occurs. Terman (1943) called attention to the fact that in many networks, such as those used to couple amplifier stages together, when the low frequency sine wave response is 99.94%, a 2 degree phase shift error is encountered which results in a 10% tilt to the top of square wave of the same frequency.

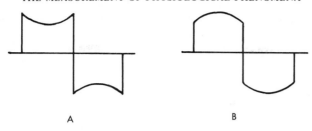

A

B

Loss of Low Frequency Response

(No Phase Distortion)

Increased Amplification of Low Frequencies
(No Phase Distortion)

FIG. 15.23. Amplitude distortion. (From Terman, F. E. *Radio engineers handbook*. New York: McGraw-Hill.)

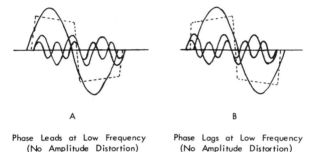

A

B

Phase Leads at Low Frequency
(No Amplitude Distortion)

Phase Lags at Low Frequency
(No Amplitude Distortion)

FIG. 15.24. Phase distortion.

Because phase shift and loss of amplitude response are virtually inseparable, it is often difficult to appreciate the effect of these distortions. To demonstrate the practical importance of this fact, Geddes (1951) constructed a variable frequency oscillator which produced a sine wave having a notch at its peak positive amplitude. The location of the notch (square pulse) was fixed but the frequency of the complex wave was variable. This wave was used to test electroencephalographs to estimate their ability to faithfully reproduce the familiar spike-and-wave complex found in recordings from patients with petit mal epilepsy.

The wave was applied to one of several EEG machines meeting existing standards; the frequency was varied and the output recorded. Figure 15.25*A* is a sketch of the input wave form. The reproduction at various frequencies is shown in Fig. 15.25, *B* to *E*. In Fig. 15.25*B*, recorded at 1 cps, it is obvious that there is a 45° of phase shift. Increasing the frequency to 2 and 3 cps, as shown in *C* and *D*, places the spike more nearly in its correct position where it appears when the frequency is 6 cps. However, it is to be noted that although the phase distortion is minimal in *E*, at 6 cps, the amplitude of the spike de-

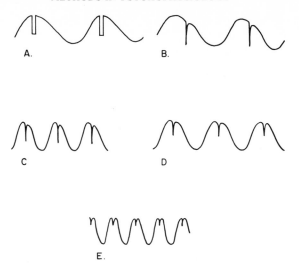

FIG. 15.25. Amplitude and phase distortion in a complex wave.

creased because the system had inadequate high frequency response to pass the frequency components contained in the spike.

The practical significance of phase distortion was reinvestigated by Saunders and Jell (1959) who recorded the effect in a unique way by using two identical channels of an EEG machine. The output of the first channel was attenuated and fed into the second; the output of both channels appeared on the same record. They first tested the system for phase distortion using 3 cps sine wave. Using a typical EEG machine in which a 3 cps sine wave was attenuated insignificantly, they recorded a time delay between channels amounting to 51.3 msec or 55.4°. It is to be noted that this testing technique demonstrated the phase shift in the second channel only. Next, in a practical study, stimulus response waves, eye blink artifacts, and spike and wave patterns all suffered time distortions in the second channel. A time separation of 75 msec between the spike and wave recorded on the first channel was reduced to 63 msec after passing through the second channel.

From the examples given it is apparent that the three criteria, amplitude linearity, frequency response, and phase linearity must be satisfied to guarantee the faithful reproduction of an event. Amplitude linearity occurs when output and input are proportional. Frequency response is usually described in terms of bandwidth which is designated as the frequency range between the lowest and highest sine wave frequencies at which a satisfactory amplitude response is obtained. It is frequently designated as the spectrum between the two frequencies at which the output has fallen to 70%. In some instances the 50, 90, or 95% points are specified.

For practical testing of a system, a form of square wave, which changes abruptly from one level to another is of considerable value. Such a wave is called a step function and is frequently employed as a calibration signal in many bioelectric recording instruments. Since the sine wave frequency response curves of most devices are given by equipment manufacturers, it will be illuminating to apply the step function to systems with various frequency response curves.

If such a wave (Fig. 15.26A) is applied to a system which does not possess a sine wave frequency response extending to 0 cps (Fig. 15.26B) but has an infinite high frequency response, the reproduced wave is of exponential form and is diagrammed in Fig. 15.26C. The decay time is described as the time taken for the amplitude to fall from 100 to 37%. This time is called the time constant and is measured in seconds. The time constant is related to the sine wave frequency response by the following approximate relationship

$$T = \frac{1}{2 \pi f_L}$$

where T = time constant in seconds; f_L = frequency on the sine wave curve at which response has fallen to 70%.

As a result of the intermittent activity of a variety of cells and organs, short duration, asymmetrical (with respect to the time axis) or completely monophasic pulses are presented to the reproducing apparatus. A harmonic analysis of such wave forms reveals the presence of a frequency independent constant. Thus, faithful reproduction of such events requires the use of a direct coupled system. Frequently it is not practical to meet this requirement. Under many circumstances, a reasonable reproduction of the event can be obtained with a processing system having a time constant which is long with respect to the duration of the event. This technique is employed in the instruments which record many of the bioelectric events such as the ECG, EEG, and EMG.

The effect of time constant on the reproduction of a single monophasic flat-topped pulse is illustrated in Fig. 15.27. In this diagram, the percentage drop (tilt) on the top of the reproduced wave is compared with the ratio of the duration of the pulse to the time constant of the circuit passing it. For simplicity of illustration, the calculations were based on a single section R-C circuit.

It is readily apparent that a 10% tilt is encountered if the duration of the pulse is approximately one-tenth of the time constant of the circuit. Increasing the time constant of the circuit or decreasing the pulse duration would reduce the percentage tilt on the top of the wave.

It is to be noted that there is also an undershoot following the pulse. The amount is equal to the amplitude of the pulse minus the tilt. If the pulse duration is many times longer than the time constant, the familiar biphasic condenser charge and discharge current wave is seen.

To further improve the reproduction of short duration pulses when using

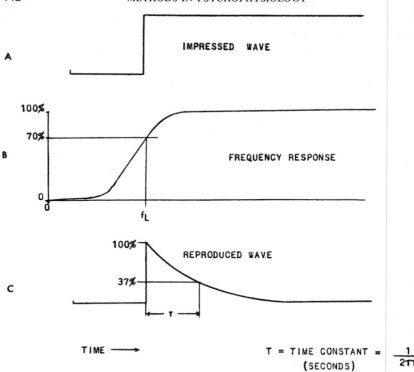

Fig. 15.26. Relationship between time constant and low frequency response.

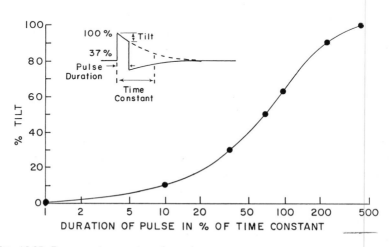

FIG. 15.27. Response to a rectangular pulse.

amplifiers without direct current response, phase and amplitude compensating networks are often added which are designed to flatten the top of a square pulse. This technique is employed in most ECG amplifiers. A good treatment of this subject is given by Valley and Wallman (1948) in the chapter of their text dealing with pulse amplifiers.

If the step function (Fig. 15.28) is now impressed on a system having a low frequency response extending to 0 cps and a high frequency response not extending to an infinitely high frequency (Fig. 15.28, *center*), the type of response encountered is shown in Fig. 15.28 (*lower*). It can be seen that the reproduced wave does not attain its final value instantly but takes a finite time to reach it. This time is called the rise or response time and is frequently described as the time in seconds for the amplitude to rise from 10 to 90% of its final value. The rise time is related to the high frequency sine wave response by the following approximate formula

$$t = \frac{1}{kf_h}$$

when t = rise time (10 to 90%) in seconds; f_h = frequency on the sine wave response curve where the response has fallen 70%, k depends on the circuit configuration and hence the rate at which the high frequency (high frequency rolloff). In most circuits, k varies between 2 and 3.

From the above it is obvious that increasing f_h, i.e. improving the high frequency response, shortens the rise time. Figure 15.29 summarizes the effect of varying the low frequency and high frequency response.

From this discussion it is readily apparent that the sharp portions of a complex wave dictate the high frequency response required. Similarly the repetition frequency or the symmetry about the time axis dictates the amount of low frequency response necessary.

Frequently in the course of measuring physiological events, as part of the channel, one encounters an important class of components in which a tendency toward resonance exists. The circuit components may be electrical, as in the case of inductances and capacitances in combination or in positive feedback circuits which tend toward instability. The resonance may be purely mechanical as in the case of devices with elasticity and mass. An elastic member experiencing deflection from its position of equilibrium and returning when the deflecting force is removed characterizes the latter type. Some of the many examples of such mechanical devices are blood pressure manometers, in which an elastic diaphragm or Bourdon tube is distorted by pressure, and moving coil recorders in which a torsion rod or spring returns the movement to its base line when the signal is removed. The actual motion of the moving element and hence the type of reproduction obtained depends on three factors and is defined in mathematical terms by the inter-relationship between three quantities which are (1) the inertial mass, (2) the elasticity or compliance, and (3) the

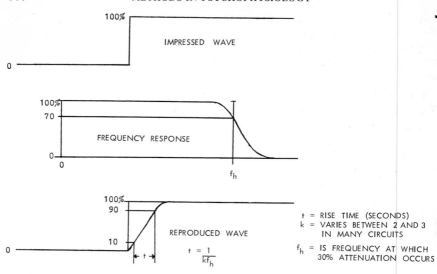

FIG. 15.28. Relationship between rise time and high frequency response.

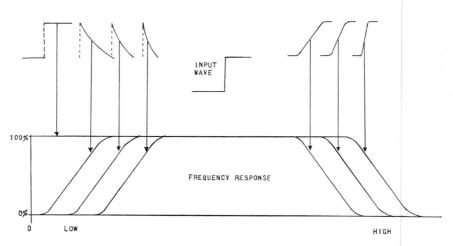

FIG. 15.29. The effect of low and high frequency response on the reproduction of a step function.

viscous damping. The first, or inertia, refers to the effect of the mass of the moving part and the direction in which it is deflected. The second, compliance, refers to the elastic behavior and is a reflection of the stiffness of the system. It is defined in terms of the force required to deflect the moving member unit distance from its position of equilibrium. Damping is the third and in many circumstances is the most important factor in determining the dynamic operating characteristics. Viscous damping is a force directed opposite to the direction of motion of the mass. The viscous force varies directly with velocity. It may be present as air resistance, fluid resistance, as in the case of a fluid-filled system in contact with the moving member, or it may exist as an electrically induced force.

Mechanical systems can be described in terms of one-to-one electrical analogues in which the behavior of both systems is described by the same mathematical equation. In mechanical systems inertia, damping, and compliance regulate the behavior. In electrical circuits these quantities correspond to inductance, resistance, and capacitance.

Because the dynamic behavior of mechanical systems is so important in physiological measurements, the interrelationship between inertia, damping, and compliance must be appreciated to understand how a given system can alter its characteristics under varying conditions. Since many of the devices can be reduced to a simple system involving only one degree of freedom, a single linear compliance and a single damping force, simple mechanical models can illustrate the behavior of most of these devices under the influence of a unit step wave of force and a constant amplitude variable frequency sinusoidal force.

Consider a mass, M, free to move on a frictionless horizontal surface coupled to a fixed support by a spring. Connected to the mass is a rod terminated by a vane dipping into a reservoir of fluid, providing viscous damping. Figure 15.30A is a sketch of such a system in which the mass, M, is free to move in a left or right hand direction only. If a force is applied to move the weight from its position of equilibrium and then the force is removed, the mass will return to its original position slowly, or rapidly and may overshoot and oscillate about the position of equilibrium several times before coming to rest, as shown in the figure. The type of motion executed depends upon the intimate relationship between the mass, stiffness, and damping. Another simple example of the same phenomenon is illustrated in Fig. 15.30B. It diagrams the essential components of a recording pen or galvanometer having a mass or moment of inertia coupled to an elastic torsion rod. If a deflecting force is applied to cause rotation, and then removed, the system will return to its position of equilibrium slowly or rapidly as in the previous case depending upon the relationship between the same three quantities. The former case deals with translation and describes the operation of blood pressure transducers and similar devices, while the latter case describes devices in which rotary motion exists. Nonetheless the displacement in both cases is described by a linear differential equation of the second order and first degree. The following mathematical expressions describe the resultant motion:

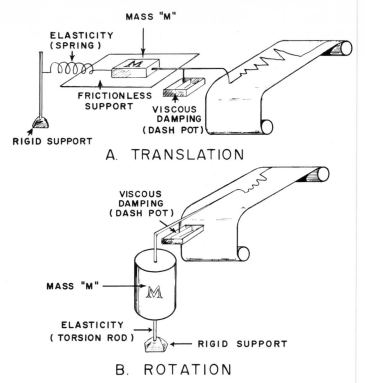

FIG. 15.30. Examples of damped systems.

Translation

$$M \frac{d^2x}{dt^2} + K_1 \frac{dx}{dt} + K_2x = \text{sum of applied forces}$$

Rotation

$$I \frac{d^2\emptyset}{dt^2} + K_1 \frac{d\emptyset}{dt} + K_2\emptyset = \text{sum of applied torques}$$

M and I are the mass inertial components; M is the mass and I is the moment of inertia. K_1 is the viscous damping constant. K_2 is the stiffness or restoring force usually represented in terms of a spring constant. x is the linear displacement and $\emptyset$ is the angular displacement. t is time.

Because these equations are of similar form the solution is the same for both except for the letter designation of terms. The solutions to the above equations involve the use of several mathematical theorems and depend on the type of force applied. In order to calculate the motion in a particular case, this mathematical knowledge is necessary. However, to understand the behavior of such systems under a variety of conditions, mathematical ability is not essential, for selected conditions can be chosen which describe the whole range of response of the systems illustrated by the simple models. The response to two types of applied force, a step function and a variable frequency sine wave will enable the reader to understand the behavior of such systems under a variety of operating conditions.

The first and probably the most important condition is that particular interrelationship between the quantities which provides just enough damping for the mass and elasticity so that the motion is nonoscillatory when a step force is applied or removed, i.e. the moving member deflects or returns to its position of equilibrium as rapidly as possible without overshoot. Such a condition is called critical damping. Less damping results in a more rapid motion with overshoot. If the damping is reduced to zero, an oscillatory condition results. While in actual practice it is never possible to achieve zero damping, a lightly damped system will oscillate for a long period before coming to rest. The frequency of force-free oscillation is called the resonant frequency of the system. When damping is made greater than critical, there is no overshoot but the time taken to reach the position of equilibrium is considerably longer. The type of response encountered with critical damping (100%) and less is summarized in Fig. 15.31. With a step force applied or removed instantly, the response (a) is nonoscillatory for critical damping. With slight damping (20%), the response (b) is partially oscillatory at a frequency less than the undamped resonant frequency of the system. Increasing the damping to 50% (c) results in an overshoot of approximately 15% followed by a heavily damped oscillation.

The time axis of the figure is plotted in percentage of the undamped period (equal to the reciprocal of the resonant frequency with zero damping). It is to be noted that as the damping is decreased, the time for the system to rise from 0 to 100% becomes shorter and the overshoot is greater. It can thus be stated that the price of elimination of transient overshoot is an increase in rise time. The method of attaining a greater rapidity of response without excessive overshoot is to use a stiffer or lighter system, i.e. one with a higher resonant frequency. Thus, the undamped resonant frequency of a system along with the damping define the rise time to be expected.

Intimately associated with the response to a step wave is the behavior of such systems when subjected to sine waves. Figure 15.32 illustrates the response when tested with a constant amplitude variable frequency sine wave of force. With 100% critical damping, the frequency response curve has a characteristic form, falling progressively as the frequency is increased. With zero damping the amplitude of motion increases and becomes larger and larger as the resonant frequency is approached. At the resonant frequency, the response theoretically approaches infinity. With driving frequencies above the resonant frequency, the amplitude is smaller and as the frequency is increased, the amplitude soon becomes immeasurably small. This condition is shown dotted in

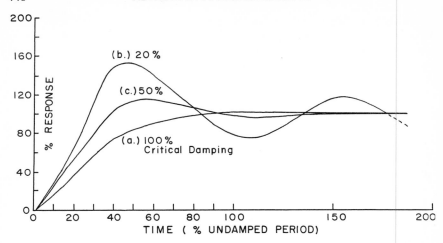

FIG. 15.31. Transient response with various degrees of damping.

Fig. 15.32 and represents a boundary condition under which all operating characteristics are to be found.

If the same procedure is carried out with various degrees of damping between zero and approximately 70%, the amplitude of motion increases slightly at first, rising to a resonant peak then falling rapidly as the frequency increases. The cases of 20 and 50% damping illustrate this point. The interesting behavior with 70% damping will be discussed in detail later.

From Fig. 15.32 it is apparent that with 100% critical damping, the system can only respond fully to sine wave frequencies up to few percent of the resonant frequency. With light damping (20%), there is a pronounced resonant rise in the frequency response curve at approximately 95% of the undamped resonant frequency. When the damping is increased to 50%, the frequency response curve is more uniform and exhibits less of a resonant peak. The frequency at these resonant peaks is less than that for undamped resonant condition. In both cases as the frequency is further increased beyond the maxima, the amplitude falls progressively.

It is thus apparent that there exists a family of curves for the various degrees of damping. Those of most interest fall between the zero and critical damping and assume a contour appropriate for their proximity to either of these boundaries.

When a periodic sine wave of force is presented to such systems, there is a time lag between the displacement of the mass and the applied force. The time lag is expressed in terms of degrees of a full cycle and is designated as phase shift. Damping has a pronounced effect on the phase characteristic of such systems. This relationship is shown in Fig. 15.32B.

It is apparent from inspection of this figure that with some damping between

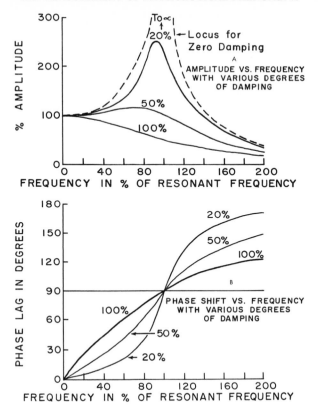

FIG. 15.32. Frequency response and phase characteristics with various degrees of damping.

50 and 100%, phase shift can be fairly linear with frequency up to 100% of the resonant frequency. Choice of an optimum damping for the best phase characteristic will be discussed in the following paragraphs.

In deciding what degree of damping should be specified, it is useful to recall the three criteria for the faithful reproduction of an event. They are linearity of amplitude and phase along with a uniform sine wave response. Because amplitude linearity is usually easy to achieve, the following discussion will deal with the effect of damping on the sine wave frequency and phase response.

In Fig. 15.33 are plotted the amplitude of the resonant rise in the sine wave frequency response curve along with the departure from phase linearity as damping is increased. On the basis of uniform sine wave frequency response a damping of 70% results in no resonant peak in the frequency response curve. Moreover this degree of damping provides a linear phase shift up to and slightly beyond 100% of the undamped resonant frequency. It is logical then to conclude that this degree of damping fulfills all the requirements for faithful

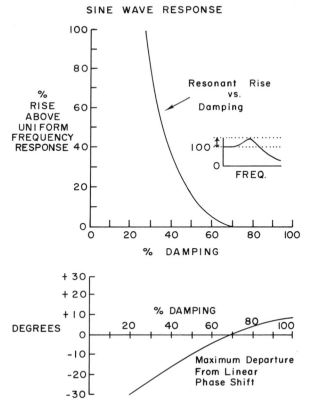

FIG. 15.33. The effect of damping on sine wave and phase characteristics.

reproduction of an event. While this is true, it must be remembered that the reproduction of a step function by a system having these constants is slightly compromised. Under these conditions, the rise time (0 to 100%) is approximately half of the undamped period. Moreover a 5% overshoot is present. It is to be recalled that decreasing the damping shortens the rise time at the expense of overshoot. Since with 70% damping some overshoot must exist, it is logical to investigate the improvement in rise time as damping is further decreased to obtain a more rapid response from the system. Just what degree of damping is to be specified usually depends on the penalty that can be paid in terms of overshoot and rise time for a step function along with distortions produced in the sine wave characteristics.

From Fig. 15.34, which relates rise time and overshoot to the various degrees of damping, it is seen that if the damping is reduced from 70 to 65%, the response time becomes 47% of the undamped period, while the overshoot increases by 2%, giving a total overshoot of 7%. Under these conditions sine

RESPONSE TO STEP FUNCTION

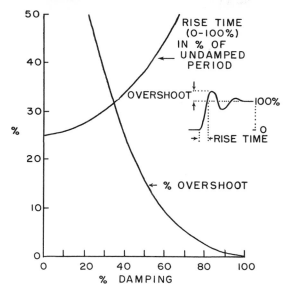

FIG. 15.34. The effect of damping on rise time and overshoot.

wave characteristics are not excessively compromised since for 65% damping, the resonant rise in the frequency response curve is slightly more than 1% and the phase error is approximately one degree.

If a larger overshoot to the step function can be tolerated, a further decrease in rise time can be attained. At 60% damping the rise time is shortened to approximately 45% of the undamped period but the overshoot is increased to about 10%. Under these conditions, the resonant rise in the sine wave curve is approximately 5% and the maximum phase shift error has increased to approximately 1.5% in the frequency range extending up to the freely resonant frequency.

Thus it is apparent that with devices in which resonance can occur, a shorter response time can be attained if a small degree of overshoot can be tolerated when a step function is applied. The improvement in rise time achieved simulates to some degree the characteristics of a stiffer system, i.e. one with a higher resonant frequency. With knowledge of the undamped resonant frequency and the degree of damping the entire behavior of a system having one degree of freedom can be predicted. Knowing the response to a step function (rise time and overshoot), the sine wave frequency and phase characteristics can be deduced. Conversely, knowledge of the sine wave frequency and phase response characteristics enables one to predict the response to a step function or a square wave.

TABLE 15.6. *Characteristics of a resonant system with 65% damping**

Step function	
Rise time (0 to 100%)	$\dfrac{1}{2.1\,f_{o}}$
Overshoot (percentage over terminal amplitude)	7%
Sine wave	
Bandwidth (to 70% amplitude)	0 to 108% f_{o}
Resonant peak (above uniform response)	1.3%
Maximum phase error (0 to 100% f_o range)	1°

*Undamped resonant frequency $= f_{o}$.

In actual practice, to obtain a good compromise between all of the factors discussed, dynamic systems are usually damped to about 65% of critical damping. With this degree of damping the approximate data shown in Table 15.6 are useful in calculation of the constants of a system.

Conclusion

Thus it is apparent that for the faithful reproduction of a complex wave coensideration must be given to its harmonic spectrum. Then the sine wave frequency and phase characteristics of the reproducing system are studied to examine their suitability fo reproduction of all of the components of the complex wave. From such an investigation one can estimate the degree of fidelity of reproduction to be expected.

REFERENCES FOR SECTION I

Benjamin, F. B., Mastrogiovanni, E., & Helveig, W. Bloodless method for continuous recording of pulse pressure in man. *J. appl. Physiol.*, 1962, *17*: 844.
Burger, H. C., & Van Milaan, J. B. Measurements of the specific resistance of the human body to direct current. *Acta med. scand.*, 1943, *114*: 584–607.
Dalla-Torre, L. Utilization d'une nouvelle méthode pour l'inrégistrement du sphygmogramme des artéres digitales. *Helv. physiol. pharmac. acta*, 1943, *1*: C14–15.
Elsner, R. W., Eagan, C. J., & Anderson, S. Impedance matching circuit for mercury strain gauge. *J. appl. Physiol.*, 1959, *14*: 871–872.
Erdos, E. G., Jackman, V., & Barnes, W. C. Instrument for recording isotonic contractions of smooth muscles. *J. appl. Physiol.*, 1962, *17*: 307–308.
Foldvari, T. L., & Lion, K. Capacitive transducers. *Instrums Control Syst.*, 1964, *37*: 77–85.
Gauer, O. H., & Gienapp, E. A miniature pressure-recording device. *Science, N.Y.*, 1950, *112*: 404–405.

Geddes, L. A., & Hoff, H. E. Graphic recording of the pressure pulse wave. *J. appl. Physiol.,* 1960, *15*: 959-960.

Geddes, L. A., Hoff, H. E., Moore, A., G. & Hinds, M. An electrical caliper myograph. *Am. J. pharm. Educ.,* 1966, *30*: 209-211.

Geddes, L. A., Hoff, H. E., & Spencer, W. A. The Center for Vital Studies—A new laboratory for the study of bodily functions in man. *I.R.E. Trans. med. Electron.,* 1961, *8*: 33-45.

Gelb, G. H., Marcus, B. D., & Dropkin, D. Manufacture of fine wire thermocouple probes. *Rev. scient. Instrum.,* 1964, *35*: 80-81.

Handbook of chemistry and physics. (44 ed.) Cleveland, Ohio: The Chemical Rubber Publishing Company, 1962-1963.

Hayward, J. N., Ott, L. H., Stuart, D. G., & Cheshire, F. C. Peltier biothermodes. *Am. J. med. Electron.,* 1965, *4*: 11-19.

Hertzman, A. The blood supply of various skin areas as estimated by the photoelectric plethysmograph *Am. J. Physiol.,* 1938, *124*: 328-340.

Hoff, H. E., & Geddes, L. A. *Experimental physiology.* Houston: Baylor Medical College, 1955.

Honda, N. Temperature compensation for mercury strain gauge used in plethysmography, *J. appl. Physiol.,* 1962, *17*: 572-574.

Lawton, R. W., & Collins, C. C. Calibration of an aortic circumference gauge. *J. appl. Physiol.,* 1959, *14*: 465-467.

Lax, H., Feinberg, A. W., & Cohen., B. M. Studies of the arterial pulse wave. *J. chron. Dis.,* 1956, *3*: 618-631.

Leeds and Northrup Bulletin 15A-RP 1.4. Pittsburgh, Pa.: The Instrument Society of America.

Lion, K. Non-linear twin-T network for capacitance transducers. *Rev. scient. Instrum.,* 1964, *35*: 353-356.

Miller, A., & White, P. D. Crystal microphone for pulse wave recording. *Am. Heart J.,* 1941, *21*: 504-510.

Müller, A. Uber die Pulsform und Wellengeschwindigkeit in den Fingerarterien. *Arch. Kreislaufforsch .,* 1942, *11*: 198-206.

Pascoe, J.E. A technique for introduction of intracellular electrodes. *J. Physiol., Paris,* 1955, *128*: 26P-27P.

Pieper, H. P. Registration of phasic changes of blood flow by means of a catheter type flowmeter. *Rev. scient. Instrum.,* 1958, *29*: 965-967.

Rappaport, M. B., & Luisada, A. Indirect sphygmomanometry. *J. Lab. clin. Med.,* 1944, *29*: 638-656.

Reed, R. P., & Kampwirth, R. T. Thermocouples of micron size by vapor-deposition. *Direction,* 1964, *10*: 8.

Rein, H., Hampel, A. A., & Heinemann, W. A. Photoelektrische Transmission-manometer zur Blutdruckschreibung. *Arch. ges. Physiol.,* 1940, *243*: 329-335.

Rein, H. Magnetische O_2 Analyse in Gasigemischen. *Arch. ges. Physiol.,* 1944, *247*:570-592.

Rosenthal, R. L., & Tobias, C. W. Measurement of the electric resistance of human blood use in coagulation studies and cell volume determinations. *J. Lab. clin. Med.,* 1946, *33*: 1110-1122.

Rushmer, R. F. Heart size and stroke volume. *Minn. Med.,* 1954, *37*: 19-29. (a)

Rushmer, R. F. Continuous measurements of left ventricular dimensions in intact unanesthetized dogs. *Circularion Res.,* 1954, *2*: 14-21. (b)

Rushmer, R. F. Pressure circumference relations in the aorta. *Am. J. Physiol.,* 1955, *183*: 545-549. (a)

Rushmer, R. F. Length-circumference relations of the left ventricle. *Circulation Res.,* 1955, *3*: 639-644. (b)

Rushmer, R. F. Pressure circumference relations in the left ventricle. *Am. J. Physiol.,* 1956, *186*: 115-121.

Schaevitz, H. The linear variable differential transformer. *Proc. Soc. Stress Analysis,* 1947, *4*: 79-88.

Schafer, P. W., & Shirer, H. W. An impedance gauging system for measurement of biologic pressure variables. *Surgery,* 1949, *26*: 446-451.

Scher, A. M., Weiger, T. H., & Young, A. C. Compact flowmeters for use in the unanesthetized animal, an electronic version of Chauveau's hemodrometer. *Science, N.Y.*, 1953, *118*: 82-84.

Swenson, C. A., & Emslie, A. G. Low temperature electronics. *Proc. Inst. Radio Engrs*, 1954, *42*: 402-413.

Thermistor data book. Union, N. J.: Victory Engineering Corporation.

Thompson, S. P. *The life of William Thomson, Baron Kelvin of Largs*. London: Macmillan, 1910.

Tucker, M. J. A linear transducer for the electrical measurement of displacement. *Electron. Engng.*, 1952, *24*: 420-422.

Wetterer, E. Eine neue manometrische Sonde mit elektrischer Transmission. *Z. Biol.*, 1943, *101*: 333-350.

Wheeler, H. A. Simple inductance formulas for radio coils. *Proc. Inst. Radio Engrs*, 1928, *16*: 1398-1400.

Whitney, R. J. The measurement of changes in human limb-volume by means of a mercury-in-rubber strain gauge. *J. Physiol., Paris*, 1949, *109*: 5P-6P.

Whitney, R. J. The measurement of volume changes in human limbs. *J. Physiol., Paris*, 1953, *121*: 1-27.

Whitney, R. J. Circulatory changes in the forearm and hand of man with repeated exposure to heat. *J. Physiol., Paris*, 1954, *125*: 1-24.

Wood, E. H., Knutson, J. R. B., & Taylor, B. E. Measurement of blood content and blood pressure in the human ear. *Proc. Staff Meet. Mayo Clin.*, 1950, *25*: 398-405.

Yamazaki, Z. Medical application of thermoelectric cooling. *Jap. Electron. Engng*, 1965, *2*: 32-35.

REFERENCES FOR SECTION II

Allison, R. D., Holmes, E. L., & Nyboer, J. Volumetric dynamics of respiration as measured by electrical impedance plethysmography. *J. appl. Physiol.*, 1964, *19*: 166-173.

Bagno, S. Impedance measurements of living tissue. *Electronics*, 1959, *32*: 62-63.

Baker, L. E., & Geddes, L. A. Quantitative evaluation of impedance spirometry in man. *Am. J. med. Electron.*, 1965, *4*: 73-77.

Bonjer, F. H., van der Berg, J., & Dirken, M. N. J. The origin of the variations of body impedance occurring during the cardiac cycle. *Circulation*, 1952, *1*: 415-420.

Brazier, M. A. B. *The electrical activity of the nervous system*. London: Sir Isaac Pitman & Sons, Ltd., 1951.

Dubuisson, M. Rechérches sur les modifications que surviennent dans la conductibilité électrique du muscle au cours de la contraction. *Archs int. Physiol.*, 1933, *37*: 35-57.

Geddes, L. A. Recording respiration and the EKG with common electrodes. *Aerospace Med.*, 1962, *33*: 791-93.

Geddes, L. A. An electrical caliper myograph. *Am. J. pharm. Educ.*, 1966, *30*: 209-211.

Geddes, L. A., & Hoff, H. E. The measurement of physiological events by electrical impedance. *Am. J. med Electron.*, 1964, *3*: 16-27.

Geddes, L. A., Hoff, H. E., Hall, C. W., & Millar, H. D. Rheoencephalography. *Cardiovascular Res cent. Bull.*, 1964, *2*: 112-121.

Geddes, L. A., Hoff, H. E., Hickman, D. M. & Moore, A. G. The impedance pneumograph. *Aerospace Med.*, 1962, *33*: 28-33.

Geddes, L. A., McCrady, J. D., & Hoff, H. E. The impedance nystagmogram—a record of the level of anesthesia in the horse. *SWest. Vet.*, 1965, *19*: 23-25.

Goldensohn, E. S., & Zablow, L. An electrical impedance spirometer. *J. appl. Physiol.*, 1959, *14*: 463-464.

Hamilton, L., Beard, J. D., & Kory, R. C. Impedance measurement of tidal volume and ventilation. *J. appl. Physiol.*, 1965, *20*: 565-568.

Hickman, D. M., Geddes, L. A., Hoff, H. E., Hinds, M., Moore, A. G., Francis, C. K., & Engen, T. A portable miniature transistorized radiofrequency coupled cardiac pacemaker. *I.R.E. Trans. med. Electron.*, 1963, *8*: 258-262.

Jenkner, F. *Rheoencephalography*. Springfield, Ill.: Charles C Thomas, 1962.

Kris, C. Vision: electro-oculography. *Med. Phys.*, 1960, *3*: 1-754.

Kubicek, W. G., Kinnen, E., & Edin, A. Calibration of an impedance pneumograph. *J. appl. Physiol.*, 1964, *19*: 557-560.

Lifschitz, K. Rheoencephalography. I. Review of the technique. *J. nerv. ment. Dis.*, 1963, *136*: 388-398. (a)

Lifshitz, K. Rheoencephalography. II. Survey of clinical application. *J. nerv. ment. Dis.*, 1963, *137*: 285-296. (b)

McCally, M., Barnard, G. W., Robins, K. E. & Marko, A. Observations with an electrical impedance respirometer. *Am. J. med. Electron.*, 1963, *2*: 322-327.

McHenry, L. C. Rheoencephalography. *Neurology, Minneap.*, 1965, *15*: 507-517.

Nyboer, J. Electrical impedance plethysmography. *Med. Phys.*, 1944, *1*: 1-744.

Nyboer, J. Electrical impedance plethysmography. *Circulation*, 1950, *2*: 811-821.

Nyboer, J. *Electrical impedance plethysmography.* Springfield, Ill.: Charles C Thomas, 1959.

Patterson, R., Kubicek, W. G., Kinnen, E., Noren, G., & Witsoe, D. Development of an electrical impedance plethysmograph system to monitor cardiac output. *1st Ann. Rocky Mount. Conf. Biomed. Engng, Colorado Springs, Colorado, May, 1964.*

Robinson, D. A. A method of measuring eye movements using a scleral search coil in a magnetic field. *I.R.E. Trans. med. Electron.*, 1963, *10*: 137-145.

Schwan, H. P. Electrical properties of body tissues and impedance plethysmography. *I.R.E. Trans. med. Electron.*, 1955, *3*: 32-46.

Schwan, H. P. Determination of biological impedances. *Physical techniques in biological research.* New York: Academic Press, 1963. Vol. VIB.

Schwan, H. P., & Kay, C. F. Capacitive properties of body tissues. *Circulation Res.*, 1957, *5*: 439-443.

Schwan, H. P., & Li, K. Capacitance and conductivity of body tissues at ultra high frequencies. *Proc. Inst. Radio Engrs*, 1953, *41*: 1735-1740.

Sullivan, G., & Weltman, G. The impedance oculogram—a new technique. *J. appl. Physiol.*, 1963, *18*: 215-216.

REFERENCES FOR SECTIONS III AND IV

Adrian, E. D., & Bronk, D. W. Impulses in motor nerve fibers, Part II. *J. Physiol.*, 1929, *67*: 119-151.

Atkins, A. R. Measuring heart rate of an active athlete. *Electron. Engng,* 1961, *33*: 457.

Asa, M. M., Crews, A. H., Rothfield, E. L., Lewis, E. S., Zucker, I. R., & Bernstein, A. High fidelity radioelectrocardiography. *Am. J. Cardio.*, 1964, *14*: 530-532.

Barnett, A. The basic factors involved in proposed electrical methods for measuring thyroid function. *West. J. Surg. Obstet. Gynec.*, 1937, *45*: 540-554.

Bell, G. H., Knox, J. A. C., & Small, A. J. Electrocardiograph electrolytes. *Br. Heart J.*, 1939, *1*: 229-236.

Blank, I. H., & Finesinger, T. G. Electrical resistance of the skin. *Archs Neurol. Psychiat., Chicago,* 1946, *54*: 544-557.

Burns, R. C. Study of skin impedance. *Electronics*, 1950, *23*: 190 and 196.

Burr, H. S. Potential gradients in living systems and their measurements. *Med. Phys.,* 1944, *1*: 1117-1121.

Burr, H. S. Bioelectricity. *Med. Phys.,* 1950, *2*: 90-94.

Clark, L. C., & Lacey, T. J. An improved skin electrode. *J. Lab. clin. Med.*, 1950, *35*: 786-787.

Curtis, H. J., & Cole, K. S. Transverse electric impedance of the squid giant axon. *J. gen. Physiol.*, 1938, *21*: 757-765.

Day, J., & Lippitt, M. A long term electrode system for electrocardiography and impedance pneumography. *Psychophysiology*, 1964, *1*: 174-182.

Dowben, R. M., & Rose, J. E. A metal filled microelectrode. *Science, N.Y.*, 1953, *118*: 22-24.

Edelberg, R., & Burch, N. R. Skin resistance and galvanic skin response. *Archs gen. Psychiat.*, 1962, *7*: 163-169.

Forbes, A., Cobb, S., & Cattell, M. An electrocardiogram and an electromyogram in an elephant. *Am. J. Physiol.*, 1921, *55*: 385-389.

Forbes, T. W. An improved electrode for the measurement of potentials on the human body. *J. Lab. clin. Med.*, 1934, *19*: 1234-1238.

Frank, K., & Becker, M. Microelectrodes for recording and stimulation. In G. Oster & A. W.

Pollister (Eds.), *Physical techniques in biological research*. New York: Academic Press, 1964. Vol. 5.

Geddes, L. A. Cortical electrodes. *Electroenceph. clin. Neurophysiol.*, 1949, *1*: 523, Illustrated on cover of *Scient. Am.*, 1948, *4*: 179.

Geddes, L. A., McCrady, J. D., Hoff, H. E., & Moore, A. Electrodes for large animals. *S West. Vet.*, 1964, *18*: 56–57.

Gesteland, R. C., Howland, B., Lettvin, J. Y., & Pitts, W. H. Comments on microelectrodes. *Proc Inst. Radio Engrs*, 1959, *47*: 1856–1862.

Grahame, D. C. Properties of the electrical double layer at a mercury surface. *J. Am. chem. Soc.*, 1941, *63*: 1207–1214.

Gray, J. A. G., & Svaetichin, G. Electrical properties of platinum tipped microelectrodes. *Acta physiol. scand.*, 1951, *24*: 278–284.

Greenwald, D. U. Electrodes used in measuring electrodermal responses. *Am. J. Psychol.*, 1936, *48*: 658–662.

Grundfest, H., & Campbell, B. Origin, conduction and termination of impulses in dorsal spino-cerebellar roots of cats. *J. Neurophysiol.*, 1942, *5*: 275–294.

Grundfest, H., Sengstaken, R. W., & Oettinger, W. H. Stainless steel microneedle electrodes made by electro-pointing. *Rev. scient. Instrum.*, 1950, *21*: 360–361.

Guld, C. A glass-covered platinum microelectrode. *Med. Electron. Biol. Engng.*, 1964, *2*: 317–327.

Handbook of chemistry and physics. (44 ed.) Cleveland, Ohio: The Chemical Rubber Publishing Company, 1962–1963.

Hendler, E., & Santa Maria, L. J. Response of subjects to some conditions of a simulated orbital flight pattern. *Aerospace Med.*, 1961, *32*: 126–133.

Henry, F. Dependable electrodes for the galvanic skin response. *J. gen. Psychol.*, 1938, *18*: 209–211.

Hubel, D. H. Tungsten microelectrode for recording from single units. *Science, N.Y.*, 1957, *125*: 549–550.

James, W. B., & Williams, H. B. The electrocardiogram in clinical medicine. *Am J. med. Sci.*, 1910, *140*: 408–421.

Janz, G. J., & Kelly, F. J. Reference electrodes. In C. A. Hampel (Ed.), *Encyclopedia of electrochemistry*. New York: Reinhold, 1964.

Janz, G. J., & Taniguchi, H. The silver-silver halide electrodes. *Chem. Rev.* 1953, *53*: 397–437.

Jasper, H. H., Johnson, R. T., & Geddes, L. A. The RCAMC electromyograph. *Can. Army Med. Report C6174*, 1945.

Jenks, J. L., & Graybiel, A. A new simple method of avoiding high resistance and overshooting in taking standardized electrocardiograms. *Am Heart J.*, 1935, *10*: 683–695.

Kado, R. T., Adey, W. R., & Zweizig, J. R. Electrode system for recording EEG from physically active subjects. *Proc. 17th Ann. Conf. Engng Med. Biol., Cleveland, Ohio.* Washington, D.C.: MacGregor and Werner, 1964.

Kahn, A. Fundamentals of biopotentials and their measurement. Biomedical Sciences Instrumentation, 1964. Dallas, Texas. *Am. J. pharm. Educ.*, 1964, *28*: 805–814.

Kahn, A. Motion artifacts and streaming potentials in relation to biological electrodes. *Int. Conf. Med. Electron. Biol. Engng, 1965, Tokyo, Japan.* Conference Digest, pp. 562–563.

Kennard, D. W. Glass microcapillary electrodes. In P. E. K. Donaldson (Ed.), *Electronic apparatus for biological research*. London: Butterworth, 1958, Chap. 35.

Lewis, T. Polarisable as against non-polarisable electrodes. *J. Physiol.*, 1915, *49*: L–Lii.

Lucchina, G. G., & Phipps, C. G. A vectorcardiographic lead system and physiologic electrode configuration for dynamic readout. *Aerospace Med.*, 1962, *33*: 722–729.

Lucchina, G. G., & Phipps, C. G. An improved electrode for physiological recording. *Aerospace Med.*, 1963, *34*: 230–231.

Lykken, D. T. Properties of electrodes used in electrodermal measurement. *J. comp. physiol. Psychol.*, 1959, *52*: 629–634.

Marmont, G. Studies on the axon membrane. *J. cell. comp. Physiol.*, 1949, *34*: 351–382.

O'Connell, D. N., & Tursky, B. Special modifications of the silver-silver chloride sponge electrode for skin recording. USAF Office of Scientific Research, Contract AF 49(638)-728, 1960.

O'Connell, D. N., Tursky, B., & Orne, M. T. Electrodes for recording skin potential. *Archs gen. Psychiat.* 1960, *3*: 252–258.

Offner, F. F. Electrical properties of tissues in shock therapy. *Proc. Soc. exp. Biol. Med.*, 1942, *49*: 571–575.

Pardee, H. E. B. Concerning the electrodes used in electrocardiography. *Am. J. Physiol.*, 1917, *44*: 80–83.

Parsons, R. Electrode double layer. In C. A. Hampel (Ed.), *The encyclopedia of electrochemistry*. New York: Reinhold, 1964.

Plutchik, R., & Hirsch, H. R. Skin impedance and phase angle as a function of frequency and current. *Science, N.Y.*, 1963, *141*: 927–928.

Roman, J., & Lamb, L. Electrocardiography in flight. *Aerospace Med.*, 1962, *33*: 527–544.

Roth, I. A self-retaining skin contact electrode for chest leads in electrocardiography. *Am. Heart J.* 1933, *9*: 526–529.

Rothschild, L. The polarization of a calomel electrode. *Proc. R. Soc.*, 1938, *125*: 283–290.

Rowley, D. A., Glagov, S., & Stoner, P. Fluid electrodes for monitoring the electrocardiogram during activity and for prolonged periods of time. *Am. Heart J.*, 1961, *62*: 263–269.

Schmitt, O. H., Okajima, M., & Blaug, M. Skin preparation and electrocardiographic lead impedance. *Dig. I.R.E. Internat. Conf. Med. Electron., New York, 1961*. Washington, D. C.: MacGregor and Werner.

Schwan, H. P. Determination of biological impedances. In B. W. Nastuk (Ed.), *Physical techniques in biological research*. New York: Academic Press, 1963.

Schwan, H. P., & Maczuk, J. G. Electrode polarization impedance; limits of linearity. *Proc. 18th Ann. Conf. Engng. Biol. Med., Philadelphia, Pa.* Washington, D. C.: MacGregor and Werner, 1965.

Shackel, B. A rubber suction cup surface electrode with high electrical stability. *J. appl. Physiol.*, 1958, *13*: 153–158.

Shackel, B. Skin drilling: a method for diminishing galvanic skin potentials. *Am. J. Psychol.*, 1959, *72*: 114–121.

Simons, D. G., Prather, W., & Coombs, F. K. Personalized telemetry medical monitoring and performance data-gathering for the 1962 SAM-MATS fatigue study. SAM-TR-65-17. USAF Brooks AFB, Texas, 1965.

Skov, E. R., & Simons, D. G. EEG electrodes for in-flight monitoring. SAM-TR-65-18. USAF Brooks AFB, Texas, 1965.

Sullivan, G. H., & Weltman, G. A low mass electrode for bioelectric recording. *J. appl. Physiol.*, 1961, *16*: 939–940.

Svaetichin, G. Low resistance microelectrode. *Acta physiol. scand.*, 1951, *24*: (suppl. 86) 1–13.

Tasaki, I. Properties of myelinated fibers in a frog sciatic nerve and in spinal cord as examined with microelectrodes. *Jap. J. Physiol., 1952, 3*: 73–94.

Telemedics, Inc. *Med. Electron. News*, 1961, *1*: 9.

Terman, F. E. *Radio engineers handbook*. (1st ed.) New York: McGraw-Hill, 1943.

Thompson, N. P., & Patterson, J. A. Solid salt bridge contact electrodes. System for monitoring the ECG during body movement. *Tech. Rep. 58-453, ASTIA Doc. AD215538*, 1958.

Ungerleider, H. E. A new precordial electrode. *Am. Heart J.*, 1939, *18*: 94.

Weale, R. A. A new micro-electrode for electrophysiological work. *Nature, Lond.*, 1951, *167*: 529.

Weinman, J., & Mahler, J. An analysis of electrical properties of metal electrodes. *Med. Electron. Biol. Engng.* 1964, *2*: 299–310.

REFERENCES FOR SECTION V

Geddes, L. A. A note on phase distortion. *Electroenceph. clin. Neurophysiol.*, 1951, *3*: 517–518.

Hansen, A. T. Pressure measurement in the human organism. Copenhagen: Technisk Forlag, 1949.

Radar Electronic Fundamentals. War Dept. Tech. Manual TM 11–466. Washington, D. C.: United States Government Printing Office, 1946.

Saunders, M. G., & Jell, R. M. Time distortion in electroencephalograph amplifiers. *Electro-enceph. clin. Neurophysiol.*, 1959, *11*: 814–816.

Terman, F. E. *Radio engineers handbook.* New York: McGraw-Hill, 1943.

Valley, G. E., & Wallman, H. *Vacuum tube amplifiers.* York, Pa.: McGraw-Hill, 1948.

16

*The Laboratory Computer in Psychophysiology**

BERNARD WEISS, Ph.D., and LOUIS SIEGEL, B.S.E.E.

Psychophysiology characteristically deals with large amounts of information and complex interrelations among variables. In these respects it is typical of much of biology and medicine. Volume and complexity of data alone, one would think, should make the biomedical sciences the most prominent beneficiaries of advances in computer technology. Regrettably, it is not so. In part, the lag on the part of biological scientists can be laid to the time consumed by having to learn the skills necessary to apply computer technology. It is no small decision to put aside current problems and well tried techniques to grapple with a new discipline. In part, however, the lag is also the fault of computer designers and manufacturers, and their orientation toward business machines. They have made it more difficult than it should ever have been for scientists to use digital computers as the exquisite tools they have the potential to be.

Quite recently, however, a number of new computers have been introduced which now make it feasible to consider them as laboratory instruments. Moreover, the intense activity within the computer industry directed toward the design of shared-time systems (Martin, 1965) promises to extend the functional equivalent of a laboratory computer to many scientists who might otherwise not have access to one. For these reasons, we shall orient this chapter toward the laboratory computer.

Nearly every experimenter soon becomes aware that the immense volumes of data that an experiment can generate can be dealt with only by a computer. Analyses by hand are out of the question if anything exceeding the most superficial analysis is to be performed. Such an application is obvious. Not so obvious are some other points.

---

*The preparation of this chapter was supported in part by National Institutes of Health Grant MH-11752 and by a contract with the United States Atomic Energy Commission.

Perhaps first is the advantage that one gains from learning the results of an experiment shortly after its completion. It can change an investigator's outlook completely. No longer is he compelled to continue experimenting blindly or to stop experimenting altogether while he awaits the results of an analysis. Rapid access to a computer allows him to modify his procedures and perhaps his problems from day to day, or even during the course of an experiment. With rapid enough access to a computer, experiments can be designed to use sequential statistics, at a significant saving in time in many cases, particularly if reliable data are hard to come by.

A second advantage of the laboratory computer is its ability to serve not only as a device for analyzing data rapidly, but to control an ongoing experiment. In the future, this will perhaps turn out to be the most useful and far reaching application of computer technology to psychophysiology in particular and biology in general.

Although many experiments do not require on-line monitoring by direct coupling to the computer, the advantages of a computer in the laboratory, even in these cases, are most cogent. Consider, first of all, that any experiment in which many variables are being recorded gives rise to perturbations which are not immediately clear to the investigator. These may range from changes in electrode resistance to, say, subtle, long term periodicities in heart rate. When the variability from sources such as these is added to the inherent variability of experimental observations, it may obscure whatever regularities are present. If it were possible to monitor the experiment with a computer, one could write programs to make continuous evaluations of the incoming data, perhaps with a view toward preprocessing to eliminate or reduce extraneous factors.

For those problems which are best attacked by modifying parameters quickly during an experiment, or which require keeping track of large numbers of stimuli and responses, or which must generate random processes, or which need to synthesize many different stimuli according to a specified plan, the laboratory computer is an indispensable partner.

In this chapter, we will discuss some of the ways in which laboratory computers may be used, how they work, what skills are needed to operate them, and where their contribution is likely to lie.

Computer Organization and Function

The kind of computer that is useful for the laboratory is one that can serve as a process controller. In such a mode of operation, the computer senses signals arriving from devices in the environment and emits other signals which modify and control actions of the environment. In the sections that immediately follow, we will discuss some basic features of computers and their use in the laboratory. We shall illustrate many features of computer usage by describing the operation of the LINC computer, which we employ. The LINC can be viewed as a prototype of the new generation of small machines oriented toward on-line functions (Clark & Molnar, 1965).

A general purpose digital computer is designed to execute a series of operations called instructions. A sequence of instructions is called a program. A particular computer model is designed with a given set of instructions in its repertoire. These are used to process data and to perform other functions, and programming consists of placing the proper instructions in sequence. Figure 16.1 is a block diagram of a digital computer. As we describe the function of the various components, the organization of a digital computer will become clearer.

Memory or storage. In the earlier electronic computers, the order in which instructions were executed was arranged by patchboards or similar devices. These required considerable time to set up and possessed little flexibility. Modern computers are designed to operate by programs stored in an internal memory which also contains the data upon which the calculations are made. The use of a stored program and internal memory revolutionized computer design. In the first place, it allowed data and instructions to be transmitted between such a unit and the processing unit, thereby performing the computing more rapidly than by other means. In addition, it meant that instructions themselves could be treated as numbers and modified by the program.

The typical internal storage device presently used consists of a matrix of ferrite cores or beads which can be magnetized in one direction or the other. The two directions correspond to 0 and 1 in binary arithmetic, which we will discuss in the next section. The memory is organized as a large number of memory boxes or registers, with each register being assigned a distinct numerical *address* or *location*. The information put into a register, which consists of a string of ferrite cores, is called a *word*. Data and instruction words look alike, that is sequences of 0's and 1's, and the computer must be told explicitly which addresses contain instructions and which contain data. The number of binary digits or bits in a word is called the word length. The LINC· uses a word length of 12 bits, and its core memory contains 2048 words. Information can be read into or out of a particular memory location by specifying its address in an instruction. For example, an instruction might read, "Store the sum just computed in memory register 1000."

Processor. The processor, sometimes called the arithmetic unit, is the actual site of the computations or data modifications performed by the computer. Words are transferred back and forth from the processor and the memory. In most modern computers, only one word at a time can be transferred between the processor and the memory. In order to perform an operation such as addition, therefore, the first number must be held in the arithmetic unit temporarily while the second number is being transferred. The accumu-

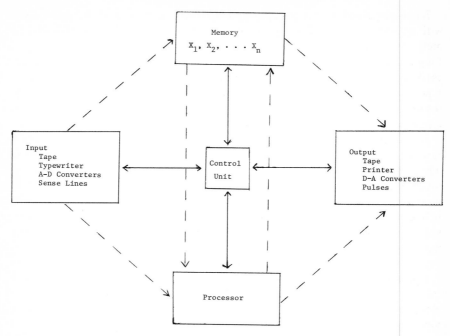

FIG. 16.1. Schematic block diagram of a general purpose digital computer. Some of the possible input-output devices that can be connected are listed in the appropriate squares.

lator is a special kind of register in the processor that performs this function of temporary storage, and it is the site of most of the operations that a computer performs. Most of the basic instructions in a computer's repertoire, therefore, refer to the accumulator (or accumulators).

To add two numbers, the accumulator is used in the following way. Assume the numbers to be located in memory addresses 100 and 101, and that we wish the sum to be placed in register 1000.

Instruction 1. Set the contents of the accumulator equal to the contents of register 100. (Note that the information in register 100 is not destroyed.)

Instruction 2. Add the contents of register 101 to the contents of the accumulator.

Instruction 3. Store the contents of the accumulator in register 1000; that is, set the contents of register 1000 equal to the contents of the accumulator.

Logical manipulations of various kinds are also carried out in the accumulator. For example, setting specified bits equal to 1 or 0, performing Boolean operations such as logical *or*, occluding parts of a word, examining a word bit by bit, shifting the accumulator contents right or left a specified number of places, and so on.

Input-output devices. A computer would be a useless piece of machinery without some means of transferring information into and out of it. Numerous methods of doing so have been developed, therefore. Typical input devices for getting data and programs into the computer are magnetic tape, punched cards, punched paper tape, magnetic drums, analogue to digital converters, typewriter keyboards, etc. Output devices are typically designed so that the results of computations can be presented to the user. These include printers, typewriters, XY plotters, oscilloscopes, etc.

If a computer is to be used on-line in the laboratory, the input-output facilities assume overwhelming importance. Provision has to be made for extensive and versatile facilities that make it easy to get information into and out of the machine and which accept and emit a variety of control signals. The LINC, via its input facilities, will accept 12-bit binary words and analogue signals and will respond to control signals in the form of pulses and levels. It can emit individually controlled pulses, levels, and relay closures, and it can transfer complete words to another computer. Such an input-output facility greatly eases the job of the experimenter trying to incorporate a computer into his laboratory.

Control unit. Some means must obviously exist within the computer for interpreting instructions, sending them on to the processor in their proper electrical code, executing the instructions in sequence, transferring data from memory to processor and vice versa, controlling the flow of input and output signals, and so on. These functions are performed by the control unit. The control unit contains a program counter for following the sequence in which instructions are executed, an instruction decoder, and means for carrying out the instructions, and, in most computers, a clock that synchronizes the operations of the computer. The internal circuitry is so connected to the clock that pulses are allowed to travel only at times when a clock pulse is received. The function of the clock has been compared to that of an orchestra conductor, who has the responsibility for keeping time and synchronizing the notes produced by the musicians.

An indispensable feature for a laboratory computer is an informative and versatile console or control panel. Such a console has three main functions. One is to enable the user to prepare the computer for the execution of a program, and to monitor it during the execution of the program. A second is to aid in checking, or "debugging," programs. And a third is to help track down maintenance problems. The console is, therefore, the main communications link between the user and the machine. By means of the console, the computer can be started and stopped, computation can be initiated or stopped at specified points in the program, instructions can be executed manually one at a time or at a slow rate, magnetic tapes can be positioned, and other input-output equipment controlled, etc. The console also displays the contents of various registers such as the accumulator, the program counter, the instruction decoder, etc. It should also permit, via switches or buttons, the insertion of data or instructions or their alteration by manual means. A loudspeaker is also useful for monitoring or checking programs in progress.

Binary Arithmetic and Notation

All modern digital computers are binary machines in that they use a two-valued logic. Both data and instructions are represented as words made up of 0's and 1's, standing for the two voltage levels which represent *off* and *on*, respectively, within the machine. Binary logic is preferred to decimal systems because it is easier to represent two states electrically than 10.

In the decimal number system, successive digit positions from right to left represent ascending powers of 10. For example, the number $4375 = 4 \times 10^3 + 3 \times 10^2 + 7 \times 10^1 + 5 \times 10^0$, or, 4 thousands, 3 hundreds, 7 tens, and 5 ones.

In the binary number system, the successive columns from right to left represent ascending powers of 2. For example, $101,011 = 1 \times 2^5 + 0 \times 2^4 + 1 \times 2^3 + 0 \times 2^2 + 1 \times 2^1 + 1 \times 2^0$, or, one 32, no 16's, one 8, no 4's, one 2, and one 1. The equivalent decimal number is $32 + 8 + 2 + 1$, 43.

Because binary numbers are so much less compact than decimal numbers, they are cumbersome for purposes of communication. This can be overcome by introducing a number system derived from the base 8, or the *octal* number system. The eight characters in this system are the arabic numerals 0 through 7. Binary can be converted to octal (and the reverse) very easily because a group of three binary digits is equivalent to one octal digit. For this reason, when various registers within a computer are displayed on a console, they are often divided into groups of three bits. Table 16.1 gives some equivalent values in all three systems, decimal, octal, and binary. The decimal number 43, represented above as 101,011 in binary, is equal to 53 in octal form.

TABLE 16.1. *Number representation in three number systems*

Decimal	Binary	Octal
0	000	0
1	001	1
2	010	2
3	011	3
4	100	4
5	101	5
6	110	6
7	111	7
8	1 000	10
9	1 001	11
10	1 010	12
29	11 101	35
40	101 000	50
100	1 100 100	144
3739	111 010 011 011	7233

Most newer machines tend to use pure binary arithmetic in their internal processing, converting to decimal representation when needed, such as printing out computational results. Other machines use a coding more akin to decimal; for example, binary-coded-decimal or biquinary systems. These systems tend to be slower and more wasteful of memory capacity than pure binary systems. In all cases, however, both data and instructions appear as strings of 0's and 1's within the computer. This form is called machine language.

Programming

Despite all the technological innovations of the past few years, the design and construction of large memory, long word length, extremely fast machines, computers are still not giant brains. A computer is a responsive and subservient clerk, relentlessly performing every action it is instructed to perform, but showing no initiative of its own (Green, 1963). It requires guidance at every step of the way. This is why programming is such a time consuming task, and why it takes immense attention to detail and thorough knowledge of the computer to practice this skill at its highest level.

We shall turn to the LINC for examples of computer programming. The sorts of instructions which the LINC computer makes available can be grouped in the following categories. They are not different in principle from those which apply to other modern computers (Clark & Molnar, 1964, p. 655):

"1) Arithmetic instructions which perform addition, multiplication, counting, etc. 2) Logic instructions which perform simple logical manipulations. 3) Data transfer instructions which move information from one computer location to another. 4) Indexing instructions which provide a convenient means of referring to tables. 5) Input-output instructions which transfer information to and from external equipment. 6) Magnetic tape instructions which control various digital magnetic tape operations. 7) Control instructions that determine which of alternative sets of instructions are to be executed according to various criteria."

For some purposes and some computers it suffices to have a knowledge of an artificial language such as FORTRAN, which, through what is called a compiler, translates common algebraic statements into machine language. If, however, one is using a computer on-line, with a specialized configuration of input and output equipment, then a knowledge of machine language and binary arithmetic is virtually indispensable.

Most computers, fortunately, ease the task of communicating in machine language by providing an *assembly program* which allows the programmer to substitute short mnemonics, of three or four letters, say, for the actual binary form of the instruction. The assembly program converts these into the proper binary codes. These programs also permit insertions and deletions to be made in the regular program and will renumber addresses accordingly.

As an example of a simple program, consider a sequence which adds the numbers in memory locations 100 and 101 and stores the sum in location 1000. The

TABLE 16.2. *Program for simple addition*

Location	Octal	Mnemonic	Description
20	11	CLR	Clear accumulator (set it to 0)
21	2100	Add 100	Add the contents of register 100 to accumulator
22	2101	Add 101	Add the contents of register 101 to accumulator
23	4100	STC 1000	Store the contents of accumulator in register 1000 and clear accumulator

sequence, mnemonics, and octal codes are given in Table 16.2. We shall start the program in location 20. We first set the accumulator to 0. Then we add the contents of register 100 to the accumulator and the contents of 101 to that entry, giving us the sum. The sum is stored in 1000.

A more complex program is given in Table 16.3. If we wish to obtain the sum of several numbers, it conserves program space in memory if we make the process a recurrent one rather than going down the list of registers one by one. The program in Table 16.3 uses what is called a loop to perform the addition, i.e. a sequence of instructions that keeps repeating until it reaches a present criterion. Assume the numbers to be added are in locations 100 to 117.

Here, we introduce some new features. The instruction occupying registers 21 and 22 is a two word instruction. This instruction does not disturb the accumulator contents, and is used to make the contents of one register equal to the contents of another register. In this case, we have made the contents of register 1 equal to the contents of register 22.

An index register is a useful device in programming; its contents may be automatically incremented in units of 1 without having to use the accumulator. In the program in Table 16.3, the index register used, 1, is set to 77 because the indexing is carried out before the associated instruction. (The next register, in the octal system, is 100.)

Instruction 23 shows how the indexing feature is used. The instruction ADAi 1 performs two functions. In the first place, it is used for what is called *indirect addressing*. Instead of designating register 100 directly, we tell the computer that the address to which we wish to refer is designated by the contents of register 1. The *i* in this instruction tells the computer to index register 1 before carrying out the instruction. Thus, the first time instruction 23 is executed,

TABLE 16.3. *Program for adding several numbers*

Location	Octal	Mnemonic	Description
20	11	CLR	Set accumulator to 0
21	61	SETi 1	Set index register 1 to the number 77
22	77	77	
23	1121	ADAi 1	Increment register 1, then add the contents of the register designated by 1 to accumulator
24	4003	STC 3	Store the contents of accumulator in register 3, then clear accumulator
25	1000	LDA	Load accumulator with the contents of register 1
26	1	1	
27	1460	SAEi	Skip the next instruction if accumulator equals 117; otherwise, execute the next instruction
30	117	117	
31	6034	JMP 34	Jump to register 34, resume program there
32	5000	STC 1000	Store contents of accumulator in 1000, then clear accumulator
33	0000	HLT	Halt the program
34	11	CLR	Clear accumulator
35	2003	ADD 3	Add the contents of register 3 to accumulator
36	6023	JMP 23	Jump to register 23, resume program there

the computer adds to the accumulator the contents of register 100; the second time, it adds the contents of 101; the third time the contents of 102, etc. We store the result temporarily in register 3.

We have to determine whether we have added our entire list of numbers, so in instruction 25–26 (a two word instruction), we place the contents of our index register in the accumulator. The next instruction, 27–30, is a conditional instruction. It states that if the accumulator is equal to 117 (the last register in our list), skip the next instruction, located in register 31, and go on to the instruction in register 32, which commands it to store the contents of the accumulator in register 1000. It then goes on to the instruction in 33, which halts the program.

If the addition of the complete list has not yet been accomplished, the program resumes at register 31. The instruction here, *Jump*, informs the computer not to take the next instruction, but to begin a new sequence at another location, in this case, register 34. At this point, the accumulator is cleared, the contents of register 3 are added (temporary storage), and the program returns to location 23.

Even with such a simple program it is possible to appreciate the flexibility that a stored program permits. A small alteration in one instruction can make a significant difference in the program.

This flexibility is even more pronounced when, instead of using the computer merely to perform arithmetic, we use it to control an experiment. Let us start with simple continuous reinforcement (CRF), as in Table 16.4. In the LINC's instruction repertoire are commands which refer to input lines to which external devices may be connected. Suppose, for instance, that an operandum is connected, via intervening circuitry, to input line 7. We will also connect an output line (number 11) to deliver a pulse for reinforcement. The first two instructions merely reset the response counter. The SXL instruction tells the computer to examine input line 7. If an appropriate signal is found there, the next instruction is skipped, and the program goes on to register 24. OPR 11 delivers the reinforcement. The next four instructions increment the response counter set aside in register 17. If no response is seen, the computer continues searching input line 7.

TABLE 16.4. *Continuous reinforcement*

Location	Octal	Mnemonic	Description
20	11	CLR	Clear accumulator
21	4017	STC 17	Store accumulator in 17 (set 17 = 0)
22	407	SXL 7	Skip if there is a signal on input line 7
23	6022	JMP 22	Jump to 22
24	511	OPR 11	Emit a signal on output line 11
25	1020	LDAi	Load the number 1 in accumula-
26	1	1	tor; i.e. set accumulator = 1
27	2017	ADD 17	Add the contents of 17 to accumulator
30	4017	STC 17	Store the sum (contents of accumulator) in 17
31	6022	JMP 22	Jump to register 22, resume program there

Let us now complicate the problem further by switching from CRF to a fixed ratio schedule, say FR6 (Table 16.5). This means that we have to set aside a memory location as a counter. Make this location 16. Again, we continue searching input line 7 until a response is made. Then, at 25, we load the accumulator with the number 1, and execute the instruction *add to mem-*

TABLE 16.5. *Fixed ratio routine*

Location	Octal	Mnemonic	Time	Description
			μsec	
20	11	CLR	8	Clear accumulator and regis-
21	4016	STC 16	16	ters 16 and 17
22	4017	STC 17	16	
23	407	SXL 7	8	Skip if there is a signal on input line 7
24	6023	JMP 23	16	Jump to register 23, resume program there
25	1020	LDAi	16	Load the number 1 in
26	1	1		accumulator
27	1140	ADM	32	Add the contents of 16 to ac-
30	16	16		cumulator and put the sum both in accumulator and in 16
31	1460	SAEi	16	Skip the next instruction if accumulator = 6
32	6	6		
33	6037	JMP 37	16	Jump to register 37, resume program there
34	511	OPR 11	16	Emit a signal from output line 11
35	11	CLR	8	Clear accumulator and clear
36	4016	STC 16	16	the FR counter (register 16)
37	1020	LDAi	16	Load the number 1 in
40	1	1		accumulator
41	1140	ADM	32	Add accumulator contents to
42	17	17		17 and leave the results both in the accumulator and in 17
43	6023	JMP 23	16	Jump to register 23, resume program there

ory, which adds the contents of the accumulator and the contents of the specified memory location, and leaves the result in both places. We wish the sum to remain in the accumulator because now we will ask whether it is large enough to produce reinforcement. If it is not, we simply increment the response counter and return to examining input line 7. If the FR is fulfilled, we reinforce by the pulse from output line 11, then reset our FR counter to 0 before going on to count the reinforcement.

In one of the columns, we have placed the times required to execute each of the instructions in this program. Note that the speed of the program militates against using it as is for operant work because a response will surely hold a circuit closed for several milliseconds, and the program can run through many cycles during that time. The most facile solution to the problem lies in the proper design of the external equipment; we have responses set flip-flops which are reset by output pulses.

We can enhance the flexibility of such a program quite simply. For example, suppose we wished to change the FR requirement easily. This is done by changing the contents of register 32. If we wished to do so while the program was running, we could add the sequence in Table 16.6, which would begin at register 43. This sequence allows us to punch a key on the LINC keyboard. The associated number then is entered in the FR register. Note that location 24 now will have to tell us to jump to register 43 instead of 23.

An additional refinement is measuring inter-response times (IRTs). We can do so in two ways. One is to insert a timing loop in the program that executes the same operation a prescribed number of times. If, for example, the instruction requires 16 μsec and the jump another 16 μsec, we could achieve a resolution of 3.2 msec by going through this loop 100 times.

TABLE 16.6. *Fixed ratio alteration*

Location	Octal	Mnemonic	Description
24	6043	JMP 43	Jump to register 43, resume program there
43	415	KST	Skip the next instruction if a key has been struck
44	6023	JMP 23	Jump to register 23, resume program there
45	535	OPRi 15	Enter the key code in accumulator
46	4032	STC 32	Store the contents of accumulator in register 32 (FR setting)
47	6023	JMP 23	Jump to register 23, resume program there

TABLE 16.7. *IRT counter*

Location	Octal	Mnemonic	Description
50	406	SXL 6	Skip if there is a signal on input line 6
51	6023	JMP 23	Jump to register 23, resume program there
52	1020	LDAi	Load the number 1 in accumulator
53	1	1	
54	1140	ADM	Add the contents of accumulator
55	15	15	register 15 and leave the results in both
56	6023	JMP 23	Jump to register 23, resume program there

Usually, because we would have to worry about equalizing the duration of several of the program branches with such a scheme, an external clock is an easier and more flexible solution. Suppose the clock output is connected to input line 6. Now, referring to Table 16.6, we replace location 44 with the instruction JMP 50. At 50 we insert the sequence shown in Table 16.7. After finding no response on input line 7, we search input line 6. If no clock level is present, we return to searching line 7. If a clock level is present, we increment the IRT counter, located in register 15, and return to search input line 7. In addition to these instructions, it would also be necessary to insert a sequence earlier that, upon a response, stores the contents of the IRT counter in a specified register and resets the time counter to 0.

Applications

A Computer-generated Reinforcement Schedule

As one example of the application of computer technology to operant behavior experiments, we will discuss a reinforcement schedule studied in this laboratory which would have been difficult, if not impossible, to study in any other way. This is the autoregressive schedule described by Weiss and Laties (1965).

The basis of the ARG schedule is diagrammed in Fig. 16.2. The probability of reinforcement associated with a response depends on the similarity of IRT (X_i) to the previous IRT (X_{i-1}), or to the mean of the last N IRTs. To measure the similarity, the LINC computes the quotient of the two IRTs, always placing the larger number in the numerator. As shown by Fig. 16.2, the closer the quotient is to 1.0, the higher the probability of reinforcement. Since such a requirement is best met by emitting IRTs that vary mini-

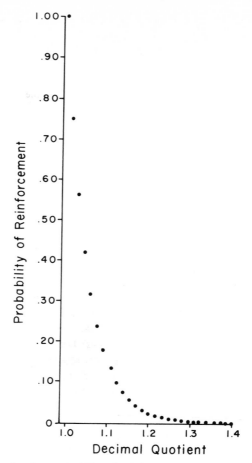

FIG. 16.2. Function showing probability of reinforcement on the ARG schedule versus the quotient of IRTi/IRTi + 1 (or the reverse). If the two IRTs are identical, the probability is 1.0 (from B. Weiss & V. G. Laties. *Science, N.Y.*, 1965, *148*: 658–661).

mally from one to the other, it can be seen that the ARG schedule is one way to reinforce differentially a low IRT variability.

From this relatively simple algorithm, we have expanded in two ways. In a further set of experiments, we added a ratio contingency. Instead of reinforcing each time a reinforcement came due, reinforcement occurred every Nth time. In another variation, instead of making the decision about reinforcement on the basis of the last two IRTs, it was made by comparing the last IRT with the mean of the previous n IRTs. Both of these variations were aimed at further decreasing the variability of IRTs.

The computer program that controls the ARG schedule offers several illustrations of how such a program is constructed. A flow chart is shown in Fig. 16.3, and we will refer to it in discussing the program.

At the start of the program, which is read from one of the tape units into the memory, switches on the console are used to give the appropriate session duration in minutes and to designate the first tape block on which the data are to be written. There are two banks of these switches, each bank equal to 12 switches, or the word length of the computer.

The computer then halts to await a number from the keyboard which designates the ratio requirement. Once this information is received, the computer program executes a group of bookkeeping instructions which include setting certain registers in the memory to correspond to the starting points for data storage.

The main part of the program then begins. Three monkeys are studied simultaneously, so that three different input lines must be scanned for responses. In addition, an external 10 msec clock is connected to another input line to provide a count for IRT duration. The computer program first examines the input level from the clock to determine whether the clock FF (flip-flop) has been set by a clock pulse. If it has, the program then jumps to a subroutine that increments the IRT time counters of each monkey and the session time counter. It compares the session time counter to the value previously designated by the switches. If the session is over, the remaining data are written on tape and the interface apparatus turned off by a pulse which actuates a relay. If the session is not over, the program then returns to its main routine and begins to examine, in turn, the input lines from the three monkeys. If the clock FF had not been set, the program would have gone directly from the clock query to the section which scans the lines from the monkeys.

Each response input line is examined in turn. If none of the response FF's are set, the program examines the inputs again. Thus, much of the time the computer waits for inputs.

If a response FF is found to be set, the program then executes its major routine, that of deciding whether to reinforce the response and recording all of the relevant information. The identity of the monkey is recorded first; a number is assigned to correspond to the source of the input line. The program then continues on to a subroutine which computes the mean of the last n waiting times, then the quotient of

$$X_i \Big/ \sum_{j=i-1}^{i-n} x_j$$

or the reverse, depending on which is larger. If the quotient is greater than two, it jumps to the routine for simply recording the information. If the quotient is less than two, a number is selected from a location in a table stored

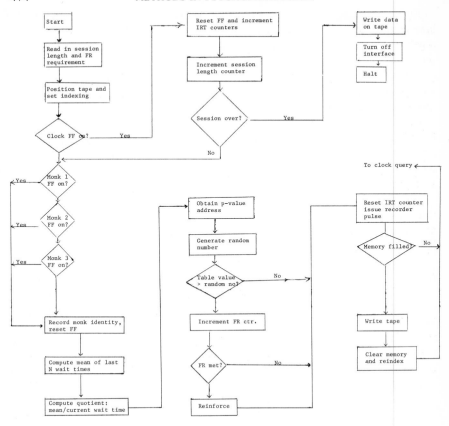

FIG. 16.3. Flow chart of the ARG reinforcement schedule. See explanation in text.

in memory. This number corresponds to a specified probability of reinforcement. Suppose that our random number generator generates a rectangular distribution of numbers between 0 and 1000. If the table entry selected is 300, this means that there is a 0.3 probability that the random number generated will be less than the table entry. Thus, the next step, after obtaining the table entry and generating the random number, is to compare these two values. If the table value is greater than the random number, we continue the routine leading to a decision about reinforcement. If it is less, that section is skipped.

If the table entry is larger than the random number, the program then increments the FR counter and asks whether the FR condition has been met. If it has, the appropriate reinforcement relay is closed for a specified period of time, and the solenoid on the liquid feeder releases a predetermined amount of fluid. The reinforcement counter is then incremented, and the current IRT labeled as reinforced by putting a 1 in the 12th bit, which ordinarily designates algebraic sign. The total time taken to process one monkey's response is no more than 3 msec.

All IRTs, reinforced or not, are recorded in a two word format. The first word gives the IRT duration. The second gives the monkey number and can also give information about discriminative stimuli present, etc.

After every IRT entry, the program determines whether the memory has been filled. If it has, instead of returning to the scanning routine, the program first jumps to a set of instructions which cause the data in memory to be written on tape and the data storage registers to be cleared for further input. It requires about 280 msec every 512 responses to write tape.

Although the program requires several hundred instructions, it is simpler than it seems because it contains a great deal of simple bookkeeping routines and because it deals with three monkeys at once, providing some duplication in program structure.

Evoked Potential Averaging

Another example of on-line programming comes from a technique widely used in psychophysiology, especially in the study of evoked potentials: response averaging. In this technique, a stimulus event begins a recording which continues for a specified period of time. The responses to successive repetitions of the signal are added algebraically. Averaging helps to recover signals obscured by noise when the noise is statistically stationary, i.e. does not vary with time in a systematic manner.

The signal enhancement is due to the fact that the noise adds in RMS fashion, while the signal sums algebraically. Following Cox (1965), the signal to noise ratio of the sum of N signals is given by

$$\frac{\sigma_{s'}}{\sigma_{n'}} = \sqrt{\frac{N^2\,\sigma_{s^2}}{N\,\sigma_{n^2}}} = \sqrt{N}\left(\frac{\sigma_s}{\sigma_n}\right)$$

where σ_s is the RMS value of the signal and σ_n is the RMS value of the noise. The values $\sigma_{s'}$ and $\sigma M_{n'}$ are the values of signals and noise after computation of the sum. N^2 is used in the numerator because the signal sums coherently (it is phase locked) and N is used in the denominator because the noise sums incoherently (the phase relations are random). A number of devices are now on the market that can be used for averaging. How do these compare to a general purpose computer?

A computer such as the LINC can easily be programmed to perform averaging. A sample program, which appears on the description of the LINC by Clark and Molnar (1965), is reproduced, in modified form, in Table 16.8. Note that it requires only a few instructions to do averaging.

TABLE 16.8. *Response averaging program**

Location	Octal	Mnemonic	Description
20	62	SETi2	Set up the number of responses to be
21	7730	−40	averaged ($= 32_{10}$)
22	63	SETi3	Set up index register 3 to store 512_{10}
23	7700	−77	samples in register 1000–1777
24	505	OPR5	Emit triggering pulse on output line 5
25	110	SAM 10	Take sample from analog channel 10 and convert to binary, put in accumulator
26	1143	ADMi3	Add contents of accumulator to sum in the appropriate register between 1000–1777
27	203	XSK3	Skip next instruction if 512 samples completed
30	6025	JMP25	Return to sampling
31	222	XSKi2	Skip next instruction if 32_{10} responses have been completed
32	6022	JMP22	Return to set up indexing
33	0	HLT	Halt

*Data from W. A. Clark & C. E. Molnar. In *Computers in biomedical research*, 1965.

Since many other instruments can perform averaging, and cost perhaps one-quarter of the LINC, one might well ask what advantages such a general purpose digital computer possesses. Again, its main virtue is flexibility. If, for example, one wishes to subject the data to quantitative treatment, a way must be found to transform the data into a computer compatible format. Although many, if not most, of the special purpose instruments have facilities for transferring the data to punched cards, punched paper tape, and so on, these additional functions naturally add considerably to the cost of the basic machine.

Even after means have been added to permit the transfer of data to an external storage device a certain deficiency still exists. If one wishes to use the data analysis as the basis for modifications in the experimental procedures or parameters, a delay is introduced. The data must be taken to a computer installation for analysis and the results returned. Making changes during the course of an experiment is thus out of the question. Moreover, the cost of computer time is generally not a trivial amount.

By the time one adds the logical equipment to perform special and very limited analyses, e.g. histograms and auto- and cross-correlations, one already has an investment equivalent in cost to a small general purpose digital computer, but still lacks the flexibility built into the latter device.

One example of how a digital computer may be used in signal averaging is provided by Lowy and Weiss (in press). Averaging of evoked potentials is used quite commonly now in experiments in neurophysiology. The result, however, is difficult to evaluate. In some experiments, an investigator chooses an arbitrary number of recurrences of the stimulus and then examines an analogue plot of the wave form to determine whether a signal is present. In other experiments, the number of recurrences is indeterminate. The experimenter continues presenting stimuli until he believes that a definite pattern has emerged.

A computer can be programmed to do what the eye does, namely, look for consistent, identifiable features, but do it better. Lowy and Weiss programmed a LINC to examine averages built up by odd-numbered and even-numbered trials, respectively. If a signal is present, it is assumed that it will produce a wave form with a definite minimum, maximum, or both. The computer program determines whether the minimum, maximum, or both (an option selected by the experimenter) coincide in location, i.e. in latency from the stimulus marker. If they do, the LINC can issue control signals which alter the stimulus, or can display and store the data. A system of this kind can easily be used to conduct Bekesy-type psychophysical experiments with the amplitude of the signal in the evoked potential serving as the response.

After each sweep, the 256 registers containing the odd-or even-averaged signal are collected into 16 sums of 16 entries each. This procedure makes it easier to find a reliable minimum and maximum. In order to avoid overflow, the 256 entries are scaled down before summing. The mean is then computed so that the maximum and minimum appear as positive and negative deviations, which makes the search program easier to write. Figure 16.4 shows an averaged evoked potential recorded from cat auditory cortex.

A number of other methods have been and can be devised to analyze evoked potentials on-line. The amount of computing power required to perform the fairly simple analyses that would be done is not excessive, and can be met by nearly all of the small laboratory computers now on or about to enter the market. Another advantage of the general purpose computer over the current type of averaging device is its ability to conduct a certain amount of preprocessing, such as digital filtering, which may also be helpful in enhancing the signal (Stauffer, Dill, & Stacy, 1965).

Synthesizing Stimuli

The versatility of the digital computer is further exemplified by its ability to synthesize stimuli. Recently, two articles have been published in *Science*, one dealing with computer music (Hiller & Beauchamp, 1965), and the other with

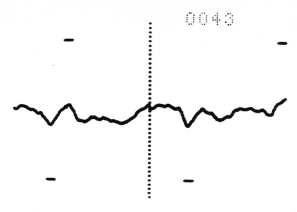

FIG. 16.4. Averaged evoked potential from cat auditory cortex. The display is sectioned into two halves by the *dotted line*. The function on the left is the averaged value (256 points spaced 1 msec apart) of the odd-numbered sweeps. The one on the right corresponds to the even-numbered sweeps. The total number of sweeps before the program found a consistent minimum in both odd- and even-numbered sweep averages was 43, the number displayed on the photograph. The *short horizontal lines at the bottom* correspond to the minima; *those at the top* correspond to the maxima. The photograph was made from a LINC-generated display.

animated cartoons (Knowlton, 1965). Both applications illustrate how with proper output facilities it is possible to use a computer to generate, on-line, stimuli of enormous complexity. The reader can find additional examples in the book by Green (1963) and the chapter by White (1962). We will provide a simple example from the LINC.

An oscilloscope provides a quick and effective readout for a computer, particularly if the data are in the form of functions rather than numbers. But the oscilloscope can also be used to draw displays which are under program control. Suppose, for example, that an experimenter wished to draw a geometric figure, such as a square, on the face of the scope.

Display oscilloscopes are usually controlled by using two registers to designate a point, one of which gives an abscissa value, the other of which gives an ordinate value. (A third register may sometimes be used to control intensity.) These values are represented in digital form, of course. In order to be able to control the position of a point, they enter digital to analogue converters which produce voltages corresponding to the binary values in the registers. A display command then briefly illuminates the designated point on the scope face. The LINC display scope is equivalent to a matrix of $(512)_{10}$ points, each of which is individually brightened.

In the program shown in Table 16.9, three parameters of the square are controlled: horizontal position, vertical position, and size. Since the LINC contains 8 potentiometers that can be used as analogue inputs, they provide a convenient means of varying these parameters. They could just as conveniently be set by

TABLE 16.9. *Program for displaying a square of variable size and position (Courtesy of P. Knauf)*

2A	SAM1 ADAi 1200 ROL1 STA 4 STC1	Sample Knob 1, convert to a form that can be used to set abscissa position, and store it away in appropriate register
	SAM3 ROLil STC3A	Sample Knob 3, store as ordinate position
	SAM2 ADAi 200 ROL1 STA 3 COM STC2	Sample Knob 2 and process the number resulting so as to give the size of the square; store this value and also its complement (the latter is used for counting purposes)
	LDA 3A ADA 3 STC4A	Add together the ordinate value and the size value to give the vertical dimension.
1A 3A 4A	LDAi DIS1 LDAi DISil XSKi2 JMP1A	Display, alternately, points on the lower and upper edges; display the number of points equivalent to the size value.
	LDAi 1 ADM 4A LDA 4 ADM 3 LDA 3A	Draw the sides of the square, first setting the upper limit, then displaying, by alternation, corresponding points on both sides; increment the ordinate each time until the sides are complete; then return to the beginning of the program
5A	DIS4 DIS3 ADAi 1 SAE 4A JMP5A JMP2A	

the keyboard, or be made to vary according to some programmed option. For example, if one were interested in generalization to size, subroutines could be written to provide squares of different sizes, the display changing after the behavior emitted with the previous size has been sampled. Or, one could program the computer to start with a large difference and reduce the difference gradually until a specified criterion, such as response rate, shows that the difference is not discriminated by the subject.

By following the flow chart, the reader can see that the program is really rather simple. It requires only 49 registers and 34 instructions. Figure 16.5 shows a photograph of the oscilloscope screen with squares of different sizes and in different positions. The ease with which such a program can be written is an excellent illustration of the adaptability of a laboratory computer.

Auditory stimuli can also be generated, without using external oscillators, and one can, therefore, synthesize extremely complex frequency modulated sound patterns.

Analogue to Digital Conversion

The psychophysiologist is concerned primarily with the analyses of variables whose characteristics change continuously with time. For computer analyses, these variables must be represented as discrete quantities, that is, binary numbers. The process of converting time varying signals (analogue signals) to binary form is called analogue to digital conversion (A-D conversion). The ability to perform this conversion under program control as well as the reverse one, that is, digital to analogue, is a necessary feature of any computer to be used in the laboratory.

The basic element of the analogue to digital conversion system is the comparator. This device can be considered as having two input terminals and one output terminal. Applied to one input is the analogue signal of unknown magnitude while to the other is a constant reference voltage. If the output is normally at 0 v, it switches to 5 v if the reference input is larger than the unknown signal. By connecting a number of comparators together such that the unknown signal is applied to one input of each comparator and reference signals differing from each other by a constant amount are applied to the remaining input terminals, a binary output will be generated reflecting the magnitude of the applied unknown analogue signal. It is this digital information that the computer then processes.

More efficient methods of A-D conversion employ a single comparator circuit and a reference supply which may be varied accurately over a wide range completely under digital control. It should be noted here that a digitally controlled variable reference voltage supply is simply a digital to analogue converter. Every digital number supplied to the input of the D-A converter produces a unique output voltage. If the input is arranged as a counting circuit that increases by

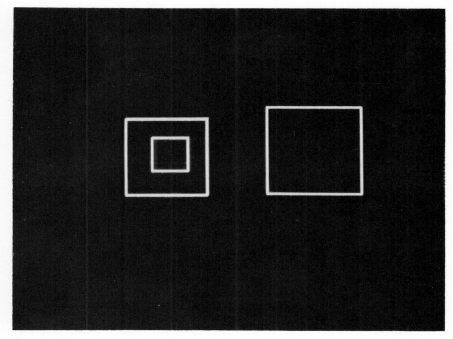

FIG. 16.5. Squares of different size and position generated on an oscilloscope screen by the program of Table 16.9.

1 unit periodically, the output of the single comparator may be used to halt automatically the counting when equality between the reference signal and the unknown signal is reached. One difficulty with this method is that the N bit counter must complete 2_N counts in a cyclic fashion.

By replacing this counter with one that may be decremented as well as incremented, the converter may be made to follow the analogue signal in a continuous fashion. This method employs an up-down counter with a logical gate controlling the direction of the counter.

Often it is necessary to know exactly when in time the input signal equalled the reference voltage. In addition, it may be desirable to extend the duration of an input for purposes of accurate conversion. The technique for accomplishing both of these goals is called sample and hold. One method uses a capacitor or storing element on the unknown signal input. When the capacitor is connected to the input it follows the voltage variations; when it is disconnected the capacitor retains the voltage applied to it at the instant it was disconnected.

Terms associated with sample and hold circuits include acquisition time, the time required for the voltage on the storing element to equal the input voltage after initial connection; aperture time, the time necessary for connection and disconnection of the input to the storing element; and holding time, the total time the storing element can retain a certain percentage of the input voltage after being disconnected.

Many experiments require the simultaneous conversion of analogue signals emanating from different sources. One method of achieving this is to use as many A-D systems as there are different signals. A more economical method employs the technique known as multiplexing. Multiplexing involves the sequential connection of each analogue signal to a central converting system. This is accomplished using either mechanical switches (relays) or solid state switches (transistors). When simultaneity is required, sample and hold circuits are used before each switch of the multiplexer in order that conversion takes place on voltages sampled at the same point in time.

There are three basic types of errors that occur in A-D conversion systems. The first is called the quantization error and occurs because of the binary nature of the output. This error is equal to the smallest measurable output increment, in this case the least significant bit of the resulting binary word. Usually this error is centered so that it is between $\pm \frac{1}{2}$ the least significant bit when the system is considered as a whole. The second type of error is due to noise. External transients, particularly 60 cycle pickup from power supplies or power cables affect the switching characteristics of the converter. The effect of this is that the same input voltage may not always produce the same binary output. The third source of error is variation in the direct current reference potentials. Since these potentials are vital in producing the correct output they must always be kept in adjustment to ensure accurate operation of the system.

The LINC is equipped with an A-D conversion system having 15 input channels. Channels to be sampled are chosen using the SAM n instruction, where n ranges from 0 to 14.

Seven of these channels are available as connectors on a special data terminal unit. Each channel accepts a voltage whose magnitude varies between ± 1 v and upon execution of the SAM instruction converts it to a binary number between ± 177 octal (8 bits) and deposits the result in the accumulator. This process takes 24μ sec. Effectively then a 2 v range is divided into one of 255 decimal different numbers. The remaining eight analogue channels are available on the console of the LINC as potentiometers. These channels are useful in modifying and controlling programs such as displays on the on-line oscilloscope.

Analogue and Hybrid Computers

Since so much of psychophysiology deals with analogue signals, it will be useful to discuss the available means of treating such signals for computation.

In fact, for certain limited purposes, analogue computers can do most of what an experimenter wishes. Since analogue computers handle continuous variables, typically representing them electrically, the real system and its representation are isomorphic.

An analogue computer typically consists of a number of computing modules, each of which performs one or more mathematical operations on voltages applied to their input terminals. The voltages applied to the terminals are analogues of some quantity that may arise from the outputs of other analogue modules, from transducers indicating physiologic changes, or from electrical signal generators. The input and output terminals of these modules appear at the computer patch panel, and programming the computer consists of patching the modules into a pattern which corresponds to the particular mathematical expression being evaluated. Because the analogue computer is faster than the digital computer and because parameters may be adjusted more easily, the analogue computer is more suitable for solving problems such as differential equations meant to be first approximations to dynamic biological processes.

Another feature of the analogue computer is that the input, the intermediate, and output voltages that appear from an analogue computation are analogues and measures of quantities in the original biological problem. These voltages are modified by passing them through electronic components such as coding operational amplifiers, potentiometers, and integrating and differentiating circuits. The time variation of many intermediate voltages, when viewed on an oscilloscope, gives the investigator a visual display of how the individual biological quantity is being represented or varying with time. The display feature, of course, is not limited to the analogue computer. Since the machine language of the analogue computer is so similar to the language of the problems being studied, there is no particular need to acquire programming skill; of course, a certain skill is required to wire the analogue computer for any particular problem. Although the analogue computer is suited for operating on-line with experimental equipment, that is, it is easily connected to transducers, the analogue computer functions without the precision and data storage features of digital computation. Also, the number of operational amplifiers limits the complexities of the expression for which the analogue computer can evaluate. The restriction of the analogue computer largely to processes that can be represented by differential equations makes it further unsuitable for many biological phenomena.

The combination of the analogue and digital computer forms a hybrid type of computing system which confers certain advantages but compounds certain difficulties because it involves the skills needed to program both types of computers individually. There are four ways to classify the hybrid computer, depending upon the way they incorporate the separate analogue and digital components: (1) an analogue computer with digital logic added, (2) a digital computer with analogue elements added, (3) a digital computer linked to an analogue computer, and (4) the true hybrids containing neither an analogue nor digital computer intended for independent existence. Computers of the first type are usually the analogue computer previously discussed with some parallel patchable digital logic used for controlling iterations of the analogue elements. These usually take the form of electromechanical relays or, more recently, the form of digitally controlled solid state analogue signal switches and banks of patchable flip-flops, gates, and counters. Computers of the second class are usually digital systems to which analogue elements are added (see Macy, 1964). They are under close program control of the digital computer and communicate via an I/O channel and A to D or D to A converters. The analogue elements are not intended to function independently of the digital computer. Instead, they are organized to take up some of the digital processor's computing workload. Computers of the third type are formed by linking separate analogue and digital computers. These are readily available commercially and are widely used for engineering simulation and in the field of biomedical research. With the advances that have been made in the input-output capabilities of digital computers, computers of the third type are now easier to design. High speed multiplexers and A to D converters now make possible A to D conversion at rates of approximately 100 kc. (D to A conversion data transfers at the 100 kc rate have been possible for some time.) Linkage systems are now available with multiplying D to A converters capable of serving as digitally controlled analogue attenuators so that digital values fed into the linkage system from the digital computer can directly set coefficients in the transfer functions of analogue signal paths within the analogue computer. Hybrid computers of the fourth class, the true hybrids, contain neither a separate analogue nor separate digital computer intended for independent use. This fourth class of computers differs from the other hybrid types in that a more intimate combination of analogue and digital techniques are possible.

Functionally, one of the differences between the two types of computers, analogue and digital, is that a digital computer executes its instructions sequentially, while an analogue computer performs its operations simultaneously or in parallel. This limitation of the digital computer is offset by its extraordinary flexibility, memory, and precision compared to the analogue computer. Furthermore, the digital computer is capable of solving any problem which may be solved by an analogue computer. The range of problems which may be solved on an analogue type computer is more limited but its programming, especially in the solution of differential equations, is usually much easier. A strong point of the digital computer lies in its great facility for logical operations, especially decision making, but also the manipulation of data and the modification of instructions. Although it is possible to store some information using analogue techniques, the digital computer is far superior in this respect.

What Kind of Computer?

Presuming that an investigator decides to equip his laboratory with a small digital computer, what features should he look for in order to provide the greatest possible usefulness? Some, of course, depend upon his particular area of interest. No single computer is superior for all applications, although the designer can include enough versatility to make the machine a reasonable choice for a broad range of these. Certain features should be common to all laboratory computers, however.

Binary words. A computer used for on-line work should be a pure binary machine. That is, data should be represented within it according to the binary number system and not according to some binary analogue, such as binary-coded-decimal (BCD). One disadvantage of the BCD and similar formats is that they waste memory space. It requires more bits to represent a number with the coded systems than with a pure binary system. Even more important, a pure binary machine allows individual bits in a word to be manipulated directly and easily in a way that greatly speeds certain operations. For example, most computers contain instructions which can shift the contents of the accumulator right or left. This is an easy way to divide and multiply by powers of 2. By shifting right two spaces, i.e. setting the contents of bit i to bit $i + 2$, the number in the accumulator is divided by 4. This kind of operation takes much less time than the ordinary divide instruction, which often is executed by a subroutine. Instructions are also available which serve as logical AND, OR, and exclusive OR, and these make most sense in a binary machine.

Instruction code. The machine should have a flexible, versatile set of instructions which make it relatively easy to write machine language, especially I/O instructions and manipulations of individual bits. It is difficult to write efficient compilers, such as FORTRAN, for the kind of program that is used in laboratory computers, one reason being the difference from one experimenter to the other in how he organizes the interface electronics. Moreover, laboratory computers are small, and memory space may be wasted by a compiler. The designers of the LINC, for example, went to great pains to provide an instruction repertoire that allowed the machine's capacity to be pushed to the fullest and that made it relatively easy to learn to use.

Input-output facilities. Exceeding everything else in importance is a flexible input-output system and germane commands. A laboratory computer should allow the experimenter to attach with little trouble a great variety of peripheral devices to control experiments and to transfer information in and out of the machine. The lack of such features has been the prime deficiency of past machines. The instruction repertoire should contain specific commands for transferring the contents of certain registers to the interface and the reverse, and for emitting and responding to control signals. In this respect, one useful feature is a priority interrupt. This allows a signal coming in over an input line to cause the program to branch to a location in memory which, in the usual case, begins a subroutine used to find which of the external devices has issued the signal. Once this device is serviced, the program resumes where it left off.

It does not take much imagination to see how useful a computer in the laboratory can be. But a word of caution is in order. An investigator must know his computer as well as he knows the other equipment he uses for his research. This means, primarily, that he must learn programming. Many biological scientists are reluctant to do so, feeling that this skill can be hired. Unfortunately, this is not the case. In the first place, trained persons with the skills needed to program computers for on-line use in a laboratory setting and who can communicate with biological scientists are exceedingly rare. In the second place, it is doubtful that the full potential of a laboratory computer can be reached if the investigator does not take an active role in interface design and programming. After all, he is the one who knows what he wants done, and can communicate effectively only when he is on intimate terms with the system.

In our experience, learning to program the LINC is not excessively time consuming provided adequate tutoring and machine time are available. Mathematical expertise is far less essential than attention to detail, a trait that many biologists must possess in abundance anyway. Macy (1964) has had considerable success, he reports, in training biological scientists to program.

There is no question, moreover, that programming takes a lot of time. Miller, Bregman, and Norman (1965) point out that one of the most frequent mistakes scientists make is to underestimate how much time is required to prepare (and debug) programs, particularly those of an unconventional character, as on-line programs are apt to be. The rewards, however, are more than commensurate with the effort, for the effort adds a new dimension to science.

REFERENCES

Clark, W. A., & Molnar, C. E. The LINC: A description of the laboratory instrument computer. *Ann. N.Y. Acad. Sci.*, 1964, *115*: 653–668.
Clark, W. A., & Molnar, C. E. A description of the LINC. In R. W. Stacy & B. Waxman (Eds.), *Computers in biomedical research*. New York: Academic Press, 1965, Vol. 2.

Cox, J. R., Jr. Special-purpose digital computers in biology. In R. W. Stacy & B. Waxman (Eds.), *Computers in biomedical research*. New York: Academic Press, 1965, Vol. 2.

Green, B. F., Jr. *Digital computers in research*. New York: McGraw-Hill, 1963.

Hiller, L., & Beauchamp, J. Research in music with electronics. *Science, N.Y.*, 1965, *150*: 161–169.

Knowlton, K. C. Computer-produced movies. *Science, N.Y.*, 1965, *150*: 1116–1120.

Lowy, K., & Weiss, B. One-line estimate of the significance of evoked potentials. *Fed. Proc. Fedn Am. Socs exp. Biol.*, in press.

Macy, J., Jr. Hybrid computer techniques for physiology. *Ann. N.Y. Acad. Sci.*, 1964, *115*: 568–590.

Martin, J. *Programming real-time computer systems*. New Jersey: Prentice-Hall, 1965.

Miller, G. A., Bregman, A. S., & Norman, D. A. The computer as a general purpose device for the control of psychological experiments. In R. W. Stacy & B. Waxman (Eds.), *Computers in biomedical research*. New York: Academic Press, 1965, Vol. 1.

Stauffer, W. M., Dill, J. C., & Stacy, R. W. Real-time numerical filtering of physiological signals. *IEEE Trans. Biomed. Engng*, 1965, *12*: 195–197.

Weiss, B., & Laties, V. G. Reinforcement schedule generated by an on-line digital computer. *Science, N.Y.*, 1965, *148*: 658–661.

White, B. W. Studies of perception. In H. Borko (Ed.), *Computer applications in the behavioral sciences*. New Jersey: Prentice-Hall, 1962.

Index